GENERALIZED FUNCTIONS

and

DIRECT OPERATIONAL METHODS

PRENTICE–HALL PARTIAL DIFFERENTIAL EQUATIONS SERIES

MURRAY PROTTER, editor

GENERALIZED FUNCTIONS

and

DIRECT OPERATIONAL METHODS

VOLUME I

NON-ANALYTIC GENERALIZED FUNCTIONS IN ONE DIMENSION

T. P. G. LIVERMAN

Professor of Mathematics
The George Washington University

PRENTICE–HALL, INC.

Englewood Cliffs, New Jersey

PRENTICE-HALL INTERNATIONAL, INC., *London*
PRENTICE-HALL OF AUSTRALIA, PTY., LTD., *Sydney*
PRENTICE-HALL OF CANADA, LTD., *Toronto*
PRENTICE-HALL OF INDIA (PRIVATE) LTD., *New Delhi*
PRENTICE-HALL OF JAPAN, INC., *Tokyo*
PRENTICE-HALL DE MEXICO, S.A., *Mexico City*

Library of Congress Catalog No. 64–16438
Printed in the United States of America
35100 C

This

Book

is

Dedicated

to

M

P *T*^{2}

PREFACE

Familiarity with the theory of generalized functions (also called ideal functions or distributions) is now becoming indispensable for the consumer no less than the practitioner of mathematical analysis. This is attested to by the stream of applications and extensions of this theory appearing in the current literature of mathematics and the physical sciences, much of it stemming from the ideas presented in 1950–51 by Laurent Schwartz in his fundamental treatise "Théorie des Distributions." This trend is in large part due to the physical significance of g.f.'s (generalized functions) and to the simplicity and generality which they bring to the solution of many linear functional equations.

Such g.f.'s as the Dirac delta function and its derivatives have long been standard fare for physicists and have now found their way into undergraduate engineering curricula. As often as not, though, these mathematical objects are presented to beginners in an entirely intuitive context. While this may whet the student's appetite, giving him a glimpse of a more unified universe, he is also apt to end up with the impression that some irregular verbs have been slipped into an otherwise consistent grammar of mathematics.

This book is the first of two volumes meant as an introduction to the theory of g.f. classes and one of its major fields of application: the solution of differential and partial differential equations, by operational methods here characterized as direct because they rest on the direct manipulation of differential and integral operators, in the manner of Heaviside. This introduction is intended for applied mathematicians, engineers, and physical scientists, as well as for classroom use by students in these areas.

In this first volume, my aim, however incompletely the following pages may fulfill it, has been to make accessible to the student, or reader, whose mathematical background amounts to those topics of elementary and advanced calculus that are common to most undergraduate curricula in mathematics, the physical sciences, and engineering, relevant portions of g.f. theory, and to give some idea of its incisiveness as a tool; without derogating from reasonable standards of mathematical rigor. I have attempted this by concentrating most of the exposition on one particular class of g.f., the so-called $\mathscr{D}'_+$ space. This choice has a twofold attraction: the definition and derivations of the properties of $\mathscr{D}'_+$ are computationally simple, a feature that makes it easy to bring out a pattern of reasoning which is equally applicable to the study of other g.f. classes (as illustrated by the exercises marked O.C. and by Chapter VIII); it is easy to justify the one-dimensional Heaviside operational calculus in $\mathscr{D}'_+$, and, by using it as a practical tool for the explicit solution of linear differential equations with constant coefficients, to illustrate the importance of g.f.'s in physical and technological applications.

A preliminary chapter is devoted to a heuristic introduction to g.f.'s and direct operational methods; it also touches on the physical significance of g.f.'s. The next two chapters present the definition and basic properties of $\mathscr{D}'_+$ g.f.'s in terms of weakly convergent sequences of piecewise continuous functions, following a simplified version of the approach first exposed in some detail by G. Temple in 1953 and 1954. The operational calculus in one dimension is rigorously developed in Chapter III and used to prove a fundamental existence and uniqueness theorem for differential equations with constant coefficients by means that foreshadow the approach to similar theorems for partial differential equations in Volume II. The practical uses of this calculus take up the rest of this chapter, which also includes both an intuitive and a mathematically rigorous discussion of the Green's function for the initial-value problem for linear d.e.'s with constant coefficients. Chapter IV deals with further applications of the operational calculus; its application to systems of d.e.'s especially illustrates the advantages of formulating physical problems in terms of g.f.'s.

Chapters V and VI, which cover some deeper properties of $\mathscr{D}'_+$ g.f.'s, are addressed primarily to the mathematician. The pace here is somewhat less leisurely, and occasional use is made of a result whose proof is proposed as an exercise. The relationship between different approaches to g.f. theory is discussed and elementary proofs given of fundamental structure theorems in close correspondence with those of L. Schwartz relating $\mathscr{D}'_+$ g.f.'s to continuous functions. These proofs, by methods of classical analysis are, so far as I am aware, new.

Chapters VII and VIII constitute a brief and partial introduction to the Laplace transform of $\mathscr{D}'_+$ g.f.'s and to a g.f. version of Fourier series. They are partly intended as background material on the solution by indirect (integral transform) methods of partial differential equations for the reader who does not embark on the study of more direct methods dealt with in Volume II.

Chapters, sections, and problems not marked with stars constitute the more elementary portions of this book; they require little technical knowledge beyond ordinary calculus, though they do assume some mathematical maturity of the student. A one star marking indicates "intermediate level" topics—in these, use is made of concepts like uniform continuity, uniform convergence, and improper double integrals. Double star markings indicate an "advanced" topic—for these, a good background in Advanced Calculus is assumed on the part of the reader, not for the technical knowledge involved, but for the maturity that such a background is expected to confer. The text may be read at any one of these levels without loss of continuity: sections at one level are independent of those at higher levels.

Three types of exercises are given: direct applications of material developed in the text; A.R. (alternative route) exercises that propose variations on the main theme; O.C. (other class) exercises that lead the student to develop the theory of other g.f. classes by following the line of argument given in the text for $\mathscr{D}'_+$.

While Chapters I through VI represent a portion of the lecture notes used in a graduate course on Operational Methods, they can, by themselves, serve for an introductory course on g.f.'s for advanced undergraduate mathematics students.

For an intermediate-level undergraduate course for a physically oriented audience, the unstarred sections of Chapters I through IV constitute a simple introduction to g.f.'s and their applications. A more complete coverage of basic engineering mathematics would include Chapter VIII, or, if time permits, Chapters VII and VIII. The latter being, perhaps, somewhat condensed for students making their first contact with Fourier series, the instructor may wish to supplement it with introductory material of his own.

ACKNOWLEDGEMENTS

Aid, in the form of a lightened teaching load and financial assistance for typing the manuscript, was contributed by The George Washington University. For this I am most grateful; as I am for the steady encouragement of my colleague, and friend, Prof. Nels D. Nelson.

My warm thanks go to Prof. Russell Remage, Jr. who read a major portion of the manuscript and contributed many helpful suggestions. To Mr. Donald D. Boyer I am much indebted for drawing up the index and aid in proofreading.

The translation in the footnote on Page 11 I owe to Dr. Eduard Farber. He persuaded me that it is better to be faithful to Mach's personal style than risk misrendering his thought in English by too glib a turn of phrase.

The preparation of the manuscript was carried out by Mrs. Amalya Johnson, whose competence it is a pleasure to acknowledge.

My greatest debts, as regards this work, are in the intellectual realm: to Laurent Schwartz, whose ideas, as embodied in his publications, are an inspiration to many; to George Temple, whose paper [51] in the Proceedings of the Royal Society of London of 1955 made me, among others, realize the existence, and see the direction, of an elementary approach to distributions.

CONTENTS

CHAPTER **0.** INTRODUCTORY, HEURISTIC BACKGROUND 1

1. Introduction, 1. **2.** Operational solution of an elementary initial-value problem, 3. **3.** The Dirac delta function, 6. **4.** Operational solution of a partial differential equation initial-value problem, 8. **5.** Operational solution of P.D.E. initial-boundary-value problems, 9. **6.** Historical indications, 10. **7.** Outline and background, 12.

CHAPTER **I.** OPERATIONAL CALCULUS ON $\mathscr{D}_-$ 14

1. Terminology, 14. **2.** Test functions of class $\mathscr{D}_-$, 14. **3.** The test space $\mathscr{D}_-$. Derivative polynomials on $\mathscr{D}_-$, 16. **4.** The inversion of the operator D, 19. **5.** Operational calculus on $\mathscr{D}_-$. Existence and uniqueness of solutions of differential equations, 23. **6.** Computational considerations. Partial fraction expansion of operators, 25. **7.** An example, 27. **8.** The space $\mathscr{D}_+$, 28. ****9.** The operator $(D - r)^\lambda$ for arbitrary real λ, 28. Appendix. Complex-valued functions of a real variable, 33. Exercises, 34.

CHAPTER **II.** THE SPACE $\mathscr{D}'_+$ OF GENERALIZED FUNCTIONS 38

A. DEFINITION OF $\mathscr{D}'_+$, 38

1. Terminology, 38. **2.** $\mathscr{K} + (R)$ functions as functionals on $\mathscr{D}_-$, 39. **3.** Generalized functions of class $\mathscr{D}'_+$, 41. **4.** Equivalence classes of fundamental sequences, 43. **5.** Basic operations in $\mathscr{D}'_+$, 44. **6.** Differentiation of g.f.'s, 47. **7.** Identification of $\mathscr{K}_+(R)$ functions and functionals, 51. **8.** Local identification of g.f.'s, 54. **9.** Physical significance of g.f.'s 59. **10.** Analogy between g.f. theory and real number theory, 56. **11.** The class $\mathscr{D}'_-$ of g.f.'s, 57.

B. THE DIFFERENTIAL CALCULUS AND CONVERGENCE IN $\mathscr{D}'_+$, 57

1. Differentiation of $\mathscr{K}_+(R)$ g.f.'s, 57. **2.** Application to differential equations, 60. **3.** Rules of differentiation in $\mathscr{D}'_+$, 62. **4.** Convergence of sequences and series in $\mathscr{D}'_{+}$, 64. **5.** Parametric g.f.'s of class $\mathscr{D}'_{+}$, 71. **6.** Relation between pointwise and $\mathscr{D}'_{+}$ convergence of functions, 74. ***7.** Differentiation and integration with respect to a real parameter, 75.

C. Singular function G.F.'s, 79

1. The g.f. log t_+, 79. **2.** The g.f.'s t_+, 80. ***3.** The g.f. $t_+^{\lambda-1}/\Gamma(\lambda)$, 82. ***4.** The g.f. $t_+ \log t$, 113. Exercises. 84.

CHAPTER **III.** THE OPERATIONAL SOLUTION OF DIFFERENTIAL EQUATIONS 90

A. Elementary Operational Calculus in $\mathscr{D}'_{+}$, 90

1. Derivative polynomials on $\mathscr{D}'_{+}$, 90. **2.** The operator $(D - r)^{-p}$, (Integer $p \geqslant 0$) on $\mathscr{D}'_{+}$, 91. **3.** Operational calculus on $\mathscr{D}'_{+}$. Existence, uniqueness of solutions of differential equations, 94. **4.** Computation of $(D - r)^{-p}F$ (integer $p \geqslant 0$). Auxiliary formulae, 95. **5.** Continuity of operators on $\mathscr{D}'_{+}$, 99. **6.** Operational calculus on $\mathscr{D}'_{-}$, 101. ****7.** $(D - r)^p$ on $\mathscr{D}'_{+}$, p noninteger, 101.

B. The Initial-Value Problem for a Differential Equation with Constant Coefficients, 103

1. Initial-value problem for D. E. with constant coefficients. Equation of evolution, 104. **2.** Example. The I. V. problem for the D. E. of a free vibrating system, 112. **3.** Explicit solution of the preceding problem, 113. **4.** I. V. problem for a forced vibrating system, 117. **5.** Infinite series solutions of I. V. problems, 119.

*C. Convolution in $\mathscr{D}'_{+}$, 120

1. Green's function—Intuitive and physical basis, 120. **2.** Convolution of $\mathscr{K}_{+}(R)$ functions, 124. **3.** The Green's function. Mathematical basis, 129. **4.** Résumé of the operational method—Example, 130. **5.** Convolution in $\mathscr{D}'_{+}$, 132. Exercises, 136.

CHAPTER **IV.** SYSTEMS OF DIFFERENTIAL EQUATIONS—OTHER APPLICATIONS 141

A. Operational Solution of Simultaneous Differential Equations, 141

1. Example of I. V. problem for simultaneous D. E.'s, 141. **2.** The system of equations of evolution, 146. **3.** Operational form of Cramer's rule, 149. **4.** The Chiò method for computing determinants, 153. **5.** The I. V. problem for normal systems, 155. ***6.** Computational considerations, 156. ***7.** I. V. problem for a nonnormal system, 159. ***8.** Mathematical and physical aspects of nonnormal systems, 164.

B. OTHER APPLICATIONS OF THE OPERATIONAL CALCULUS IN $\mathscr{D}_+$, 165

1. Boundary-value problems for linear D. E.'s with constant coefficients, 165. ***2.** Integro-differential equations of convolution type, 166. **3.** The algebra of translation operators on $\mathscr{D}'_+$, 171. **4.** Operational solution of the I. V. problem for linear difference equations with constant coefficients, 174. **5.** The operational method of Mikusiński, 178. Exercises, 179.

CHAPTER **V. THE STRUCTURE OF $\mathscr{D}'_+$. INDIVIDUAL G.F.'s 184

A. G. F.'s AS CONTINUOUS FUNCTIONALS, 184

1. Preface, 184. **2.** Positive G.F.'s of class $\mathscr{D}'_+$, 185. **3.** Boundedness properties of fundamental sequences on $\mathscr{D}_-$, 186. **4.** $\mathscr{D}'_+$ G.F.'s as continuous linear functionals, 191. **5.** The limit definition of G.F. differentiation, 196. **6.** Characterization of positive G.F.'s, 197.

B. $\mathscr{D}'_+$ G.F.'s AS DERIVATIVES OF FUNCTIONS, 199

1. The fundamental structure theorems, 199. **2.** Some consequences, 204. **3.** The carrier of a g.f., 207. **4.** Convolution in $\mathscr{D}'_+$, 209. Exercises, 212.

CHAPTER **VI. THE STRUCTURE OF $\mathscr{D}'_+$. COMPLETENESS 216

A. COMPLETENESS OF $\mathscr{D}'_+$, 216

1. The Lebesgue method of resonance, 217. **2.** Bounded sequences in $\mathscr{D}'_+$, 220. **3.** Completeness of $\mathscr{D}'_+$, 225. **4.** Parametric Derivatives and Integrals, 226. **5.** The problem of division, 227. **6.** Relative compactness of $\mathscr{D}'_+$, 230. Exercises, 233.

*CHAPTER **VII.** THE LAPLACE TRANSFORM 237

1. The Laplace transform of a function, 237. **2.** Principle of application to differential equations with constant coefficients, 241. **3.** Uniqueness of the inverse Laplace transform, 243. **4.** The inverse Laplace transform, 247. **5.** Laplace transforms of $\mathscr{D}'_{++}$ g.f.'s of exponential type, 250. **6.** Laplace transform images of operations on $\mathscr{D}'_{++}$, 256. **7.** Correspondence between Laplace transforms and Green's functions, 258. **8.** Applications to mixed difference-differential equations, 258. **9.** Application to differential equations with polynomial coefficients, 261. **10.** A partial differential equation problem, 265. **11.** Application of the Laplace transform, 268. **12.** Relation to problem A, 271. **13.** A practical L. T. routine for P. D. E. problems, 276. Exercises, 280.

*CHAPTER **VIII.** PERIODIC G.F.'s; INTRODUCTION TO FOURIER SERIES 283

1. Preliminaries, 283. **2.** The class $\mathscr{P}'_{2L}$ of g.f.'s with period $2L$, 287. **3.** The basic operations in $\mathscr{P}'_{2L}$, 290. **4.** Relation between ordinary and g.f. derivatives in $\mathscr{K}_{2L}(R)$, 292. **5.** Convergence in $\mathscr{P}'_{2L}$. Parametric derivatives and integrals, 294. **6.** The Fourier series for $\delta_{2L}(x - \xi)$, 294. **7.** Fourier series of $\mathscr{P}'_{2L}$ g.f.'s, 298. **8.** Ordinary convergence of Fourier series, 302. **9.** Primitive of a $\mathscr{P}'_{2L}$ g.f., 304. **10.** The finite Fourier transforms, 307. ****11.** The structure of $\mathscr{P}'_{2L}$ g.f.'s, 312. Exercises, 320.

APPENDIX: TABLE OF INVERSE OPERATOR VALUES (GREEN'S FUNCTIONS), 324
SUPPLEMENTARY TABLE OF INVERSE OPERATOR VALUES, 325
TABLE OF LAPLACE TRANSFORMS, 326

BIBLIOGRAPHY 327

INDEX OF NOTATION 331

INDEX 335

GENERALIZED FUNCTIONS

and

DIRECT OPERATIONAL METHODS

CHAPTER 0

INTRODUCTORY HEURISTIC BACKGROUND

1. Introduction

Consider the differential equation

$$\frac{dx}{dt}(t) + x(t) = t,$$

and put it in the familiar form

$$(D + 1)x = t. \tag{1.1}$$

In a spirit of naïve experimentation, one might write

$$\begin{aligned} x(t) &= \frac{1}{D+1}\,t \\ &= (1 - D + D^2 - \cdots + (-1)^n D^n + \cdots)t \\ &= t - 1, \end{aligned} \tag{1.2}$$

which substitution in (1.1) proves to be a correct solution.

With equal abandon, one might indulge in the following:

$$\begin{aligned} x(t) &= \frac{1}{D+1}\,t = \frac{1}{D}\,\frac{1}{1 + 1/D}\,t \\ &= \frac{1}{D}\left[1 - \frac{1}{D} + \frac{1}{D^2} + \cdots + \frac{(-1)^n}{D^n} + \cdots\right]t. \end{aligned} \tag{1.3}$$

As a not unreasonable guess interpret $1/D$, by its effect on functions of t, to be such that $(1/D)f(t) = \int_0^t f(\tau)\,d\tau$. One then arrives at

$$\begin{aligned} x(t) &= \left(\frac{1}{D} - \frac{1}{D^2} + \cdots + \frac{(-1)^n}{D^{n+1}} + \cdots\right)t \\ &= \frac{t^2}{2!} - \frac{t^3}{3!} + (-1)^n \frac{t^{n+1}}{(n+1)!} + \cdots, \end{aligned}$$

$$x(t) = e^{-t} + t - 1. \tag{1.4}$$

This, too, is a correct solution of (1.1).

A third approach, closely related to (1.3) and (1.4), recasts (1.1) as

$$e^{-t}D[e^{t}x(t)] = t, \tag{1.5}$$

and then proceeds, with the aid of integration by parts, thus:

$$\begin{aligned} D[e^{t}x(t)] &= te^{t} \\ e^{t}x(t) &= \frac{1}{D}(te^{t}) = \int_{0}^{t} \tau e^{\tau}\, d\tau \\ &= \tau e^{\tau}\Big|_{0}^{t} - \int_{0}^{t} e^{\tau}\, d\tau = te^{t} - e^{t} + 1; \end{aligned} \tag{1.6}$$

whence the conclusion that

$$x(t) = t - 1 + e^{-t}, \tag{1.7}$$

which coincides with the result of (1.4).

These computations illustrate in simplistic fashion the methods of operational calculus, also called symbolic calculus, a powerful tool for the solution of ordinary and partial differential equations of the kind encountered in physical applications.

The purpose of this text is to show the student that, far from being empty exercises in formalism, such methods are perfectly respectable; each one conforms to all the canons of mathematical propriety so long as it is employed in the correct environment (e.g., all three methods were successful in the above case, but replacing t on the right-hand side of (1.1) by e^{t} makes the procedure (1.2) inoperable, whereas procedures like that of (1.3) and that of (1.6) retain their usefulness). We shall study operational procedures appropriate to each of several classes of ordinary and partial differential equations prevalent in applied mathematics, physics, and engineering, and shall see that besides their usefulness in computing explicit solutions these methods also yield important theorems on the existence and uniqueness of solutions to such equations.

The interest of such theorems is not confined exclusively to mathematicians. A physicist or engineer, faced with an equation that purports to be a picture of some physical process or engineering system, will find it worthless unless he can be certain that a solution exists under the conditions specified by his laboratory data. On the other hand, if he is not assured that the solution is unique, either the equation is an insufficient mathematical model, because it furnishes an indeterminate description, or else he should return to the laboratory to see whether his experiment might not yield other equally valid results.

The operational method applied to one class of problem, say some types of partial differential equations with constant coefficients and given initial conditions, often differs a good deal from that which serves for a different class, say a partial differential equation with variable coefficients and given boundary values. Consequently, it is often considered appropriate to speak of different operational calculi. In this sense, we shall study three calculi: (a) one, for the solution of problems connected with linear differential equations with constant coefficients, and illustrated by the procedure of (1.6) above; (b) another, related to the procedure (1.3) (1.4), for partial differential equations with constant coefficients; (c) the third, a generalization of procedure (1.2), for the solution of certain classical linear partial differential equations, with constant or variable coefficients, of mathematical physics.

In spite of considerable differences in details of mathematical technique between these calculi, many essential ideas on which their justification and use are based in this book are common to all three. These ideas, which center on the study of generalized functions, an outgrowth of the distributions of L. Schwartz, are most apparent in case (a), where the foliage of computation and technical details is scanty enough not to encumber the view. For this reason, this case is treated at a leisurely pace and in detail over four chapters, I–IV, even though it is much more elementary and less applicable than (b) or (c). The study of the latter two, which occupies the second volume of this text, will thereby be simplified; the general pattern of reasoning behind the g.f. approach to operational calculus will by then be familiar to the student, and he will be in a position to study the technical details particular to cases (b) and (c) without losing sight of their role in the theory.

The rest of the present chapter is devoted to elementary samples of the three types of problem to which our operational calculi apply. These illustrative sections are designed to introduce some basic mathematical and physical ideas, and are followed by a few summary indications on the history of our subject and the manner of its presentation.

2. Operational Solution of an Elementary Initial-Value Problem

The simplest initial-value problem for ordinary differential equations consists in finding the function $x(t)$, defined for $t > 0$, which satisfies the equation

(2.1) $$Dx(t) = f(t) \qquad (t > 0)$$

and assumes the initial value

(2.2) $$x(+0) = 0.^{\dagger}$$

† $x(+0)$ stands for the limit of $x(t)$ as t tends to zero from the right ($t \to +0$).

Defining the operator D^{-1}, under appropriate restrictions on the operand, by

$$D^{-1}f = \int_0^t f(\tau)\, d\tau, \tag{2.3}$$

the solution of the problem takes the form

$$x(t) = D^{-1}f. \tag{2.4}$$

One is tempted to say that the application of the operators D^{-1} and D to both sides of (2.1) and (2.4), respectively, gives

$$D^{-1}(Dx) = x = D^{-1}f \quad \text{and} \quad Dx = D(D^{-1}f), \tag{2.5}$$

so that one writes the operator relation

$$DD^{-1} = D^{-1}D = I. \tag{2.6}$$

Here I, the identity operator, is defined by its effect on functions $w(t)$ by $Iw = w$.

One can in all legitimacy yield to this temptation, providing restrictions are placed on the class of functions (operands) to which the operators D and D^{-1} are applied. Indeed, confining the operands to functions $w(t)$, defined and continuously differentiable for $t > 0$, and for which $w(+0) = 0$, gives

$$D^{-1}(Dw) = \int_0^t w(\tau)\, d\tau = w(t) - w(+0) = w(t) \tag{2.7a}$$

$$D(D^{-1}w) = \frac{d}{dt}\int_0^t w(\tau)\, d\tau = w(t), \tag{2.7b}$$

thus proving the validity of the operator identity (2.6) *for this class of operands.*

It is impossible to apply this rudimentary operator algebra directly to the solution of equation (2.1) with the *non*vanishing initial condition

$$x(+0) = x_0 \neq 0, \tag{2.8}$$

because in this case $DD^{-1}x \neq D^{-1}Dx$.

One way to circumvent this difficulty is to first transform the problem (2.1) (2.8) into one with vanishing initial conditions by changing the dependent variable to $y(t) = x(t) - x_0$. While this makes it possible to build up an operational calculus applicable to problems with nonvanishing initial conditions it does not get at the heart of the matter—which is that, by broadening the class of operands to include certain "generalized functions," and by broadening the meaning of D and D^{-1}, one regains the commutativity of multiplication of these operators.

Broadly speaking, the approach consists in obtaining the solution of (2.1) (2.8) as the limit (in a sense to be touched on in § 3 below and defined in Chapters II and III) of the solutions $x_n(t)$ of a sequence of initial-value problems, each involving vanishing initial values $x_n(+0) = 0$ $(n = 1, 2, \ldots)$.

Specifically, consider the following sequence of problems $(n = 1, 2, \ldots)$:

$$Dx_n = x_0 q_n(t) + f(t) \qquad (t > 0), \tag{2.9}$$

$$x_n(+0) = 0, \tag{2.10}$$

where the $q_n(t)$ are the "pulse" functions

$$q_n(t) = \begin{cases} 0 & \text{for } t < 0 \\ n & \text{for } 0 \leqslant t \leqslant 1/n \\ 0 & \text{for } 1/n < t. \end{cases} \tag{2.11}$$

Because of (2.10), $D^{-1}Dx_n = DD^{-1}x_n = x_n(t)$. Therefore, the operational method applies to each of these problems, the solutions being

$$x_n(t) = D^{-1}f + x_0 D^{-1} q_n. \tag{2.12}$$

Since

$$D^{-1}q_n = \int_0^t q_n(\tau)\, d\tau = \begin{cases} nt & \text{for } 0 \leqslant t \leqslant 1/n \\ 1 & \text{for } 1/n \leqslant t \end{cases}$$

we find, for every $t > 0$,

$$\lim_{n\to\infty} x_n(t) = x_0 + \int_0^t f(\tau)\, d\tau, \tag{2.13}$$

which is the correct solution $x(t)$ of (2.1) (2.8), so that we may write

$$x(t) = x_0 \lim_{n\to\infty} (D^{-1}q_n) + D^{-1}f. \tag{2.14}$$

This suggests that, rather than solve an infinite sequence of problems and then compute the limit of their solutions, we first take the "limit problem" of the sequence and solve it. In other words, that we try to invert the order of application of the lim and D^{-1} operations in (2.14). To do this, set down the purely formal expression

$$\delta(t) = \lim_{n\to\infty} q_n \tag{2.15}$$

and make a formal exchange in the first term on the right in (2.9) and (2.14). This gives the "limit equation" and its "solution"

$$Dx = x_0\delta(t) + f(t), \tag{2.16}$$

$$x(t) = x_0 D^{-1}\delta + D^{-1}f. \tag{2.17}$$

In terms of ordinary calculus, all this is meaningless, since, by (2.11) and (2.15),

$$\delta(t) = \begin{cases} 0 & \text{for } t \neq 0 \\ +\infty & \text{for } t = 0 \end{cases} \tag{2.18}$$

is neither a function, nor does

$$D^{-1}\delta = \int_0^t \delta(\tau)\, d\tau$$

stand for anything but empty formalism.

The beauty of g.f. theory is that, not only does it infuse into such formalism a mathematically vigorous substance, but it provides a generalization of the analysis of functions that is in many respects much simpler than ordinary calculus, especially in its application to the solution of linear ordinary and partial differential, and other functional equations.

In terms of physical intuition, what we have done here is definitely meaningful and relevant. If we momentarily violate alphabetic tradition, denoting by $x(t)$ the momentum, mv, of a particle of constant mass, say, in motion on a straight line, and subject to a force $f(t)$ along this line, then equation (2.1) is an expression of Newton's second law and the initial condition $x(+0) = x_0$ represents the initial momentum, mv_0, of the particle.

On the other hand, equations (2.9) (2.10) characterize the motion of this same particle when the initial momentum vanishes, but when, in addition to $f(t)$, there is applied between $t = 0$ and $t = 1/n$ a brief "pulse" of force of intensity $x_0 q_n(t)$. The term $D^{-1}x_0 q_n$ in (2.12) then represents what physicists call the amount of *impulse*† of the force $x_0 q_n$. A hammer blow of given impulse x_0 on the particle at $t = 0$ is idealized by letting $n \to \infty$, and so is considered as an "infinite pulse" of force $x_0\, \delta(t)$. The fact that (2.1) with the initial value $x(+0) = 0$ has the same solution as (2.10) with the initial value $\lim_{n\to\infty} x_n(+0) = 0$ then expresses the following physical fact: two particles of mass m subject to the force $f(t)$ $(t > 0)$, one with initial velocity $v_0 \neq 0$ (initial momentum $x_0 = mv_0$), and the other with initial velocity zero but subjected at $t = 0$ to a hammer blow of impulse x_0, have the same momentum $x(t)$ for all $t > 0$ (and therefore the same motion if their initial displacements are equal).

3. The Dirac Delta Function

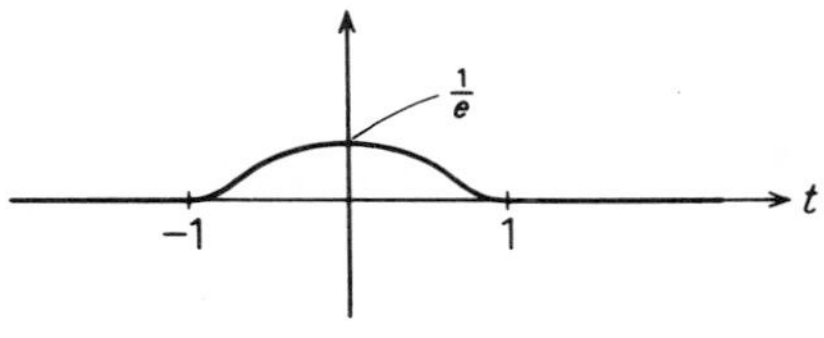

FIGURE 1

While we must defer to Chapter II the precise definition of g.f.'s, we can, at this stage, give at least an inkling of the approach that we shall follow by describing the delta function, $\delta(t)$, of Dirac.

Let $\mathscr{D}_-$ be the set of all functions $\varphi(t)$ that have continuous derivatives of every order for every real number t (these functions are called test

† It is recalled that the impulse of a force $\vec{F}(t)$ is defined in mechanics as $\int_{t_1}^{t_2} \vec{F}(t)dt$ and equals the change of momentum between t_1 and t_2 of the particle to which it is applied.

functions). An example of such a function (this will be proved in Chapter I) is

$$\varphi(t) = \begin{cases} 0 & \text{for } |t| \geqslant 1 \\ \exp\left(\dfrac{1}{t^2 - 1}\right) & \text{for } |t| < 1 \end{cases}$$

whose graph is given in Figure 1.

A function such as $q_n(t)$, defined in (2.11) above, that is continuous except for finite "jumps" and vanishes for $t < 0$, has the property that for every test function $\varphi(t)$ the integral

$$\int_{-\infty}^{\infty} q_n(t)\, \varphi(t)\, dt = n \int_0^{1/n} \varphi(t)\, dt \tag{3.1}$$

is finite. Let us represent the value of this integral by $\langle q_n, \varphi\rangle$; for a given $q_n(t)$ it defines a function whose domain is the set of test functions $\mathscr{D}_-$ and whose values are numerical. A function whose domain is another set A of functions and whose range is a set of real or complex numbers is called a *functional on* A. Thus, by means of (3.1) $q_n(t)$ defines a functional on $\mathscr{D}_-$, which we denote by q_n in the present section, and whose value at any $\varphi(t)$ in $\mathscr{D}_-$ is denoted by $\langle q_n, \varphi\rangle$.

The first distinction between the g.f. approach and ordinary calculus is that instead of studying the properties of functions like $q_n(t)$ as functions of t, one concentrates on their behavior as functionals on $\mathscr{D}_-$.

To gauge the effect of this attitude, consider the sequence $\{q_n(t)\}$. We saw in the last paragraph that, as a sequence of functions of t, it does not converge. As a sequence of functionals on $\mathscr{D}_-$, however, it behaves very much better.

By the theorem of the mean of integral calculus, we have for $n = 1, 2, \ldots$

$$\langle q_n, \varphi\rangle = n\, \frac{1}{n}\, \varphi(\tau_n) = \varphi(\tau_n), \tag{3.2}$$

where τ_n is an appropriate real number such that $0 < \tau_n < 1/n$. Consequently

$$\lim_{n\to\infty} \langle q_n, \varphi\rangle = \varphi(0), \tag{3.3}$$

and the sequence $\{q_n(t)\}$, thanks to (3.3), associates with every member $\varphi(t)$ of the set $\mathscr{D}_-$ of test functions, the number $\varphi(0)$; thereby defining a functional on $\mathscr{D}_-$. This functional is represented by the symbol δ and its value at $\varphi(t)$ by $\langle \delta, \varphi\rangle$, i.e.,

$$\langle \delta, \varphi\rangle = \varphi(0). \tag{3.4}$$

δ is called the Dirac delta function. It is not, we see, a function of t, but a functional on $\mathscr{D}_-$ (i.e., a function of φ). To summarize, the sequence q_n ($n = 1, 2, \ldots$) of *functionals on* $\mathscr{D}_-$ *does converge* and converges in fact to the functional δ on $\mathscr{D}_-$; it follows that when (2.15) is interpreted in terms of the convergence of functionals on $\mathscr{D}_-$, it takes on a well-defined meaning.

The *g.f.'s of class* $\mathscr{D}'_+$ are precisely those functionals on $\mathscr{D}_-$ which are functional limits of sequences of functionals determined by piecewise continuous functions [just as q_n is determined by $q_n(t)$ via (3.1)]. We shall see in Chapter II that we can define for these g.f.'s concepts of differentiation and integration which are true generalizations of everyday differentiation and integration.

Let us mention in passing that this definition of g.f.'s from sequences of functions is somewhat similar to the definition of real numbers in terms of sequences of rational numbers as employed in the theory of G. Cantor [25].

Remark on the physical relevance of g.f.'s. Besides the mathematical advantages of the g.f. outlook on differential equations, which we shall repeatedly encounter in later chapters, there are also serious physical reasons for considering g.f.'s. as natural mathematical models of physically observed quantities. One reason was mentioned in § 2: g.f.'s provide a means of describing such physical percussion phenomena as hammer blows or surges of electric curent. There are also other reasons, which lie in the interpretation of physical measurements. For example, suppose that $f(t)$ represents an electric current varying with time. If this current is measured in the laboratory with a thermocouple ammeter, say, is it not more realistic to interpret the "measurement at the instant t_0" as a weighted average $\int f(t)\,\varphi(t)\,dt$ over an interval of time containing the instant t_0 rather than as the actual value of $f(t_0)$? Following this interpretation, there is associated with every observation a test function. If different observations, corresponding to different test functions, are to conform to the same mathematical model, [e.g., a differential equation, such as (2.1)] the two sides of the equation must be equal when taken *as functionals* on $\mathscr{D}_-$ rather than as functions of t.

**4. Operational Solution of a Partial Differential Equation Initial-Value Problem

The operational calculus referred to as type (b) in the introduction will enable us to solve initial-value and boundary-value problems involving individual or simultaneous partial differential equations with constant coefficients in any number of variables. Such problems occur in the treatment of physical phenomena like the propagation of acoustic and electromagnetic waves, the temperature distribution in a heat conducting body, the bending of a plate subject to outside forces, etc.

To illustrate this calculus, we may consider, in a purely formal manner, the problem of finding a function $u(x, y, z, t)$, defined for all real x, y, z and for $t > 0$, given that it satisfies the equation with constant coefficients

(4.1) $$\frac{\partial u}{\partial t} = a\frac{\partial u}{\partial x} + b\frac{\partial u}{\partial y} + c\frac{\partial u}{\partial z} \qquad (t > 0)$$

and takes the initial values

(4.2) $$u(x, y, z, +0) = f(x, y, z).$$

Assuming the solution to exist, integrate both sides of (4.1) with respect to t, and use the operator notation:

$$Qg(x, y, z, t) = \int_0^t g(x, y, z, \tau)\, d\tau, \tag{4.3}$$

$$\frac{\partial g}{\partial x} = D_1 g, \qquad \frac{\partial g}{\partial y} = D_2 g, \qquad \frac{\partial g}{\partial z} = D_3 g.$$

We then obtain

$$u(x, y, z, t) - u(x, y, z, +0) = Q(aD_1 + bD_2 + cD_3)u \tag{4.4}$$

which we rewrite, in view of (4.2) (I is the identity operator),

$$[I + Q(aD_1 + bD_2 + cD_3)]u(x, y, z, t) = f(x, y, z).$$

Next put

$$u(x, y, z, t) = \frac{1}{I + Q(aD_1 + bD_2 + cD_3)} f(x, y, z), \tag{4.5}$$

and expand in a formal series

$$\begin{aligned} u(x, y, z, t) &= \sum_{n=0}^{\infty} (-1)^n Q^n (aD_1 + bD_2 + cD_3)^n f(x, y, z) \\ &= \sum_{n=0}^{\infty} (-1)^n \frac{t^n}{n!} (aD_1 + bD_2 + cD_3)^n f(x, y, z) \\ &= e^{-t(aD_1 + bD_2 + cD_3)} f(x, y, z) \end{aligned} \tag{4.6}$$

$$u(x, y, z, t) = e^{-atD_1} e^{-btD_2} e^{-ctD_3} f(x, y, z). \tag{4.7}$$

Putting the Taylor series of a function $g(x - at)$ in the form

$$g(x - at) = \sum_{n=0}^{\infty} (-1)^n \frac{a^n t^n}{n!} D_1^n g(x) = e^{-atD_1} g(x)$$

the relation (4.7) becomes

$$u(x, y, z, t) = f(x - at, y - bt, z - ct). \tag{4.8}$$

This, it is easy to check, is a correct solution, even if f does not allow expansion in a Taylor series. We shall see in Volume II that the computation which led us to it is entirely valid, providing we interpret it in terms of generalized functions of certain classes. These g.f.'s differ from those mentioned in § 3 in that they are functionals on a set of test functions $\varphi(x, y, z, t)$, which are analytic in x, y, z and which, as functions of t, resemble those of class $\mathscr{D}_-$. This operational method also serves to solve many classical boundary-value problems of mathematical physics, as we shall see later.

**5. Operational Solution of P.D.E. Initial-Boundary-Value Problems

The third type of operational method, called (c) in the introduction, is applicable to problems such as that of § 4 above, as well as to certain P.D.E.'s with variable coefficients. Such equations arise in the treatment of mixed initial- and boundary-value problems related to heat conduction, wave propagation, and other physical phenomena in spatial regions having particular geometric configurations. The method will be studied in Volume II. It is based on the use of g.f.'s which are functionals on sets of test functions that are analytic. To form an idea of its use, let us consider a formal solution of a P.D.E. initial-value problem. As in the two previous illustrations, we take an equation involving only first-order derivatives merely to make the example simple. Later, when we engage more seriously in the subject, we shall deal mostly with P.D.E.'s of higher orders.

The problem in question is: find $u(x, t)$, defined for $t > 0$ and x real, given the initial condition

$$u(x, +0) = f(x) \tag{5.1}$$

and the equation

$$\frac{\partial u}{\partial t} + tu = \frac{\partial u}{\partial x}. \tag{5.2}$$

Here we shall manipulate the operator $\partial/\partial x$ like a number, writing the equation as

$$\frac{\partial u}{\partial t} + \left(t - \frac{\partial}{\partial x}\right) u = 0 \tag{5.3}$$

so that it is analogous to an ordinary differential equation in t, which is linear. It is solved by means of the identity

$$\frac{d}{dt}\left(e^{\int a(t)dt} g(t)\right) = e^{\int a(t)dt}\left(\frac{dg}{dt} + a(t)\, g(t)\right),$$

where we take

$$a(t) = t - \frac{\partial}{\partial x}, \int a(t)\, dt = \frac{t^2}{2} - t\frac{\partial}{\partial x},$$

and put

$$\frac{\partial u}{\partial t} + \left(t - \frac{\partial}{\partial x}\right) u = e^{-t^2/2 + t\partial/\partial x} \cdot \frac{\partial}{\partial t}\left(e^{t^2/2 - t\partial/\partial x} u\right) = 0.$$

Formally, this suggests that

$$e^{t^2/2 - t\partial/\partial x} u(x, t) = c$$

where c is independent of t.

On letting $t \to +0$ and using (5.1) we find $c = f(x)$, and so

$$u(x, t) = e^{-t^2/2} e^{+t\partial/\partial x} f(x), \tag{5.4}$$

$$u(x, t) = e^{-t^2/2} f(x + t). \tag{5.5}$$

That this is a correct solution of the problem is instantly verified by substitution. When we justify this procedure, we shall see that this solution is unique.

6. Historical Indications

The history of operational methods and of generalized functions vividly testifies to the fruitfulness of cross-fertilization between mathematics, the physical sciences, and engineering. It is, however, far too vast a subject—it begins with Leibniz in the seventeenth century—for us to enter upon; a few names, and the barest of indications about their roles, is all we shall set down here.

The first extensive development of operational methods directed at problems of mathematical physics and engineering is due to O. Heaviside (1850–1925). Posthumously his genius received a fair share of praise, including the description of his calculus by E. T. Whittaker, as one of the three most important mathematical advances of the last quarter of the nineteenth century. Initially, the reaction of the mathematical community was anything but graceful—partly because much of this illuminating work consisted of a combination of ad hoc devices so devoid of mathematical rigor that it was difficult to see why the method works. Heaviside, himself, confessed his ignorance of the real reasons as to why his formal methods often gave correct solutions in the statement: "Shall I refuse my dinner because I do not fully understand the process of digestion?"† Sometimes, he also got incorrect solutions.

Since 1919 (T. J. Ia Bromwich [5]), there have appeared many and diverse mathematically rigorous justifications of this method, a preponderant number among them confined to the operator calculus for ordinary differential equations with constant coefficients. Broadly speaking, they stand in two categories: the *direct*, operator, *methods* (in which algebras of operators D, $D^{-1}, f(D)$ are constructed directly) and the *indirect*, integral transform, *methods*. The latter, of which the Laplace transform procedure, familiar to most engineers, is representative, is in a sense an evasion of the mathematical issue posed by Heaviside. Indeed, with it a differential equation relating an unknown $x(t)$ and a known $f(t)$ is not solved directly; instead, one solves an algebraic equation in an "image space" of complex-valued functions which relates the images

$$\bar{x}(s) = \int_0^\infty e^{-st}\, x(t)\, dt, \qquad \bar{f}(s) = \int_0^\infty e^{-st} f(t)\, dt;$$

after which one seeks the explicit form of the "original" $x(t)$ of $\bar{x}(s)$. Note that an equation like $Dx(t) = e^{t^2}$ with $x(+0)$ given does not submit to this approach since $\int_0^\infty e^{-st}e^{t^2}\, dt$ does not exist. It does, however, submit to the direct method.

In this book, it is on the direct method that we concentrate; for each of the three types of operational calculi mentioned earlier, the algebraic

† A remark made by the physicist Ernst Mach in a different context (*The Science of Mechanics* (4th German ed.), chap. IV, § IV.5) is worth recalling: "Whoever pursues mathematics without procuring for himself enlightenment in the indicated direction must often receive the uncomfortable impression that paper and pencil surpass him, as it were, in intelligence."

manipulation of such symbols as

$$D, \qquad D^{-1}, \qquad \sum_{n=0}^{\infty} a_n D^{-n} \frac{\partial^{2n}}{\partial x^n \, \partial y^n}$$

is rigorously justified by treating them as operators on appropriate classes of operands consisting of generalized functions.

The first comprehensive development of the theories of different classes of g.f.'s was given by L. Schwartz in 1948. He applied some of these classes to the justification of parts of the Heaviside calculus in the treatise "Théorie des Distributions." These distributions are functionals (cf. § 3 above) on sets of infinitely differentiable functions.

When the test functions are also analytic, the corresponding functionals are sometimes called hyperdistributions (Ehrenpreis [15]) or analytic distributions. Their systematic investigation and application to the direct operational method for Partial Differential Equations was initiated by Gel'fand and Šilov (see [22] for an account). Distributions, as well as hyperdistributions, are called generalized functions—whence our adoption of the abbreviation g.f., introduced by Lighthill [34], to designate either one of these types of functionals.

7. Outline and Background

The division of topics is this:

A. Operational Calculus for G.F.'s of Class $\mathscr{D}'_+$

This is the operational calculus exemplified in § 2 above. We shall apply it to ordinary linear differential equations with constant coefficients and to systems of such equations, as well as to some integral equations. The presentation, which occupies Chapters I–IV of this volume, is based on the work of L. Schwartz [43, vol. II] and is rendered elementary by an adaptation and simplification of G. Temple's sequence approach to g.f.'s.

Sources: Schwartz [43] [46], Temple [50] [51], Doetsch [14].

B. Structure of $\mathscr{D}'_+$ *G.F.'s*

Some deeper properties of g.f.'s are studied and basic theorems proved within the framework of classical analysis (Chapters V–VI). This treatment is addressed primarily to the student of mathematics with a solid advanced calculus background. The basic ideas are simple enough, but some of the computational details require attention on the part of the student.

Sources: Schwartz [43], Halperin [26].

C. Laplace Transforms in $\mathscr{D}'_+$

Introduction to the Laplace transform in $\mathscr{D}'_+$. Introduction to the application of the L.T. (Laplace transform) to differential, difference, and partial differential equations.

Sources: Schwartz [46], Doetsch [14], Widder [54] [56].

D. Periodic G.F.'s—Fourier Series

An introductory study of periodic g.f.'s. The treatment is elementary and illustrates the wide applicability of the pattern of ideas introduced in Chapter II. The g.f. version of Fourier series is considerably more accessible than the classical theory. It is given here in elementary terms.

Sources: Schwartz [46], Temple [51].

These four subjects are gathered in Volume I. As they are approached mostly within the framework of functions of a single real variable, and without the use of analytic function theory, the demands on the student's mathematical background are kept within modest bounds.

Volume II will center on the study of g.f. classes for which the operational calculi illustrated in §§ 4 and 5 above are valid. Some knowledge of analytic function theory is required there. Many of the basic ideas, however, are the same as in Volume I.

SUGGESTED READING

Courant and Hilbert, "Methods of Mathematical Physics" [12], preface to vol. I.

CHAPTER I

OPERATIONAL CALCULUS ON $\mathscr{D}_-$

1. Terminology

The overwhelming majority of functions with which we shall deal are complex-valued (have their range in the set of complex numbers). It will simplify our language if we now agree once and for all that, except when otherwise explicitly specified, the term *function on D* designates a complex-valued function whose domain is D.

A function, $f(t)$,† on R is a $C^k(R)$ *function* ($k \geqslant 0$, integer) if $f(t), f'(t), \ldots, f^{(k)}(t)$ are continuous on R (i.e., the *real-valued* functions $f_1(t), \ldots, f_1^{(k)}(t)$ and $f_2(t), \ldots, f_2^{(k)}(t)$, where $f(t) = f_1(t) + if_2(t)$ are all continuous on R). When this holds for every positive integer k we write $C^\infty(R)$ and call $f(t)$ infinitely differentiable.

The carrier (supporting set) of a function on R is the *closure*, $\bar{\Delta}$, of the subset Δ of R on which the function does not vanish. Whenever a set S contains the carrier of a function f, f is said to be *carried in S*. In the case of functions on R, the containing set S considered will frequently be a *forward half-line* $[a, +\infty)$, a backward half-line $(-\infty, b]$, a closed interval $[a, b]$, or an open interval (a, b).

A scalar is a complex number.

An appendix to this chapter summarizes a few essentials of the calculus of complex-valued functions of a real variable.

2. Test Functions of Class $\mathscr{D}_-$

A $C^\infty(R)$ function $\varphi(t)$ that is carried in a *backward half-line* $(-\infty, b]$ will be called a test function of class $\mathscr{D}_-$, and one writes $\varphi \in \mathscr{D}_-$, $\varphi(t) \in \mathscr{D}_-$. One such function is the identically zero function on R. There are also

† It is more precise to use the symbol f to denote a function, reserving $f(t)$ for its value at the element t of its domain. However, following a well-established tradition, we shall often use $f(t)$ to designate either the function, or its value, relying on the context to indicate which of the two is meant. This has some advantages and should cause no difficulty.

nontrivial functions of class $\mathscr{D}_-$; an example is $\varphi(t)$, defined by

$$(2.1) \qquad \varphi(t) = \begin{cases} 0 & \text{for } t \geqslant 0 \\ e^{1/t} & \text{for } t < 0, \end{cases}$$

which, being positive for $t < 0$, is nontrivial.

Let us prove that $\varphi \in \mathscr{D}_-$:

(1) *$\varphi(t)$ is a function on R and is carried in a backward half-line.*

Indeed $\varphi(t)$ is well defined at every $t \in R$ and vanishes for $t \geqslant 0$, so that it is carried in the half-line $(-\infty, 0]$. In fact this half-line is actually the carrier of $\varphi(t)$.

(2) $\varphi(t) \in C^\infty(R)$.

At every $t \neq 0$, φ is obviously continuous. At $t = 0$, $\varphi(0) = 0 = \varphi(+0)$. Also the left-hand limit $\varphi(-0) = 0$ so φ is continuous at $t = 0$ also.

The elementary computations leading to

$$(2.2) \qquad \frac{d\varphi}{dt} = -\frac{1}{t^2} e^{1/t}$$

$$(2.2') \qquad \frac{d^2\varphi}{dt^2} = \frac{1 + 2t}{t^4} e^{1/t}$$

when $t < 0$ suggest that, for all $n \geqslant 1$,

$$(2.3) \qquad \frac{d^n\varphi}{dt^n} = \frac{P_{n-1}(t)}{t^{2n}} e^{1/t} \qquad \text{if } t < 0,$$

where $P_{n-1}(t)$ is a polynomial in t of degree $n - 1$. On differentiating both sides of (2.3), we get

$$(2.4) \qquad \frac{d^{n+1}\varphi}{dt^{n+1}} = \frac{P'_{n-1}(t)t^2 - (2nt + 1)P_{n-1}(t)}{t^{2n+2}} e^{1/t}.$$

If $P_{n-1}(t)$ were of degree $(n - 1)$, the degree of the numerator in (2.4) would then be n. Since for $n = 1$ $P_{n-1}(t)$ is, in fact, of degree $n - 1$, we have proved by induction that (2.3) is true for all $n \geqslant 1$ as well.

From this and (2.1), we conclude that $\varphi^{(n)}(t)$ exists and is continuous at every $t \neq 0$ with

$$(2.5) \qquad \varphi^{(n)}(t) = \begin{cases} 0 & \text{for } t > 0 \\ \dfrac{P_{n-1}(t)}{t^{2n}} e^{1/t} & \text{for } t < 0, \end{cases}$$

also

$$(2.6) \qquad \varphi^{(n)}(+0) = 0.$$

Let us now prove that

$$(2.7) \qquad \lim_{t \to -0} \frac{d^n e^{1/t}}{dt^n} = \varphi^{(n)}(-0) = 0.$$

Taking $1/t = -x$ we find

$$\lim_{t \to -0} \frac{e^{1/t}}{t^{2n}} = \lim_{x \to +\infty} \frac{(-x)^{2n}}{e^{+x}} = 0. \tag{2.8}$$

To see this, note that, for $x \geqslant 0$, Taylor's formula proves that $e^x \geqslant 1 + x^{2n+1}/(2n+1)!$, so that

$$0 \leqslant \frac{x^{2n}}{e^x} \leqslant \frac{x^{2n}}{1 + x^{2n+1}/(2n+1)!},$$

where the right-hand side has the limit 0 as $x \to +\infty$.

This, with the fact that $P_{n-1}(t)$ is bounded on every interval of finite length, allows us to conclude from (2.5) that (2.7) is indeed true.

The theorem of the mean of differential calculus ensures for every $h \neq 0$ the existence of $\theta_h < 1$ such that

$$\frac{\varphi(h) - \varphi(0)}{h} = \varphi'(\theta_h h).$$

Letting $h \to 0$, it results from (2.6) and (2.7) that $\varphi'(0)$ exists and equals 0. Repetition of this argument proves that $\varphi^{(n)}(t)$ exists and that

$$\varphi^{(n)}(0) = 0. \tag{2.9}$$

With this, the proof that $\varphi^{(n)}(t)$ is continuous on R is complete.

Other examples of test functions of class $\mathscr{D}_-$ are

$$\varphi(t) = \begin{cases} 0 & \text{for } t \geqslant b \\ \exp \dfrac{1}{(t-b)^\alpha} & \text{for } t < b \quad (\text{integer } \alpha > 0); \end{cases} \tag{2.10}$$

these are carried in the backward half-line $(-\infty, b]$.

Yet another example of a $\mathscr{D}_-$ function is

$$\rho_\varepsilon(t) = \begin{cases} 0 & \text{for } |t| \geqslant \varepsilon > 0 \\ \dfrac{k}{\varepsilon} e^{\varepsilon^2/(t^2-\varepsilon^2)} & \left(\text{here } k = 1\Big/\int_{-1}^{1} e^{1/(t^2-1)}\, dt\right). \end{cases} \tag{2.11}$$

We shall make repeated use of this particular function later on. Observe that its carrier is the interval $[-\varepsilon, \varepsilon]$, that $\rho_\varepsilon(t) \geqslant 0$ and that $\int_{-\infty}^{\infty} \rho_\varepsilon(t)\, dt = 1$.

3. The Test Space $\mathscr{D}_-$. Derivative Polynomials on $\mathscr{D}_-$

$\mathscr{D}_-$, the set of all $C^\infty(R)$ functions, each of which is carried in a backward half-line, is called a test space. It is a *linear space*, which implies that it has the property:

$$c_1, c_2 \in C;\ \varphi_1, \varphi_2 \in \mathscr{D}_- \Rightarrow c_1\varphi_1 + c_2\varphi_2 \in \mathscr{D}_-. \tag{3.1}$$

(The function $c_1\varphi_1 + c_2\varphi_2$ is called a *linear combination* of the functions φ_1 and φ_2.)

Definition 3.1. *An operator* Ω *on a set* A *(of operands) is a transformation which carries every element* f *of* A *into one well-defined element* Ωf *of* A.

The simplest operator is the identity operator I, which transforms $f \in A$ into $If = f$.

Our concern in this section is with certain operators (called derivative polynomials) *on the particular set of operands* $\mathscr{D}_-$. Differentiation is a transformation applicable to every element $\varphi \in \mathscr{D}_-$ and which carries it into the well-defined element $\varphi' \in \mathscr{D}_-$. This transformation defines the derivative or differentiation operator D on $\mathscr{D}_-$ and we write $D\varphi$ or $D\varphi(t)$ for the derivative $\varphi'(t)$.

If Ω_1 and Ω_2 are operators on the same set of operands A, one writes $\Omega_2\Omega_1$ for the operator which takes every $f \in A$ into the element $\Omega_2(\Omega_1 f)$, and one denotes by $\Omega_1\Omega_2$ the operator which carries every $f \in A$ into the element $\Omega_1(\Omega_2 f)$. $\Omega_2\Omega_1$ and $\Omega_1\Omega_2$ are called *products* of the operators Ω_1 and Ω_2. Of course, this form of multiplication is *not always commutative*: $\Omega_2\Omega_1$ and $\Omega_1\Omega_2$ may very well be different operators (two *operators* Ω and Ω' *are equal* (as operators on A) *if and only if*, $\Omega f = \Omega' f$ for every $f \in A$).† Operator multiplication is, however, always associative: for any three operators Ω_1, Ω_2, Ω_3 on A it is always true that $\Omega_1(\Omega_2\Omega_3) = (\Omega_1\Omega_2)\Omega_3$; thus the parentheses are superfluous and this product may, without ambiguity, be represented by $\Omega_1\Omega_2\Omega_3$. An operator product $\Omega \cdots \Omega$ of p identical operators is symbolized by Ω^p.

The derivative of any order p in $\mathscr{D}_-$ is then the result of applying the product operator D^p

$$\varphi^{(p)}(t) = D^p\varphi,$$

and for any positive integers p, q there holds on the operand set $\mathscr{D}_-$ the relation

$$D^pD^q = D^qD^p = D^{p+q}, \tag{3.2}$$

since for every $\varphi(t) \in \mathscr{D}_-$, $D^p(D^q\varphi) = D^q(D^p\varphi) = D^{p+q}\varphi$.

If $r, s, \ldots$ are complex numbers and $\varphi(t) \in \mathscr{D}_-$ the functions $r\varphi(t)$, $s\varphi(t), \ldots$ also $\in \mathscr{D}_-$. Thus, every complex number defines an operator on $\mathscr{D}_-$; it is denoted by the same symbol as the number (this is simpler than denoting it by rI where I is the identity operator on $\mathscr{D}_-$).

---

† It may well happen that Ω and Ω' are operators on a set B that contains A and that $\Omega f = \Omega' f$ for $f \in A$, while for some $f \in B$, $f \notin A$, $\Omega f \neq \Omega' f$. Therefore, in discussing the properties of operators, it is essential always to specify the set of operands with which one is dealing.

Besides the multiplication of operators one defines addition and linear combinations, providing these are possible in the set A of operands [and by (3.1) they are in the particular case $A = \mathscr{D}_-$]. The *product* $c\Omega$ of the operator Ω *by the scalar* c and the *linear combination* $c_1\Omega_1 + c_2\Omega_2$ are then defined in the obvious way by their action on A: viz., for every $f \in A$,

$$(c\Omega)f = c(\Omega f)$$
$$(c_1\Omega_1 + c_2\Omega_2)f = c_1(\Omega_1 f) + c_2(\Omega_2 f).$$

(If $c_1 = c_2 = 1$, this last gives $\Omega_1 + \Omega_2$, called the sum of Ω_1 and Ω_2.)

In the case of the *operand space* $\mathscr{D}_-$, the operators r and s, defined by two complex numbers, and the derivative operators $D^p D^q$ can be combined into the sums $D^p + r$ and $D^q + s$. These sums can be multiplied, yielding for every $\varphi(t) \in \mathscr{D}_-$

$$(D^p + r)(D^q + s)\varphi = (D^q + s)(D^p + r)\varphi = (D^{p+q} + rD^q + sD^p + rs)\varphi.$$

Thus $(D^p + r)$, $(D^q + s)$ commute under operator multiplication and we have proved the validity of the operator identity (on $\mathscr{D}_-$):

(3.3) $$(D^p + r)(D^q + s) = (D^q + s)(D^p + r) = D^{p+q} + rD^q + sD^p + rs.$$

Of course all this is trivial; (3.2) and (3.3) are known from elementary calculus. Our reason for harping on these matters has been to introduce the notion and language of operators on $\mathscr{D}_-$. This has now been done in sufficient detail for the reader to verify for himself that all the properties of ordinary algebraic polynomials in the indeterminate x which depend on addition and multiplication alone directly yield corresponding properties for the operator (on $\mathscr{D}_-$) expressions obtained when D is substituted for x. These operator expressions we shall call *derivative or differentiation polynomials.*

In particular, it is clear that, just as an algebraic polynomial

$$P(x) = a_0x^p + a_1x^{p-1} + \cdots + a_{p-1}x + a_p$$

can be factored in the form

$$P(x) = a_0(x - r_1)^{p_1}(x - r_2)^{p_2} \cdots (x - r_l)^{p_l},$$

where the complex numbers $r_1, r_2, \ldots, r_l$ are the zeros of $P(x)$ of orders $p_1, p_2, \ldots, p_l$ respectively $(p_1 + p_2 + \cdots + p_l = p)$, so we have the operator identity for $P(D)$:

(3.4) $$a_0D^p + a_1D^{p-1} + \cdots + a_{p-1}D + a_p$$
$$\equiv a_0(D - r_1)^{p_1}(D - r_2)^{p_2} \cdots (D - r_l)^{p_l}.$$

Indeed, the application of the left-hand side of this relation to any $\varphi(t) \in \mathscr{D}_-$ gives the same function $P(D)\varphi \in \mathscr{D}_-$ obtained on applying the right-hand side.

The binomial expansion of algebra has as its analogue the binomial expansion of the operator $(D - r)^p$ on $\mathscr{D}_-$:

$$(D - r)^p = \sum_{n=0}^{p} (-1)^{p-n} \binom{p}{n} r^{p-n} D^n. \tag{3.5}$$

There is, however, a considerably simpler way of computing $(D - r)^p$ than as a linear combination of derivative monomials $r^{p-n}D^n$, and that is by means of the important *shift relation* for nonnegative p:

$$(D - r)^p \varphi = e^{rt} D^p [e^{-rt} \varphi(t)]. \tag{3.6}$$

For $p = 1$ its truth is obvious:

$$e^{rt} D(e^{-rt}\varphi(t)) = e^{rt}e^{-rt}(D\varphi - r\varphi) = (D - r)\varphi.$$

For integer $p > 1$ an easy induction on p proves it. For $p = 0$ it holds because we define $(D - r)^0$ to be the identity operator on $\mathscr{D}_-$.

4. The Inversion of the Operator D

Whenever one encounters, as above, a situation to which part of a familiar symbolism (in this case, addition and multiplication of polynomials) can be extended, one instinctively seeks to extend the rest of the symbolism or, if that is impossible, to determine the nature of the obstacles to such a generalization. This attitude has led to the development and rigorous formulation of various Operational Calculi for the solution of differential, partial differential, and other equations, as we shall see on repeated occasions beginning with the present one.

The algebra of derivative polynomials so far considered is applicable not simply to the operand space $\mathscr{D}_-$, but to the much larger set of $C^\infty(R)$ functions. However, when it comes to extending this algebra to include the "division" of one derivative polynomial by another, it is necessary to restrict the operand space, as was seen in § 2 of the previous chapter. For our purposes, a very convenient restriction is to $\mathscr{D}_-$ (the advantages of this choice will become obvious in Chapter III).

The first essential step towards a theory of division of our operators is to find an operator on $\mathscr{D}_-$, call it D^{-1}, of course, which is inverse to D; by which we mean that for every $\varphi \in \mathscr{D}_-$

$$D^{-1}(D\varphi) = D(D^{-1}\varphi) = \varphi, \tag{4.1}$$

a relation which in operator form is

$$D^{-1}D = DD^{-1} = I. \tag{4.2}$$

Because $D\varphi(t) = \varphi'(t)$, one is liable to take antidifferentiation to define D^{-1}; that is

$$D^{-1}\varphi = \int \varphi(t)\,dt = \Phi(t) + C_1$$

where $\Phi(t)$ is a primitive function of $\varphi(t)$. This will not do, however, for these reasons: C_1 being an arbitrary constant, $D^{-1}\varphi$ is not uniquely defined; also $D^{-1}D\varphi(t) = \int \varphi'(t)\,dt = \varphi(t) + C_2$ (C_2 is an arbitrary constant) whereas

$$DD^{-1}\varphi = D(\Phi(t) + C_1) = \varphi(t)$$

so that $DD^{-1}\varphi$ and $D^{-1}D\varphi$ are not necessarily equal.

These defects do not occur if we use a definite integral for D^{-1}:

Definition 4.1. *The operator D^{-1} on the operand space $\mathscr{D}_-$ is defined by its action on every $\varphi(t) \in \mathscr{D}_-$ by the relation*

$$D^{-1}\varphi(\tau) = \int_{+\infty}^{t} \varphi(\tau)\,d\tau \left(= -\int_{t}^{+\infty} \varphi(\tau)\,d\tau \right). \tag{4.3}$$

To every $\varphi(t) \in \mathscr{D}_-$ corresponds $b_\varphi \in R$ such that $\varphi(t) = 0$ for $t \geqslant b_\varphi$, (4.3) is therefore the same as

$$D^{-1}\varphi(t) = \int_{b_\varphi}^{t} \varphi(\tau)\,d\tau. \tag{4.3$'$}$$

Thus $D^{-1}\varphi$ belongs to $\mathscr{D}_-$ and is unique, i.e., well-defined, being the only element of $\mathscr{D}_-$ into which φ is transformed by the definite integral on the right. It is immediately verified that (4.1) is always true with this definition of D^{-1} and so (4.2) is always true on the set $\mathscr{D}_-$ of operands.

Let us agree to represent the identity operator I on $\mathscr{D}_-$ by D^0 (in accordance with the prevalent practice of considering a function φ as the derivative of order zero of φ). The operator relation (4.2) is then written in the more suggestive form

$$D^{-1}D = DD^{-1} = D^0. \tag{4.4}$$

This relation expresses the fact that on the operand space $\mathscr{D}_-$, D^{-1} is a left-inverse of D (i.e., $D^{-1}D = D^0$) and also a right-inverse of D (i.e., $DD^{-1} = D^0$). Such a situation is a particular case of the conditions described in the following general theorem:

Theorem 4.1. *Let Ω_1 and Ω_2 be operators on the operand set A such that Ω_1 is both a left-inverse and a right-inverse of Ω_2. Then Ω_1 is the only left-inverse and the only right-inverse of Ω_2 on A. For this reason, it is called the inverse of Ω_2.*

Proof. Let us show that Ω_1 is the only left-inverse of Ω_2.

Suppose there were another left-inverse Ω_1'. We would then have

$$\Omega_1'\Omega_2 = I.$$

Multiplying both sides on the right by Ω_1 gives

$$\Omega_1'\Omega_2\Omega_1 = I\Omega_1,$$

which, since $\Omega_2\Omega_1 = I$ by hypothesis, gives, in view of the associativity of operator multiplication,

$$\Omega_1'I = I\Omega_1.$$

But for any operator Ω we have $\Omega I = I\Omega = \Omega$ (since $\Omega If = \Omega(If) = \Omega f$ and $I\Omega f = I(\Omega f) = \Omega f$ for every $f \in A$ by the definition of the identity operator), so finally

$$\Omega_1' = \Omega_1.$$

The proof that Ω_1 is also the only right-inverse of Ω_2 on A proceeds along similar lines and is left to the reader. ∎

Corollary. *The operator D^{-1} on $\mathscr{D}_-$ defined in* (4.3) *is the only inverse of D.*

Remark. This corollary can be proved without the general algebraic Theorem 4.1 since it is a fact resulting from elementary calculus that $\int_{b_\varphi}^t \varphi(\tau)\, d\tau$ is the only primitive function of φ that belongs to $\mathscr{D}_-$. The explanation for our choice of this algebraic proof of the uniqueness of the inverse of D is that it happens to be a prototype of proofs of some much deeper results of operational calculus that we shall meet later.

From the definition of D^{-1}, it follows that the product $(D^{-1})^p$ ($p > 0$, integer), which we symbolize by D^{-p}, transforms $\varphi(t) \in \mathscr{D}_-$ into

$$D^{-p}\varphi = \int_{+\infty}^{t} \int_{+\infty}^{t_{p-1}} \cdots \int_{+\infty}^{t_1} \varphi(t_0)\, dt_0 \cdots dt_{p-2}\, dt_{p-1}. \tag{4.5}$$

Let us momentarily write $\Phi_p(t) = D^{-p}\varphi$; (4.5) can then be stated as

$$\Phi_p(t) = \int_{+\infty}^{t} \Phi_{p-1}(\tau)\, d\tau = \int_{b_\varphi}^{t} \Phi_{p-1}(\tau)\, d\tau$$

which on integrating by parts gives ($d_\tau(t - \tau) = -d\tau$)

$$\Phi_p(t) = -(t - \tau)\Phi_{p-1}(\tau)\Big|_{\tau=b_\varphi}^{\tau=t} + \int_{b_\varphi}^{t} (t - \tau)\Phi_{p-2}(\tau)\, d\tau$$

$$= \int_{+\infty}^{t} (t - \tau)\Phi_{p-2}(\tau)\, d\tau.$$

Again integrating by parts ($-d_\tau (t-\tau)^2/2! = (t-\tau)\,d\tau$)

$$\Phi_p(t) = -\frac{(t-\tau)^2}{2!}\Phi_{p-2}(\tau)\Big|_{\tau=b\varphi}^{\tau=t} + \int_{b\varphi}^{t} \frac{(t-\tau)^2}{2!}\Phi_{p-3}(\tau)\,d\tau$$

$$= \int_{+\infty}^{t} \frac{(t-\tau)^2}{2!}\Phi_{p-3}(\tau)\,d\tau.$$

Continuing thus we find that (4.5) can be replaced by

$$D^{-p}\varphi = \int_{+\infty}^{t} \frac{(t-\tau)^{p-1}}{(p-1)!}\varphi(\tau)\,d\tau. \tag{4.5'}$$

From (4.5) it follows that whenever p, q are nonnegative integers and $\varphi \in \mathscr{D}_-$:

$$D^{-q}D^{-p}\varphi = D^{-p}D^{-q}\varphi = D^{-p-q}\varphi,$$

$$D^{q}D^{-p}\varphi = D^{-p}D^{q}\varphi = D^{q-p}\varphi,$$

providing D^0 is taken, as before, to represent the identity operator on $\mathscr{D}_-$. Thus we have derived the following generalization of (3.2) for all integer p, q (positive, negative, or zero):

$$D^pD^q = D^qD^p = D^{p+q}. \tag{4.6}$$

Given $\varphi \in \mathscr{D}_-$, $r \in C$ (the class of complex numbers), *p a nonnegative integer*, denote momentarily by Ω the operator on $\mathscr{D}_-$ defined by

$$\Omega\varphi(t) = e^{rt}D^{-p}(e^{-rt}\varphi(t)).$$

In view of the shift relation (3.6) and (4.6) we have

$$(D-r)^p\{\Omega\varphi(t)\} = e^{rt}D^p\{e^{-rt}e^{rt}D^{-p}(e^{-rt}\varphi(t))\} = \varphi(t)$$

and

$$\Omega\{(D-r)^p\varphi(t)\} = e^{rt}D^{-p}\{e^{-rt}e^{rt}D^{p}(e^{-rt}\varphi(t))\} = \varphi(t),$$

proving that Ω is both a left- and a right-inverse of $(D-r)^p$ on $\mathscr{D}_-$. Applying Theorem 4.1 we see that it is the *unique inverse operator of $(D-r)^p$ on $\mathscr{D}_-$*. For this reason Ω will henceforth be denoted by $(D-r)^{-p}$. We may combine this with the shift formula (3.6) and state

Theorem 4.2. *For any integer p, any complex number r and $\varphi \in \mathscr{D}_-$, there holds the shift relation*

$$(D-r)^p\varphi(t) = e^{rt}D^p(e^{-rt}\varphi(t)). \tag{4.7}$$

With this and (4.6) one easily proves for any integers p and q the following operator identity on $\mathscr{D}_-$ which generalizes (4.6):

$$(D-r)^p(D-r)^q = (D-r)^q(D-r)^p = (D-r)^{p+q} \tag{4.8}$$

Also from (4.7) we deduce (Exercise I.10) that for any scalars r, s and arbitrary integers p, q we have on $\mathscr{D}_-$:

(4.9) $$(D - r)^p(D - s)^q = (D - s)^q(D - r)^p.$$

5. Operational Calculus on $\mathscr{D}_-$. Existence and Uniqueness of Solutions of Differential Equations

The basic algebra of polynomials in the operator D on $\mathscr{D}_-$ is entirely analogous to that of polynomials in one variable in ordinary algebra. This is a consequence of the addition and multiplication properties derived in the last two sections and explains the convenience of operational calculus on $\mathscr{D}_-$.

Among the problems which can be handled by this operational method are: (A) the solution of a linear differential equation of arbitrary order with constant coefficients and (B) the solution of a system of simultaneous differential equations of this kind. In the present section, we treat the single-equation case. The other case will be considered in the more general context of Chapter IV. It must be pointed out that while we shall confine the known and unknown functions in our problem to $\mathscr{D}_-$ at this stage, the procedures and the algebraic manipulations carry over verbatim to generalized function operands.

Problem A. *Given $\psi \in \mathscr{D}_-$ find $\varphi \in \mathscr{D}_-$ such that*

(5.1) $$a_0 \frac{d^p\varphi}{dt^p} + a_1 \frac{d^{p-1}\varphi}{dt^{p-1}} + \cdots + a_p\varphi = \psi,$$

where $t \in R$ and $a_0, a_1, \ldots, a_p$ are real- or complex-valued constants ($a_0 \neq 0$).

This differential equation of order p, expressed in operational form, is

(5.1′) $$(a_0D^p + a_1D^{p-1} + \cdots + a_p)\varphi = \psi,$$

or more briefly, writing $P(D)$ for the operator polynomial on the left,

(5.1″) $$P(D)\varphi = \psi.$$

Solution. Factoring the algebraic polynomial $P(x)$ as

$$a_0x^p + a_1x^{p-1} + \cdots + a_p = a_0(x - r_1)^{p_1}(x - r_2)^{p_2} \cdots (x - r_l)^{p_l},$$

where $r_1, r_2, \ldots, r_l$ ($l \leqslant p$) are the distinct zeros of $P(x)$; r_1 being of order p_1, r_2 of order $p_2, \ldots, r_l$ of order p_l ($p_1 + p_2 + \cdots + p_l = p$), we may, following (3.4), rewrite (5.1) in the form

(5.2) $$a_0(D - r_1)^{p_1}(D - r_2)^{p_2} \cdots (D - r_l)^{p_l}\varphi = \psi.$$

In view of the commutativity of operator multiplication, the order of the factors $(D - r_i)^{p_i}$ on the left is, of course, indifferent.

The commutativity and associativity of multiplication of the operators involved and identity (4.8) prove that the operator on $\mathscr{D}_-$,

$$P^{-1}(D) = \frac{1}{a_0}(D - r_1)^{-p_1}(D - r_2)^{-p_2} \cdots (D - r_l)^{-p_l}, \tag{5.3}$$

is the inverse of $P(D)$; it is a right-inverse,

$$P(D)\,P^{-1}(D) = I; \tag{5.4a}$$

and it is a left-inverse,

$$P^{-1}(D)\,P(D) = I. \tag{5.4b}$$

By Theorem 4.1, P^{-1} is then the unique inverse of P and this proves that (5.1) has the solution $P^{-1}\psi$ and that it is unique. It is instructive to further analyze the role of P^{-1}. First, the fact that $P^{-1}(D)$ is a right-inverse of $P(D)$ ensures the existence of a solution, since by (5.4a) the $\mathscr{D}_-$ function

$$\varphi = P^{-1}(D)\psi \tag{5.5}$$

satisfies the given equation (5.1). Second, the fact that P^{-1} is a left-inverse ensures the uniqueness of this solution. Indeed, every solution $\varphi(\in \mathscr{D}_-)$ of

$$P(D)\varphi = \psi$$

also verifies

$$P^{-1}(D)\,P(D)\varphi = P^{-1}(D)\psi,$$

so that, by (5.4b),

$$\varphi = P^{-1}(D)\psi,$$

i.e., these solutions are all identical. This result deserves formal expression as

Theorem 5.1. *The equation*

$$P(D)\varphi = \psi, \tag{A}$$

where $\psi \in \mathscr{D}_-$, *and where* $(a_0 \neq 0)$

$$P(D) = a_0(D - r_1)^{p_1}(D - r_2)^{p_2} \cdots (D - r_l)^{p_l}, \tag{B}$$

has a unique solution, $\varphi \in \mathscr{D}_-$, *explicitly given by*

$$\varphi = P^{-1}(D)\psi \tag{C}$$

with

$$P^{-1}(D) = \frac{1}{a_0}(D - r_1)^{-p_1}(D - r_2)^{-p_2} \cdots (D - r_l)^{-p_l}. \tag{E}$$

The existence of the solution is guaranteed by the fact that $P^{-1}(D)$ is a right-inverse of $P(D)$ on $\mathscr{D}_-$; its uniqueness is guaranteed by the fact that $P^{-1}(D)$ is a left-inverse of $P(D)$.

Remark 1. Proofs of existence and uniqueness theorems for solutions of ordinary differential equations abound. The interest of the present one is not just that it is obtained as an easy by-product of the derivation of an explicit analytic formula for the solution in terms of ordinary integrals, but that it provides a prototype for similar proofs applicable to linear partial differential equations, as will be seen in Volume II.

6. Computational Considerations. Partial Fraction Expansion of Operators

To compute

$$\frac{1}{a_0}(D - r_1)^{-p_1}(D - r_2)^{-p_2} \cdots (D - r_l)^{-p_l}$$

directly by the repeated application of (4.5′) and (4.7) is laborious. Fortunately there is a way of reducing these iterated integrations to a sum of simpler integrals, and that is by the decomposition of rational operators in D into partial fractions, which we shall now develop.

We begin by recalling in outline the method of decomposing rational algebraic functions into partial fractions [2] [7] [19].

If $A(x)$ and $B(x)$ are polynomials in the variable x without common factors, the usual division of polynomials gives†

$$\frac{A(x)}{B(x)} \equiv Q(x) + \frac{R(x)}{B(x)}, \tag{6.1}$$

where $Q(x) \equiv 0$ if the degree of $B(x)$ exceeds the degree of $A(x)$, and is a polynomial otherwise. The degree of the polynomial $R(x)$ is less than that of $B(x)$, so that $R(x)/B(x)$ is a proper fraction in which the zeros of $B(x)$ all differ from the zeros of $R(x)$.

Let the factorization of $B(x)$ be

$$B(x) = a_0(x - r_1)^{p_1}(x - r_2)^{p_2} \cdots (x - r_l)^{p_l}. \tag{6.2}$$

Then the decomposition of $R(x)/B(x)$ into simple partial fractions takes the form

$$\frac{R(x)}{B(x)} \equiv \sum_{k=1}^{p_1} \frac{\alpha_k}{(x - r_1)^k} + \sum_{k=1}^{p_2} \frac{\beta_k}{(x - r_2)^k} + \cdots + \sum_{k=1}^{p_l} \frac{\lambda_k}{(x - r_l)^k}. \tag{6.3}$$

This decomposition is unique and the values of the numerical coefficients

† The identity symbol is used here and in equation (6.3) to indicate equality of the two sides of the relation for all values of x that do not make the denominator, $B(x)$, vanish.

$\alpha_k, \beta_k, \ldots, \lambda_k$ can be obtained by any one of several classical computational procedures. Of these, we describe the one that follows, which is often employed in actual applications involving numerical data.

Since the relation (6.3) is an identity valid for all but a finite number of x values, we can compute the $\alpha_k, \beta_k, \ldots, \lambda_k$ by using conveniently chosen particular values for x.

Thus, to find α_{p_1} multiply both sides of (6.3) by $(x - r_1)^{p_1}$ and then let $x \to r_1$. This gives

$$R(r_1) \lim_{x \to r_1} \frac{(x - r_1)^{p_1}}{B(x)} = \alpha_{p_1}, \tag{6.4}$$

which we shall agree to write in the form

$$\alpha_{p_1} = \left[\frac{R(x)(x - r_1)^{p_1}}{B(x)}\right]_{x=r_1}, \tag{6.4'}$$

though it must be understood that actually the right-hand side is a limit value as $x \to r_1$ [which in practice is computed by substituting r_1 for x *after* the division $(x - r_1)^p/B(x)$ has been performed].

In the same way one finds

$$\beta_{p_2} = \left[\frac{R(x)(x - r_2)^{p_2}}{B(x)}\right]_{x=r_2}, \ldots, \lambda_{p_l} = \left[\frac{R(x)(x - r_l)^{p_l}}{B(x)}\right]_{x=r_l}. \tag{6.4''}$$

To find α_k $(k < p_1)$ multiply both sides of (6.3) by $(x - r_1)^{p_1}$ and differentiate $(p_1 - k)$ times with respect to x. After this, the only nonzero term on the right which does not contain the factor $(x - r_1)$ will be the term

$$\alpha_k \frac{d^{p_1-k}}{dx^{p_1-k}} (x - r_1)^{p_1-k} = (p_1 - k)!\, \alpha_k.$$

Therefore, letting $x \to r_1$, the limit of the right-hand side is precisely this term, and we have

$$\alpha_k = \frac{1}{(p_1 - k)!} \left[\frac{d^{p_1-k}}{dx^{p_1-k}} \left\{\frac{R(x)(x - r_1)^{p_1}}{B(x)}\right\}\right]_{x=r_1}. \tag{6.5}$$

Similarly one finds

$$\beta_k = \frac{1}{(p_2 - k)!} \left[\frac{d^{p_2-k}}{dx^{p_2-k}} \left\{\frac{R(x)(x - r_2)^{p_2}}{B(x)}\right\}\right]_{x=r_2},$$

(6.5′). . . . .

$$\lambda_k = \frac{1}{(p_l - k)!} \left[\frac{d^{p_l-k}}{dx^{p_l-k}} \left\{\frac{R(x)(x - r_l)^{p_l}}{B(x)}\right\}\right]_{x=r_l}.$$

These include (6.4) and (6.4′) as particular cases.

After this digression into ordinary algebra, we can now return to the matter at hand, which is:

Theorem 6.1. *Every operator on $\mathscr{D}_-$ of the form $A(D)B^{-1}(D)$, where $A(D)$ and $B(D)$ are polynomials in the operator D without common factors, and where the factored form of $B(D)$ is*

$$B(D) = a_0(D - r_1)^{p_1}(D - r_2)^{p_2} \cdots (D - r_l)^{p_l} \neq 0, \tag{6.6}$$

has a unique decomposition into the sum of a polynomial $Q(D)$ in D and of simple "partial fractions" in D which has the form

$$A(D)\, B^{-1}(D) = Q(D) + \sum_{k=1}^{p_1} \alpha_k (D - r_1)^{-k} + \cdots + \sum_{k=1}^{p_l} \lambda_k (D - r_l)^{-k}. \tag{6.7}$$

The polynomial $Q(D)$ and the scalar coefficients $\alpha_k, \beta_k, \ldots, \lambda_k$ of this decomposition are obtained in precisely the same way as the corresponding elements of the decomposition of the rational algebraic fraction $A(x)/B(x)$ [cf. formulas (6.1), (6.5), (6.5′)].

Proof. In ordinary algebra we have the identity between *polynomials*:

$$A(x) \equiv B(x)\, Q(x) + \sum_{k=1}^{p_1} \alpha_k \frac{B(x)}{(x - r_1)^k} + \cdots + \sum_{k=1}^{p_l} \lambda_k \frac{B(x)}{(x - r_l)^k}\,. \tag{6.8}$$

If in (6.8) we replace x by the operator D we obtain an identity between operator polynomials on $\mathscr{D}_-$, valid because those laws of operator algebra enumerated in § 3 and § 4 above (in particular the commutativity of multiplication), are the same as those of the algebra of polynomials.

Multiplying both sides of this identity by $B^{-1}(D)$ gives (6.7), and proves it to be an identity since B^{-1} is the unique inverse of $B(D)$. ∎

7. An Example

To illustrate the application of Theorems 5.1 and 6.1, let us find $\varphi \in \mathscr{D}_-$ such that

$$(12D^3 - 8D^2 - 3D + 2)\varphi = \psi, \tag{7.1}$$

where $\psi(t) \in \mathscr{D}_-$ is a given function.

The first necessary step in the solution of this problem is the factorization of the derivative polynomial on the left. It is obtained from the algebraic relation

$$12x^3 - 8x^2 - 3x + 2 = (2x - 1)(2x + 1)(3x - 2) \tag{7.2}$$

which enables us to rewrite equation (7.1) in the form

$$12(D - \tfrac{1}{2})(D + \tfrac{1}{2})(D - \tfrac{2}{3})\varphi = \psi. \tag{7.3}$$

This has, by Theorem 5.1, the unique solution

$$\varphi = \tfrac{1}{12}(D - \tfrac{1}{2})^{-1}(D + \tfrac{1}{2})^{-1}(D - \tfrac{2}{3})^{-1}\psi. \tag{7.4}$$

Decomposing the operator on the right in the manner of Theorem 6.1 gives

$$\varphi = \{-\tfrac{1}{2}(D - \tfrac{1}{2})^{-1} + \tfrac{1}{14}(D + \tfrac{1}{2})^{-1} + \tfrac{3}{7}(D - \tfrac{2}{3})^{-1}\}\psi. \tag{7.5}$$

By (4.5) this is

$$\varphi(t) = -\tfrac{1}{2}\int_{+\infty}^{t} e^{(t-\tau)/2}\,\psi(\tau)\,d\tau + \tfrac{1}{14}\int_{+\infty}^{t} e^{-(t-\tau)/2}\,\psi(\tau)\,d\tau + \tfrac{3}{7}\int_{+\infty}^{t} e^{2(t-\tau)/3}\,\psi(\tau)\,d\tau. \tag{7.6}$$

Remark. When $\psi \in \mathscr{D}_-$, integrals such as those on the right in (7.6) can only in rare cases be worked out explicitly in terms of familiar functions. The point of the above example is that the easy formalism leading from (7.1) to (7.5) is typical of the operational method studied in Chapters III and IV, and which applies to an operand space considerably broader and more interesting, mathematically and physically, than $\mathscr{D}_-$.

8. The Space $\mathscr{D}_+$

Let $\varphi(t) \in \mathscr{D}_-$ and set $\psi(t) = \varphi(-t)$. The set of functions $\psi(t)$ is called $\mathscr{D}_+$; it is the collection of all $C^\infty(R)$ functions carried in forward half-lines.

For such functions define

$$(D - r)^{-1}\psi(t) = e^{rt}\int_{-\infty}^{t} e^{-r\tau}\,\psi(\tau)\,d\tau, \tag{8.1}$$

$$(D - r,^{-p}\psi(t) = e^{rt}\int_{-\infty}^{t} \frac{(t-\tau)^{p-1}}{(p-1)!}\,e^{-r\tau}\,\psi(\tau)\,d\tau, \qquad (p > 0, \text{ integer}), \tag{8.2}$$

while D^p, $(D - r)^p$ $(p \geqslant 0)$ are defined as in $\mathscr{D}_-$.

It is a trivial exercise to verify that with these operators one obtains an operational calculus entirely analogous to that which we have just developed on $\mathscr{D}_-$.

**9. The Operator $(D - r)^\lambda$ for Arbitrary Real λ

Almost every text on advanced calculus includes a treatment of the gamma function, defined for $\lambda > 0$ by

$$\Gamma(\lambda) = \int_0^\infty t^{\lambda-1}\,e^{-t}\,dt, \tag{9.1}$$

and of the beta function, defined for $\lambda > 0$, $\mu > 0$ by

(9.2) $$B(\lambda, \mu) = \int_0^1 t^{\lambda-1}(1-t)^{\mu-1}\,dt.$$

These treatments include a proof of the important identity

(9.3) $$B(\lambda, \mu) = \frac{\Gamma(\lambda)\,\Gamma(\mu)}{\Gamma(\lambda+\mu)}.$$

Integration by parts easily gives the identity $\Gamma(\lambda) = (\lambda-1)\Gamma(\lambda-1)$ which, when $\lambda = p$, a positive integer, leads to

(9.4) $$\Gamma(p) = (p-1)!$$

and justifies considering the gamma function as the extension of the factorial function to nonintegers.

Substituting (9.4) in the relation (4.5′) leads to defining the operator $D^{-\lambda}$ on $\mathscr{D}_-$ for any real $\lambda > 0$ by its action on test functions as

(9.5) $$D^{-\lambda}\varphi = \int_{+\infty}^{t} \frac{(t-\tau)^{\lambda-1}}{\Gamma(\lambda)}\,\varphi(\tau)\,d\tau.$$

[By $(t-\tau)^{\lambda-1}$ we understand $(-1)^{\lambda-1}(\tau-t)^{\lambda-1}$ with $(-1)^{\lambda-1}$ defined as $e^{(\lambda-1)\pi i}$, i.e., we take for $\log(z)$, where z is negative, the principal branch of the complex-valued log function. With this convention the identity $z^\lambda z^\mu = z^{\lambda+\mu}$ remains true for any λ, μ values.]

This is called an integral of order λ of φ; clearly it converges for any $\lambda > 0$. That this definition is fruitful results from the fact that, given any $\lambda > 0$, $\mu > 0$, the following identity between operators on $\mathscr{D}_-$ holds:

(9.6) $$D^{-\lambda}D^{-\mu} = D^{-\mu}D^{-\lambda} = D^{-\mu-\lambda} \qquad (\lambda, \mu > 0).$$

To prove this, take any $\varphi \in \mathscr{D}_-$ and let $(-\infty, b]$ be a backward half-line carrying this function. Then by (9.5)

(9.7) $$D^{-\mu}D^{-\lambda}\varphi = \frac{1}{\Gamma(\lambda)\,\Gamma(\mu)}\int_b^t (t-\tau)^{\mu-1}\int_b^\tau (\tau-\sigma)^{\lambda-1}\,\varphi(\sigma)\,d\sigma\,d\tau.$$

This repeated integral corresponds to a double integral over the triangle *ABC* of the accompanying diagram (Figure 2).

If $\lambda > 1$ and $\mu > 1$ this is a proper integral, its integrand is continuous, and the order of integration may be inverted, so that, integrating with respect to τ first and to σ next,

(9.8) $$D^{-\mu}D^{-\lambda}\varphi = \frac{1}{\Gamma(\lambda)\,\Gamma(\mu)}\int_b^t \varphi(\sigma)\int_\sigma^t (t-\tau)^{\mu-1}(\tau-\sigma)^{\lambda-1}\,d\tau\,d\sigma.$$

[When one or both of the positive exponents λ and μ are < 1, the integrals are improper but the passage from (9.7) to (9.8) can still be justified by an obvious modification to this argument where the integral over ABC is taken as a limit of integrals over slightly smaller triangles.]

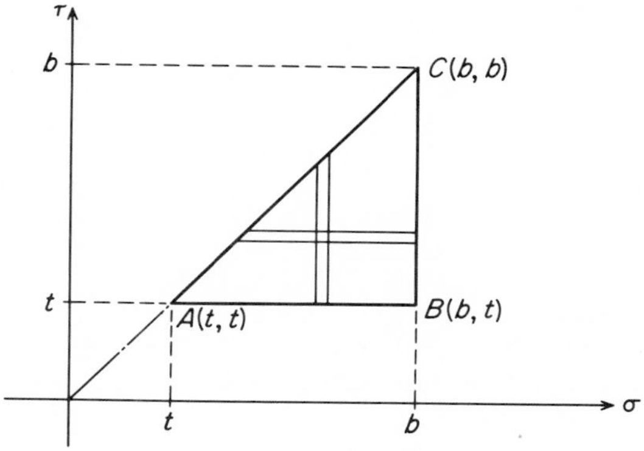

FIGURE 2

The change of variables $u = \dfrac{\tau - \sigma}{t - \sigma}\left(du = \dfrac{d\tau}{t - \sigma}\right)$ and (9.3) give

$$\begin{aligned}\int_\sigma^t (t-\tau)^{\mu-1}(\tau-\sigma)^{\lambda-1}\,d\tau &= (t-\sigma)^{\lambda+\mu-1}\int_0^1 u^{\lambda-1}(1-\mu)^{\mu-1}\,d\mu\\ &= (t-\sigma)^{\lambda+\mu-1}B(\lambda,\mu)\\ &= (t-\sigma)^{\lambda+\mu-1}\frac{\Gamma(\lambda)\,\Gamma(\mu)}{\Gamma(\lambda+\mu)},\end{aligned}$$

which substituted in (9.7) leaves

$$D^{-\mu}D^{-\lambda}\varphi(t) = \frac{1}{\Gamma(\lambda+\mu)}\int_b^t (t-\sigma)^{\lambda+\mu-1}\,\varphi(\sigma)\,d\sigma = D^{-\lambda-\mu}\varphi(t),$$

proving half of (9.6). Exchanging λ and μ in this argument proves the other half.

To define differentiation of noninteger order $\lambda > 0$ on $\mathscr{D}_-$ we set

$$D^\lambda\varphi = D^{[\lambda]+1}D^{+\lambda-[\lambda]-1}\,\varphi, \tag{9.9}$$

where $[\lambda]$ = largest integer $\leqslant \lambda$ (so $\lambda - [\lambda] - 1 < 0$) and, in view of (9.5),

$$D^\lambda\varphi(t) = D^{[\lambda]+1}\left(\int_{+\infty}^t \frac{(t-\tau)^{[\lambda]-\lambda}}{\Gamma([\lambda]+1-\lambda)}\,\varphi(\tau)\,d\tau\right). \tag{9.10}$$

Since $\varphi(t) = 0$ for $t \geqslant b$, changing variables in the integral to $u = t - \tau$ transforms (9.10) into

$$D^\lambda \varphi(t) = D^{[\lambda]+1} \int_0^{t-b} \frac{u^{[\lambda]-\lambda}}{\Gamma([\lambda] + 1 - \lambda)} \varphi(t - u)\, du. \tag{9.11}$$

There is a well-known formula of Leibniz,

$$\frac{\partial}{\partial \alpha} \int_a^{g(\alpha)} f(\alpha, t)\, dt = f(\alpha, g(\alpha)) \frac{dg}{d\alpha} + \int_a^{g(\alpha)} \frac{\partial f(\alpha, t)}{\partial \alpha}\, dt, \tag{9.12}$$

which is valid when $f(\alpha, t)$ and $\dfrac{\partial f}{\partial \alpha}(\alpha, t)$ are continuous functions of the point (α, t) and $g(\alpha)$ is differentiable. Its proof results from the observation that the integral depends on α directly as well as through $g(\alpha)$,

$$\int_a^{g(\alpha)} f(\alpha, t)\, dt = F(\alpha, g(\alpha)),$$

so that

$$\frac{dF(\alpha, g(\alpha))}{d\alpha} = \left(\frac{\partial F}{\partial \alpha}\right)_g + \left(\frac{\partial F}{\partial g}\right)_\alpha \frac{dg}{d\alpha},$$

where the subscript on a partial derivative indicates the variable that is being held constant in the differentiation.

Applying the Leibniz formula and $\varphi^{(n)}(b) = 0$ to (9.11) we find

$$D^{[\lambda]+1} \int_0^{t-b} \frac{u^{[\lambda]-\lambda}}{\Gamma([\lambda] + 1 - \lambda)} \varphi(t - u)\, du = \int_0^{t-b} \frac{u^{[\lambda]-\lambda}}{\Gamma([\lambda] + 1 - \lambda)} \varphi^{([\lambda]+1)}(t - u)\, du. \tag{9.13}$$

Changing variables to $\tau = t - u$ transforms the right-hand side into

$$\int_b^t \frac{(t - \tau)^{[\lambda]-\lambda}}{\Gamma([\lambda] + 1 - \lambda)} \varphi^{([\lambda]+1)}(\tau)\, d\tau,$$

and we have proved that for real λ

$$D^{[\lambda]+1} D^{\lambda-[\lambda]-1} \varphi = D^{\lambda-[\lambda]-1} D^{[\lambda]+1} \varphi. \tag{9.14}$$

It is now an easy exercise to verify that the identity (9.6) generalizes to

$$D^\lambda D^\mu = D^\mu D^\lambda = D^{\mu+\lambda}, \tag{9.15}$$

valid for any real λ and μ.

The definition of the operator $(D - r)^\lambda$ on $\mathscr{D}_-$ for any real λ follows from that of D^λ in (9.5) and (9.9) by the shift relation

$$(D - r)^\lambda \varphi = e^{rt} D^\lambda[e^{-rt}\varphi(t)]. \tag{9.16}$$

Very little effort is now required to justify with the relations of this section the conclusion that all the previous operator identities of this chapter hold true when the integer exponents are replaced by arbitrary real numbers. While we have no cause here to go into the matter, let it be mentioned that the theory extends to arbitrary complex-valued exponents [23] [43].

APPENDIX TO CHAPTER I

COMPLEX-VALUED FUNCTIONS OF A REAL VARIABLE

For the benefit of the reader unfamiliar with this topic, we list some basic facts.

A complex-valued function $f(t)$ of the real variable t is a function whose values are given by

$$f(t) = f_1(t) + if_2(t), \tag{α.1}$$

where both $f_1(t)$ and $f_2(t)$ are real-valued functions of t and are often designated by $\mathscr{R}f(t)$ and $\mathscr{I}f(t)$, respectively, to stress their roles as the real and imaginary components of $f(t)$. Continuity is defined in the usual way, and $f(t)$ is continuous if, and only if, both $f_1(t)$ and $f_2(t)$ are individually continuous.

The ordinary derivative $f'(t)$ is defined by

$$f'(t) = \frac{df}{dt} = \lim_{h\to 0}\frac{f(t+h) - f(t)}{h}, \tag{α.2}$$

and is computed with the easily verified identity

$$f'(t) = f_1'(t) + if_2'(t), \tag{α.3}$$

whose repeated use gives

$$f^{(p)}(t) = f_1^{(p)}(t) + if_2^{(p)}(t). \tag{α.4}$$

The integral $\int_a^b f(t)\,dt$ is defined by

$$\int_a^b f(t)\,dt = \int_a^b f_1(t)\,dt + i\int_a^b f_2(t)\,dt, \tag{α.5}$$

and so exists if, and only if, the functions $f_1(t), f_2(t)$ are individually integrable on $[a, b]$.

There follows from (α.5)

$$\left|\int_a^b f\,dt\right| \leqslant \left|\int_a^b f_1\,dt\right| + \left|\int_a^b f_2\,dt\right| \leqslant \int_a^b |f_1|\,dt + \int_a^b |f_2|\,dt. \tag{α.6}$$

The last two of the inequalities

$$(\alpha.7)\qquad \begin{gathered} |f(t)| \leqslant |f_1(t)| + |f_2(t)|, \\ |f_1(t)| \leqslant |f(t)|, \qquad |f_2(t)| \leqslant |f(t)| \end{gathered}$$

applied on the right in (α.6) yield

$$(\alpha.8)\qquad \left|\int_a^b f\,dt\right| \leqslant 2\left|\int_a^b |f|\,dt\right|.$$

A better inequality is

$$(\alpha.9)\qquad \left|\int_a^b f\,dt\right| \leqslant \left|\int_a^b |f|\,dt\right|.$$

Its proof, however, is not quite so simple as that of (α.8) as it involves the "Riemann sums" for integrals (cf. Exercise 22, Chapter I). This proof is not included here because, though we shall repeatedly encounter (α.9) in the pages to come, the reader can, whenever it occurs, verify for himself that the arguments in which it is used remain valid when it is replaced by the less precise inequality (α.8).

Taylor's formula with integral remainder holds also for complex-valued functions of a real variable:

$$f(t) = f(a) + \frac{(t-a)}{1!}f'(a) + \cdots + \frac{(t-a)^n}{n!}f^{(n)}(a) + \int_a^t \frac{(t-\tau)^n}{n!}f^{(n+1)}(\tau)\,d\tau.$$

To see this, apply the Taylor formula for real-valued functions to $f_1(t)$ and $f_2(t)$.

Unless $f(t)$ is real-valued, the Taylor formula with Lagrange form of the remainder does *not* apply to $f(t)$. Instead we have

$$(\alpha.11)\qquad f(t) = f(a) + \frac{t-a}{1!}f'(a) + \cdots + \frac{(t-a)^n}{n!}f^{(n)}(a) + \frac{(t-a)^{n+1}}{(n+1)!}[f_1^{(n+1)}(\tau_1) + if_2^{(n+1)}(\tau_2)],$$

where τ_1 and τ_2 are points in the open interval (a, t) which coincide only in exceptional cases.

EXERCISES

Section 2

1. Prove (2.8) by means of l'Hopital's rule.

2. Prove the Leibniz formula

$$(\alpha(t)\ \varphi(t))^{(n)} = \sum_{k=0}^{n} \binom{n}{k} \alpha^{(n-k)}\varphi^{(k)}$$

where $\alpha, \varphi \in C^\infty(R)$.

3. Prove that $\rho_\epsilon(t)$ defined in (2.11) is a $C^\infty(R)$ function. (Use the Leibniz formula.)

4. (O.C.) The class of $C^p(R)$ functions, φ, each of which is carried in a backward half-line $(-\infty, b]$, is called $\mathscr{D}^p_-$. Give an example of a $\mathscr{D}^p_-$ function which is not $C^{p+1}(R)$. Also give an example of such a function that is carried in the finite interval $[a, b]$.

***5.** The p'th difference, with argument h, of φ is defined by

$$\Delta^p\varphi(t) = \sum_{k=0}^{p} \binom{p}{k} (-1)^{p-k}\varphi(t + kh).$$

If the real-valued function $\varphi \in C^p(R)$ show that

$$\frac{1}{h^p}\Delta^p\varphi(t) = \varphi^{(p)}(t + \theta ph)$$

where $\theta = \theta(t, h)$ satisfies $0 < \theta < 1$. Conclude that when the real-valued $\varphi \in \mathscr{D}^p_-$ and $h \neq 0$ is constant, the function of t

$$\varphi^{(p)}(t + \theta(t)ph) \in \mathscr{D}^p_-$$

and compare the carrier of this function with that of $\varphi(t)$. (Notice that $\Delta^p\varphi = \Delta(\Delta^{p-1}\varphi)$ and proceed by induction.)

***6.** Given $\varphi(t) \in \mathscr{D}_-$, $\varphi(t_0) = 0$. Prove the existence of $\varphi_1(t) \in \mathscr{D}_-$ such that $\varphi(t) = (t - t_0)\varphi_1(t)$. $\varphi_1(t_0) = ?$

7. (O.C.) $\mathscr{S}$ is the set of $C^\infty(R)$ functions such that for every pair of integers $k, p > 0$,

$$\lim_{|t|\to+\infty} \frac{\varphi^{(p)}(t)}{|t|^k} = 0.$$

Show that $e^{-t^2} \in \mathscr{S}$ and give other examples of functions in this class.

8. (O.C.) Given $\varphi_0 \in \mathscr{D}$ (the set of $C^\infty(R)$ functions carried in finite intervals), where

$$\int_{-\infty}^{\infty} \varphi_0(t)\, dt = 1,$$

show that for any $\varphi \in \mathscr{D}$, $\varphi = k\varphi_0 + \psi$, where k is a constant depending on φ and where $\psi \in \mathscr{D}$ has

$$\int_{-\infty}^{\infty} \psi(t)\, dt = 0$$

and is the derivative of a $\mathscr{D}$ function.

Section 3

9. Prove (3.6) for integer $p > 1$.

Section 4

10. Prove the identity (4.9) on the operand set $\mathscr{D}_-$. [*Hint:* (a) first prove it with $p, q \geqslant 0$; (b) for $p \leqslant 0, q \geqslant 0$ multiply $(D - r)^p(D - s)^q$ by $I = (D - r)^{-p}(D - r)^p$ and use (a); (c) for $p \leqslant 0, q \leqslant 0$ use (b).]

11. The function defined in (2.11), $\rho_\varepsilon(t) \in \mathscr{D}_-$. What are the values of $D^{-1}\rho_\varepsilon(t - t_0)$ (constant $t_0 \in R$) for $t \leqslant t_0 - \varepsilon$, for $t \geqslant t_0 + \varepsilon$? Does this function take positive values?

12. Given the finite intervals $[a, b]$, $[c, d]$ with $a < c < d < b$, exhibit a real, nonnegative valued $\mathscr{D}_-$ function $\varphi(t)$ carried in $[a, b]$, and such that $\varphi(t) \equiv 1$ for $t \in [c, d]$. (Use the result of Exercise 11 to obtain two functions whose product gives φ.)

***13.** Show that the function

$$\varphi(t) = \int_{c-\varepsilon}^{d+\varepsilon} \rho_\varepsilon(t - \tau)\, d\tau,$$

where $\rho_\varepsilon(t)$ is defined by (2.11), and where $\varepsilon < \min\left(\frac{c - a}{2}, \frac{b - d}{2}\right)$, is a $\mathscr{D}_-$ function carried in $[a, b]$ and that $\varphi(t) \equiv 1$ for $t \in [c, d]$. Assume $a < c < d < b$.

Section 5

***14.** (O.C.) Given a fixed integer $p > 1$, the operators D^k, D^{-k} are defined for appropriate integer k on the operand set $\mathscr{D}_-^p$ (Exercise 4 above) quite as on the operand set $\mathscr{D}_-$. To what extent can the operator algebra of §§ 3, 4, 5 be developed on $\mathscr{D}_-^p$? Give an appropriate version of Theorem 5.1.

Sections 5, 6, 7

Express as a sum of definite integrals the solution $\varphi \in \mathscr{D}_-$ of each of the following equations ($\psi \in \mathscr{D}_-$ is given); check the solution.

15. $(D^2 + 1)(D^2 + 4)\varphi = \psi$.

16. $(D^2 + 2)^2\varphi = \psi$.

17. $D(D^2 + 2)\varphi = \psi$.

18. $D(D - 1)(D^2 + 4)\varphi = \psi$.

19. $D(D - 1)[(D + 2)^2 + 1]\varphi = \psi$.

20. $\psi_1, \psi_2 \in \mathscr{D}_-$ are given. Find $\varphi_1, \varphi_2 \in \mathscr{D}_-$ in integral form when $(D + 1)\varphi_1 + D\varphi_2 = \psi_1$, $(D + 2)\varphi_1 + 2(D + 1)\varphi_2 = \psi_2$.

Section 8

***21.** Without making use of the results of § 8, observe that a plausible definition of the operator $D^{-1/2}$ on $\mathscr{D}_-$ suggested by (4.5′) is

$$D^{-1/2}\varphi = k \int_{+\infty}^{t} (t - \tau)^{-1/2}\, \varphi(\tau)\, d\tau,$$

where k is an unknown constant. If one requires $D^{-1/2}D^{-1/2} = D^{-1}$, the value of k can be determined without using the gamma or beta functions. Find it.

(*Ans.* $k = 1/\sqrt{\pi}$.)

Appendix

***22.** Prove that when $a < b$ and $f(t)$, complex-valued, is continuous there holds the relation

$$\left| \int_a^b f(t)\, dt \right| \leqslant \int_a^b |f(t)|\, dt.$$

(Compare Riemann sums for the two integrals.)

23. Show that

$$\int_a^b e^{\beta t}\, dt = \frac{e^{\beta b} - e^{\beta a}}{\beta}$$

when β is a complex number and $a, b \in R$.

CHAPTER II

THE SPACE $\mathscr{D}'_+$ OF GENERALIZED FUNCTIONS

Every g.f. has derivatives of every order. Differentiation is a continuous operation—in the sense that, for example, an infinite series of g.f.'s whose sum is S may be differentiated term by term, the resulting series being convergent to the derivative of S. These properties, which do not hold for ordinary functions, except in restrictive circumstances, constitute basic mathematical reasons why the use of g.f.'s so radically simplifies the treatment of very many problems of mathematics and mathematical physics.

In this chapter, we shall define a class of g.f.'s, develop a calculus for it, and derive continuity properties of g.f.'s, as well as other properties that are especially useful.

A. DEFINITION OF $\mathscr{D}'_+$

1. Terminology

While we shall continue to use the terminology of Chapter I, some new terms must be added:

Functional on A: any function (i.e., complex-valued function) whose domain is a collection, A, of functions. The value of a functional F at $f(t) \in A$ is often denoted by $\langle F, f \rangle$.

Linear functional on A: Let A be a linear space of functions—$(c_1 f_1(t) + c_2 f_2(t)) \in A$ whenever c_1 and c_2 are scalars and $f_1(t), f_2(t) \in A$. Then a functional F on A is called linear if

(A.1.1) $$\langle F, c_1 f_1 + c_2 f_2 \rangle = c_1 \langle F, f_1 \rangle + c_2 \langle F, f_2 \rangle.$$

Piecewise continuous function on R: A function defined at every $t \in R$, except possibly a countable sequence $\{t_i\}_{i=-\infty}^{i=+\infty}$ of points $(\cdots < t_{-1} < t_0 < t_1 < \cdots)$ of which at most a finite number lie in any interval of finite length, is called piecewise continuous if it is continuous in each of the open intervals (t_i, t_{i+1}) and the limits $f(t_i - 0), f(t_i + 0)$ all exist and are finite.

Piecewise $C^k(R)$ function: a function $f(t)$ which is piecewise continuous and whose derivatives $f'(t), f''(t), \ldots, f^{(k)}(t)$ are piecewise continuous on R.

2. $\mathscr{K}_+(R)$ functions as functionals on $\mathscr{D}_-$

Definition A.2.1. *A function $f(t)$ on R is a $\mathscr{K}_+(R)$ function if and only if the following conditions are satisfied:*

(*a*) *There exists a point $a_f \in R$ and a monotonic sequence*† $\{t_i\}$ *of points of R such that $a_f \leqslant t_1 < t_2 < \cdots < t_i < \cdots$ and such that at most a finite number of these points lies in any interval of finite length* ($\{t_i\}$ has no finite point of accumulation)*;*
(*b*) *$f(t)$ is carried in the forward half-line $[a_f, +\infty)$ and is undefined at t_i $(i = 1, 2, 3, \ldots)$;*
(*c*) *$f(t)$ is continuous at every $t \neq t_i$ $(i = 1, 2, \ldots)$ and the limits $f(t_i - 0)$, $f(t_i + 0)$ exist and are finite;*
(*d*) *$f(t_i - 0) \neq f(t_i + 0)$ $(i = 1, 2, \ldots)$.*

To a piecewise continuous function, $f(t)$, on R that is carried in a forward half-line there corresponds the $\mathscr{K}_+(R)$ function obtained by disregarding any values $f(t_i)$ at those t_i where $f(t_i + 0) \neq f(t_i - 0)$, and by redefining $f(t_i)$ as $f(t_i + 0)$ at those t_i where $f(t_i + 0) = f(t_i - 0)$. For example, to the piecewise continuous function $q_n(t)$, defined in (0.2.11), corresponds the $\mathscr{K}_+(R)$ function, $p_n(t)$, defined by

$$\text{(A.2.1)} \qquad p_n(t) = \begin{cases} 0 & \text{for } t < 0 \\ n & \text{for } 0 < t < 1/n \\ 0 & \text{for } 1/n < t. \end{cases}$$

If c_1, c_2 are scalars and $f_1(t), f_2(t) \in \mathscr{K}_+(R)$, *the function $c_1 f_1(t) + c_2 f_2(t)$ is piecewise continuous and there is associated with it a $\mathscr{K}_+(R)$ function which we temporarily denote by*

$$\text{(A.2.2)} \qquad c_1 f_1(t) \dotplus c_2 f_2(t).$$

Thus, the function defined in (A.2.1) gives for

$$p_n(t) \dotplus (-1) p_n(t)$$

the identically zero function.

---

† This sequence may be infinite, finite, or even empty.

From the definition of $\mathscr{K}_+(R)$ functions it follows that any two of them, $f_1(t)$ and $f_2(t)$, are *equal* if and only if they have the *same points of discontinuity*, t_i $(i = 1, 2, \ldots)$, *and* $f_1(t) - f_2(t) = 0$ *for* $t \neq t_i$.

Let $f(t) \in \mathscr{K}_+(R)$ be carried in the half-line $[a_f, +\infty)$ and have the points of discontinuity $a_f \leqslant t_1 < t_2 < \cdots < t_i < \cdots$ and let the test function $\varphi(t) \in \mathscr{D}_-$ be carried in the half-line $(-\infty, b_\varphi]$. Then, by the definition of the improper integrals given in elementary calculus for discontinuous functions, we have

(A.2.3)

$$\int_{-\infty}^{\infty} f(t)\, \varphi(t)\, dt = \int_{a_f}^{b_\varphi} f(t)\, \varphi(t)\, dt = \left(\int_{a_f}^{t_1} + \int_{t_1}^{t_2} + \cdots + \int_{t_{n-1}}^{t_n} + \int_{t_n}^{b_\varphi}\right) f(t)\, \varphi(t)\, dt$$

if the only points of discontinuity of $f(t)$ in the interval $[a_f, b_\varphi]$ are $t_1, \ldots, t_n$ (this does not exclude $a_f = t_1$ and $t_n = b_\varphi$). If $b_\varphi \leqslant a_f$ this integral has the value zero. Otherwise each of the integrals in this sum is an improper integral of the simplest kind since the integrands are not defined at the t_i but have left and right limits there:

(A.2.4) $$\int_{t_i}^{t_{i+1}} f(t)\, \varphi(t)\, dt = \lim_{\substack{\varepsilon \to 0 \\ \eta \to 0}} \int_{t_i+\varepsilon}^{t_{i+1}-\eta} f(t)\, \varphi(t)\, dt \qquad (\varepsilon > 0, \eta > 0),$$

with obvious simplifications for the case where a_f, b_φ are points of continuity of $f(t)$.

The expression (A.2.3), for any given $f \in \mathscr{K}_+(R)$, associates with every $\varphi \in \mathscr{D}_-$ a well-defined, finite, complex number. Consequently f *defines a functional on* $\mathscr{D}_-$.

This functional is designated by the symbols f or $f(t)$;† its value, at any $\varphi \in \mathscr{D}_-$, by either of the symbols

(A.2.5) $$\langle f, \varphi \rangle = \langle f(t), \varphi(t) \rangle = \int_{-\infty}^{\infty} f(t)\, \varphi(t)\, dt.$$

It was noted in § I.3 that $\mathscr{D}_-$ is a linear space. By the elementary properties of integrals, it follows that the functional defined on $\mathscr{D}_-$ by $f \in \mathscr{K}_+(R)$ is a *linear functional*. We shall denote it by the same symbols f, or $f(t)$, as the function (more on this in § 7 below).

Definition A.2.2 (Fundamental Sequence). *A fundamental sequence on* $\mathscr{D}_-$ *is a sequence* $\{f_n\}$ *of* $\mathscr{K}_+(R)$ *functions, all of which are carried in the same forward half-line* $[a_F, +\infty)$, *and which has the property that for every*

---

† This notation, which might seem misleading insofar as the functional f is a function of φ, and not of t, is nevertheless widely accepted because of its usefulness in many contexts, e.g., Definition A.5.1 below.

$\varphi \in \mathscr{D}_-$, $\lim_{n\to\infty} \langle f_n, \varphi\rangle$ exists. This quantity is called the value of the sequence at φ. The sequence is said to be carried in $[a_F, +\infty)$.

A fundamental sequence defines a functional on $\mathscr{D}_-$ whose value at each test function is the value of the sequence at that function. Such a functional is what we call a g.f. of class $\mathscr{D}'_+$.

3. Generalized Functions of Class $\mathscr{D}'_+$

Definition A.3.1. (G.F. of Class $\mathscr{D}'_+$). *A g.f. of class $\mathscr{D}'_+$ is a functional, F, on $\mathscr{D}_-$ whose values are those of a fundamental sequence $\{f_n\}$ on $\mathscr{D}_-$. That is, there is associated with F a fundamental sequence on $\mathscr{D}_-$, $\{f_n\}$, such that, for every $\varphi \in \mathscr{D}_-$,*

$$\langle F, \varphi\rangle = \lim_{n\to\infty}\langle f_n, \varphi\rangle. \tag{A.3.1}$$

The set of these functionals is denoted by $\mathscr{D}'_+$.

Remark Concerning Notation. Though a g.f. $F \in \mathscr{D}'_+$ is a function whose domain is the space of functions $\mathscr{D}_-$, it is frequently very helpful to denote it by the symbol $F(t)$. This does not mean that F is a function of t, rather it serves to indicate that it is *defined* by *a fundamental sequence of functions of t*.†

Furthermore, with this notation the value $\langle F, \varphi\rangle$ of F at $\varphi(t) \in \mathscr{D}_-$ is denoted by either of the symbols

$$\langle F(t), \varphi(t)\rangle, \quad \int_{-\infty}^{\infty} F(t)\,\varphi(t)\,dt, \quad F(\varphi), \quad F\cdot\varphi.$$

In accordance with (A.3.1) the "integral" here simply stands for a limit of integrals, viz.,

$$\int_{-\infty}^{\infty} F(t)\,\varphi(t)\,dt = \lim_{n\to\infty}\int_{-\infty}^{\infty} f_n(t)\,\varphi(t)\,dt. \tag{A.3.2}$$

Throughout the following pages only the notations $\langle F, \varphi\rangle$ and $\langle F(t), \varphi(t)\rangle$ will be used. (The literature on g.f.'s, as yet, has not fully settled on any consistent notation—except insofar as mathematicians with an eye to rigor favor $\langle F, \varphi\rangle$, $F(\varphi)$, and $F\cdot\varphi$, whereas physicists and applied mathematicians sometimes use $\int_{-\infty}^{\infty} F(t)\,\varphi(t)\,dt$ for its greater suggestiveness in certain situations.)

Example 1. *The $\mathscr{K}_+(R)$ g.f.'s.* If $f(t) \in \mathscr{K}_+(R)$, designate by $\{f(t)\}$ or $\{f\}$ the sequence $\{f_n(t)\}$ in which $f_n(t) = f(t)$ $(n = 1, 2, \ldots)$. This sequence is fundamental on $\mathscr{D}_-$ and it defines the g.f. $f(t) \in \mathscr{D}'_+$ whose value is

$$\langle f, \varphi\rangle = \int_{-\infty}^{\infty} f(t)\,\varphi(t)\,dt. \tag{A.3.3}$$

---

† Except in exercises marked (O.C.) and in Chapter VIII the term "fundamental sequence" will henceforth be used in the sense of "fundamental sequence on $\mathscr{D}_-$."

This shows that the set of $\mathscr{K}_+(R)$ functions considered as functionals on $\mathscr{D}_-$ is a subset of $\mathscr{D}'_+$. The g.f. defined by the identically zero function is denoted by the symbol 0 or $0 \in \mathscr{D}'_+$.

Example 2. *The Heaviside function $H(t)$.* This is the $\mathscr{K}_+(R)$ function

(A.3.4)
$$H(t) = \begin{cases} 0 & \text{for } t < 0 \\ 1 & \text{for } t > 0. \end{cases}$$

It determines the $\mathscr{D}'_+$ g.f. $H(t)$ whose value is

(A.3.5)
$$\langle H, \varphi \rangle = \int_0^\infty \varphi(t)\, dt.$$

Example 3. *The Dirac delta "function" $\delta(t)$.* Consider the sequence $\{p_n(t)\}$ of the $\mathscr{K}_+(R)$ functions defined in (A.2.1). This sequence is fundamental on $\mathscr{D}_-$. Indeed, given any real-valued $\varphi \in \mathscr{D}_-$ there exists, by the Theorem of the Mean of integral calculus, τ_n, with $0 < \tau_n < 1/n$, such that

$$\int_{-\infty}^{\infty} p_n(t)\, \varphi(t)\, dt = n\int_0^{1/n} \varphi(t)\, dt = \varphi(\tau_n).$$

But, φ being continuous, and since $\lim_{n\to\infty} \tau_n = 0$, we have

$$\lim_{n\to\infty} \langle p_n, \varphi \rangle = \lim_{n\to\infty} \varphi(\tau_n) = \varphi(0).$$

If $\varphi = \varphi_1 + i\varphi_2$ is complex-valued, we have

$$\lim_{n\to\infty} \langle p_n, \varphi \rangle = \lim_{n\to\infty} \langle p_n, \varphi_1 \rangle + i \lim_{n\to\infty} \langle p_n, \varphi_2 \rangle,$$

so

$$\lim_{n\to\infty} \langle p_n, \varphi \rangle = \varphi_1(0) + i\varphi_2(0) = \varphi(0).$$

The $\mathscr{D}'_+$ g.f. defined by the sequence $\{p_n\}$ is denoted by the symbols δ or $\delta(t)$ and called the *Dirac delta function* (it is not a function of t but of φ), and has the value

(A.3.6)
$$\langle \delta, \varphi \rangle = \varphi(0).$$

Historically, this is the earliest nonfunction g.f. defined [13]. That it is not definable by any single $\mathscr{K}_+(R)$ (or even merely absolutely integrable) function $f(t)$ follows from the fact that if we take $\varphi_\varepsilon(t) = \exp \dfrac{\varepsilon^2}{t^2 - \varepsilon^2}$ for $|t| < \varepsilon$ and $\varphi_\varepsilon(t) = 0$ for $|t| \geqslant \varepsilon$ then

$$\lim_{\varepsilon\to 0} \int_{-\infty}^{\infty} f(t)\, \varphi_\varepsilon(t)\, dt = 0,$$

whereas $\langle \delta, \varphi_\varepsilon \rangle = 1/e$ for all $\varepsilon > 0$ so that

$$\lim_{\varepsilon\to 0} \langle \delta, \varphi_\varepsilon \rangle = \frac{1}{e}.$$

Example 4. *The Dirac g.f., $\delta(t - h)$.* $p_n(t)$ being defined as in (A.2.1) and h a fixed point of the real axis, consider the sequence $\{p_n(t - h)\}$ of functions of t.

Quite as in Example 3 this sequence is seen to be fundamental on $\mathscr{D}_-$ and to have the value

$$\lim_{n\to\infty} \langle p_n(t-h), \varphi(t)\rangle = \varphi(h).$$

The g.f. defined by this sequence is denoted by $\delta(t-h)$. Its value is then represented by

$$\langle \delta(t-h), \varphi(t)\rangle = \varphi(h). \tag{A.3.7}$$

$\delta(t-h)$, like $\delta(t)$, is an example of a g.f. that is not a functional on $\mathscr{D}_-$ merely defined by a single ordinary function of t.

Theorem A.3.1. *Every $F \in \mathscr{D}'_+$ is a linear functional.*

This is obvious enough. Take $\varphi_1, \varphi_2 \in \mathscr{D}_-$ and the complex numbers c_1, c_2. Then, if $\{f_n\}$ is a fundamental sequence defining F, it follows from

$$\langle f_n, c_1\varphi_1 + c_2\varphi_2\rangle = c_1\langle f_n, \varphi_1\rangle + c_2\langle f_n, \varphi_2\rangle$$

that, in the limit $(n \to \infty)$,

$$\langle F, c_1\varphi_1 + c_2\varphi_2\rangle = c_1\langle F, \varphi_1\rangle + c_2\langle F, \varphi_2\rangle. \tag{A.3.8}$$

4. Equivalence Classes of Fundamental Sequences

Different fundamental sequences on $\mathscr{D}_-$ may very well have the same values. For example, the sequence $\{s_n(t)\}$ of "triangle" functions, whose elements are

$$s_n(t) = \begin{cases} 0 & \text{for } t < -\dfrac{1}{n} \\ n^2\left(t + \dfrac{1}{n}\right) & \text{for } \dfrac{1}{n} < t < 0 \\ -n^2\left(t - \dfrac{1}{n}\right) & \text{for } 0 < t < \dfrac{1}{n} \\ 0 & \text{for } t > \dfrac{1}{n}, \end{cases} \tag{A.4.1}$$

can be shown, by reasoning similar to that of Example 3, above, to have the value

$$\lim_{n\to\infty} \langle s_n, \varphi\rangle = \varphi(0).$$

Therefore, the sequences $\{p_n\}$ and $\{s_n\}$ both define the same g.f., $\delta \in \mathscr{D}'_+$. Different fundamental sequences that define the same element of $\mathscr{D}'_+$ are called equivalent:

Definition A.4.1. *Two fundamental sequences on $\mathscr{D}_-$, $\{f_n\}$ and $\{g_n\}$, are called equivalent (write $\{f_n\} \sim \{g_n\}$) if and only if they have the same values on $\mathscr{D}_-$. That is, if and only if to every $\varphi \in \mathscr{D}_-$ and to every $\varepsilon > 0$ corresponds a positive integer $N(\varepsilon, \varphi)$ such that*

$$n > N(\varepsilon, \varphi) \Rightarrow |\langle f_n - g_n, \varphi\rangle| < \varepsilon. \tag{A.4.2}$$

The elementary properties of sequences of complex numbers make plain that the two statements in this definition are entirely equivalent. For similar reasons the relation just defined has the properties:

(a) For every fundamental sequence $\{f_n\}$, $\{f_n\} \sim \{f_n\}$ (reflexivity).

(b) If $\{f_n\} \sim \{g_n\}$ then $\{g_n\} \sim \{f_n\}$ (symmetry).

(c) If $\{f_n\} \sim \{h_n\}$ and $\{g_n\} \sim \{h_n\}$ then $\{f_n\} \sim \{g_n\}$ (transitivity).

Any relation having these three properties is called an *equivalence relation.*

Consider F and G, two different g.f.'s of class $\mathscr{D}'_+$ (i.e., for at least one $\varphi \in \mathscr{D}_-$ $\langle F, \varphi\rangle \neq \langle G, \varphi\rangle$) which are determined by the fundamental sequences $\{f_n\}$ and $\{g_n\}$ respectively. Let C_F be the set of all fundamental sequences equivalent to $\{f_n\}$ and C_G the set of all fundamental sequences equivalent to $\{g_n\}$. C_F and C_G are disjoint subsets of Σ_+, the set of all fundamental sequences on $\mathscr{D}_-$ [if they were not, there would exist $\{h_n\}$, a fundamental sequence belonging to the intersection $C_F \cap C_G$, and then it would follow from the transitivity property (c) above that $\langle F, \varphi\rangle = \langle G, \varphi\rangle$ for every $\varphi \in \mathscr{D}_-$, i.e., F and G would not be different g.f.'s]. C_F, which thus characterizes precisely one element $F \in \mathscr{D}'_+$ and none other, is called the *equivalence class* of F. We have in this manner obtained a one-to-one correspondence between $\mathscr{D}'_+$ and the collection of these equivalence classes. For this reason we shall designate each equivalence class by the same symbol as the g.f. defined by the fundamental sequences it contains. For example, C_F is denoted by F, C_G by G; furthermore, *to indicate that $\{f_n\}$ is a defining sequence of $F \in \mathscr{D}'_+$ we shall henceforth write $\{f_n\} \in F$.*

Definition A.4.2. *$F \in \mathscr{D}'_+$ is carried in the half-line $[a, +\infty)$ if and only if some $\{f_n\} \in F$ is carried in $[a, +\infty)$.*

5. Basic Operations in $\mathscr{D}'_+$

Let c_1, c_2 be two scalars; $f(t)$, $g(t)$ be two $\mathscr{K}_+(R)$ functions; h a real number; and $\alpha(t) \in C^\infty(R)$. Then each of

$$c_1 f(t) + c_2 g(t), \quad f(t - h), \quad \alpha(t) f(t) \tag{A.5.1}$$

is also a $\mathscr{K}_+(R)$ function.

If now we consider the $\mathscr{D}'_+$ g.f.'s defined by these functions, the operations (A.5.1) will be reflected by operations on the corresponding functionals. Furthermore, since these operations are applicable to the elements of fundamental sequences, this suggests that they can be defined for any g.f.'s in $\mathscr{D}'_+$ by means of the following:

Definition A.5.1. *Let F, $G \in \mathscr{D}'_+$ with $\{f_n(t)\} \in F$ and $\{g_n(t)\} \in G$; c_1, c_2 complex numbers; $h \in R$; $\alpha \in C^\infty(R)$. Then*

(a) *$c_1F(t) + c_2G(t)$ (a linear combination of F and G) is the g.f. defined by $\{c_1f_n(t) + c_2g_n(t)\}$;*

(b) *$F(t - h)$ (the translation of $F(t)$ by h*[†] *is the g.f. defined by $\{f_n(t - h)\}$;*

(c) *$\alpha(t)F(t)$ (the product of F by α) is the g.f. defined by $\{\alpha(t)f_n(t)\}$.*

This definition is correct. However, we cannot accept it as such *unless we are first assured that each one of its statements is consistent and devoid of ambiguity*. Specifically, it is necessary to show that each of the operations described is effectively applicable to any $F, G, c_1, c_2, h, \alpha(t)$ combination called for in the description, and that each time the result is a single well-defined g.f. of class $\mathscr{D}'_+$.

The procedure for carrying out the proof that Definition A.5.1 is indeed consistent is perfectly simple. We shall do it in full detail for statement (a) only [after that, cases (b) and (c) will be obvious to the reader]. For this, we need to establish two facts:

(i) *Given any two fundamental sequences on $\mathscr{D}_-$, $\{f_n(t)\}$ and $\{g_n(t)\}$, the sequence $\{c_1f_n(t) + c_2g_n(t)\}$ is also fundamental on $\mathscr{D}_-$* (i.e., the definition defines a linear combination g.f. for any F, $G \in \mathscr{D}'_+$).

To prove this, take $\varphi(t) \in \mathscr{D}_-$. Since $\{f_n(t)\}$ and $\{g_n(t)\}$ are fundamental, the limits $\lim_{n\to\infty} \langle f_n, \varphi\rangle$ and $\lim_{n\to\infty} \langle g_n, \varphi\rangle$ exist. From the elementary properties of convergent sequences of complex numbers, it follows that $\{\langle c_1f_n + c_2g_n, \varphi\rangle\}$ is a convergent sequence and that

$$\lim_{n\to\infty} \langle c_1f_n + c_2g_n, \varphi\rangle = c_1 \lim_{n\to\infty} \langle f_n, \varphi\rangle + c_2 \lim_{n\to\infty} \langle g_n, \varphi\rangle.$$

Since the functions $c_1f_n(t) + c_2g_n(t)$ are $\mathscr{K}_+(R)$ functions, the sequence $\{c_1f_n(t) + c_2g_n(t)\}$ conforms to Definition A.2.2.

[†] The translation of a function, f, or of a g.f., F, by h is also sometimes designated by the symbol τ_hf. This practice will not be followed here (except in Chapter IVB). It is partly because of its inconvenience in lengthy formulas that we use the notation $F(t)$ for g.f.'s even though they are not functions of t.

(ii) *If* $\{k_n(t)\} \sim \{f_n(t)\}$ *and* $\{l_n(t)\} \sim \{g_n(t)\}$ *then the sequence*

$$\{c_1k_n(t) \dotplus c_2l_n(t)\}$$

defines the same g.f. as does $\{c_1f_n \dotplus c_2g_n\}$ (in other words, the definition gives a single well-defined g.f. $c_1F + c_2G$ for $F, G \in \mathscr{D}'_+$).

The proof of this also follows immediately from the elementary properties of convergent sequences of complex numbers. Since we have

$$\lim_{n\to\infty} \langle c_1f_n \dotplus c_2g_n, \varphi\rangle = c_1 \lim_{n\to\infty} \langle f_n, \varphi\rangle + c_2 \lim_{n\to\infty} \langle g_n, \varphi\rangle$$

and

$$\lim_{n\to\infty} \langle c_1k_n \dotplus c_2l_n, \varphi\rangle = c \lim_{n\to\infty} \langle k_n, \varphi\rangle + c_2 \lim_{n\to\infty} \langle l_n, \varphi\rangle,$$

and since the right-hand sides are equal, the left-hand sides are also equal; which proves, in accordance with Definition A.4.1, that

$$\{c_1 f_n(t) \dotplus c_2g_n(t)\} \sim \{c_1k_n(t) \dotplus c_2l_n(t)\}. \quad \blacksquare$$

A final point to be examined about Definition A.5.1 is whether the operations on $\mathscr{D}'_+$ that it describes are simply extensions to $\mathscr{D}'_+$ of classical operations on $\mathscr{K}_+(R)$ functionals or whether they are entirely new operations even when applied to the latter subset of $\mathscr{D}'_+$. For any $f(t)$, $g(t) \in \mathscr{K}_+(R)$ and $\varphi(t) \in \mathscr{D}_-$ we have

(A.5.2)

$$\int_{-\infty}^{\infty} (c_1f(t) + c_2g(t))\, \varphi(t)\, dt = c_1 \int_{-\infty}^{\infty} f(t)\, \varphi(t)\, dt + c_2 \int_{-\infty}^{\infty} g(t)\, \varphi(t)\, dt;$$

it follows that for the corresponding g.f.'s

(A.5.3) $$\langle c_1f + c_2g, \varphi\rangle = c_1\langle f, \varphi\rangle + c_2\langle g, \varphi\rangle.$$

Comparison of (A.5.2) and (A.5.3) shows that linear combinations as defined by (a) are simply extensions to $\mathscr{D}'_+$ of linear combinations as defined for $\mathscr{K}_+(R)$. [In fact it was this desire for a straightforward extension of a known operation which suggested the form of Definition A.5.1(a) in the first place.]

Similar remarks concerning the translation and multiplication operation in $\mathscr{D}'_+$ as direct extensions of operations in $\mathscr{K}_+(R)$ apply to parts (b) and (c) of Definition A.5.1. Furthermore, as the reader can verify with the aid of the elementary properties of limits of sequences of complex numbers, the counterparts to (A.5.3) for these operations are†

(A.5.4) $$\langle F(t-h), \varphi(t)\rangle = \langle F(t), \varphi(t+h)\rangle,$$

(A.5.5) $$\langle \alpha(t)F(t), \varphi(t)\rangle = \langle F(t), \alpha(t)\, \varphi(t)\rangle.$$

† $\varphi(t+h)$ and $\alpha(t)\,\varphi(t)$ are clearly $\mathscr{D}_-$ test functions.

Remark. Because of (A.5.3) $\mathscr{D}'_+$ *is a linear space* over the field of complex numbers. We therefore speak of the "*space* $\mathscr{D}'_+$" as well as of the "class $\mathscr{D}'_+$."

Remark. The reader may be surprised that no more general form of multiplication than that by $\alpha(t) \in C^\infty(R)$ has been defined in $\mathscr{D}'_+$. The fact is that the product of two arbitrary g.f.'s, $F \in \mathscr{D}'_+$ and $G \in \mathscr{D}'_+$, cannot be defined in any direct manner [44]. For example, if we wished to define $[\delta(t)]^2$ as the functional related to the sequence $\{[p_n(t)]^2\}$, where $p_n(t)$ is given by (A.2.1), we would not succeed, for $\lim_{n\to\infty} \int_{-\infty}^{\infty} p_n^2\,(t)\,\varphi(t)\,dt$ does not exist for every $\varphi(t) \in \mathscr{D}_-$. (Exercise 11).

6. Differentiation of G.F.'s

Several times already we have mentioned the fact that there can be defined in $\mathscr{D}'_+$ a calculus which is a generalization of the calculus of ordinary functions of t. We now begin to do so by defining the derivative of $F \in \mathscr{D}'_+$.

We want this new concept of derivative to be an *extension* of the classical one, and not some radically new operation only remotely related to it. We will, therefore, be well advised to consider the effect of ordinary differentiation on the functional on $\mathscr{D}_-$ defined by a $\mathscr{K}_+(R)$ function $f(t)$ which happens to have an ordinary derivative $f'(t) \in \mathscr{K}_+(R)$. That such functions exist, we know; take $f(t) \in \mathscr{D}_+$ for example.

The g.f. defined by $f(t) \in \mathscr{D}_+$ has, at $\varphi(t) \in \mathscr{D}_-$, the value $\int_{-\infty}^{\infty} f(t)\,\varphi(t)\,dt$. But $f'(t)$ also defines a g.f. and its value is $\int_{-\infty}^{\infty} f'(t)\,\varphi(t)\,dt$. Let $[a, +\infty)$ be a forward half-line carrying $f(t)$, and therefore carrying $f'(t)$ too. Let $(-\infty, b]$ be a backward half-line carrying $\varphi(t)$. Then, integrating by parts, we find

$$\int_{-\infty}^{\infty} f'(t)\,\varphi(t)\,dt = \int_a^b f'(t)\,\varphi(t)\,dt = f(t)(\varphi(t))\Big|_a^b - \int_a^b f(t)\,\varphi\,(t)\,dt,$$

which, since $f(a) = \varphi(b) = 0$, reduces to

$$\int_{-\infty}^{\infty} f'(t)\,\varphi(t)\,dt = -\int_{-\infty}^{\infty} f(t)\,\varphi'(t)\,dt. \tag{A.6.1}$$

Naturally, we would like to define the *derivative of the functional* $f \in \mathscr{D}'_+$ as the *functional* $Df \in \mathscr{D}'_+$, which is determined by the $\mathscr{K}_+(R)$ function $f'(t)$. If we define Df in terms of its values at $\varphi \in \mathscr{D}_-$ we can do so by means of the relation

$$\langle Df, \varphi\rangle = -\langle f, \varphi'\rangle. \tag{A.6.2}$$

This enables us to compute $\langle Df, \varphi\rangle$ by means of the integral $\int_{-\infty}^{\infty} f(t)\,\varphi'(t)\,dt$ *which requires no knowledge whatsoever of the function* $f'(t)$.

The quantity $\langle f, \varphi'\rangle$ is perfectly well defined for any $f \in \mathscr{K}_+(R)$ whether it has a derivative in the ordinary (function) sense or not. In fact, $\langle F, \varphi'\rangle$ is defined for any $F \in \mathscr{D}'_+$.

Rather surprisingly these elementary considerations suffice to lead us to the appropriate general definition of the derivative of any g.f. of class $\mathscr{D}'_+$:

Definition A.6.1. *The derivative of $F \in \mathscr{D}'_+$ is the functional on $\mathscr{D}_-$ (denoted by the symbols DF, $DF(t)$) whose values are computed from those of F by the relation*

$$\langle DF, \varphi \rangle = -\langle F, \varphi' \rangle. \tag{A.6.3}$$

A direct and striking consequence of this definition is the fact that *all* g.f.'s of class $\mathscr{D}'_+$ are differentiable. A question immediately raised by this definition is whether DF itself belongs to $\mathscr{D}'_+$ or not. The answer is provided by the important

Theorem A.6.1. *Whenever $F \in \mathscr{D}'_+$, the derivative $DF \in \mathscr{D}'_+$.*

Proof. Given $F \in \mathscr{D}'_+$ let $\{f_n\} \in F$ and let $[a_F, +\infty)$ be a forward half-line in which every f_n $(n = 1, 2, \ldots)$ is carried. We need only construct a fundamental sequence $\{g_n\}$ that determines the functional DF to prove the theorem. First, define the positive quantities $(n = 1, 2, \ldots)$

$$M_n = \sup_{a_F \leqslant t \leqslant n} |f_n(t)|, \qquad h_n = \min\left(\frac{1}{n}, \frac{1}{nM_n}\right) \tag{A.6.4}$$

and the $\mathscr{K}_+(R)$ functions

$$g_n(t) = \frac{1}{h_n}(f_n(t + h_n) - f_n(t)). \tag{A.6.5}$$

Using the fact that $\int_{-\infty}^{\infty} f_n(t + h)\, \varphi(t)\, dt = \int_{-\infty}^{\infty} f_n(t)\, \varphi(t - h)\, dt$ we may write

$$\begin{aligned}(\text{A.6.6}) \quad \left|\left(\int_{-\infty}^{\infty} g_n(t)\, \varphi(t)\, dt\right) - \left(-\int_{-\infty}^{\infty} f_n(t)\, \varphi'(t)\, dt\right)\right| &= \left|\int_{-\infty}^{\infty} f_n(t)\left[\frac{\varphi(t - h_n) - \varphi(t)}{h_n} + \varphi'(t)\right] dt\right| \\ &= \left|\int_{-\infty}^{\infty} f_n(t)\left[\frac{1}{h_n}\int_t^{t-h_n} (\varphi'(\tau) - \varphi'(t))\, d\tau\right] dt\right|.\end{aligned}$$

If $\varphi(t)$ is carried in $(-\infty, b]$ the function $\varphi(t - h)$ is carried in $(-\infty, b + h]$. Therefore, since $0 < h_n \leqslant 1$ $(n = 1, 2, \ldots)$, all the terms in (A.6.6) are carried in $(-\infty, b + 1]$ and so vanish if $b \leqslant a_F - 1$ since $f_n(t)$ vanishes for $t < a_F$. Let us therefore consider the case $b > a_F - 1$. The right-hand side of (A.6.6) is then majorized by

$$\begin{aligned}&\int_{a_F}^{b+1} |f_n(t)| \left|\frac{1}{h_n}\int_t^{t-h_n} \left(\int_t^{\tau} |\varphi''(\sigma)|\, d\sigma\right) d\tau\right| dt \\ &\qquad \leqslant \sup_{a_F \leqslant t \leqslant b+1} |f_n(t)|\, (b + 1 - a_F)\, \frac{|h_n|}{2} \max_{a_F - 1 \leqslant t \leqslant b+1} |\varphi''(t)|;\end{aligned}$$

consequently, as soon as $n \geqslant b + 1$, we have, in view of (A.6.4),

$$|\langle g_n, \varphi\rangle - (-\langle f_n, \varphi'\rangle)| \leqslant \frac{b+1-a_F}{2} h_n M_n \max_{a_F-1\leqslant t\leqslant b+1} |\varphi''(t)|$$

$$\leqslant \frac{1}{n}\frac{b+1-a_F}{2} \max_{a_F-1\leqslant t\leqslant b+1} |\varphi''(t)|.$$

Therefore, for any $\varphi \in \mathscr{D}_-$,

$$\lim_{n\to\infty} \langle g_n, \varphi\rangle = -\langle F, \varphi'\rangle. \quad ∎$$

Corollary A.6.1. *For any integer $p > 0$, $F \in \mathscr{D}'_+$ has a derivative of order p, $D^pF \in \mathscr{D}'_+$. The values of F and D^pF are related by*

(A.6.7) $$\langle D^pF, \varphi\rangle = (-1)^p\langle F, \varphi^{(p)}\rangle.$$

Proof. This is a corollary of the previous theorem. Since $DF \in \mathscr{D}'_+$ this g.f. has a derivative by Definition A.6.1. This derivative is, of course, what we call D^2F, the second derivative of F. But $D^2F \in \mathscr{D}'_+$ by the last theorem, and the argument repeats itself. Relation (A.6.7) follows from the repeated application of (A.6.3). ∎

Corollary A.6.2. *If p, q are positive integers and $F \in \mathscr{D}'_+$ then*

$$D^p(D^qF) = D^q(D^pF) = D^{p+q}F.$$

Remark. *Henceforth the terms derivative and differentiation will always be taken in the sense of Definition A.6.1 unless specific mention to the contrary is made.*

Example 1. *Derivative of the translated Heaviside g.f., $H(t - h)$.* The Heaviside function $H(t)$ was defined in Example 2 of § A.3; h being a real number, the function $H(t - h)$ is called a translation, by h of the Heaviside function. The derivative of the corresponding g.f. $H(t - h)$ is, following (A.6.3), given by

$$\langle DH(t-h), \varphi(t)\rangle = -\langle H(t-h), \varphi'(t)\rangle.$$

The right-hand side is the integral of a $\mathscr{K}_+(R)$ function and equals

$$-\int_h^\infty \varphi'(t)\, dt = \varphi(h).$$

On the other hand, since the g.f. $\delta(t - h)$ has at every $\varphi \in \mathscr{D}_-$ the same value,

$$\langle \delta(t-h), \varphi(t)\rangle = \varphi(h),$$

we can assert that

(A.6.8) $$DH(t-h) = \delta(t-h).$$

Example 2. *Derivatives of $\delta(t - h)$.* From (A.6.7) we find the pth derivative of

$\delta(t-h)$ to be the g.f. $\delta^{(p)}(t-h) = D^p\,\delta(t-h)$ whose value at $\varphi(t) \in \mathscr{D}_-$ is

(A.6.9) $$\langle \delta^{(p)}(t-h), \varphi(t)\rangle = (-1)^p \langle \delta(t-h), \varphi^{(p)}(t)\rangle = (-1)^p\,\varphi^{(p)}(h).$$

We observe in passing that $\delta^{(p)}(t-h)$, like $\delta(t-h)$, is a g.f. which is not defined by an ordinary function.†

Example 3. *Derivative of* $|t|\,H(t+h)$. Take $h > 0$ first. Then by (A.6.3)

$$\langle D\,|t|\,H(t+h), \varphi\rangle = -\int_{-h}^{\infty} |t|\,\varphi'(t)\,dt$$
$$= \int_{-h}^{0} t\,\varphi'(t)\,dt - \int_{0}^{\infty} t\,\varphi'(t)\,dt.$$

Integrating by parts (φ is carried in $(-\infty, b_\varphi]$ so $\varphi(b_\varphi) = \varphi'(b_\varphi) = 0$),

$$\int_{-h}^{0} t\,\varphi'(t)\,dt = \left[h\varphi(-h) - \int_{-h}^{0} \varphi(t)\,dt\right],$$

$$-\int_{0}^{b_\varphi} t\,\varphi'(t)\,dt = \int_{0}^{b_\varphi} \varphi(t)\,dt.$$

Therefore

$$\langle D\,|t|\,H(t+h), \varphi\rangle = h\varphi(-h) + \int_{-h}^{\infty} \operatorname{sgn} t \cdot \varphi(t)\,dt,$$

where sgn t is the $\mathscr{K}_+(R)$ function

(A.6.10) $$\operatorname{sgn} t = \begin{cases} -1 & \text{for } t < 0 \\ +1 & \text{for } t > 0. \end{cases}$$

Thus, we may write

(A.6.11) $$D\,|t|\,H(t+h) = h\delta(t+h) + \operatorname{sgn} t \cdot H(t+h).$$

This has been proved so far for the case $h > 0$. The simpler case, $h \leqslant 0$, is obtained analogously, the answer being again (A.6.11).

Theorem A.6.2. *If $F \in \mathscr{D}'_+$ and $DF = 0$ then $F = 0$.*

Proof. The notation 0 stands for the $\mathscr{D}'_+$ g.f. defined by the identically vanishing function of t (Example 1, § A.3).

Suppose the conclusion were false. There would then exist $\varphi \in \mathscr{D}_-$ such that $\langle F, \varphi\rangle \neq 0$. The function $\psi(t) = D^{-1}\,\varphi(t)$, as defined in Chapter I, is also in $\mathscr{D}_-$ and $D\psi(t) = \varphi(t)$. By (A.6.3)

$$\langle DF, \psi\rangle = -\langle F, D\psi\rangle = -\langle F, \varphi\rangle \neq 0.$$

This contradicts the hypothesis $DF = 0$. ∎

Remark. The property of $\mathscr{D}'_+$ established by this theorem is similar to the property of $\mathscr{D}_-$ vis-à-vis ordinary differentiation: if $\varphi \in \mathscr{D}_-$ and $D\varphi(t) \equiv 0$ then $\varphi(t) \equiv 0$.

---

† While the symbol D^pF is habitually used in this book (instead of $F^{(p)}$) to indicate the p'th derivative of $F \in \mathscr{D}'_-$, exception is made for the particular g.f. $\delta \in \mathscr{D}'_+$.

7. Identification of $\mathscr{K}_+(R)$ Functions and Functionals

The study of $\mathscr{D}'_+$ as we have carried it up to this point has yielded the remarkable result that every g.f. in this space has derivatives of every order. Before going on with the development of this theory, we must examine the cost at which this result has been achieved.

Instead of dealing with functions of t, we have turned to a set of functionals on the function space $\mathscr{D}_-$. While in the language of ordinary calculus a function, $f(t)$, and its derivative, $f'(t)$, if it exists, are defined by their values at every point t of the real axis, this precision is lost when we consider f as a g.f. In that case, we *no longer consider the function-value at any given* $t \in R$.[†] We shall be content instead with the *weighted averages*

$$\langle f, \varphi \rangle = \int_{-\infty}^{\infty} f(t)\, \varphi(t)\, dt$$

of such values at points, the weighting functions being restricted to the test functions $\varphi \in \mathscr{D}_-$.

In view of this blurring of values at individual points of R, it seems quite possible that two different functions of t could, as functionals on $\mathscr{D}_-$, be indistinguishable. This does not happen in the case of $\mathscr{K}_+(R)$ functions, as attested by the following theorem.

Theorem A.7.1. *The $\mathscr{K}_+(R)$ functions $f(t)$ and $g(t)$ are identical if and only if $\langle f, \varphi \rangle = \langle g, \varphi \rangle$ at every $\varphi \in \mathscr{D}_-$.*

Proof. The necessity of the condition $\langle f, \varphi \rangle = \langle g, \varphi \rangle$ for all $\varphi \in \mathscr{D}_-$ is obvious. Indeed, if $f(t)$ and $g(t)$ are equal, these two functions have the same points $\{t_i\}$ of discontinuity, while $f(t) = g(t)$ for all $t \neq t_i$. It follows that

$$\int_{-\infty}^{\infty} f(t)\, \varphi(t)\, dt = \int_{-\infty}^{\infty} g(t)\, \varphi(t)\, dt,$$

whatever the function $\varphi \in \mathscr{D}_-$ that appears in the integrands.

The converse is proved by contradiction.

Suppose $f(t)$ and $g(t)$ were two different $\mathscr{K}_+(R)$ functions and that they were real-valued, we shall show that there would then exist a function

$$\varphi(t) \in \mathscr{D}_- \quad \text{such that} \quad \langle f(t), \varphi(t) \rangle \neq \langle g(t), \varphi(t) \rangle.$$

[†] Actually at any point of continuity τ of $f(t)$ we do have

$$f(\tau) = \lim_{\varepsilon \to 0} \langle f(t), \rho_\varepsilon(t - \tau) \rangle$$

where ρ_ε is the function defined in (I.2.11). However, this means of obtaining function values from functional values will not be extended to $\mathscr{D}'_+$ g.f.'s here. For the concept of value of a g.f. at a point the reader is referred to [35].

To this end, note first that, in view of Definition A.2.1, $f(t)$ and $g(t)$ can differ if and only if $f(h) - g(h) = d \neq 0$ at some point $h \in R$ where both these functions are continuous. There is no loss of generality in supposing $d > 0$. In that case there exists $\varepsilon > 0$ such that, when t is confined to the interval $[h - \varepsilon, h + \varepsilon]$, we have

$$f(t) - g(t) \geqslant \frac{d}{2} > 0. \tag{A.7.1}$$

Now consider the function

(A.7.2)

$$\rho_\varepsilon(t - h) = \begin{cases} 0 & \text{for } t \leqslant h - \varepsilon \\ C_\varepsilon \exp\left(\dfrac{\varepsilon/2}{t - h - \varepsilon}\right) \exp\left(\dfrac{\varepsilon/2}{h - \varepsilon - t}\right) & \text{for } |t - h| < \varepsilon \\ 0 & \text{for } t \geqslant h + \varepsilon, \end{cases}$$

where C_ε is a normalizing constant chosen so that

$$\int_{-\infty}^{\infty} \rho_\varepsilon(t - h)\, dt = 1.$$

This function is a test function in $\mathscr{D}_-$ of the kind defined in (I.2.11). It vanishes outside the interval $[h - \varepsilon, h + \varepsilon]$, whereas inside this interval it is nonnegative.

It follows from this and (A.7.1) that

$$\int_{-\infty}^{\infty} (f(t) - g(t))\rho_\varepsilon(t - h)\, dt \geqslant \frac{d}{2}\int_{-\infty}^{\infty} \rho_\varepsilon(t - h)\, dt = \frac{d}{2} > 0.$$

This proves the converse for real-valued $\mathscr{K}_-(R)$ functions. The proof for complex-valued $\mathscr{K}_+(R)$ functions is obtained by applying the same reasoning to its real and imaginary parts separately. ∎

Remark 1. Expressed in loose terms, the gist of this theorem is that the set $\mathscr{D}_-$ contains test functions that are sufficiently "fine" to discriminate between different $\mathscr{K}_-(R)$ functions. This is the reason why there is no risk of ambiguity in designating $f(t) \in \mathscr{K}_+(R)$ and the g.f. $f \in \mathscr{D}'_+$ that it defines by the same symbol $f(t)$. We have here a *one-to-one correspondence between $\mathscr{K}_+(R)$ and a subset of $\mathscr{D}'_+$* and shall freely speak of $\mathscr{K}_+(R)$ as being a subset of $\mathscr{D}'_+$. This convenient lapse of language cannot cause any confusion in view of this correspondence.

Remark 2. Let $f(t)$ be a piecewise continuous function carried in a forward half-line, and let $g(t)$ be the $\mathscr{K}_+(R)$ function associated with it in the fashion described in § A.2 above. Then

$$\int_{-\infty}^{\infty} f(t)\, \varphi(t)\, dt = \int_{-\infty}^{\infty} g(t)\, \varphi(t)\, dt$$

for every $\varphi \in \mathscr{D}_-$. These two functions determine the same g.f., even though, as functions of t, they differ (albeit only at the isolated points t_i, that is, in an inessential manner). Thus, we could have used the set of such piecewise continuous functions in place of $\mathscr{K}_+(R)$ when we defined fundamental sequences—providing we had included a definition of "essentially equal" or "equivalent" functions of this kind.

****Remark 3.** Another approach would be to use locally Lebesgue integrable functions in place of $\mathscr{K}_+(R)$ functions. Two such functions define the same g.f. if and only if they are almost everywhere equal. While this would require the student to be familiar with Lebesgue integration, it leads to precisely the same set $\mathscr{D}'_+$ that we have reached by a more accessible path. In any case, from the point of view of physical applications, $\mathscr{K}_+(R)$ functions are more relevant.

Remark 4. It might seem, a priori, that removal from Definition A.2.1 of the requirement that all the f_n of a fundamental sequence be carried in the same forward half-line $[a, +\infty)$ could lead to a larger class of functionals on $\mathscr{D}_-$ than $\mathscr{D}'_+$.

This is not so, for there holds the following (compare [41])

***Proposition.** *To a sequence $\{f_n\}$ of $\mathscr{K}_+(R)$ functions such that, for every $\varphi \in \mathscr{D}_-$, there exists $\lim\limits_{n\to\infty} \langle f_n, \varphi\rangle$, there corresponds a forward half-line $[a, +\infty)$ in which every element of the sequence is carried.*

Proof. By contradiction. The proof is given for real-valued f_n. The case of complex-valued f_n is then immediate.

Let $[a_n, +\infty)$ be the smallest half-line carrying f_n, so that $f_n(t) = 0$ for $t < a_n$, while there exists at least one point in $[a_n, a_n + 1)$ (and, because of the piecewise continuity, an interval of nonzero length), such that f_n does not vanish there. If there exists no single half-line carrying all the f_n there must exist a subsequence $\{f_{n'}\}$ of $\{f_n\}$ such that the corresponding $a_{n'}$ satisfy

$$a_{(n+1)'} < a_{n'} - 1 \qquad \text{(so that } \lim_{n'\to\infty} a_{n'} = -\infty)$$

and whose first index $1'$ is such that $a_{1'} < 0$.

Since the interval $[a_{n'}, a_{n'} + 1)$ contains a subinterval throughout which $f_{n'}$ does not vanish, a subinterval $I_{n'}$ of nonzero length of that exists, in which $f_{n'}$ is continuous and satisfies for some $d_{n'} > 0$ the relation

$$|f_{n'}(t)| \geqslant d_{n'} > 0.$$

Reasoning as in the proof of Theorem A.7.1, we can find a $\varphi_{n'} \in \mathscr{D}_-$ carried in $I_{n'}$ such that

$$\langle f_{n'}, \varphi_{n'}\rangle \geqslant d_{n'} > 0.$$

[For $\varphi_{n'}$ take a translation of $\rho_\varepsilon(t)$ of (I.2.11), with small enough ε to be carried in $I_{n'}$, and multiply by $+1$ or -1, whichever makes $\langle f_{n'}, \varphi_{n'}\rangle$ positive.]

It follows that for the test function $\psi_{1'} = (1/d_{1'})\varphi_{1'}$ we get

$$\langle f_{1'}, \psi_{1'}\rangle = 1.$$

A constant $c_{2'}$ can be found such that

$$c_{2'}\langle f_{2'}, \varphi_{2'}\rangle + \langle f_{2'}, \psi_{1'}\rangle \geqslant 1';$$

we then denote by $\psi_{2'}$ the function $c_{2'}\varphi_{2'}$.

This is the beginning of an induction procedure yielding the test functions

$$\psi_{n'}(t) = c_{n'}\varphi_{n'}(t),$$

where the constants $c_{n'}$ are chosen to satisfy:

$$c_{n'}\langle f_{n'}, \varphi_{n'}\rangle + \langle f_{n'}, \psi_{(n-1)'} + \psi_{(n-2)'} + \cdots + \psi_{1'}\rangle \geqslant n'.$$

The series

$$\varphi(t) = \sum_{n'=1'}^{\infty} \psi_{n'}(t)$$

represents a $\mathscr{D}_-$ function carried in $(-\infty, 0]$, for each of its terms is carried in one of the $I_{n'}$ and no two of these intervals have points in common.

We see that

$$\langle f_{n'}, \varphi\rangle = \langle f_{n'}, \psi_{n'} + \psi_{(n-1)'} + \cdots + \psi_{1'}\rangle \geqslant n'$$

so that, as $n' \to \infty$, $\langle f_{n'}, \varphi\rangle$ increases indefinitely.

This contradicts the hypothesis that $\lim_{n\to\infty} \langle f_n, \varphi\rangle$ exists for every $\varphi \in \mathscr{D}_-$, and proves that the assumption $\lim_{n'\to\infty} a_{n'} = -\infty$ is untenable. ■

It should be noted that quite analogously it can be shown that any piecewise continuous function $f(t)$ such that $\int_{-\infty}^{\infty} f(t)\,\varphi(t)\,dt$ is finite for every $\varphi \in \mathscr{D}_-$ must be carried in a forward half-line.

8. Local Identification of G.F.'s

If (a, b) is an open interval, finite or infinite,† of R then two $\mathscr{K}_+(R)$ functions $f(t)$ and $g(t)$ coincide at every point of this interval if and only if $\langle f, \varphi\rangle = \langle g, \varphi\rangle$ at every $\varphi(t) \in \mathscr{D}_-$ which is carried in this interval. The proof is part of the proof, just given, of Theorem A.7.1. From this property, we are led to

Definition A.8.1. *The G.F.'s $F \in \mathscr{D}'_+$ and $G \in \mathscr{D}'_+$ are called equal (coincident) on the open interval (a, b) if and only if*

(A.8.1) $$\langle F, \varphi\rangle = \langle G, \varphi\rangle$$

for every $\varphi(t) \in \mathscr{D}_-$ that is carried in (a, b).

The g.f. $F \in \mathscr{D}'_+$ is said to equal zero on the open interval (a, b) if and only if

(A.8.2) $$\langle F, \varphi\rangle = 0$$

for every $\varphi \in \mathscr{D}_-$ carried in (a, b).

Thus, even though a g.f. has no value at a point of R, we can compare two g.f.'s or a g.f. and a $\mathscr{K}_+(R)$ function of t on an *open* interval (a, b).

---

† $(-\infty, b)$, $(b, +\infty)$ are called infinite open intervals.

For example, the g.f.'s $\delta^{(p)}(t - h)$ are zero on the open intervals $(-\infty, h)$ and $(h, +\infty)$. We shall say that $\delta^{(p)}(t - h)$ is carried by the point $h \in R$ (§ V.B.3).

9. Physical Significance of G.F.'s

Mathematically g.f.'s provide a more natural medium for the treatment of linear differential and partial differential equations than do ordinary functions. This is borne out by the remarkable simplicity and generality that their use brings, both to the theory, and to the computations of their solutions.

Physically, too, there are serious grounds for viewing g.f.'s as the appropriate language for the mathematical depiction of experimental facts concerning linear phenomena. While this is not the place to go into profound, and, as yet, only partially resolved, questions of epistemology, it is fitting that we touch upon some relevant points for the benefit of the reader to whom mathematics is above all a tool that serves to correlate the numerical data supplied by physical observations.

To the physicist, a partial differential equation is an idealized model of some observed phenomenon. For the engineer, a given differential equation may be the simplified picture of a system of assembled "hardware"—a "black box." In such equations appear terms like: $u(x, y, z, t)$, the temperature at the "point" (x, y, z) at the "instant" t; $V(x, y, z)$, the electric potential at the "point" (x, y, z) of a conductor; $i(t)$, the current at the "instant" t.

Though V, i, u are treated as functions of "points" in space, time, or space-time, it is, to say the least, debatable what experimental meaning should be ascribed to the concept of "point." The temperature and the potential are measured with probes—and these, be they optical or metallic, test over a finite region of nonzero volume. The intensity of an alternating current may be measured with a thermocouple, whose molecules, as well as those of the current-carrying wire, are in motion—so that, experimentally, instantaneous temperature or current is a fiction. Surely, then, it is eminently reasonable to interpret such *experimental measurements* as representing "*weighted averages*" *over some finite neighborhood of a point*. Thus, even if we consider that, ideally, $V(x, y, z)$, $i(t)$, $u(x, y, z, t)$ exist as functions of points, the numerical yields of particular measurements may represent

$$\int_{-\infty}^{\infty} i(t)\, \varphi_2(t)\, dt,$$

$$\iiiint_{-\infty}^{\infty} u(x, y, z, t)\, \varphi_3(x, y, z, t)\, dx\, dy\, dz\, dt,$$

$$\iiint_{-\infty}^{\infty} V(x, y, z)\, \varphi_1(x, y, z)\, dx\, dy\, dz,$$

respectively; where the averaging process corresponds to the *test functions* $\varphi_1(x, y, z)$, $\varphi_2(t)$, $\varphi_3(x, y, z, t)$.

The physically oriented reader, confronted with the conversion of $\mathscr{K}_+(R)$ functions into functionals on $\mathscr{D}_-$ in § A.2 above, and the abandonment of functions in favor of functionals on a test space in § A.3, may have felt some uneasiness at what, at first sight, might seem artificial and juggling for the sake of mathematical convenience alone. The above remarks concerning measurements, even if they do raise more questions in his mind than they answer (among others, questions of statistics and the relation between observational errors in measurement of the dependent and independent variables have been deliberately evaded here),† are inserted for the sole purpose of persuading him that *treating physical variables as generalized functions is no less plausible physically than viewing them as ordinary functions.*

10. Analogy Between G.F. Theory and Real Number Theory

To every $F \in \mathscr{D}'_+$ corresponds the collection of all fundamental sequences [of $\mathscr{K}_+(R)$ functions] any one of which serves to compute the value of F at $\varphi \in \mathscr{D}_-$. There is a one-to-one correspondence between $\mathscr{D}'_+$ and the set of equivalence classes of fundamental sequences.

This is rather analogous to Cantor's manner of defining real numbers from the set R of rational numbers [25].

A fundamental sequence of rationals $\{r_n\}$ is by definition a sequence such that to every rational $\varepsilon > 0$ corresponds a positive integer N such that

$$n, m > N \Rightarrow |r_n - r_m| < \varepsilon.$$

Every fundamental sequence of rationals determines a real number (e.g., 1.4, 1.41, 1.414, . . . determines $\sqrt{2}$). In fact, every real number is identified with an equivalence class of fundamental sequences of rationals ($\{r_n\} \sim \{r'_n\}$ if to every rational $\varepsilon > 0$ corresponds a positive integer K such that $n > K \Rightarrow |r_n - r'_n| < \varepsilon$). It is apparent that $\mathscr{K}_+(R)$ plays a role similar to that of the rationals while $\mathscr{D}'_+$ is analogous to the reals. Thus the g.f. $\delta(t)$, which is not defined by a single function of t, is in a relation to $\mathscr{K}_+(R)$ comparable to that of any irrational number to the rationals.

† Such questions are intimately tied to the choice of test functions. For instance, many $\mathscr{D}_-$ functions represent probability density functions for sums of independent random variables with rectangular probability densities (this follows from a result of S. Mandelbrojt [36, pp. 79–84]). The weighted average $\int i(t)\, \varphi(t)\, dt$ can, in such a case, be interpreted as the expected value of a measurement which is in fact instantaneous, but about whose occurrence only the probability density $\varphi(t)$ is known. On the physical interpretation of g.f.'s see [24] [27].

The parallelism between the two theories goes even further; the generalization to $\mathscr{D}'_+$ of operations of the calculus of ordinary functions resembles the extension to the real numbers of the operations of the arithmetic of rational numbers.

The interested student is referred to the quoted literature on Cantor's theory and encouraged to make the comparison with g.f. theory as it develops in later chapters.

11. The Class $\mathscr{D}'_-$ of Generalized Functions

If in the theory, so far given and to be continued in the rest of this chapter, the $\mathscr{K}_+(R)$ functions and the $\mathscr{D}_-$ functions are all subjected to the change of variables $\tau = -t$ one obtains what are, of course, called $\mathscr{K}_-(R)$ functions and $\mathscr{D}_+$ functions. The class of g.f.'s obtained is called $\mathscr{D}'_-$.

If, given $f(t) \in \mathscr{K}_-(R)$, $\varphi(t) \in \mathscr{D}_+$, we then define

(A.11.1) $$\langle f, \varphi \rangle = \int_{-\infty}^{\infty} f(t)\, \varphi(t)\, dt,$$

and for $\{f_n\} \in F \in \mathscr{D}'_-$

(A.11.2) $$\langle F, \varphi \rangle = \lim_{n \to \infty} \langle f_n, \varphi \rangle.$$

The g.f. derivative of F, DF, is then defined so that it satisfies the same relation as in the $\mathscr{D}'_+$ case:

(A.11.3) $$\langle DF, \varphi \rangle = -\langle F, \varphi' \rangle.$$

Obvious changes in the development given so far of $\mathscr{D}'_+$ g.f.'s directly yield the appropriate results for $\mathscr{D}'_-$.

B. THE DIFFERENTIAL CALCULUS AND CONVERGENCE IN $\mathscr{D}'_+$

1. Differentiation of $\mathscr{K}_+(R)$ G.F.'s

In the applications of g.f. theory to differential and partial differential equations, the subset $\mathscr{K}_+(R)$ of $\mathscr{D}'_+$ plays a particularly important role. This is because data are very often represented mathematically either by $\mathscr{K}_+(R)$ functions or by g.f. derivatives thereof.

Definition B.1.1. *$\mathscr{K}^p_+(R)$ functions. A function $f(t)$ on R is a $\mathscr{K}^p_+(R)$ function if and only if it is a $\mathscr{K}_+(R)$ function carried in a forward half-line $[a_f, +\infty)$ where the following conditions are verified:*

(a) *There exist monotonic sequences*† $\{t_i^{(l)}\}_{i=1}^{i=\infty}$ $(l = 0, 1, 2, \ldots, p)$ *such that*

(B.1.1) $$a_f \leqslant t_1^{(l)} < t_2^{(l)} < \cdots < t_i^{(l)} < \cdots$$

and such that for any l only a finite number of points $t_i^{(l)}$ is contained in any interval of finite length (i.e., $\{t_i^{(l)}\}_i$ $(l = 0, 1, \ldots, p)$ has no finite points of accumulation).

(b) *The ordinary derivative $f^{(l)}(t)$ $(l = 0, 1, \ldots, p)$ is undefined at the $t_i^{(l)}$ and is continuous at every $t \neq t_i^{(l)}$.*

(c) *The limits*

$$f^{(l)}(t_i^{(l)} + 0), \quad f^{(l)}(t_i^{(l)} - 0) \quad (l = 0, 1, \ldots, p; i = 1, 2, \ldots)$$

are defined.

The quantity

(B.1.2) $$f^{(l)}(t_i^{(l)} + 0) - f^{(l)}(t_i^{(l)} - 0) = s_i^{(l)}$$

is called the saltus, or jump, of $f^{(l)}(t)$ at the point t_i.

For example, any function $f(t) \in C^p(R)$ and carried in a forward half-line $[a_f, +\infty)$ is of class $\mathscr{K}_+^p(R)$. (The sequences $\{t_i^{(l)}\}_i$ for such a function are empty.)

In brief, a $\mathscr{K}_+^p(R)$ function is a $\mathscr{K}_+(R)$ function $f(t)$ which has ordinary derivatives $f^{(l)}(t)$ of orders $1, 2, \ldots, p$ except at isolated points, each of these derivatives being itself a piecewise continuous function. [$\mathscr{K}_+(R)$ in this notation would be designated by $\mathscr{K}_+^0(R)$.] With each of these derivatives one can then associate a $\mathscr{K}_+(R)$ function in the manner indicated right after Definition A.2.1.

There is a simple relationship between the g.f. derivatives of the g.f. defined by such a function and the $\mathscr{D}'_+$ g.f.'s defined by its ordinary derivatives. It is expressed in the next theorem and its corollary. Stated in very rough fashion, the theorem indicates that the g.f. derivative of f equals its ordinary derivative plus "point-masses" of magnitude proportional to the jumps in f and located at the jump points $\{t_i^{(0)}\}_i$ of f. In every open interval between two adjacent points of discontinuity, the ordinary derivative and the g.f. derivative of a $\mathscr{K}_+(R)$ function are equal in the sense of § A.8.

Theorem B.1.1. *Let $f(t) \in \mathscr{K}_+^1(R)$ and let $[Df]$ be the $\mathscr{D}'_+$ g.f. defined by the $\mathscr{K}_+(R)$ function associated with the ordinary derivative df/dt, while Df designates the g.f. derivative of $f \in \mathscr{D}'_+$. Then Df, $[Df]$ and the salti (jumps) $s_i^{(0)}$ $(i = 1, 2, \ldots)$ of the function $f(t)$ are related by the expression*

(B.1.3) $$Df = [Df] + \sum_{i=1}^{\infty} s_i^{(0)} \delta(t - t_i^{(0)}).$$

† Which may be infinite, finite, or even empty.

Proof. Compute the values of Df at $\varphi(t) \in \mathscr{D}_-$. By definition $\langle Df, \varphi \rangle = -\langle f, \varphi' \rangle$, i.e.,

$$\langle Df, \varphi \rangle = -\int_{-\infty}^{\infty} f(t)\, \varphi'(t)\, dt = -\int_{a_f}^{t_1^{(0)}} f\varphi'\, dt - \sum_{i=1}^{\infty} \int_{t_i^{(0)}}^{t_{i+1}^{(0)}} f(t)\, \varphi'(t)\, dt$$

(when $a_f = t_1^{(0)}$ the first integral on the right does not appear), where the sum on the right has only a finite number of nonzero terms, since $\varphi(t) = 0$ for $t \geqslant b$ and there is only a finite number of $t_i^{(0)}$ points in the interval $[a_f, b]$, so there is no ambiguity in the use of the symbol $\sum\limits_{i=1}^{\infty}$.

Integrating each term on the right by parts gives

$$\begin{aligned} \langle Df, \varphi \rangle = &-[f(t_1^{(0)} - 0)\, \varphi(t_1^{(0)}) - f(a_f + 0)\, \varphi(a_f)] + \int_{a_f}^{t_1^{(0)}} \frac{df}{dt}\, \varphi\, dt \\ &- \sum_{i+1}^{\infty} [f(t_{i+1}^{(0)} - 0)\, \varphi(t_{i+1}^{(0)}) - f(t_i^{(0)} + 0)\, \varphi(t_i^{(0)})] \\ &+ \sum_{i=1}^{\infty} \int_{t_i^{(0)}}^{t_{i+1}^{(0)}} \frac{df}{dt}\, \varphi(t)\, dt \end{aligned}$$

(when $a_f = t_1^{(0)}$ the terms on the right in the first line do not appear).

Therefore, rearranging the integrated terms and gathering integrals together, we find

$$\text{(B.1.4)} \quad \langle Df, \varphi \rangle = \sum_{i=1}^{\infty} [f(t_i^{(0)} + 0) - f(t_i^{(0)} - 0)]\, \varphi(t_i^{(0)}) + \int_{a_f}^{+\infty} \frac{df}{dt}\, \varphi\, dt.$$

With the notation of (B.1.2) and our knowledge of $\delta(t - t_i)$, as defined earlier, we may rewrite (B.1.4) as

$$\langle Df, \varphi \rangle = \sum_{i=1}^{\infty} s_i^{(0)} \langle \delta(t - t_i), \varphi(t) \rangle + \langle [Df], \varphi \rangle.$$

This identity holds for every $\varphi(t) \in \mathscr{D}_-$, and therefore proves (B.1.3). ∎

Example 1. *Application of* (B.1.3) *to the determination of*

$$D(e^{2\pi i t} H(t + h)\, H(h - t))\ (h > 0).$$

In the open interval $(-h, h)$, $e^{2\pi i t}\, H(t + h)\, H(t - h)$ coincides with $e^{2\pi i t}$. At $t = -h$ there is a jump from 0 to $e^{-2\pi i h}$, at $t = h$ there is a jump from $e^{2\pi i h}$ to 0. The theorem therefore yields

$$\begin{aligned} D(e^{2\pi i t}\, H(t + h)\, H(h - t)) = {} & e^{-2\pi i h} \delta(t + h) \\ & + 2\pi i e^{2\pi i t}\, H(t + h)\, H(t - h) - e^{2\pi i h}\, \delta(t - h). \end{aligned}$$

Example 2. *Application of* (B.1.3) *to the finite "sawtooth" function*

$$S_n(t) = ([t] - t + \tfrac{1}{2})\, H(t)\, H(n - t) \qquad (\textit{integer } n > 0)$$

([*t*] *designates the integer portion of t*).

The graph of the function (Figure 3) shows clearly that

$$DS_n(t) = \tfrac{1}{2}\delta(t) + \sum_{j=1}^{n-1} \delta(t - j) + \tfrac{1}{2}\delta(t - n) - H(t)\, H(n - t).$$

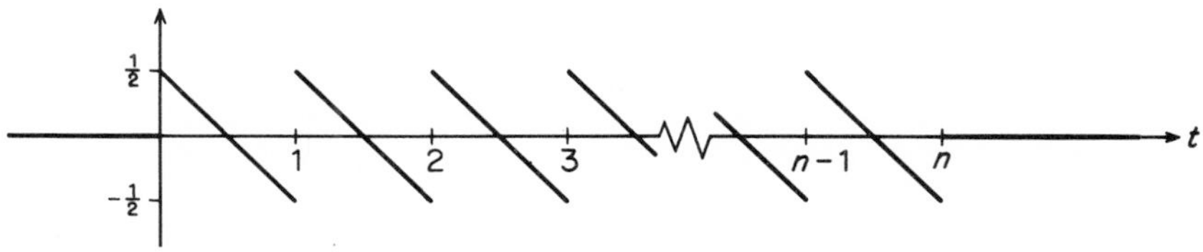

FIGURE 3

Corollary B.1.1. *Given* $f(t) \in \mathscr{K}^p_+(R)$, *designate by* $[D^pF]$ *the g.f. of class* $\mathscr{D}'_+$ *defined by the* $\mathscr{K}_+(R)$ *function associated with the piecewise continuous function* d^pf/dt^p. *Then the g.f. derivative* D^pf *and the g.f.* $[D^pf]$ *satisfy the identity*

$$\text{(B.1.5)} \qquad D^pf = [D^pf] + \sum_{i=1}^{\infty} s_i^{(0)}\delta^{(p-1)}(t - t_i^{(0)}) + \sum_{i=1}^{\infty} s_i^{(1)}\, \delta^{(p-2)}(t - t_i^{(1)})$$

$$+ \cdots + \sum_{i=1}^{\infty} s_i^{(p-1)}\, \delta(t - t_i^{(p-1)}).$$

Proof. (B.1.5) follows directly from repeated application of the previous theorem and the obvious identity (B.3.1) below. (Exercise 21)

Remark. In the terminology of § A.8, this theorem indicates that D^pf and $d^pf(t)/dt^p$ coincide in every open interval where the ordinary derivative $d^pf(t)/dt^p$ is continuous.

2. Application to Differential Equations

A differential equation initial-value problem formulated in terms of functions can be reformulated in terms of $\mathscr{D}'_+$ g.f.'s with the help of the two propositions of the last section. The interest of such a reformulation is that the new equation, providing it is linear with constant coefficients, can be solved by operational methods as simple as those of the last chapter, and whose development is the object of the next chapter.

For a single differential equation, the kind of problem we have in mind is a particularization of the following:

Problem. Find the function $x(t)$ which with its ordinary derivatives $\frac{dx}{dt}, \dots, \frac{d^{p-1}x}{dt^{p-1}}$ is defined and continuous for $t > 0$, while its ordinary derivative $\frac{d^p x}{dt^p}$ is continuous, except possibly at isolated points t_i ($i = 1, 2, \dots$) $\left(\text{where } \frac{d^p x}{dt}(t_i + 0) \text{ and } \frac{d^p x(t_i - 0)}{dt^p} \text{ exist}\right)$, given that, for $t > 0$ and $t \neq t_i$ ($i = 1, 2, \dots$), this function satisfies the equation

$$\text{(B.2.1)} \qquad a_0(t)\frac{d^p x}{dt^p} + a_1(t)\frac{d^{p-1}x}{dt^{p-1}} + \cdots + a_{p-1}(t)\frac{dx}{dt} + a_p(t)x = f(t).$$

Here the $a_j \in C^\infty(R)$, and the "forcing" function $f(t)$ is defined and continuous for $t > 0$, except possibly at isolated points t_i ($i = 1, 2, \dots$) where $f(t_i + 0)$ and $f(t_i - 0)$ exist and $f(t_i + 0) - f(t_i - 0) \neq 0$ (the set $\{t_i\}$ may be empty). We are also given the initial values

$$\text{(B.2.2)} \qquad x(+0) = x_0, \quad \frac{dx}{dt}(+0) = x_1, \dots, \frac{d^{p-1}x}{dt}(+0) = x_{p-1}.$$

To convert this into a g.f. problem, we simply "*continue $x(t)$ and $f(t)$ by zero*" for $t < 0$. This means that we define the functions $X(t)$ and $F(t)$, which belong to $\mathscr{K}_+^p(R)$ and $\mathscr{K}_+(R)$ respectively:

$$\text{(B.2.3)} \qquad X(t) = \begin{cases} 0 & \text{for } t < 0 \\ x(t) & \text{for } t > 0, \end{cases}$$

$$\text{(B.2.4)} \qquad F(t) = \begin{cases} 0 & \text{for } t < 0 \\ f(t) & \text{for } t \neq t_i \ (i = 1, 2, \dots) \text{ and } t > 0. \end{cases}$$

While $x(t)$, $f(t)$ satisfy (B.2.1) for $t > 0$ and $t \neq t_i$, the new functions $X(t)$, $F(t)$ also satisfy this equation for $t < 0$. Being $\mathscr{K}_+(R)$ functions, they define g.f.'s $X \in \mathscr{D}'_+$ and $F \in \mathscr{D}'_+$. As theorem A.7.1 guarantees that every $\mathscr{K}_+(R)$ function is identifiable with one and only one $\mathscr{D}'_+$ g.f. to say that $X(t)$ and $F(t)$ satisfy (B.2.1) *implies that the following relation holds*:

$$\text{(B.2.1')} \quad a_0(t)[D^p X] + a_1(t)[D^{p-1}X] + \cdots + a_{p-1}(t)[DX] + a_p(t)X = F,$$

where, in accordance with the notation of § B.1 above, $[D^l X]$ is the g.f. defined by the $\mathscr{K}_+(R)$ function $d^l X/dt^l$ ($l = 1, 2, \dots, p$).

From Corollary B.1.1 above, and the initial condition (B.2.2) of our problem, we obtain the expressions ($l = 1, 2, \dots, p$)

$$\text{(B.2.5)} \quad [D^l X] = D^l X - (x_0\delta^{(l-1)}(t) + x_1\delta^{(l-2)}(t) + \cdots + x_{l-1}\,\delta(t))$$

relating the g.f. derivatives and the ordinary derivatives of $X(t)$.

Substituting these in (B.2.1′) and rearranging terms, we end up with the following equation, all of whose terms are g.f.'s of class $\mathscr{D}'_+$:

(B.2.6)
$$\begin{aligned} a_0(t)D^pX + a_1(t)D^{p-1}X + \cdots + a_p(t)X \\ = \left(\sum_{l=0}^{p-1} a_l(t)x_{p-1-l}\right)\delta(t) \\ + \left(\sum_{l=0}^{p-2} a_l(t)x_{p-2-l}\right)\delta'(t) + \cdots + \left(\sum_{l=0}^{p-1-j} a_l(t)x_{p-1-j-l}\right)\delta^{(j)}(t) \\ + \cdots + a_0(t)x_0\delta^{(p-1)}(t) + F. \end{aligned}$$

The original problem required the separate statement of the differential equation and of the initial conditions. This reformulated problem requires the statement of a g.f. equation alone, the initial conditions being part of the "forcing" term on the right-hand side. (This g.f. equation is called the equation of evolution of the given problem.)

This argument proves

Theorem B.2.1. *If the initial-value problem* (B.2.1), (B.2.2) *has an ordinary function solution, $x(t)$, of the kind described in the statement of this problem, then the g.f. $X(t) \in \mathscr{D}'_+$ determined by the function $X(t)$ defined by* (B.2.3) *is a solution of the g.f. differential equation* (B.2.6).

Note that we have in no way shown that (B.2.6) is equivalent to the problem (B.2.1) (B.2.2). All we can say at this stage is that the solution of the original problem, if it exists, will be found *among* the (a priori possibly several) solution(s) of the equation of evolution. It turns out (Chapter III) that the latter is very easy to solve when the a_j are constants.

In passing, let it be pointed out that the same reformulation procedure applies to initial-value problems for systems of simultaneous differential equations in several unknowns, as we shall see later.

3. Rules of Differentiation in $\mathscr{D}'_+$

Many of the rules of classical differentiation have their counterparts in the differentiation of g.f.'s. This is to be expected, since the latter is defined by means of the identity (A.6.3). We now list some of these rules:

(1) *Derivative of a linear combination.* If c_1, c_2 are complex constants and $F_1, F_2 \in \mathscr{D}'_+$ we have

(B.3.1)
$$D(c_1F_1 + c_2F_2) = c_1DF_1 + c_2DF_2.$$

The proof is immediate by (A.6.3).

(2) *Derivative of a translated g.f.*

(B.3.2)
$$DF(t-h) = (DF)(t-h) \qquad (h \in R).$$

The notation on the right here stands for the g.f. differentiation of $F(t) \in \mathscr{D}'_+$, followed by a translation by the amount h, so that (B.3.2) simply states that in $\mathscr{D}'_+$ the operations of differentiation and translation *commute*. The proof follows on invoking (A.6.3) and (A.5.4), which yield at once:

$$\begin{aligned}\langle DF(t-h), \varphi(t)\rangle &= -\langle F(t-h), \varphi'(t)\rangle \\ &= -\langle F(t), \varphi'(t+h)\rangle \\ &= \langle (DF)(t-h), \varphi(t)\rangle.\end{aligned}$$

(3) *Derivative of the product* $\alpha(t)F(t)$ ($\alpha(t) \in C^\infty(R)$, $F(t) \in \mathscr{D}'_+$).

(B.3.3) $$D(\alpha F) = (D\alpha)F + \alpha DF.$$

By (A.6.3) and (A.5.5), for any $\varphi \in \mathscr{D}_-$,

$$\langle D(\alpha F), \varphi\rangle = -\langle \alpha F, D\varphi\rangle = -\langle F, \alpha D\varphi\rangle.$$

Ordinary calculus gives $D(\alpha\varphi) - \varphi D\alpha = \alpha D\varphi$, which substituted above, and recalling that every g.f. in $\mathscr{D}'_+$ is a linear functional, leaves

$$\begin{aligned}\langle -F, \alpha D\varphi\rangle &= -\langle F, D(\alpha\varphi)\rangle + \langle F, \varphi D\alpha\rangle \\ &= \langle DF, \alpha\varphi\rangle + \langle (D\alpha)F, \varphi\rangle \\ &= \langle \alpha DF, \varphi\rangle + \langle (D\alpha)F, \varphi\rangle,\end{aligned}$$

which proves (B.3.3).

(4) *Leibniz' theorem* (integer $p \geqslant 0$).

(B.3.4) $$D^p(\alpha F) = \sum_{l=0}^{p} \binom{p}{l} (D^l\alpha) D^{p-l}F$$

(p integer $\geqslant 0$; $\alpha(t) \in C^\infty(R)$; $F \in \mathscr{D}'_+$). For $p = 1$ this has just been proved. For $p > 1$ use induction on p.

(5) *An identity for* $\alpha(t)\, \delta^{(p)}(t-h)$ ($\alpha(t) \in C^\infty(R)$; integer $p \geqslant 0$). From (A.5.5) and the definition of the g.f. $\delta(t-h)$, we obtain for every $\varphi(t) \in \mathscr{D}_-$

$$\langle \alpha(t)\, \delta(t-h), \varphi(t)\rangle = \langle \delta(t-h), \alpha(t)\, \varphi(t)\rangle = \alpha(h)\, \varphi(h).$$

On the other hand, $\alpha(h)$ being a complex constant, we also have

$$\langle \alpha(h)\, \delta(t-h), \varphi(t)\rangle = \alpha(h)\, \langle \delta(t-h), \varphi(t)\rangle = \alpha(h)\, \varphi(h).$$

Thus we get

(B.3.5) $$\alpha(t)\, \delta(t-h) = \alpha(h)\, \delta(t-h).$$

Now consider $D(\alpha(t)\, \delta(t-h))$, which by this last relation is the same as

(B.3.6) $$D(\alpha(h)\, \delta(t-h)) = \alpha(h)\, \delta'(t-h),$$

while by (B.3.3) we have

(B.3.7) $$\begin{aligned}D(\alpha(t)\, \delta(t-h)) &= \alpha'(t)\, \delta(t-h) + \alpha(t)\, \delta'(t-h) \\ &= \alpha'(h)\, \delta(t-h) + \alpha(t)\, \delta'(t-h).\end{aligned}$$

Comparison of (B.3.6) and (B.3.7) gives

$$\alpha(t)\,\delta'(t-h) = \alpha(h)\,\delta'(t-h) - \alpha'(h)\,\delta(t-h). \tag{B.3.8}$$

Using the Leibniz formula, one obtains, for integer $p > 0$, the general identity

$$\alpha(t)\,\delta^{(p)}(t-h) = \sum_{l=0}^{p} (-1)^l \binom{p}{l} \alpha^{(l)}(h)\,\delta^{(p-l)}(t-h). \tag{B.3.9}$$

Example

$$t^k\,\delta^{(p)}(t) = \begin{cases} 0 & \text{if } k > p \\ (-1)^k \dfrac{p!}{(p-k)!}\,\delta^{(p-k)}(t) & \text{if } k \leqslant p. \end{cases} \tag{B.3.10}$$

This can also be obtained directly from

$$\langle t^k\,\delta^{(p)}, \varphi\rangle = (-1)^p\,\langle \delta, D^p(t^k\varphi)\rangle.$$

4. Convergence of Sequences and Series in $\mathscr{D}'_+$

Let $\{f_n(t)\}$ be a sequence of functions on R. In the classical calculus, two modes of convergence are studied. The simplest, *pointwise convergence*, occurs if there exists a function $f(t)$ such that for every $t \in R$

$$\lim_{n\to\infty} f_n(t) = f(t). \tag{B.4.1}$$

Because the sequence of derivatives, or the sequence of integrals, of the elements $f_n(t)$ very often does not converge, even though (B.4.1) is verified, one introduces the concept of uniform convergence, which, in a variety of special cases, enables one to relate the convergence of a sequence of functions to that of its definite integrals. However, it is no panacea. Indeed, though uniform convergence suffices to ensure some simple relations [e.g., if each $f_n(t)$ is continuous, then $f(t)$ is continuous if it is the uniform limit of $f_n(t)$], it is by no means a necessary condition. As a result, questions concerning the continuity, integration and differentiation of sequences and series of functions, and of differentiation with respect to y of integrals such as $\int_a^b f(t, y)\,dt$, usually require a detailed and sometimes involved examination of technical aspects of the particular case at hand. Such questions concerning the commutativity of successive limit processes arise constantly in ordinary and partial differential equations problems related to physical applications.

In $\mathscr{D}'_+$, and in all the other g.f. classes to be studied later, no such complications arise. The simplest convergence definition is also the *natural* one, inasmuch as it makes rigorously valid all sorts of analytical manipulations that in the ordinary calculus are either downright wrong or else require elaborate justification. This remarkable gain in simplicity is due to the fact that the domain of a g.f. is a set of test functions, and that these test functions are particularly smooth [e.g., in $\mathscr{D}_-$ every $\varphi(t)$ is $C^\infty(R)$ and $\varphi(t) = 0$ for all $t \geqslant b_\varphi$, b_φ finite].

Convergence in $\mathscr{D}'_+$ is defined, in direct analogy with the pointwise convergence of everyday calculus, as convergence at every element $\varphi \in \mathscr{D}_-$ (also called *weak* convergence in $\mathscr{D}'_+$):

Definition B.4.1. *A sequence $\{F_n\}$ of g.f.'s of class $\mathscr{D}'_+$ is said to converge to $F \in \mathscr{D}'_+$ if and only if for every $\varphi \in \mathscr{D}_-$*

$$\lim_{n\to\infty} \langle F_n, \varphi\rangle = \langle F, \varphi\rangle. \tag{B.4.2}$$

To indicate that $\{F_n\}$ converges to F in this sense, one writes

$$\operatorname*{Lim}_{n\to\infty} F_n = F \tag{B.4.3}$$

or

$$\operatorname*{Lim}_{n\to\infty} F_n(t) = F(t). \tag{B.4.3'}$$

Right away we see that this is precisely the kind of convergence enjoyed by every fundamental sequence $\{f_n\}$ on $\mathscr{D}_-$, since every $f_n \in \mathscr{K}_+(R)$ is identified (§ A.7) with a g.f. of class $\mathscr{D}'_+$ and $F \in \mathscr{D}'_+$ defined by $\{f_n\}$ satisfies the relation (A.3.1), which is a particular case of (B.4.2).

More briefly,

$$\{f_n(t)\} \in F \Leftrightarrow \operatorname*{Lim}_{n\to\infty} f_n(t) = F(t).$$

Definition B.4.2. *A series $\sum_{n=0}^{\infty} F_n$ of $\mathscr{D}'_+$ g.f.'s is convergent if and only if for some $F \in \mathscr{D}'_+$ the partial sums converge to F, i.e.,*

$$F = \operatorname*{Lim}_{N\to\infty} \sum_{n=0}^{N} F_n. \tag{B.4.4}$$

Note that the right hand sides of relations (B.1.3) and (B.1.5) contain infinite series of g.f.'s when the points of discontinuity $\{t_i^{(l)}\}$ form infinite sequences. (As the meaning of the particular series $\sum_{i=1}^{\infty} s_i^{(0)}\, \delta(t - t_i^{(0)})$ was made plain in the course of the proof of Theorem B.1.1 we did not require Definition B.4.2 at the time.)

Using the same notation as in § A.5, we can enunciate

Theorem B.4.1. *If*

$$\operatorname*{Lim}_{n} F_n = F \quad \textit{and} \quad \operatorname{Lim} G_n = G,$$

where $F_n, G_n \in \mathscr{D}'_+$ $(n = 1, 2, \ldots)$ *and* $F, G \in \mathscr{D}'_+$, *then, also,*

(B.4.5) $$\operatorname*{Lim}_{n\to\infty} (c_1F_n + c_2G_n) = c_1F + c_2G \qquad (c_1, c_2 \in C),$$

(B.4.6) $$\operatorname*{Lim}_{n\to\infty} F_n(t-h) = F(t-h) \qquad (h \in R),$$

(B.4.7) $$\operatorname*{Lim}_{n\to\infty} \alpha(t)\, F_n(t) = \alpha(t)\, F(t) \qquad (\alpha \in C^\infty(R)).$$

Proof. Obvious. In each case apply the elementary properties of convergent sequences of complex numbers and the relation (B.4.2).

We now come to the first of the simplifications of the calculus in $\mathscr{D}'_+$: the automatic term by term differentiability of sequences. The proof is disconcertingly simple, as are those of other more general versions to be considered in Volume II.

Theorem B.4.2. *If* $F \in \mathscr{D}'_+$, $F_n \in \mathscr{D}'_+$ $(n = 1, 2, \ldots)$ *and*

(B.4.8) $$\operatorname*{Lim}_{n\to\infty} F_n = F,$$

then, for every integer $p \geqslant 0$,

(B.4.9) $$\operatorname*{Lim}_{n\to\infty} D^pF_n = D^pF.$$

Proof. For any $\varphi \in \mathscr{D}_-$,

(B.4.10) $$\langle D^pF_n, \varphi\rangle = (-1)^p\langle F_n, \varphi(p)\rangle.$$

But, since $\varphi^{(p)}(t) \in \mathscr{D}_-$, it follows from the hypothesis (B.4.8) that

(B.4.11) $$(-1)^p \lim_{n\to\infty} \langle F_n, \varphi^{(p)}\rangle = (-1)^p\langle F, \varphi^{(p)}\rangle.$$

On the other hand, the term on the right equals $\langle D^pF, \varphi\rangle$; this and (B.4.10) substituted in (B.4.11) yield

$$\langle D^pF, \varphi\rangle = \lim_{n\to\infty} \langle D^pF_n, \varphi\rangle. \quad \blacksquare$$

Corollary B.4.1. *Let* $F_n \in \mathscr{D}'_+$ $(n = 0, 1, 2, \ldots)$, $F \in \mathscr{D}'_+$ *and*

(B.4.12) $$\sum_{n=0}^{\infty} F_n = F.$$

Then, for any integer $p \geqslant 0$,

(B.4.13) $$\sum_{n=0}^{\infty} D^pF_n = D^pF.$$

Proof. Apply the previous theorem to $S_N = \sum_{n=0}^{N} F_n$. ∎

Remark. A question that immediately suggests itself in connection with the definition and propositions just given is this: does there exist in $\mathscr{D}'_+$ an analogue of the Cauchy convergence principle for functions? In other words: given a sequence $\{F_n\}$ of $\mathscr{D}'_+$ g.f.'s such that, for every positive integer p, $\operatorname*{Lim}_{n\to\infty} (F_n - F_{n+p}) = 0 \in \mathscr{D}'_+$, does it follow that there exists $F \in \mathscr{D}'_+$ such that $\operatorname*{Lim}_{n\to\infty} F_n = F$?

The answer is yes, as will be proved in Chapter VI. For most physical applications this fact is not needed, which is why we defer its proof.

Example 1. $F_n(t) = (\sin nt)\, H(t)$. As a sequence of $\mathscr{K}_+(R)$ functions, $\{F_n(t)\}$ does not, as $n \to \infty$, converge pointwise at any point of the forward half-axis $[0, +\infty)$ which is not a multiple of π, so that, in the sense of ordinary calculus, this sequence of functions is not convergent. However, considered as a sequence of $\mathscr{D}'_+$ g.f.'s it does converge. Indeed

$$\langle \sin nt\, H(t), \varphi(t)\rangle = \int_0^{b_\varphi} \sin nt\, \varphi(t)\, dt$$

whenever $\varphi(t) \in \mathscr{D}_-$ is carried in $(-\infty, b_\varphi]$ and $b_\varphi > 0$. Integrating by parts gives

$$\langle \sin nt \cdot H(t), \varphi(t)\rangle = -\frac{\cos nt}{n}\varphi(t)\Big|_0^{b_\varphi} + \int_0^{b_\varphi} \frac{\cos nt}{n}\varphi'(t)\, dt$$
$$= -\frac{\varphi(0)}{n} + \int_0^{b_\varphi} \frac{\cos nt}{n}\varphi'(t)\, dt.$$

From

$$\left|\int_0^{b_\varphi} \frac{\cos nt}{n}\varphi'(t)\, dt\right| \leqslant \frac{1}{n}\int_0^{b_\varphi} |\varphi'(t)|\, dt$$

it follows that, for $b_\varphi > 0$,

$$\lim_{n\to\infty} \langle \sin nt \cdot H(t), \varphi(t)\rangle = 0,$$

which, since, obviously, $\langle F_n, \varphi\rangle = 0$ when $b_\varphi < 0$, gives

(B.4.14) $$\operatorname*{Lim}_{n\to\infty} (\sin nt \cdot H(t)) = 0 \in \mathscr{D}'_+.$$

By Theorem B.4.2 we then also have

$$\operatorname*{Lim}_{n\to\infty} D(\sin nt \cdot H(t)) = D0 \in \mathscr{D}'_+;$$

but $D0 = 0$ and so, by identity (B.3.3), we get

$$\operatorname*{Lim}_{n\to\infty} (n \cos nt \cdot H(t) + \sin nt\, \delta(t)) = 0.$$

By (B.3.5) $\sin nt\, \delta(t) = 0$, so we have finally

(B.4.15) $$\operatorname*{Lim}_{n\to\infty} (n \cos nt \cdot H(t)) = 0 \in \mathscr{D}'_+.$$

In summary, then, the given sequence, though not convergent in the pointwise sense of functions, not only converges as a sequence of $\mathscr{D}'_+$ g.f.'s, but has a convergent sequence of derivatives.

Example 2. A sequence of functions which does not converge pointwise may very well converge in the sense of $\mathscr{D}'_+$. This fact was illustrated by Example 1. It is reasonable to ask whether a sequence $\{f_n(t)\}$ of functions of t which does converge pointwise automatically converges in $\mathscr{D}'_+$ as well. The answer is *no* and is illustrated by the functions

$$f_n(t) = \begin{cases} 0 & \text{for } t \leqslant 0 \\ n^2 & \text{for } 0 < t \leqslant 1/\text{n} \\ 0 & \text{for } 1/n < t, \end{cases}$$

for which $\lim\limits_{n\to\infty} f_n(t) = 0$ at every $t \in R$, whereas $\lim\limits_{n\to\infty} \langle f_n, \varphi\rangle = +\infty$, if for $\varphi(t) \in \mathscr{D}_-$ we take

$$\varphi(t) = \begin{cases} 0 & \text{for } |t| \geqslant 0 \\ e^{1/(t^2-1)} & \text{for } |t| < 1. \end{cases}$$

***Example 3.** *Another fundamental sequence for* $\delta(t)$. The sequence

$$\left\{\frac{2 \sin nt}{\pi t} H(t)\right\},$$

where $H(t)$ is the Heaviside function, converges to $\delta(t)$:

$$\operatorname*{Lim}_{n\to\infty} \left[\frac{2 \sin nt}{\pi t} H(t)\right] = \delta(t). \tag{B.4.16}$$

The graph of $f_n(t) = \dfrac{2 \sin nt}{\pi t} H(t)$ is given in Figure 4. Since

$$\frac{\sin nt}{t} = n \frac{\sin nt}{nt} \quad \text{and} \quad \lim_{t\to 0} \frac{\sin nt}{nt} = 1,$$

we see that, as t approaches 0 from the right, we have

$$f_n(+0) = \frac{2n}{\pi}.$$

When $\varphi \in \mathscr{D}_-$ is carried in a half-line $(-\infty, b_\varphi]$ with $b_\varphi \leqslant 0$ we have $\langle f_n, \varphi\rangle = 0$ and $\langle \delta, \varphi\rangle = 0$, which is consistent with (B.4.16) for these particular test functions.

Referring to any Advanced Calculus text (e.g. [1] [6] [11] [19] [49] [55]) we find the Dirichlet relation ($nt = x$)

$$\frac{2}{\pi} \int_0^\infty \frac{\sin x}{x} dx = 1 = \lim_{n\to\infty} \frac{2}{\pi} \int_0^b \frac{\sin nt}{t} dt \quad \text{if } b > 0. \tag{B.4.17}$$

Let $b_\varphi > 0$; we wish to show that in that case

$$\lim_{n\to\infty} \langle f_n, \varphi\rangle = \varphi(0). \tag{B.4.18}$$

From (B.4.17) we obtain the equality

$$\varphi(0) = \lim_{n\to\infty} \frac{2}{\pi} \int_0^{b_\varphi} \frac{\sin nt}{t} \varphi(0)\, dt,$$

so that we can write

$$\lim_{n\to\infty} [\langle f_n, \varphi\rangle - \varphi(0)] = \lim_{n\to\infty} \frac{2}{\pi} \int_0^{b_\varphi} \frac{\sin nt}{t} (\varphi(t) - \varphi(0))\, dt,$$

in which the integral is the usual simple type of improper integral:

$$\int_0^{b_\varphi} = \lim_{\eta\to 0} \int_\eta^b, \qquad \eta > 0.$$

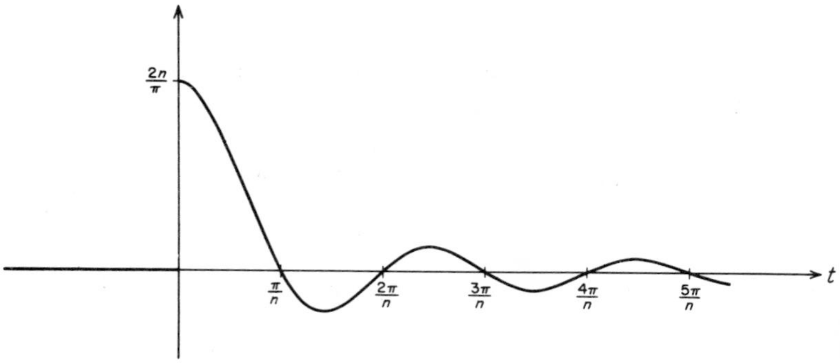

FIGURE 4

Once again we integrate by parts:

$$\text{(B.4.19)} \qquad \lim_{n\to\infty} [\langle f_n, \varphi\rangle - \varphi(0)] = \lim_{n\to\infty} \frac{2}{\pi} \left[-\frac{\cos nt}{n} \left(\frac{\varphi(t) - \varphi(0)}{t}\right)\Bigg|_0^{b_\varphi} + \frac{1}{n}\int_0^{b_\varphi} \cos nt\, \frac{t\varphi'(t) - \varphi(t) + \varphi(0)}{t^2}\, dt\right].$$

Taylor's formula with $t > 0$ gives, for real-valued $\varphi \in \mathscr{D}_-$,

$$\varphi(0) = \varphi(t) - t\varphi'(t) + \frac{t^2}{2!} \varphi''(t\theta(t)),$$

where $0 < \theta(t) < 1$, and where $(t^2/2!)\varphi''(t\theta(t))$ is a $C^\infty(R)$ function of t, because it is equal to a linear combination of $C^\infty(R)$ functions. It follows that

$$\frac{t\varphi'(t) - \varphi(t) + \varphi(0)}{t^2} = \varphi''(t\theta(t))$$

is a continuous function for $t \neq 0$, while as $t \to 0$ it approaches $\varphi''(0)$ since $0 < \theta(t) < 1$. The integrand on the right in (B.4.19) is thus continuous on R, so that it is bounded by some $M_2 > 0$ when $0 < t \leqslant b_\varphi$. Similarly

$$\left|\frac{\varphi(t) - \varphi(0)}{t}\right| \leqslant M_1 < \infty,$$

so (B.4.19) yields

$$|\lim_{n\to\infty} [\langle f_n, \varphi\rangle - \langle \delta, \varphi\rangle]| \leqslant \lim_{n\to\infty} \frac{1}{n}\left[\frac{2M_1}{\pi} + \frac{2b_\varphi}{\pi} M_2\right].$$

Letting $n \to \infty$ we arrive at (B.4.18) for real-valued φ. For complex-valued φ, the usual decomposition $\varphi = \varphi_1 + i\varphi_2$ applies, and (B.4.18) follows easily for all $\varphi \in \mathscr{D}_-$. This proves (B.4.16).

If we take

$$\alpha_n(t) = \begin{cases} \dfrac{\sin nt}{\pi t} & \text{for } t \neq 0 \\ 1 & \text{for } t = 0, \end{cases}$$

and properly define $\alpha_n^{(p)}(t)$ at $t = 0$ we obtain $\alpha_n(t) \in C^\infty(R)$ and $f_n(t) = \alpha_n(t)\, H(t)$. We can then apply (B.3.3) to get

$$Df_n = \alpha_n'(t)\, H(t) + \alpha_n(t)\, \delta(t),$$

which, since $\alpha_n(0) = 1$, assumes as a result of (B.3.5) the form

$$Df_n = \frac{2n}{\pi t}\left(\cos nt - \frac{\sin nt}{nt}\right) H(t) + \delta(t).$$

As $\operatorname*{Lim}_{n\to\infty} f_n = \delta(t)$ by (B.4.16) we have only to apply Theorem B.4.2 to obtain

$$\text{(B.4.20)} \qquad \operatorname*{Lim}_{n\to\infty} \frac{2n}{\pi}\left[\frac{1}{t}\left(\cos nt - \frac{\sin nt}{nt}\right) H(t) + \delta(t)\right] = \delta'(t)$$

This gives $\delta'(t)$ as a limit of g.f.'s which are not of $\mathscr{K}_+(R)$ type. Further applications of Theorem B.4.2 will yield sequences for $\delta^{(p)}(t)$.

Example 4. *The g.f. $P_h(t + a)$ defined by*

$$P_h(t + a) = \sum_{n=0}^{\infty} \delta(t + a - nh).$$

If a and h are real numbers, this series converges in $\mathscr{D}'_+$. Indeed for any $\varphi \in \mathscr{D}_-$ carried in $(-\infty, b_\varphi]$ there exists an integer N such that $(N + 1)h \geqslant b_\varphi$, thus

$$\langle P_h(t + a), \varphi(t)\rangle = \sum_{n=0}^{N} \varphi(nh - a),$$

which is finite.

Example 5

$$[t]H(t) = \sum_{n=1}^{\infty} H(t - n)$$

then

$$D([t]H(t)) = \sum_{n=1}^{\infty} \delta(t - n)$$

($[t]$ = integer portion of t).

Example 6. As an instance of a series of g.f.'s that does *not* converge in $\mathscr{D}'_+$ (though it does converge in certain other classes of g.f.'s) we may cite

$$\sum_{n=1}^{\infty} \delta\left(t - \frac{1}{n}\right).$$

Indeed, take for $\varphi(t) \in \mathscr{D}_-$ the function equal to $e^{1/(t^2-1)}$ for $|t| < 1$ and vanishing for $|t| \geqslant 1$. Then

$$\sum_{n=0}^{N} \left\langle \delta\left(t - \frac{1}{n}\right), \varphi(t) \right\rangle \geqslant (N-1)e^{-4/3},$$

which shows that the partial sums of the series do not converge for every $\varphi \in \mathscr{D}_-$.

5. Parametric G.F.'s of Class $\mathscr{D}'_+$

Let Λ be a set of complex numbers which may be the entire complex plane C. If with every $\lambda \in \Lambda$ there is associated a g.f. $F_\lambda \in \mathscr{D}'_+$, we shall say that this g.f. is a *function of the parameter* λ *and that* Λ *is its domain.* Also one says that F_λ is a *parametric g.f.* of class $\mathscr{D}'_+$, or that the set of all $F_\lambda \in \mathscr{D}'_+$ constitutes a *parametric family of* $\mathscr{D}'_+$ *g.f.'s on* Λ.

Any sequence $\{F_n\}$, where $F_n \in \mathscr{D}'_+$ $(n = 1, 2, \ldots)$, is an example of a parametric family of g.f.'s on the set Λ of nonnegative integers.

Naturally we want to extend the convergence concepts of § B.4 to more general parametric families. Before doing so, let us agree on the following

Definition. *A point* $\lambda_0 \in C$ *is called a limit point (point of accumulation) of the subset* Λ *of* C *if and only if to every* $\varepsilon > 0$ *there corresponds a point* $\lambda \in \Lambda$ *such that* $|\lambda - \lambda_0| < \varepsilon$. $\Lambda \subset C$ *is said to have the point at infinity (denoted by* ∞*) as a limit point if and only if to every* $K > 0$ *there corresponds a point* $\lambda \in \Lambda$ *such that* $|\lambda| > K$.

We now come to the following generalization of Definition B.4.1.

Definition B.5.1. *Given a parametric g.f.* $F_\lambda \in \mathscr{D}'_+$ *with the domain* $\Lambda \subset C$, *let* λ_0 *be a limit point of* Λ. *Then* F_λ *is said to converge to* $F \in \mathscr{D}'_+$ *as* λ *approaches* λ_0, *and we write*

(B.5.1) $$\operatorname*{Lim}_{\lambda \to \lambda_0} F_\lambda = F,$$

if and only if for every $\varphi(t) \in \mathscr{D}_-$

(B.5.2) $$\lim_{\lambda \to \lambda_0} \langle F_\lambda, \varphi \rangle = \langle F, \varphi \rangle.$$

If $|\lambda_0| < \infty$ *this means that to every* $\varphi(t) \in \mathscr{D}_-$ *and every* $\varepsilon > 0$ *there corresponds* $\eta = \eta(\varphi, \varepsilon)$ *such that, whenever* $\lambda \in \Lambda$,

$$|\lambda - \lambda_0| < \eta \Rightarrow |\langle F_\lambda, \varphi \rangle - \langle F, \varphi \rangle| < \varepsilon.$$

If $\lambda_0 = \infty$ it means that to every $\varphi \in \mathscr{D}_-$ and every $\varepsilon > 0$ there corresponds $K = K(\varphi, \varepsilon)$ such that, whenever $\lambda \in \Lambda$,

$$|\lambda| > K \Rightarrow |\langle F_\lambda, \varphi\rangle - \langle F, \varphi\rangle| < \varepsilon.$$

Remark on terminology. In the future we shall not bother to explicitly specify that λ_0 is a point of accumulation of Λ. Whenever we write $\operatorname*{Lim}_{\lambda\to\lambda_0} F_\lambda = F$ or state that F_λ converges as $\lambda \to \lambda_0$ *it will be tacitly understood* that the λ_0 in question conforms to the definition above.

Theorem B.5.1. *Let $F_\lambda \in \mathscr{D}'_+$, $G_\lambda \in \mathscr{D}'_+$ be parametric g.f.'s with the same domain Λ and let*

$$\operatorname*{Lim}_{\lambda\to\lambda_0} F_\lambda = F, \qquad \operatorname*{Lim}_{\lambda\to\lambda_0} G_\lambda = G. \tag{B.5.3}$$

Then, if c_1, c_2 are scalars, $h \in R$, $\alpha(t) \in C^\infty(R)$, and p integer $\geqslant 0$, the following properties hold:

$$\operatorname*{Lim}_{\lambda\to\lambda_0} (c_1F_\lambda + c_2G_\lambda) = c_1F + c_2G, \tag{B.5.4}$$

$$\operatorname*{Lim}_{\lambda\to\lambda_0} F_\lambda(t-h) = F(t-h), \tag{B.5.5}$$

$$\operatorname*{Lim}_{\lambda\to\lambda_0} \alpha(t)F_\lambda(t) = \alpha(t)F(t), \tag{B.5.6}$$

$$\operatorname*{Lim}_{\lambda\to\lambda_0} D^pF_\lambda = D^pF. \tag{B.5.7}$$

This proposition is the analog for parametric g.f.'s of Theorems B.4.1 and B.4.2, and its proof is practically the same. The only distinction is that $\langle F_\lambda, \varphi\rangle$ is a convergent set of complex numbers instead of a sequence.

Example 1. $e^{\lambda t}\,H(t)$, Λ = *imaginary axis of C.* In this case we obtain

$$\operatorname*{Lim}_{\lambda\to\infty} e^{\lambda t}H(t) = 0 \in \mathscr{D}'_+ \tag{B.5.8}$$

for, integrating by parts and with $\varphi(t) \in \mathscr{D}_-$,

$$\int_0^\infty e^{\lambda t}\,\varphi(t)\,dt = \frac{1}{\lambda}\,e^{\lambda t}\,\varphi(t)\Big|_0^{b_\varphi} - \frac{1}{\lambda}\int_0^{b_\varphi} e^{\lambda t}\,\varphi'(t)\,dt.$$

But, since $\lambda = il$ with $l \in R$, $|e^{\lambda t}| = 1$ and therefore

$$\lim_{\lambda\to\infty} \langle e^{\lambda t}, \varphi(t)\rangle = 0.$$

Example 1 of § B.4 can be deduced from this since

$$\sin nt = \frac{e^{int} - e^{-int}}{2i}.$$

Example 2. *Derivatives as limits.* Let $f(t) \in \mathscr{K}_+(R)$, The g.f. derivative of f, which was defined in § A.6 in terms of its values on $\mathscr{D}_-$, can also be obtained as the g.f. limit of a difference quotient analogous in form to that of ordinary calculus. More precisely, we have

(B.5.9) $$Df = \lim_{h\to 0} \frac{1}{h}(f(t+h) - f(t)).$$

Take $\varphi(t) \in \mathscr{D}_-$, then

$$\left\langle \frac{1}{h}(f(t+h) - f(t)), \varphi(t) \right\rangle = \left\langle f(t), \frac{1}{h}(\varphi(t-h) - \varphi(t)) \right\rangle.$$

From the Taylor formula for real-valued $\varphi(t - h)$ follows

$$\int_0^{b_\varphi} f(t) \frac{\varphi(t-h) - \varphi(t)}{h} dt = -\int_0^{b_\varphi} f(t)\, \varphi'(t)\, dt + \frac{h}{2} \int_0^{b_\varphi} f(t)\, \varphi''(t - \theta(t,h)h)\, dt$$

where $0 < \theta(t, h) < 1$ and $\varphi''(t - \theta(t, h)h)$, being a sum of continuous functions of t, is itself continuous and uniformly bounded by $M_1 < \infty$ for $0 \leqslant t \leqslant b_\varphi$ when $|h| \leqslant 1$. $f(t) \in \mathscr{K}_+(R)$ is bounded by $M_2 < \infty$ in this interval so we have

$$\left| \int_0^{b_\varphi} f(t) \frac{\varphi(t-h) - \varphi(t)}{h} dt + \int_0^{b_\varphi} f(t)\, \varphi'(t)\, dt \right| \leqslant \frac{h}{2} M_1 M_2 b_\varphi,$$

and this tends to zero as $h \to 0$, which proves (B.5.9) for real-valued $\varphi \in \mathscr{D}_-$. The case of complex-valued φ follows automatically by decomposition.

More generally, one shows that *any g.f. of the form* $F = D^p f$, *where* $f \in \mathscr{K}_+(R)$, has the property

(B.5.10) $$DF(t) = \operatorname{Lim}_{h\to 0} \frac{1}{h}(F(t+h) - F(t)).$$

To prove it, simply apply the reasoning of the previous case to

$$\lim_{h\to 0} \left\langle \frac{1}{h}(f(t+h) - f(t)), \varphi^{(p)}(t) \right\rangle = -\langle f(t), \varphi^{(p+1)}(t) \rangle.$$

It follows from this and $\delta(t) = DH(t)$ that

(B.5.11) $$\delta'(t) = \operatorname{Lim}_{h\to 0} \frac{1}{h}(\delta(t+h) - \delta(t)),$$

(B.5.12) $$\delta^{(p+1)}(t) = \operatorname{Lim}_{h\to 0} \frac{1}{h}(\delta^{(p)}(t+h) - \delta^{(p)}(t)),$$

relations which can also be proved more directly.

Remark. An overwhelming majority of g.f.'s encountered in the physical applications of $\mathscr{D}'_+$ are of the form $F = D^p f$, $f \in \mathscr{K}_+(R)$,† so that their derivatives

† Such g.f.'s are said to be of finite K-order (§ III.C.5.1).

can be obtained as limits of the above type. In § V.B.1 it is shown that this mode of definition, far from being restricted to such g.f.'s, is actually valid for every member of $\mathscr{D}'_+$ on every backward half-line.

*6. Relation between Pointwise and $\mathscr{D}'_+$ Convergence of Functions

No clear pattern as to the relationship between the pointwise convergence of a sequence $\{f_n(t)\}$ of $\mathscr{K}_+(R)$ functions and its convergence as a sequence of g.f.'s is immediately apparent in the above examples. In some cases pointwise convergence is accompanied by $\mathscr{D}'_+$ convergence; in others, there is $\mathscr{D}'_+$ convergence without pointwise convergence; in still others, we saw that one may have pointwise convergence without $\mathscr{D}'_+$ convergence. It is often useful to have some widely applicable propositions indicating forms of function convergence that imply $\mathscr{D}'_+$ convergence. We shall therefore consider two such theorems which, though simple, cover a multitude of applications.

Theorem B.6.1. *Let $f_\lambda(t)$ be a parametric family of $\mathscr{K}_+(R)$ functions carried in the same forward half-line $[a, +\infty)$ and which converges uniformly to $f(t) \in \mathscr{K}_+(R)$ on every interval of finite length as $\lambda \to \lambda_0$. Then $\operatorname{Lim}_{\lambda\to\lambda_0} f_\lambda = f$.*

Proof. Take $\varphi \in \mathscr{D}_-$, it is carried in some half-line $(-\infty, b]$. As $f_\lambda(t)$ tends to $f(t)$ uniformly on $[a, b]$ there corresponds to any $\varepsilon > 0$ an $\eta > 0$ such that

$$|\lambda - \lambda_0| < \eta \Rightarrow \sup_{a\leqslant t\leqslant b} |f_\lambda(t) - f(t)| < \varepsilon.$$

Consequently, when $|\lambda - \lambda_0| < \eta$,

$$\left|\int_{-\infty}^{\infty} (f_\lambda(t) - f(t))\, \varphi(t)\, dt\right| \leqslant \varepsilon \int_a^b |\varphi(t)|\, dt$$

so

$$\lim_{\lambda\to\lambda_0} \langle f_\lambda, \varphi\rangle = \langle f, \varphi\rangle.$$

(The proof for $\lambda_0 = \infty$ is equally obvious.) ∎

As a preliminary to the next theorem, we require this

Lemma. *If $f(t)$, $g(t)$ are positive or zero-valued piecewise continuous functions on the finite interval $[a, b]$ there holds Schwarz's inequality:*

(B.6.1) $$\left(\int_a^b f(t)g(t)\, dt\right)^2 \leqslant \int_a^b (f(t))^2\, dt \int_a^b (g(t))^2\, dt.$$

Proof. Consider $\int_a^b (f(t) + rg(t))^2\, dt$, where r is any fixed real number. This is nonnegative, so that

$$0 \leqslant \int_a^b (f + rg)^2\, dt = \int_a^b f^2\, dt + 2r \int_a^b gf\, dt + r^2 \int_a^b g^2\, dt.$$

As this holds for all real r the quadratic polynomial in r on the right cannot have distinct real roots. Therefore its discriminant must be negative or zero, i.e.,

$$\left(\int_a^b fg\,dt\right)^2 - \left(\int_a^b f^2\,dt\right)\left(\int_a^b g^2\,dt\right) \leqslant 0. \quad \blacksquare$$

Definition B.6.1. *A parametric family of functions $f_\lambda(t)$ is said to converge to $f(t)$ in mean square on the interval $[a, b]$ as $\lambda \to \lambda_0$ if*

$$\lim_{\lambda \to \lambda_0} \int_a^b |f_\lambda(t) - f(t)|^2\,dt = 0. \tag{B.6.2}$$

Theorem B.6.2. *Let $f_\lambda(t)$ be a parametric family of $\mathscr{K}_+(R)$ functions carried in the same forward half-line $[a, +\infty)$ and which converges in mean square to $f(t) \in \mathscr{K}_+(R)$ on every finite interval of R. Then* $\operatorname*{Lim}_{\lambda \to \lambda_0} f_\lambda = f$.

Proof. Let $(-\infty, b]$ carry $\varphi(t) \in \mathscr{D}_-$ and put

$$g_\lambda(t) = f_\lambda(t) - f(t).$$

Then

$$\left|\int_{-\infty}^{\infty} g_\lambda(t)\,\varphi(t)\,dt\right| \leqslant \int_a^b |g_\lambda(t)|\,|\varphi(t)|\,dt,$$

and, by Schwarz's inequality

$$\int_a^b |g_\lambda(t)|\,|\varphi(t)|\,dt \leqslant \sqrt{\int_a^b |g_\lambda(t)|^2\,dt \int_a^b |\varphi(t)|^2\,dt}. \tag{B.6.3}$$

The first term on the right approaches 0 as $\lambda \to \lambda_0$. The second term is finite and independent of λ. Therefore

$$\lim_{\lambda \to \lambda_0} \langle f_\lambda, \varphi \rangle = \langle f, \varphi \rangle.$$

Obvious modifications give the proof for $\lambda_0 = \infty$. $\blacksquare$

7. Differentiation and Integration with Respect to a Real Parameter

Let Λ be an interval of R, or the whole real axis, and let $F_\lambda \in \mathscr{D}'_+$ be a parametric g.f. with domain Λ. *These assumptions are retained throughout this section.*

If at $\lambda_0 \in \Lambda$ we have $\operatorname*{Lim}_{\lambda \to \lambda_0} F_\lambda = F_{\lambda_0}$, the g.f. is said to be continuous (with respect to λ) at λ_0. *F_λ is said to be continuous on Λ if it is continuous at every point of Λ.* This is equivalent to the statement that *for every* $\varphi(t) \in \mathscr{D}_-$ the function $\langle F_\lambda, \varphi \rangle$ of λ is continuous on Λ.

Definition B.7.1. *The parametric g.f. $F_\lambda(t) \in \mathscr{D}'_+$ has a derivative with respect to λ at $\lambda_0 \in \Lambda$ if and only if there exists an element of $\mathscr{D}'_+$ denoted by $\partial F_{\lambda_0}/\partial\lambda$ such that*

$$\text{(B.7.1)} \qquad \operatorname*{Lim}_{\Delta\lambda \to 0} \frac{1}{\Delta\lambda}(F_{\lambda_0+\Delta\lambda}(t) - F_{\lambda_0}(t)) = \frac{\partial F_{\lambda_0}(t)}{\partial\lambda}.$$

This is equivalent to the statement that

$$\text{(B.7.2)} \qquad \left(\frac{\partial}{\partial\lambda}\langle F_\lambda, \varphi\rangle\right)_{\lambda=\lambda_0} = \left\langle \frac{\partial F_{\lambda_0}}{\partial\lambda}, \varphi \right\rangle$$

at every $\varphi \in \mathscr{D}_-$.

***Example.**

$$F_\lambda = (\sin \lambda t)\, H(t), \qquad \Lambda = R$$

$$\frac{\partial F_\lambda}{\partial\lambda} = t \cos \lambda t\, H(t).$$

Take $\varphi(t) \in \mathscr{D}_-$. We have to show that

$$\lim_{\Delta\lambda \to 0} \left\langle \frac{\sin(\lambda + \Delta\lambda)t - \sin \lambda t}{\Delta\lambda} H(t) - t \cos \lambda t\, H(t), \varphi(t) \right\rangle = 0,$$

in other words that

$$\frac{\partial}{\partial\lambda} \int_0^{b_\varphi} \sin \lambda t\, \varphi(t)\, dt = \int_0^b \frac{\partial(\sin \lambda t)}{\partial\lambda} \varphi(t)\, dt.$$

But this we already know from advanced calculus to be correct since the integrand on the right is continuous in the joint variable (λ, t). Higher-order derivatives with respect to λ are defined in the expected manner by repeated differentiation.

Theorem B.7.1. *If $F_\lambda \in \mathscr{D}'_+$, and if $\partial^k F_{\lambda_0}/\partial\lambda^k \in \mathscr{D}'_+$ exists at $\lambda_0 \in \Lambda$, then*

$$\text{(B.7.3)} \qquad D^p \frac{\partial^k F_{\lambda_0}}{\partial\lambda^k} = \frac{\partial^k}{\partial\lambda^k}(D^p F_{\lambda_0}).$$

Proof. By the definition of $D^p(\partial^k F_{\lambda_0}/\partial\lambda^k)$ and use of (B.7.2), we have for $\varphi(t) \in \mathscr{D}_-$

$$\left\langle D^p \frac{\partial^k F_{\lambda_0}(t)}{\partial\lambda^k}, \varphi(t) \right\rangle = (-1)^p \left\langle \frac{\partial^k F_{\lambda_0}}{\partial\lambda^k}, \varphi^{(p)} \right\rangle = \left(\frac{\partial^k}{\partial\lambda^k}[(-1)^p \langle F_\lambda, \varphi^{(p)}\rangle]\right)_{\lambda=\lambda_0}$$

$$= \left(\frac{\partial^k}{\partial\lambda^k}\langle D^p F_\lambda, \varphi\rangle\right)_{\lambda=\lambda_0} = \left\langle \frac{\partial^k (D^p F_{\lambda_0})}{\partial\lambda^k}, \varphi \right\rangle.$$

Here the notation $(\partial^k/\partial\lambda^k)\, D^p F_{\lambda_0}(t)$ stands for the kth derivative with respect to λ of the parametric g.f. $D^p F_\lambda(t)$ at $\lambda = \lambda_0$. ∎

Definition B.7.2 (Definite Integral of a Parametric G.F.). *Let* $[\alpha, \beta]$ *be an interval of finite length contained in* Λ *and let* $F_\lambda(t) \in \mathscr{D}'_+$ *be continuous with respect to* λ *on* $[\alpha, \beta]$. *The definite integral*

$$G = \int_\alpha^\beta F_\lambda(t)\, d\lambda$$

is the g.f., G, of class $\mathscr{D}'_+$ *which, if it exists, satisfies the relation*

$$\int_\alpha^\beta \langle F_\lambda, \varphi\rangle\, d\lambda = \langle G, \varphi\rangle \tag{B.7.4}$$

for every $\varphi \in \mathscr{D}_-$.

If $G = \int_\alpha^\beta F_\lambda\, d\lambda$ exists in the sense of this definition we have

$$\int_\alpha^\beta F_\lambda\, d\lambda = \operatorname*{Lim}_{N\to\infty} \sum_{k=1}^{N} F_{\lambda'_k} \Delta\lambda_k, \tag{B.7.5}$$

where the sums on the right-hand side are the g.f. analogs of the Riemann sums of ordinary calculus; i.e.,

$$\Delta\lambda_k = \lambda_k - \lambda_{k-1} \qquad (k = 1, 2, \ldots, N),$$

the points $\alpha = \lambda_0 \leqslant \lambda_1 \leqslant \cdots \leqslant \lambda_{N-1} \leqslant \lambda_N = \beta$ partition the interval $[\alpha, \beta]$, λ'_k is a point in $[\lambda_{k-1}, \lambda_k]$, and as $N \to \infty$ we make all the $|\Delta\lambda_k| \to 0$.

The truth of (B.7.5) is seen by taking the value of both sides on the $\varphi \in \mathscr{D}_-$ and is left for the reader to establish.

Of course, not every $F_\lambda(t) \in \mathscr{D}'_+$ whose parametric domain contains $[\alpha, \beta]$ has a definite integral in the sense of the above definition. However, every $F_\lambda(t)$ that is continuous on $[\alpha, \beta]$ does, as we shall be able to show later with the help of a result of Chapter VI.

Example.

$$\int_0^\beta \cos \lambda t \cdot H(t)\, d\lambda \qquad \Lambda = [0, +\infty), \quad \beta > 0.$$

If the g.f. $\cos \lambda t \cdot H(t)$ is integrable with respect to the parameter λ, (B.7.4) will be satisfied. The left-hand side takes the form ($\varphi(t)$ carried in $(-\infty, b_\varphi]$)

$$\int_0^\beta \left[\int_0^{b_\varphi} \cos \lambda t\, \varphi(t)\, dt\right] d\lambda.$$

The integrand of this repeated integral, being continuous in the joint variable (t, λ), satisfies the requisite conditions for the inversion of the order of integration, and is equal, therefore, to

$$\int_0^{b_\varphi}\int_0^\beta \cos \lambda t\, \varphi(t)\, d\lambda\, dt = \int_0^{b_\varphi} \frac{\sin \beta t}{t}\, \varphi(t)\, dt.$$

Thus (B.7.4) is satisfied. The *definite integral of the g.f.* $\cos \lambda t \cdot H(t)$ *equals the* $\mathscr{D}'_+$ *g.f. defined by the* $\mathscr{K}_+(R)$ *function*

(B.7.6) $$\int_0^\beta \cos \lambda t \cdot H(t)\, d\lambda = \frac{\sin \beta t}{t} H(t).$$

Definition B.7.3 (Improper Integral of Parametric G.F. of Class $\mathscr{D}'_+$). *Let* $F_\lambda(t) \in \mathscr{D}'_+$ *have the parametric domain* $\Lambda = [0, +\infty)$ *and let the definite integral* $\int_0^\beta F_\lambda(t)\, d\lambda$ *exist for every* $\beta > 0$. *The integral* $\int_0^\infty F_\lambda(t)\, d\lambda$ *is then defined to be the g.f. of class* $\mathscr{D}'_+$, *if it exists, such that*

(B.7.7) $$\int_0^\infty F_\lambda(t)\, d\lambda = \operatorname*{Lim}_{\beta \to +\infty} \int_0^\beta F_\lambda(t)\, d\lambda.$$

This definition, like the others of this section, is a direct and obvious transcription to parametric g.f.'s of class $\mathscr{D}'_+$ of the definition of the integral over an infinite interval of an ordinary function of a real variable. Other types of improper integrals can be defined for parametric g.f.'s in the same carbon-copy fashion. It would therefore be idle to use up the space to formally write out definitions for them.

***Example.**

$$\frac{2}{\pi} \int_0^\infty \cos \lambda t \cdot H(t)\, d\lambda.$$

The improper integral of the *function*,

$$\int_0^\infty \cos \lambda t \cdot H(t)\, d\lambda,$$

does not exist, since

(B.7.8) $$\frac{2}{\pi} \int_0^\beta \cos \lambda t \cdot H(t)\, d\lambda = \frac{2 \sin \beta t}{\pi t} H(t)$$

does not converge as $\beta \to +\infty$.

However, the improper *g.f. integral*

$$\int_0^\infty \cos \lambda t \cdot H(t)\, d\lambda$$

is perfectly well defined. Indeed, in the last example it was seen that the $\mathscr{D}'_+$ g.f. defined by the function in (B.7.8) is the g.f. integral

$$\int_0^\beta \cos \lambda t \cdot H(t)\, d\lambda.$$

By Definition B.7.3 we have,

$$\frac{2}{\pi} \int_0^\infty \cos \lambda t \cdot H(t)\, d\lambda = \operatorname*{Lim}_{\beta \to \infty} \frac{2 \sin \beta t}{\pi t} H(t).$$

Referring to Example 3 of § B.4 [replacing the integer n by the real number $\beta > 0$ in the relation (B.4.16) can be immediately legitimized] we find

$$\frac{2}{\pi}\int_0^\infty \cos \lambda t\, H(t)\, d\lambda = \delta(t), \tag{B.7.9}$$

a result that is of use in mathematical physics, and which is here placed on a mathematically rigorous foundation of a type applicable to many other problems.

Remark. Throughout this section the parametric domain Λ was restricted to intervals (finite or infinite) of R. By now, it must be more than obvious to the reader that this restriction is not essential. One can take for Λ sets of k-tuples $=$ $(\lambda^1, \lambda^2, \ldots, \lambda^k)$, where the components λ^j range over intervals or regions of the complex plane. Continuity, partial differentiation with respect to the parameters λ^j $(j = 1, 2, \ldots, k)$, multiple integration, line, surface, and volume integrals, as well as contour integrals, of $F_\lambda(t) \in \mathscr{D}'_+$, are then defined exactly as one would expect.

C. SINGULAR FUNCTION G.F.'S

In this portion of Chapter II, we shall concern ourselves with the definition of some $\mathscr{D}'_+$ g.f.'s related to ordinary functions, such as $t^{-3/2}H(t)$, that have isolated singularities where they become indefinitely large.

1. The G.F. log t_+

The ordinary function $H(t)\log t$ is designated by the symbol $\log t_+$. As t approaches the origin from the right, the value of the function diverges to $-\infty$; it is therefore not a $\mathscr{K}_+(R)$ function. Nevertheless, whenever $\varphi(t) \in \mathscr{D}_-$, the improper integral

$$\begin{aligned}\int_{-\infty}^{\infty} \log t_+\, \varphi(t)\, dt &= \lim_{\substack{\varepsilon\to 0\\ \varepsilon>0}} \int_\varepsilon^{b_\varphi} \log t\, \varphi(t)\, dt \\ &= \lim_{\substack{\varepsilon\to 0\\ \varepsilon>0}} [(t\log t - t)\,\varphi(t)|_\varepsilon^{b_\varphi} \\ &\qquad - \int_\varepsilon^{b_\varphi} (t\log t - t)\,\varphi'(t)\, dt]\end{aligned} \tag{C.1.1}$$

does exist since $\lim_{\substack{\varepsilon\to 0\\ \varepsilon>0}} \varepsilon \log \varepsilon = 0$[†]. Thus, the function $\log t_+$, in spite of

[†] One way of showing this is to apply l'Hopital's Rule. A more direct procedure is to write $\log \varepsilon = -u$ so that as $\varepsilon > 0$ approaches 0, $u \to +\infty$. Then, so long as $u > 0$ and $\varepsilon < 1$,

$$\frac{-u}{1 + u + u^2/2} < -\frac{u}{e^u} = \varepsilon \log \varepsilon < 0,$$

and the result follows from $\displaystyle\lim_{u\to+\infty} \frac{u}{1 + u + u^2/2} = 0.$

its singularity at the origin, determines a functional on $\mathscr{D}_-$. This functional is a g.f. of class $\mathscr{D}'_+$ because the sequence $\{f_n(t)\}$ of the truncated functions

$$f_n(t) = \begin{cases} 0 & \text{for } t < 1/n \\ \log t & \text{for } t > 1/n \end{cases} \tag{C.1.2}$$

is a fundamental sequence of $\mathscr{K}_+(R)$ functions on $\mathscr{D}_-$ with the property

$$\int_{-\infty}^{\infty} \log t_+ \cdot \varphi(t)\,dt = \lim_{n\to\infty} \int_{-\infty}^{\infty} f_n(t)\,\varphi(t)\,dt, \tag{C.1.3}$$

a fact proved by taking $\varepsilon = 1/n$ in (C.1.1).

This $\mathscr{D}'_+$ g.f. we shall henceforth denote by the same symbol, $\log t_+$, as the function from which it originates. Note that it provides another example of a function which is not everywhere differentiable in the ordinary sense, whereas its g.f. derivatives $D^p \log t_+$ exist for every integer $p > 0$.

The translations $\log (t + h)_+$ $(h \in R)$ also define $\mathscr{D}'_+$ g.f.'s, of course.

2. The G.F.'s t_+^λ (λ Real and $\lambda \neq -1, -2, -3, \ldots$)

The function t_+^λ is defined by

$$t_+^\lambda = \begin{cases} 0 & \text{for } t \leqslant 0 \\ t^\lambda & \text{for } t > 0. \end{cases} \tag{C.2.1}$$

Here we restrict λ to being real and different from the negative integers.

For $\lambda > 0$, t_+^λ is a continuous function which coincides with the function $t^\lambda H(t)$ at every point of continuity of the latter and defines the corresponding g.f. t_+^λ in the usual manner.

For $\lambda < 0$, t_+^λ does not determine a $\mathscr{K}_+(R)$ function, since t_+^λ diverges to $+\infty$ as t approaches the origin from the right. However, when $-1 < \lambda < 0$ and $\varphi(t) \in \mathscr{D}_-$, the improper integral

$$\begin{aligned} \int_{-\infty}^{\infty} t_+^\lambda\,\varphi(t)\,dt &= \lim_{\substack{\varepsilon\to 0\\ \varepsilon>0}} \int_{\varepsilon}^{b_\varphi} t^\lambda\,\varphi(t)\,dt \\ &= \lim_{\substack{\varepsilon\to 0\\ \varepsilon>0}} \left[\frac{t^{\lambda+1}}{\lambda+1}\,\varphi(t)\Big|_{\varepsilon}^{b_\varphi} - \frac{1}{\lambda+1}\int_{\varepsilon}^{b_\varphi} t^{\lambda+1}\,\varphi'(t)\,dt\right] \end{aligned} \tag{C.2.2}$$

is well defined, so that in this case t_+^λ defines a functional on $\mathscr{D}_-$. That this functional is in fact a g.f. of class $\mathscr{D}'_+$ is seen by verifying that the truncated functions

$$g_n(t) = \begin{cases} 0 & \text{for } t < 1/n \\ t^\lambda & \text{for } t > 1/n \end{cases} \tag{C.2.3}$$

form a fundamental sequence of $\mathscr{K}_+(R)$ functions such that

$$\lim_{n\to\infty}\int_{-\infty}^{\infty} g_n(t)\,\varphi(t)\,dt = \int_{-\infty}^{\infty} t_+^\lambda\,\varphi(t)\,dt. \tag{C.2.4}$$

This g.f. will be represented by the symbol t_+^λ of the function from which it is derived.

When $\lambda < -1$ the improper integral $\int_{-\infty}^{\infty} t_+^\lambda\,\varphi(t)\,dt$ does not exist for arbitrary $\varphi(t)\in\mathscr{D}_-$. Yet, if $\varphi(t)$ is carried either in $(-\infty, 0)$ or in $(0, +\infty)$ $\int_{-\infty}^{\infty} t_+^\lambda\,\varphi(t)\,dt$ is an ordinary integral. This suggests looking for a g.f. of class $\mathscr{D}'_+$ which on these open half-lines has values equal to this integral. Let us suppose that we have found such a g.f., call it $\text{Pf}\,t_+^\lambda$ temporarily;† it is immediately apparent that *it is not unique*. Indeed, for any $\varphi(t)\in\mathscr{D}_-$ carried in $(-\infty, 0)$ or in $(0, +\infty)$ we have

$$\langle \text{Pf}\,t_+^\lambda + \delta^{(p)}(t), \varphi(t)\rangle = \langle \text{Pf}\,t_+^\lambda, \varphi(t)\rangle = \int_{-\infty}^{\infty} t_+^\lambda\,\varphi(t)\,dt.$$

For this reason, we modify the suggested problem to: find a $\mathscr{D}'_+$ g.f., $\text{Pf}\,t_+^\lambda$, which coincides with $\int_{-\infty}^{\infty} t_+^\lambda\,\varphi(t)\,dt$ on $(-\infty, 0)$ and $(0, +\infty)$ and which is a "natural" g.f. to associate with the singular function t_+^λ for non-integer $\lambda < -1$. By a "natural" association between the function t_+^λ and the g.f. $\text{Pf}\,t_+^\lambda$, we mean one such that certain basic analytic properties of the functions are reflected by their associated g.f.'s [23, p. 68]. Specifically, we should like to have for all real λ_1, λ_2 which are not negative integers (c_1, c_2 constants, $\alpha(t)\in C^\infty(R)$)

$$\begin{aligned} &\text{(a)}\quad \text{Pf}\,(c_1 t_+^{\lambda_1} + c_1 t_+^{\lambda_2}) = c_1\,\text{Pf}\,t_+^{\lambda_1} + c_1\,\text{Pf}\,t_+^{\lambda_2},\\ &\text{(b)}\quad \text{Pf}\,(\alpha(t) t_+^{\lambda}) = \alpha(t)\,\text{Pf}\,t_+^{\lambda},\\ &\text{(c)}\quad \text{Pf}\,(D^p t^\lambda)_+ = D^p(\text{Pf}\,t_+^\lambda), \end{aligned} \tag{C.2.5}$$

where, in (c), the derivative on the left-hand side is an ordinary derivative while that on the right is a g.f. derivative, and where for $\lambda > -1$ the symbol $\text{Pf}\,t_+^\lambda$ stands for the g.f. designated earlier in this section by t_+^λ.

The solution to this problem, as suggested by (C.2.5c), is:

Definition C.2.1. *For real noninteger $\lambda < -1$, the g.f. of class $\mathscr{D}'_+$ $\text{Pf}\,t_+^\lambda$ is defined by*

$$\text{Pf}\,t_+^\lambda = \frac{1}{(\lambda+1)(\lambda+2)\cdots(\lambda+k)}\,D^k t_+^{\lambda+k} \tag{C.2.6}$$

where k is any positive integer such that $\lambda + k > 0$ and where differentiation is in $\mathscr{D}'_+$.

---

† Pf stands for "pseudo-function" in the terminology of Schwartz [43].

We cannot accept this as a definition of a g.f. without first verifying that it is consistent, viz., that if k_1 and k_2 are different positive integers, such that $\lambda + k_1 > 0$, and $\lambda + k_2 > 0$, one has

$$\text{(C.2.7)} \qquad \frac{1}{(\lambda+1)\cdots(\lambda+k_1)} D^{k_1} t_+^{\lambda+k_1} = \frac{1}{(\lambda+1)\cdots(\lambda+k_2)} D^{k_2} t_+^{\lambda+k_2}.$$

Now, if $k_2 > k_1$, for instance, the functions $t_+^{\lambda+k_1}$, $t_+^{\lambda+k_1+1}, \ldots, t_+^{\lambda+k_2}$ are respectively $C(R), C^1(R), \ldots, C^{k_2-k_1}(R)$; their ordinary and their g.f. derivatives coincide by Corollary B.1.1; therefore,

$$D^{k_2-k_1} t_+^{\lambda+k_2} = \frac{1}{(\lambda+k_1+1)\cdots(\lambda+k_2)} t_+^{\lambda+k_1}.$$

Applying the g.f. derivative D^{k_1} to both sides proves the veracity of (C.2.7).

Next, it must be shown that (C.2.5a, b, c) hold true. But that the reader can immediately verify himself—remember that for $\lambda > -1$, the symbol Pf t_+^λ stands for the g.f. t_+^λ defined in the early portion of this section.

Remark. Some authors, [23] [34], drop the Pf prefix introduced in [43] and write t_+^λ instead of Pf t_+^λ, even when $\lambda < -1$. While the Pf notation was useful in the discussion above to distinguish between function and generalized function, now that the definitions have been formally stated, we can afford to follow the practice of these authors and write t_+^λ both for the function and for the g.f. defined in (C.2.6). This should not cause any confusion since the symbol $\langle t_+^\lambda, \varphi\rangle$ makes sense (when $\lambda < -1$) only when a means for computing it is given. As the only such means given here lies in Definition C.2.1, by which

$$\text{(C.2.7)} \qquad \langle t_+^\lambda, \varphi(t)\rangle = \frac{(-1)^k}{(\lambda+1)\cdots(\lambda+k)} \int_{-\infty}^{\infty} t_+^{\lambda+k} \varphi^{(k)}(t)\, dt,$$

this makes clear the g.f. interpretation of the symbol t_+^λ as the g.f. that we shall always associate with the function t_+^λ.

*3. The G.F. $t_+^{\lambda-1}/\Gamma(\lambda)$ (λ real)

The function $\Gamma(\lambda)$ has already been encountered in § I.9 for real $\lambda > 0$. Using the identity $\Gamma(\lambda+1) = \lambda\Gamma(\lambda)$ we extend the domain of $\Gamma(\lambda)$ to all real λ such that $\lambda \neq 0, -1, -2, -3, \ldots$. For this we simply define its value at $\lambda < 0$ ($\neq -1, -2, -3, \ldots$) to be

$$\Gamma(\lambda) = \frac{\Gamma([-\lambda]+\lambda+1)}{\lambda(\lambda+1)\cdots([-\lambda]+\lambda)},$$

where $[-\lambda]$ is the largest nonnegative integer that does not exceed $-\lambda$.

We now define the following g.f. of class $\mathscr{D}'_+$ for all real λ:

(C.3.1)
$$\frac{t_+^{\lambda-1}}{\Gamma(\lambda)} = \begin{cases} \dfrac{t_+^{\lambda-1}}{\Gamma(\lambda)} & \text{for real } \lambda \neq 0, -1, -2, -3, \dots \\ \delta^{(-\lambda)}(t) & \text{for } \lambda = 0, -1, -2, -3, \dots . \end{cases}$$

This definition for $\lambda \neq 0, -1, -2, \dots$ results from the multiplication of the g.f. t_+^λ of the preceding section by the finite constant $1/\Gamma(\lambda)$. As to the definition for $\lambda = 0, -1, -2, \dots$, let the reader be assured that it is not artificial; the reason for the choice $\delta^{(-\lambda)}(t)$ is that this makes the g.f. $t_+^{\lambda-1}/\Gamma(\lambda)$ continuous with respect to the parameter λ.† In this book, no use will be made of this particular property, and we therefore omit its proof and discussion, for which the interested reader is referred to [43] and [23].

*4. The G.F. t_+^λ log t (real $\lambda \neq -1, -2, -3, \dots$)

When $\lambda > 0$, $t_+^\lambda \log t$ is a continuous function on R

$$\lim_{\substack{t \to 0 \\ t > 0}} t^\lambda \log t = 0.$$

(Proof by modification of argument in footnote, p. 79.) When $\lambda > -1$ the functions

(C.4.1)
$$l_n(t) = \begin{cases} 0 & \text{for } t < 1/n \\ t^\lambda \log t & \text{for } t > 1/n \end{cases}$$

form a fundamental sequence of $\mathscr{K}_+(R)$ functions and $(\varphi(t) \in \mathscr{D}_-)$,

(C.4.2)
$$\lim_{n \to \infty} \int_{-\infty}^{\infty} l_n(t)\, \varphi(t)\, dt = \int_{-\infty}^{\infty} t^\lambda \log t\, \varphi(t)\, dt,$$

where the integral on the right is a well-defined improper integral. Furthermore, when $\lambda > -1$, both the function $t_+^\lambda \log t$ and its associated $\mathscr{D}'_+$ g.f. satisfy

(C.4.3)
$$t_+^\lambda \log t = \frac{\partial t_+^\lambda}{\partial \lambda}.$$

If $\lambda < -1$, but is not a negative integer, take any positive integer k such that $k + \lambda > 0$. Then, $t_+^{\lambda+k}$ is a continuous function of t which, with its associated g.f., satisfies (C.4.3). The kth-order g.f. derivative $D^k(\partial t_+^{\lambda+k}/\partial\lambda)$ is by Corollary A.6.1 a g.f. of class $\mathscr{D}'_+$, and Theorem B.7.1 enables us to assert that the parametric derivative $(\partial/\partial\lambda)(D^k t_+^{\lambda+k})$ exists and equals $D^k(\partial t_+^{\lambda+k}/\partial\lambda)$. Since $D^k t_+^{\lambda+k} = (\lambda + 1) \cdots (\lambda + k)\, t_+^\lambda$ by the Definition of

† See also Example 3, § VII.5.

§ C.2 above, we have proved that the parametric derivative $\partial t_+^\lambda / \partial \lambda$ exists for all real $\lambda \neq -1, -2, -3, \ldots$. In consequence, we can *define* the g.f. $t_+^\lambda \log t$ for these values of λ by the relation (C.4.3) [34].

EXERCISES

Sections A.2, A.3, A.4

1. Prove that every $\mathscr{K}_+(R)$ function can be represented as the sum of a $C(R)$ function and a series of the form $\sum_{k=1}^{\infty} a_k H(t - \tau_k)$ where the $a_k \in C$ and the $\tau_k \in R$.

2. Give several examples of fundamental sequences equivalent to $\{p_n(t)\}$. Show that $\rho_{1/n}(t)$ (ρ_ε defined in (I.2.11)) is such a sequence.

3. What g.f. is defined by the fundamental sequence $\{np_n(t - n)\}_n$?

4. Use the result of Exercise 1 to show that, when $f(t) \in \mathscr{K}_+(R)$ and when $\rho_\varepsilon(t)$ is defined by (I.2.11), the function

$$f_\varepsilon(t) = \int_{-\infty}^{\infty} f(\tau)\, \rho_\varepsilon(t - \tau)\, d\tau$$

is a $\mathscr{D}_+$ function (§ I.8).

***5.** Use the result of Exercise 4 to show that $f_\varepsilon(t)$ approaches $f(t)$ uniformly on every finite closed interval $[c, d]$ where $f(t)$ is continuous. Apply this to prove that to every $f \in \mathscr{K}_+(R)$ corresponds an equivalent fundamental sequence $\{f_n(t)\}$ of $\mathscr{D}_+$ functions.

6. (O.C.) With every piecewise continuous function carried on a forward half-line, there is associated a $\mathscr{K}_+(R)$ function (Definition A.2.1). In similar fashion, there is associated with every piecewise continuous function on R a function which we may call a $\mathscr{K}(R)$ function. (*a*) Give a precise definition of $\mathscr{K}(R)$ functions. (*Note:* the points t_i of discontinuity will be arranged in a two-sided sequence $\{t_i\}_{i=-\infty}^{i=+\infty}$.) (*b*) The set of $C^\infty(R)$ functions carried in closed finite intervals being denoted by $\mathscr{D}$, we write $\langle f, \varphi \rangle$ for

$$\int_{-\infty}^{\infty} f(t)\, \varphi(t)\, dt$$

where $f \in \mathscr{K}(R)$ and $\varphi \in \mathscr{D}$. By analogy with the $\mathscr{D}'_+$ g.f. definition, define fundamental (on $\mathscr{D}$) sequences of $\mathscr{K}(R)$ functions, equivalent (on $\mathscr{D}$) sequences, and g.f.'s of class $\mathscr{D}'$. Show that a $\delta(t) \in \mathscr{D}'$ can be defined such that $\langle \delta, \varphi \rangle = \varphi(0)$. Give examples of fundamental sequences that define $\delta(t)$ on $\mathscr{D}$ but are not fundamental on $\mathscr{D}_-$.

7. (O.C.) $\mathscr{E}$ denotes the class of $C^\infty(R)$ functions. Any $f \in \mathscr{K}_+(R)$ which is carried in a finite interval $[a, b]$ defines a linear functional on $\mathscr{E}$ with the values

$$\langle f, \varphi \rangle = \int_{-\infty}^{\infty} f(t)\, \varphi(t)\, dt \qquad (\varphi \in \mathscr{E}).$$

Following the pattern employed for $\mathscr{D}'_+$ in the text and for $\mathscr{D}'$ in Exercise 6, develop a definition of g.f.'s of class $\mathscr{E}'$. (*Note:* for simplicity define every fundamental sequence on $\mathscr{E}$ so that its members are all carried in a common finite interval. However, Remark 4 (p. 53) has an analogue for $\mathscr{E}'$.) Observe that $\delta(t)$ can be defined on $\mathscr{E}$ also.

Sections A.5, A.6, A.7, A.8

8. Prove the consistency of (b) and (c) in Definition A.5.1.

9. Show that $\alpha(t)\,\delta(t-h) = \alpha(h)\,\delta(t-h)$ when $\alpha \in C^\infty(R)$.

10. (Change of variable in a g.f.) Given $F(t) \in \mathscr{D}'_+$ and $a > 0$, define $F(at+b)$ and prove the definition to be consistent. Apply it to show

$$\delta(at+b) = \frac{1}{a}\,\delta\left(t + \frac{b}{a}\right).$$

11. Show that $\{p_n(t)\}^2$ is not a fundamental sequence.

12. (O.C.) The g.f.'s of class $\mathscr{D}'$ defined in Exercise 6 have generalized derivatives which satisfy

$$\langle DF, \varphi\rangle = -\langle F, \varphi'\rangle \qquad (F \in \mathscr{D}',\ \varphi \in \mathscr{D}).$$

Show that $DF \in \mathscr{D}'$. (See Exercise 6.)

13. (O.C.) Repeat Exercise 12, but with $\mathscr{E}$, $\mathscr{E}'$ in place of $\mathscr{D}$, $\mathscr{D}'$. (See Exercise 7.)

14. (O.C.) A sequence $\{f_n\}$ of $\mathscr{K}_+(R)$ functions is called fundamental on $\mathscr{D}^p_-$ if, for $k = 0, 1, 2, \ldots, p$, $\lim_{n\to\infty} \langle f_n, \varphi^{(k)}\rangle = \lim_{n\to\infty} \int_{-\infty}^{\infty} f_n\,(t)\,\varphi^{(k)}(t)\,dt$ exist. A g.f. is of class $\mathscr{D}'^p_+$ if it is a functional on $\mathscr{D}^p_-$ defined by such a sequence. Define generalized derivatives $DF, \ldots, D^pF$ for $F \in \mathscr{D}'^p_+$ and observe that $D^iF \in \mathscr{D}'^{p-i}_+ (i = 1, 2, \ldots, p)$. Also show that $\alpha(t)F(t)$ is defined for $F \in \mathscr{D}'^p_+$, $\alpha \in C^p\,(R)$.

15. (A.R.) For those $F \in \mathscr{D}'_+$ which are defined by fundamental sequences of $\mathscr{D}_+$ functions, Theorem A.6.1 is easy to prove directly. Do so.

***16.** (A.R.) Let $F \in \mathscr{D}'_+$ and let the fundamental sequence of $\mathscr{K}_+(R)$ functions $\{f_n(t)\} \in F$. Let

$$g_n(t) = \int_{-\infty}^{\infty} f(\tau)\,\rho_\varepsilon(t-\tau)\,d\tau \quad \text{with } \varepsilon = \frac{1}{n}.$$

By Exercise 5, $g_n \in \mathscr{D}_+$. Show that $\{g_n\} \sim \{f_n\}$. Combine this with Exercise 15 to get a new proof of Theorem A.6.1.

***17.** (O.C.) Carry out a $\mathscr{D}'$ and an $\mathscr{E}'$ version of Exercise 16.

18. Give examples showing that modifying Definition A.8.1 so as to let φ be carried in $[a, b]$ does not lead to a concept of equality of g.f.'s on closed intervals.

19. Show that

$$a_1\delta(t) + b_1\delta'(t) = a_2\delta(t) + b_2\delta'(t)$$

if and only if $a_1 = a_2$ and $b_1 = b_2$. Next, show that

$$a_1\delta + b_1\delta' + \cdots + m_1\delta^{(p)} = a_2\delta + b_2\delta' + \cdots + m_2\delta^{(p)}$$

if and only if $a_1 = a_2$, $b_1 = b_2, \ldots, m_1 = m_2$.

20. (O.C.) Verify that $\mathscr{D}'$ and $\mathscr{E}'$ versions of the discussion of §§ A.7, A.8 are very easily obtained.

Sections B.1, B.2, B.3

21. Prove Corollary B.1.1.

22. (A.R.) Use the relation (A.6.8) and Exercise 1 to give a new proof of Theorem B.1.1.

23. $F(t) = \operatorname{sgn} t \cdot H(t - h)$ [sgn t defined in (A.6.10)]. Find D^pF (integer $p > 0$).

24. $F(t) = |t|H(t - h)$; find D^pF.

25. $F(t) = H(t - h) \cdot H(t + h)$; find D^pF.

26. Find DF_N when

$$F_N(t) = (2[\sqrt{t}\,] + 1)\, H(t)\, H(N - t)$$

($[u]$ = largest integer $\leqslant u$).

27. (O.C.) State and establish $\mathscr{D}'$, $\mathscr{E}'$, and $\mathscr{D}'^p_+$ versions of Theorem B.1.1 and Corollary B.1.1. (See Exercises 6, 7, 12, 13, 14.)

28. (O.C.) Use the results of Exercises 14, 27 to get a $\mathscr{D}'^p_+$ version of Theorem B.2.1 when the coefficients $a_j(t)$ ($j = 0, 1, \ldots, p$) in equation B.2.1 are merely assumed to be $C^p(R)$ functions.

29. Prove (B.3.4).

30. Prove (B.3.9).

31. Prove (B.3.10) directly, without using (B.3.9).

***32.** (O.C.) Given $F \in \mathscr{D}'$, find a primitive (antiderivative) $G \in \mathscr{D}'$ such that $DG = F$. (Take a fundamental sequence $\{F_n\} \in F$. G is then defined by

$$\{G_n\} = \left\{\int_0^t F_n(\tau)\, d\tau + c_n\right\}_n$$

where the constants c_n are chosen arbitrarily except that they must be such that $\lim_{n \to +\infty} \langle G_n, \varphi\rangle$ exists for all $\varphi \in \mathscr{D}$. To achieve this, decompose φ as in Exercise I.8 with φ_0 an arbitrary fixed $\mathscr{D}$ function having

$$\int_{-\infty}^{\infty} \varphi_0(t)\, dt = 1.)$$

Show that any two primitives of F differ by a constant (Temple [51]).

Sections B.4, B.5, B.6

33. $\lim_{n \to \infty} D^p(n^q e^{int} H(t)) = ?$

34. Show that

$$\lim_{n \to \infty} \left\langle H(t) \frac{\sin nt,}{t} \varphi(t) \right\rangle = 0$$

when $\varphi \in \mathscr{D}_-$ has $\varphi(0) = 0$.

***35.** Given $\varphi_0(t) \in \mathscr{D}_-$ with $\varphi_0(0) = 1$, show that any $\varphi \in \mathscr{D}_-$ can be written in the form

$$\varphi(t) = c\varphi_0(t) + \psi(t)$$

(c constant, $\psi \in \mathscr{D}_-$ with $\psi(0) = 0$). Use this and Exercise 34 to prove that

$$\operatorname*{Lim}_{n\to\infty} \frac{\sin nt}{t} H(t) = k\delta(t),$$

k constant. (The value of k was indicated in Example 3, § B.4, to be $\pi/2$.)

***36.** Show that any sequence $\{F_N\}$ of $\mathscr{D}'_+$ g.f.'s such that $\lim_{N\to+\infty} \langle F_N, \varphi\rangle$ exists for every $\varphi \in \mathscr{D}_-$ has all its members carried in some forward half-line independent of N. This is not necessarily true of any parametric family F_λ for which $\lim_{\lambda\to\lambda_0} \langle F_\lambda, \varphi\rangle$ exists at every $\varphi \in \mathscr{D}_-$. Give an example to prove it.

37. $F \in \mathscr{D}'_+$ is said to be locally of finite K– order if to every backward half-line $(-\infty, a)$ correspond $G_a \in \mathscr{K}_+(R)$ and an integer $p_a \geqslant 0$ such that $F = D^{p_a}G_a$ on $(-\infty, a)$. Prove that in that case

$$D^kF = \operatorname*{Lim}_{h\to 0} \frac{1}{h^k} \Delta^k F(t)$$

where

$$\Delta^k F(t) = \sum_{j=0}^{k} (-1)^{k-j} \binom{k}{j} F(t + jh).$$

(Recall Exercise I.5.)

38. Show that if the parametric derivative $\partial F_{\lambda_0}/\partial\lambda$ of $F_\lambda \in \mathscr{D}'_+$ exists F_λ is continuous at λ_0.

39. $F_\lambda \in \mathscr{D}'_+$ being a continuous parametric g.f. on $\Lambda = R$ for which $\int_\alpha^\beta F_\lambda(t)\, d\lambda = G_\beta \in \mathscr{D}'_+$ exists, show that

$$\frac{\partial G_\beta}{\partial\beta} = F_\beta(t).$$

Compare this with

$$\int_\alpha^\beta \frac{\partial F_\lambda}{\partial\lambda}\, d\lambda \quad \left(\frac{\partial F_\lambda}{\partial\lambda} \in \mathscr{D}'_+\right).$$

40. Derive the Taylor formula with integral remainder for parametric $F_\lambda \in \mathscr{D}'_+$ such that the $\partial^k F_\lambda/\partial\lambda^k$ exist and are continuous on $\Lambda = [\alpha, \beta] \subset R$, for $k = 1, 2, \ldots, p$. Can the Lagrange form of the remainder be used in place of the integral remainder whenever the latter is valid?

41. Consider the sequence of parametric $\mathscr{D}'_+$ g.f.'s

$$\{F_{n\lambda}(t)\}_n = \left\{\frac{2 \sin n\lambda t}{t} H(t)\right\}_{n=1}^{\infty}, \qquad \Lambda = [0, +\infty).$$

Find

$$\operatorname*{Lim}_{\lambda\to 0} \operatorname*{Lim}_{n\to+\infty} F_{n\lambda} \qquad \text{and} \qquad \operatorname*{Lim}_{n\to+\infty} \operatorname*{Lim}_{\lambda\to 0} F_{n\lambda}.$$

Is the limit of a convergent sequence of parametric $\mathscr{D}'_+$ g.f.'s continuous with respect to the parameter necessarily continuous?

42. Give an example of a sequence $\{F_{n\lambda}(t)\}_{n=1}^{\infty}$ of $\mathscr{D}'_+$ parametric g.f.'s for which

$$\operatorname*{Lim}_{n\to\infty} \frac{\partial F_{n\lambda_0}}{\partial\lambda} \neq \left[\frac{\partial}{\partial\lambda}\left(\operatorname*{Lim}_{n\to+\infty} F_{n\lambda}\right)\right]_{\lambda=\lambda_0}.$$

(This shows that parametric differentiation, like ordinary differentiation of functions, does not enjoy the simple properties—à la Theorem B.4.2—that hold for g.f. differentiation.)

Sections C.1, C.2, C.3, C.4

43. Find a fundamental sequence of $\mathscr{K}_+(R)$ functions that defines $D(\log t_+)$.

44. If $h > 0$, the g.f. $H(t + h) \log |t| \in \mathscr{D}'_+$ is defined by the fundamental sequence $\{F_n(t)\}$ where

$$F_n(t) = H(t + h) \log |t| \qquad \text{for } |t| > 1/n$$

and

$$F_n(t) = 0 \qquad \text{for } |t| < 1/n.$$

Show that $\{F_n\}$ is fundamental on $\mathscr{D}_-$ and find $t\, D[H(t + h) \log |t|]$.

45. If $h > 0$ the g.f. $H(t + h)(1/t) \in \mathscr{D}'_+$ is defined by the sequence $\{G_n\}$ where

$$G_n(t) = H(t + h)\frac{1}{t} \qquad \text{for } |t| > \frac{1}{n}$$

and

$$G_n(t) = 0 \qquad \text{for } |t| < \frac{1}{n}.$$

Show that $\{G_n\}$ is fundamental and that

$$D[H(t + h) \log |t|] = (\log h)\, \delta(t + h) + H(t + h)\frac{1}{t}.$$

46. The g.f. t_+^λ is defined for real negative $\lambda \neq -1, -2, \ldots, -k, \ldots$ in (C.2.6). Show that when $-k - 1 < \lambda < -k$ $(k = 1, 2, \ldots)$ the values of this g.f. are given by

$$\langle t_+^\lambda, \varphi\rangle = \int_0^\infty t^\lambda[\varphi(t) - \varphi(0) - t\varphi'(0) - \cdots \frac{t^{k-1}}{(k-1)!}\varphi^{(k-1)}(0)]\, dt. \quad [23]$$

47. A $\mathscr{D}'_+$ g.f. is called homogeneous of degree λ [23] if for every $\alpha > 0$, $F(\alpha t) = \alpha^\lambda F(t)$. Show that this is equivalent to the condition

$$\alpha^{-1}\left\langle F(t), \varphi\left(\frac{t}{\alpha}\right)\right\rangle = \alpha^\lambda\langle F(t), \varphi(t)\rangle$$

for all $\varphi \in \mathscr{D}_-$. Prove that $\delta(t)$ is homogeneous of degree -1 and that $\delta^{(p)}(t)$ is homogeneous of degree $-p - 1$. What is the degree of homogeneity of t_+^λ? (Compare Exercise 10.)

48. A remarkable property [23] of homogeneous g.f.'s (Exercise 47) is this: if $F_1, F_2, \ldots, F_k$ are homogeneous of degrees $\lambda_1, \lambda_2, \ldots, \lambda_k$, respectively, and if no two λ_j are equal, these g.f.'s are linearly independent

$$(c_1F_1 + c_2F_2 + \cdots + c_kF_k = 0 \;\Rightarrow\; c_1 = c_2 = \cdots = c_k = 0).$$

(Note that this generalizes the result of Exercise 19.)

49. (O.C.) As a $\mathscr{D}'$ g.f. $\log |t|$ is defined by the fundamental sequence $\{F_n\}$ where

$$F_n(t) = \log |t| \qquad \text{for } |t| > \frac{1}{n}$$

and

$$F_n(t) = 0 \text{ for} \qquad \text{for } |t| < \frac{1}{n}.$$

Show that defining $\mathrm{Pf}\, t^{-k} \in \mathscr{D}'$ $(k = 1, 2, \ldots)$ by

$$\frac{(-1)^{k-1}}{(k-1)!} D^k \log |t|$$

constitutes a natural mode of definition in the sense of (C.2.5).

50. t_+^λ defined in (C.2.6) for $\lambda \neq -1, -2, \ldots$ satisfies the conditions (C.2.5). For $k = -1, -2, \ldots$ one defines t_+^{-k} with these relations ([23] [43]):

$$t_+^{-1} = D \log t_+, \quad -t_+^{-2} = Dt_+^{-1} + \delta'(t), \quad \ldots,$$
$$-kt_+^{-k-1} = Dt_+^{-k} - (-1)^k \delta^{(k)}(t).$$

Thus (C.2.5c) does not hold for t_+^{-k}. Show that $t(t_+^{-k-1}) = t_+^{-k}$, however.

CHAPTER IV

THE OPERATIONAL SOLUTION OF DIFFERENTIAL EQUATIONS

A. ELEMENTARY OPERATIONAL CALCULUS IN $\mathscr{D}'_+$

1. Derivative Polynomials on $\mathscr{D}'_+$

In Chapter I, we discussed a particular class of operators on the set of operands $\mathscr{D}_-$, the derivative polynomials. We now turn to the very much larger set of operands $\mathscr{D}'_+$—which, being, as we have seen earlier, a linear space, may be called a *space* of operands. The operators envisaged are again called derivative polynomials, but now differentiation is to be understood in the sense of h.f. differentiation.

For each of the identities for operators on $\mathscr{D}_-$ of § 3, Chapter I, we can now obtain an analogous identity for operators on $\mathscr{D}'_+$.

Let D^0 designate the identity operator on $\mathscr{D}'_+$, i.e., $D^0F = F$ whenever $F \in \mathscr{D}'_+$. This, and Corollary II.A.6.2, proves, for non-negative integers p, q, the identity for operators on $\mathscr{D}'_+$ that generalizes (I.3.2):

$$D^p D^q = D^q D^p = D^{p+q}. \tag{A.1.1}$$

If r, s are complex numbers, they define operators on $\mathscr{D}'_+$ which we also designate by r, s and whose application to $F \in \mathscr{D}'_+$ yields the ordinary products rF and sF. Then the identity (I.3.3) generalizes to

$$(D^p + r)(D^q + s) = D^{p+q} + rD^q + sD^p + rs, \tag{A.1.2}$$

where all the indicated operators now act on $\mathscr{D}'_+$ and p, q are nonnegative integers. The proof is trivial: apply both sides to $F \in \mathscr{D}'_+$ and use the elementary properties of multiplication and differentiation in $\mathscr{D}'_+$ derived in part A of Chapter II to check that they are equal.

From this, we immediately obtain the factorization of derivative polynomials on $\mathscr{D}'_+$, i.e., the generalization of (I.3.4), but with D now standing for the g.f. derivative operator

$$P(D) = a_0D^p + a_1D^{p-1} + \cdots + a_p = a_0(D - r_1)^{p_1} \cdots (D - r_l)^{p_l}. \tag{A.1.3}$$

We recall that $r_1, r_2, \ldots, r_l$ are the zeros of the algebraic polynomial $P(x) = a_0x^p + a_1x^{p-1} + \cdots + a_p$ and are of orders $p_1, p_2, \ldots, p_l$, respectively $(p_1 + p_2 + \cdots + p_l = p)$.

Definition A.1.1. *Given the derivative polynomial on* $\mathscr{D}'_+$

(A.1.4) $$P(D) = a_0D^p + a_1D^{p-1} + \cdots + a_p = a_0(D - r_1)^{p_1} \cdots (D - r_l)^{p_l},$$

the derivative polynomial on $\mathscr{D}_-$

(A.1.5) $$\bar{P}(D) = (-1)^p a_0 D^p + (-1)^{p-1} a_1 D^{p-1} + \cdots + a_p = (-1)^p a_0 (D + r_1)^{p_1} \cdots (D + r_l)^{p_l}$$

is called the transpose of $P(D)$.

Theorem A.1.1. *The derivative polynomial on* $\mathscr{D}'_+$, $P(D)$, *and its transpose,* $\bar{P}(D)$, *satisfy, for every* $F \in \mathscr{D}'_+$ *and* $\varphi \in \mathscr{D}_-$, *the relation*

(A.1.6) $$\langle P(D)F, \varphi\rangle = \langle F, \bar{P}(D)\varphi\rangle.$$

In particular, for any nonnegative integer p and scalar r, there holds:

(A.1.7) $$\langle (D - r)^pF, \varphi\rangle = (-1)^p\langle F, (D + r)^p\varphi\rangle.$$

Proof. Apply formula (II.A.6.7) to $\langle a_0D^pF + a_1D^{p-1}F + \cdots + a_pF, \varphi\rangle$.

Theorem A.1.2 (Generalized Shift Relation for Nonnegative Exponents). *Given r complex, p a nonnegative integer, and* $F \in \mathscr{D}'_+$,

(A.1.8) $$(D - r)^pF = e^{rt}D^p(e^{-rt}F).$$

Proof. For any $\varphi \in \mathscr{D}_-$ and $F \in \mathscr{D}'_+$, according to (A.1.7):

$$\langle (D - r)^pF, \varphi\rangle = (-1)^p\langle F, (D + r)^p\varphi\rangle.$$

Using the shift relation (I.3.6) on the right gives

$$\langle (D - r)^pF, \varphi\rangle = (-1)^p\langle F, e^{-rt}\, D^p(e^{rt}\varphi(t))\rangle,$$

which, by the rules of multiplication and differentiation of g.f.'s of class $\mathscr{D}'_+$, yields

$$\begin{aligned}(-1)^p\langle F, e^{-rt}D^p(e^{rt}\varphi(t))\rangle &= (-1)^p\langle e^{-rt}F, D^p(e^{+rt}\varphi(t))\rangle \\ &= (-1)^{2p}\langle D^p(e^{-rt}F), e^{+rt}\varphi(t)\rangle \\ &= \langle e^{rt}D^p(e^{-rt}F), \varphi(t)\rangle. \quad \blacksquare\end{aligned}$$

2. The Operator $(D - r)^{-p}$ (Integer $p \geqslant 0$) on $\mathscr{D}'_+$

The operator $(D - r)^{-p}$ was defined on $\mathscr{D}_-$ for nonnegative integer p by relations (I.4.5), (I.4.5′), and (I.4.7). It amounts to this:

for $p = 0$, $(D - r)^{-p}$ is the identity operator on $\mathscr{D}_-$;
for $p > 0$,

$$(D - r)^{-p}\varphi(t) = e^{rt}\int_{+\infty}^{t}\int_{+\infty}^{t_{p-1}}\cdots\int_{+\infty}^{t_1} e^{-rt_0}\,\varphi(t_0)\,dt_0\cdots dt_{p-2}\,dt_{p-1}$$

$$= e^{rt}\int_{+\infty}^{t}\frac{(t-\tau)^{p-1}}{(p-1)!}\,e^{-r\tau}\,\varphi(\tau)\,d\tau.$$

Consider $g(t) \in \mathscr{K}_+(R)$ and a positive integer p. Let Ω be the operator on $\mathscr{K}_+(R)$ defined by

(A.2.1) $$\Omega g(t) = g_p(t) = e^{rt}\int_{-\infty}^{t}\int_{-\infty}^{t_{p-1}}\cdots\int_{-\infty}^{t_1} e^{-rt_0}\,g(t_0)\,dt_0\cdots dt_{p-2}\,dt_{p-1},$$

which also belongs to $\mathscr{K}_+(R)$. Incidentally, repeated integration by parts, much as in § I.4, shows that

(A.2.2) $$g_p(t) = e^{rt}\int_{-\infty}^{t}\frac{(t-\tau)^{p-1}}{(p-1)!}\,e^{-r\tau}\,g(\tau)\,d\tau.$$

Next, we shall show that the operator Ω serves to define an inverse to the operator $(D - r)^p$ on $\mathscr{D}'_+$. At every point of continuity of $g(t)$ we have, in view of (A.2.1),

(A.2.3) $$e^{rt}D^p[e^{-rt}g_p(t)] = g(t),$$

where differentiation is taken in the ordinary sense. Now, for any $\varphi(t) \in \mathscr{D}_-$, the $\mathscr{D}_-$ function

(A.2.4) $$\psi(t) = (-1)^{-p}(D + r)^{-p}\,\varphi(t)$$

has, by § I.4, the property that

$$(-1)^p(D + r)^p\,\psi(t) = \varphi(t).$$

Consequently,

$$\langle g_p(t), \varphi(t)\rangle = (-1)^p\langle g_p, (D + r)^p\psi\rangle;$$

which, applying Theorem A.1.1 to the right-hand side, gives

$$\langle g_p, \varphi\rangle = \langle (D - r)^p g_p, \psi\rangle$$
$$= \langle e^{rt}D^p(e^{-rt}g_p(t)), \psi(t)\rangle.$$

Substituting (A.2.3), and (A.2.4), this relation takes the form

(A.2.5) $$\langle \Omega g, \varphi\rangle = \langle g, (-1)^{-p}(D + r)^{-p}\varphi\rangle.$$

Next, let $F \in \mathscr{D}'_+$ and let $\{f_n(t)\} \in F$. Applying Ω to every element of this fundamental sequence gives the sequence $\{\Omega\, f_n(t)\}$ which is also fundamental, since, by (A.2.5),

(A.2.6) $$\lim_{n\to\infty}\langle \Omega f_n, \varphi\rangle = (-1)^{-p}\lim_{n\to\infty}\langle f_n, (D + r)^{-p}\varphi\rangle;$$

where the limit on the right-hand side assuredly exists, being equal to $(-1)^{-p}\langle F, (D + r)^{-p}\varphi\rangle$. Furthermore, if $\{g_n(t)\} \sim \{f_n(t)\}$ then clearly $\{\Omega f_n(t)\} \sim \{\Omega g_n(t)\}$. Thus, it is perfectly consistent, and in accord with the precepts used in § II.A.5 for defining various operations on g.f.'s, to define Ω as an operator on $\mathscr{D}'_+$ which with every $F \in \mathscr{D}'_+$ associates $\Omega F \in \mathscr{D}'_+$, where $\{\Omega f_n\} \in \Omega F$ whenever $\{f_n\} \in F$. By (A.2.6), this operator satisfies

$$\text{(A.2.7)} \qquad \langle \Omega F, \varphi\rangle = (-1)^{-p}\langle F, (D + r)^{-p}\varphi\rangle.$$

Successively applying (A.1.7), (A.2.7), and (I.4.8) we obtain

$$\text{(A.2.8)} \qquad \begin{aligned} \langle (D - r)^p\Omega F, \varphi\rangle &= (-1)^{-p}\langle \Omega F, (D + r)^p\varphi\rangle \\ &= (-1)^{p-p}\langle F, (D + r)^{-p}(D + r)^p\varphi\rangle \\ &= \langle F, \varphi\rangle, \end{aligned}$$

while the successive use of (A.2.7), (A.1.7), and (I.4.8) gives

$$\text{(A.2.9)} \qquad \begin{aligned} \langle \Omega(D - r)^p F, \varphi\rangle &= (-1)^{-p}\langle (D - r)^p F, (D + r)^{-p}\varphi\rangle \\ &= (-1)^{p-p}\langle F, (D + r)^p(D + r)^{-p}\varphi\rangle \\ &= \langle F, \varphi\rangle. \end{aligned}$$

In other words, as operators on $\mathscr{D}'_+$, $(D - r)^p$ and Ω have the property that

$$\text{(A.2.10)} \qquad (D - r)^p\Omega = \Omega(D - r)^p = D^0.$$

Referring to the algebraic Theorem I.4.1, we conclude that Ω is the unique inverse of $(D - r)^p$ on the operand space $\mathscr{D}'_+$. We are now justified in designating Ω by $(D - r)^{-p}$ and stating:

Theorem A.2.1. *The operator $(D - r)^p$ on $\mathscr{D}'_+$ (r scalar; $p \geqslant 0$, integer) has a unique inverse, $(D - r)^{-p}$, which has these properties:*

(a) *for any $F \in \mathscr{D}'_+$ and $\{f_n\} \in F$, $\{(D - r)^{-p}f_n\} \in (D - r)^{-p}F$, where*

$$\text{(A.2.11)} \qquad (D - r)^{-p}f_n = e^{rt}\int_{-\infty}^{t} \frac{(t - \tau)^{p-1}}{(p - 1)!}\, e^{-r\tau}f_n(\tau)\, d\tau$$

for every $\mathscr{K}_+(R)$ function in the fundamental sequence $\{f_n\}$;

(b) *for any $F \in \mathscr{D}'_+$ and $\varphi \in \mathscr{D}_-$*

$$\text{(A.2.12)} \qquad \langle (D - r)^{-p}F, \varphi\rangle = (-1)^{-p}\langle F, (D + r)^{-p}\varphi\rangle.$$

The identities (A.1.7) and (A.2.12) combine into

$$\text{(A.2.13)} \qquad \langle (D - r)^p F, \varphi\rangle = (-1)^p\langle F, (D + r)^p\varphi\rangle$$

(p, arbitrary integer; $F \in \mathscr{D}'_+$, $\varphi \in \mathscr{D}_-$, r scalar).

With the help of (A.2.11), the reasoning of Theorem A.1.2 is easily extended to $(D - r)^{-p}$ where $p > 0$, immediately yielding the proof of

Theorem A.2.2 (Generalized Shift Relation). *Given r complex; p, an arbitrary integer, and $F \in \mathscr{D}'_+$,*

$$(D - r)^p F = e^{rt} D^p (e^{-rt} F). \tag{A.2.14}$$

If r, s are scalars; p, q arbitrary integers, then on $\mathscr{D}'_+$

$$(D - r)^p (D - s)^q = (D - s)^q (D - r)^p. \tag{A.2.15}$$

This results from (A.2.13) and (I.4.9). From (A.2.13) and (I.4.8), we derive the operator identity

$$(D - r)^p (D - r)^q = (D - r)^{p+q} \tag{A.2.16}$$

valid on $\mathscr{D}'_+$ for r scalar and p, q arbitrary integers.

So far, we have obtained for operators on $\mathscr{D}'_+$ the same identities as had been derived in §§ I.3, I.4, for operators on $\mathscr{D}_-$. The inversion of derivative polynomials and solution of differential equations in $\mathscr{D}_-$ treated in § I.5 can now be extended to $\mathscr{D}_+$. This is the subject of the next section.

3. Operational Calculus on $\mathscr{D}'_+$. Existence, Uniqueness of Solutions of Differential Equations

Theorem A.3.1. *The equation*

$$P(D)X = F, \tag{A.3.1}$$

where $F \in \mathscr{D}'_+$, and where

$$P(D) = a_0 (D - r_1)^{p_1} (D - r_2)^{p_2} \cdots (D - r_l)^{p_l} \qquad (a_0 \neq 0),$$

has a solution $X \in \mathscr{D}'_+$. It is the only solution in $\mathscr{D}'_+$ and is explicitly given by

$$X = \frac{1}{a_0} (D - r_1)^{-p_1} (D - r_2)^{-p_2} \cdots (D - r_l)^{-p_l} F = P^{-1}(D) F \tag{A.3.2}$$

Proof. The proof is algebraic and follows the pattern of that of the more restricted Theorem I.5.1. From identity (A.2.16) and the commutativity relation (A.2.15), it follows that, for any $F \in \mathscr{D}'_+$,

$$P(D)\, P^{-1}(D) F = F.$$

This proves that $P^{-1}(D) F \in \mathscr{D}'_+$ is a solution of (A.3.1). Thus, the existence of the solution follows from the fact that $P^{-1}(D)$ is a right-inverse of $P(D)$ on $\mathscr{D}'_+$.

But applying (A.2.15) and (A.2.16) we see that $P^{-1}(D)$ is also a left-inverse of $P(D)$ on $\mathscr{D}'_+$. Therefore, if X is any solution in $\mathscr{D}'_+$ of (A.3.1), multiplying both sides of this equation on the left by $P^{-1}(D)$ gives

$$X = P^{-1}(D)\, P(D)X = P^{-1}(D)F.$$

This proves the uniqueness of the solution in $\mathscr{D}'_+$. ∎

Note that, by (A.2.12), for any $F \in \mathscr{D}'_+$ and $\varphi \in \mathscr{D}_-$:

$$\text{(A.3.3)} \quad \langle P^{-1}(D)F, \varphi\rangle = \frac{(-1)^{-p}}{a_0} \langle F, (D + r_1)^{-p_1} \cdots (D + r_l)^{-p_l}\varphi\rangle.$$

The operator on $\mathscr{D}_-$

$$\text{(A.3.4)} \qquad \overline{P^{-1}}(D) = \frac{(-1)^{-p}}{a_0} (D + r_1)^{-p_1} \cdots (D + r_l)^{-p_l},$$

in extension of Definition A.1.1 above, is called the *transpose of* $P^{-1}(D)$.

When it comes to the actual computation of $P^{-1}(D)F$, the direct use of the product representation (A.3.2) suffers from the same disadvantages we mentioned in § I.5. Again the device of decomposing $P^{-1}(D)$ into a sum of simple partial fractions offers itself as a means of replacing high-order repeated integrations by a sum of several integrals of lower order. It suffices to reproduce the proof of Theorem I.6.1, but with operators on $\mathscr{D}'_+$ instead of on $\mathscr{D}_-$, to obtain the following

Theorem A.3.2. *Every operator on* $\mathscr{D}'_+$ *of the form* $A(D)\, B^{-1}(D)$, *where* $A(D)$ *and* $B(D)$ *are derivative polynomials without common factors, and where the factored form of* $B(D)$ *is*

$$\text{(A.3.5)} \qquad B(D) = a_0(D - r_1)^{p_1} \cdots (D - r_l)^{p_l},$$

has a unique decomposition into the sum of a derivative polynomial $Q(D)$ *and of simple partial fractions of the form*

$$\text{(A.3.6)} \quad A(D)B^{-1}(D) = Q(D) + \sum_{k=1}^{p_1} \alpha_k(D - r_1)^{-k} + \cdots + \sum_{k=1}^{p_l} \lambda_k(D - r_l)^{-k}.$$

The polynomial $Q(D)$ *and the scalars* $\alpha_k, \ldots, \lambda_k$ *in this decomposition are obtained in precisely the same way as the corresponding elements of the decomposition of the rational algebraic fraction* $A(x)/B(x)$.

4. Computation of $(D - r)^{-p}F$ (Integer $p \geqslant 0$). Auxiliary Formulae

In applying the above theorems to the explicit computation of solutions of differential equations, one repeatedly encounters the g.f.'s $(D - r)^pH(t - \xi)$ and $(D - r)^p\delta(t - \xi)$. It is therefore fitting that we work out these and other examples.

(A table of inverse operator values is given in the Appendix.)

(i) $D^{-p}H(t - \xi)$ (*integer* $p \geqslant 0$).

By Theorem A.2.1, this is the $\mathscr{D}'_+$ g.f. defined by the $\mathscr{K}_+(R)$ function

$$D^{-p}H(t - \xi) = \int_{-\infty}^{t} \frac{(t-\tau)^{p-1}}{(p-1)!} H(\tau - \xi)\, d\tau$$
$$= \begin{cases} \displaystyle\int_{\xi}^{t} \frac{(t-\tau)^{p-1}}{(p-1)!}\, d\tau & \text{for } t > \xi \\ 0 & \text{for } t \leqslant \xi. \end{cases}$$

Thus, using the notation of § II.C.2,

(A.4.1) $$D^{-p}H(t - \xi) = \frac{(t-\xi)_+^p}{p!}$$

However, we prefer to write this in the form

(A.4.2) $$D^{-p}H(t - \xi) = \frac{(t-\xi)^p}{p!} H(t - \xi).^\dagger$$

(ii) $D^{-p}\delta(t - \xi)$ (*integer* $p \geqslant 0$)

For $p = 0$, $D^{-p}\delta(t - \xi) = \delta(t - \xi)$ since D^0 is the identity operator on $\mathscr{D}'_+$. For $p \geqslant 1$, we have $DH(t - \xi) = \delta(t - \xi)$ and through the identity (A.2.16)

$$D^{-p}\delta(t - \xi) = D^{-p}DH(t - \xi) = DD^{-p}H(t - \xi) = D\frac{(t-\xi)^p}{p!} H(t - \xi).$$

Since $(t - \xi)^p/p! \in C^\infty(R)$ we have, by Leibniz's theorem for $\mathscr{D}'_+$,

$$D\left[\frac{(t-\xi)^p}{p!} H(t - \xi)\right] = \frac{(t-\xi)^{p-1}}{(p-1)!} H(t - \xi) + \frac{(t-\xi)^p}{p!} \delta(t - \xi),$$

and, since $\alpha(t)\,\delta(t - \xi) = \alpha(\xi)\,\delta(t - \xi)$ when $\alpha \in C^\infty(R)$,

(A.4.2) $$D^{-p}\,\delta(t - \xi) = \frac{(t-\xi)^{p-1}}{(p-1)!} H(t - \xi) \qquad (p \geqslant 1).$$

(iii) $(D - r)^{-p}H(t - \xi)$ ($r \neq 0$, *integer* $p > 0$).

---

† As a function of t this is everywhere continuous, except at $t = 0$ where it is undefined. The associated (in the sense of § II.A.2) $\mathscr{K}_+(R)$ function is the right-hand side of (A.4.1) which is actually a $C(R)$ function defined for all $t \in R$. The algebra of operators in D derived in the preceding sections applies to the operand set $\mathscr{D}'_+$; and *all equalities with which we shall deal are*, unless otherwise specified, *equalities between g.f.'s*. Since the right-hand sides of (A.4.1) and (A.4.2) are equal as g.f.'s, these two expressions are consistent. The same remark applies to all other formulae obtained in this book by operator algebra.

This is the g.f. defined by the $\mathscr{K}_+(R)$ function

$$(D - r)^{-p}H(t - \xi) = e^{rt}\int_{-\infty}^{t} \frac{(t - \tau)^{p-1}}{(p - 1)!} e^{-r\tau} H(\tau - \xi)\, d\tau$$
$$= e^{rt}\int_{\xi}^{t} \frac{(t - \tau)^{p-1}}{(p - 1)!} e^{-r\tau}\, d\tau\, H(\tau - \xi).$$

In the Taylor formula with integral remainder,

$$f(t) = f(\xi) + \frac{(t - \xi)}{1!} f'(\xi) + \cdots + \frac{(t - \xi)^{p-1}}{(p - 1)!} f^{(p-1)}(\xi)$$
$$+ \int_{\xi}^{t} \frac{(t - \tau)^{p-1}}{(p - 1)!} f^{(p)}(\tau)\, d\tau,$$

take $f(t) = \dfrac{(-1)^p}{r^p} e^{-rt}$. This gives

$$e^{rt}\int_{\xi}^{t} \frac{(t - \tau)^{p-1}}{(p - 1)!} e^{-r\tau}\, d\tau = \frac{(-1)^p}{r^p}\left[1 - e^{r(t-\xi)}\sum_{k=0}^{p-1} \frac{(-1)^k r^k}{k!} (t - \xi)^k\right].$$

Consequently

(A.4.3)

$$(D - r)^{-p}H(t - \xi) = \frac{(-1)^p}{r^p}\left[1 - e^{r(t-\xi)}\sum_{k=0}^{p-1} \frac{(-1)^k r^k}{k!} (t - \xi)^k\right] H(t - \xi).$$

(iv) $(D - r)^{-p}\delta^{(q)}(t - \xi) \qquad (p \geqslant 0, q \geqslant 0)$.

This could be obtained by taking $D^{q+1}(D - r)^{-p}H(t - \xi)$. Another procedure consists in using the shift relation (A.2.14) and the relation (II.B.3.9):

$$(D - r)^{-p}\delta^{(q)}(t - \xi) = e^{rt}D^{-p}[e^{-rt}\delta^{(q)}(t - \xi)]$$
$$= e^{rt}D^{-p}\left[e^{-r\xi}\sum_{l=0}^{q}\binom{q}{l} r^l \delta^{(q-l)}(t - \xi)\right].$$

Therefore

$$(D - r)^{-p}\delta^{(q)}(t - \xi) = e^{r(t-\xi)}\sum_{l=0}^{q}\binom{q}{l} r^{q-l} D^{(l-p)}\delta(t - \xi). \tag{A.4.4}$$

If $p = q + 1$ this is a $\mathscr{K}_+(R)$ function; if $p \geqslant q + 2$ it is, in view of (A.4.2), a $C^{p-q-2}(R)$ function.

(v) $(aD^2 + bD + c)^{-1}F$ (*a*, *b*, *c real; $b^2 - 4ac < 0$*).

The coefficients being real, $aD^2 + bD + c$ factors into

$$a(D - r)(D - \bar{r}),$$

where $r = \alpha + i\omega$ and $\bar{r} = \alpha - i\omega$ are complex conjugates. Then, from the algebraic partial fraction decomposition

$$\frac{1}{a(x - r)(x - \bar{r})} = \frac{1}{a(r - \bar{r})}\left[\frac{1}{x - r} - \frac{1}{x - \bar{r}}\right]$$
$$= \frac{1}{2i\omega a}\left[\frac{1}{x - \alpha - i\omega} - \frac{1}{x - \alpha + i\omega}\right]$$

it follows, by means of Theorem A.3.2 above, that for any $F \in \mathscr{D}'_+$,

(A.4.5) $$(aD^2 + bD + c)^{-1}F = \frac{1}{2i\omega a}[(D - r)^{-1} - (D - \bar{r})^{-1}]F.$$

In particular, if F is defined by a $\mathscr{K}_+(R)$ function $f(t)$, the shift-relation yields

(A.4.6) $$(aD^2 + bD + c)^{-1}f(t) = \frac{1}{2i\omega a}\int_{-\infty}^{t} [e^{r(t-\tau)} - e^{\bar{r}(t-\tau)}]f(\tau)\,d\tau,$$

which becomes, since $\sin u = \dfrac{e^{iu} - e^{-iu}}{2i}$ and $\alpha = -\dfrac{b}{2a}$,

(A.4.7) $$(aD^2 + bD + c)^{-1}f(t) = \frac{1}{\omega a}\int_{-\infty}^{t} e^{-(b/2a)(t-\tau)}\sin\omega(t - \tau)\,f(\tau)\,d\tau.$$

In the particular case $F = H(t - \xi)$ (A.4.7) gives

(A.4.8)
$$(aD^2 + bD + c)^{-1}\,H(t - \xi) = \frac{1}{\omega a}\int_{\xi}^{t} e^{-(b/2a)(t-\tau)}\sin\omega(t - \tau)\,dt\,H(t - \xi),$$

which, by an elementary computation based on integrations by parts, gives

(A.4.9)
$$(aD^2 + bD + c)^{-1}\,H(t - \xi) = -\frac{2}{b\omega}\,\frac{H(t - \xi)}{1 + 4\omega^2a^2/b^2}$$
$$\cdot\left[e^{-(b/2a)(t-\xi)}\sin\omega(t - \xi) + \frac{2a\omega}{b}\,e^{-(b/2a)(t-\xi)}\cos\omega(t - \xi) - \frac{2a\omega}{b}\right].$$

$\left(\omega = \sqrt{\dfrac{b^2}{4a^2} - \dfrac{c}{a}}\right.$ plays a particular role in physical applications, which is why it is left in this formula.$\Big)$

Next, substitute $\delta(t - \xi)$ for F in (A.4.5) or apply D to both sides of (A.4.9) to obtain

(A.4.10) $$(aD^2 + bD + c)^{-1}\,\delta(t - \xi) = \frac{1}{a\omega}\,e^{-(b/2a)(t-\xi)}\sin\omega(t - \xi)\,H(t - \xi).$$

Applying D to both sides of this equality gives

$$(aD^2 + bD + c)^{-1}\,\delta'(t - \xi)$$
$$= \frac{1}{a}\,e^{-(b/2a)(t-\xi)}\left[-\frac{b}{2a\omega}\sin\omega(t - \xi) + \cos\omega(t - \xi)\right]H(t - \xi)$$
$$+ \frac{1}{a\omega}\,e^{-(b/2a)(t-\xi)}\sin\omega(t - \xi)\,\delta(t - \xi),$$

which, since $\sin \omega(t - \xi)\, \delta(t - \xi) = 0$, leaves

$$(A.4.11) \quad (aD^2 + bD + c)^{-1}\, \delta'(t - \xi) = \frac{1}{a} e^{-(b/2a)(t-\xi)} \cdot \left[-\frac{b}{2a\omega} \sin \omega(t - \xi) + \cos \omega(t - \xi) \right] H(t - \xi).$$

5. Continuity of Operators on $\mathscr{D}'_+$

The notation of § II.B.4 and § II.B.5 is employed in this section. Let $\Omega(D) = A(D)\, B^{-1}(D)$ be the product of a derivative polynomial on $\mathscr{D}'_+$ by the inverse of a derivative polynomial on $\mathscr{D}'_+$. From (A.1.6) applied to $A(D)$ and (A.3.3) applied to $B^{-1}(D)$, we deduce that *the operator*

$$\overline{\Omega(D)} = \overline{A(D)}\, \overline{B^{-1}(D)};$$

is the transpose of $\Omega(D)$, i.e., for any $F \in \mathscr{D}'_+$ and $\varphi \in \mathscr{D}_-$,

$$(A.5.1) \qquad \langle \Omega(D)F, \varphi \rangle = \langle F, \overline{\Omega(D)}\varphi \rangle.$$

If $\{F_n\}$ is a sequence of $\mathscr{D}'_+$ g.f.'s converging to $F \in \mathscr{D}'_+$,

$$(A.5.2) \qquad \operatorname*{Lim}_{n \to \infty} F_n = F,$$

it follows from (A.5.1) that for any $\varphi \in \mathscr{D}_-$,

$$\lim_{n \to \infty} \langle \Omega(D)F_n, \varphi \rangle = \lim_{n \to \infty} \langle F_n, \bar{\Omega}(D)\varphi \rangle.$$

Applying in turn (A.5.2) and (A.5.1) to the right-hand side of this relation gives

$$\lim_{n \to \infty} \langle \Omega(D)F_n, \varphi \rangle = \langle F, \bar{\Omega}(D)\varphi \rangle = \langle \Omega(D)F, \varphi \rangle,$$

so we have proved that

$$\operatorname*{Lim}_{n \to \infty} \Omega(D)F_n = \Omega(D)F.$$

Trivial modifications to this argument complete the proof of the following generalization of Theorem II.B.4.2:

Theorem A.5.1. *An operator* $\Omega(D) = A(D)\, B^{-1}(D)$ *on* $\mathscr{D}'_+$, *where* $A(D)$ *and* $B(D)$ *are derivative polynomials on* $\mathscr{D}'_+$, *has the properties:*

(a) $\operatorname*{Lim}_{n \to \infty} F_n = F \in \mathscr{D}'_+ \Rightarrow \operatorname*{Lim}_{n \to \infty} \Omega(D)F_n = \Omega(D)F$,

(b) $\sum_{n=0}^{\infty} F_n = F \in \mathscr{D}'_+ \Rightarrow \sum_{n=0}^{\infty} \Omega(D)F_n = \Omega(D)F$,

(c) $\operatorname*{Lim}_{\lambda \to \lambda_0} F_\lambda = F \in \mathscr{D}'_+ \Rightarrow \operatorname*{Lim}_{\lambda \to \lambda_0} \Omega(D)F_\lambda = \Omega(D)F$.

Remark. This theorem is summarized in the statement, "$\Omega(D)$ *is a continuous operator on* $\mathscr{D}'_+$." It is precisely because of this property that $\mathscr{D}'_+$ is mathematically a more natural domain for the application of operator expressions in D than some set of ordinary functions on which these operators are not continuous.

The propositions of § II.B.7 can also be extended to the present situation in the form of

Theorem A.5.2. *Given the operator* $\Omega(D) = A(D)\, B^{-1}(D)$, *where* $A(D)$, $B(D)$ *are derivative polynomials, and given the parametric g.f.* $F_\lambda \in \mathscr{D}'_+$. *Then*

(a) *if the derivative* $\partial^k F_{\lambda_0}/\partial\lambda^k$ *of* F_λ *with respect to the parameter* λ *exists, then* $\dfrac{\partial^k}{\partial\lambda^k}(Q(D)F_{\lambda_0})$ *also exists and satisfies*

$$\Omega(D)\frac{\partial^k F_{\lambda_0}}{\partial\lambda^k} = \frac{\partial^k}{\partial\lambda^k}(\Omega(D)F_{\lambda_0}); \tag{A.5.2}$$

(b) *if the parametric integral* $\int_\alpha^\beta F_\lambda\, d\lambda$ *exists then* $\int_\alpha^\beta (\Omega(D)F_\lambda)\, d\lambda$ *also exists and satisfies*

$$\Omega(D)\int_\alpha^\beta F_\lambda\, d\lambda = \int_\alpha^\beta (\Omega(D)F_\lambda)\, d\lambda. \tag{A.5.3}$$

Proof. This proposition is a corollary to the preceding one.

(a) To prove (A.5.2) for $k = 1$, note that by (c) of Theorem A.5.1

$$\Omega(D)\frac{\partial F_{\lambda_0}}{\partial\lambda} = \Omega(D) \operatorname*{Lim}_{\lambda\to\lambda_0}\left[\frac{1}{\lambda-\lambda_0}(F_\lambda - F_{\lambda_0})\right]$$

$$= \operatorname*{Lim}_{\lambda\to\lambda_0}\frac{1}{\lambda-\lambda_0}[\Omega(D)F_\lambda - \Omega(D)F_{\lambda_0}] = \frac{\partial}{\partial\lambda}[\Omega(D)F_{\lambda_0}],$$

the final equality being merely the expression of the definition of the parametric derivative, at λ_0, of $\Omega(D)F_\lambda$. The result for $k > 1$ is now automatic.

(b) To prove (b), note that if $\int_\alpha^\beta (\Omega(D)F_\lambda)\, d\lambda$ exists, there exist sequences of Riemann sums (of which the sequence $\{R_n\}$ with

$$R_n = \sum_{j=1}^{n} [\Omega(D)F_{\lambda'_j}]\, \Delta\lambda_j$$

is typical) such that

$$\int_\alpha^\beta (\Omega(D)F_\lambda)\, d\lambda = \operatorname*{Lim}_{n\to\infty} R_n.$$

(Here the symbol Lim, it must be understood, indicates that $n \to \infty$, while at the same time $\max_{1\leqslant j\leqslant n} |\Delta\lambda_j| \to 0$ as in the theory of the Riemann integral for functions of a real variable.)

To show that $\int_{\alpha}^{\beta} (\Omega(D)F_{\lambda})\, d\lambda$ does indeed exist, observe that otherwise there could be found different sequences of sums like R_n which either converge to different limits or else diverge as $n \to \infty$ and max $|\Delta\lambda_j| \to 0$. But, writing $P_n = \Omega^{-1}(D)R_n$, we see that $\{P_n\}$ is a sequence of Riemann sums for $\int_{\alpha}^{\beta} F_{\lambda}\, d\lambda$. Since *this* integral exists by hypothesis, we have

$$\operatorname*{Lim}_{n\to\infty} P_n = \int_{\alpha}^{\beta} F_{\lambda}\, d\lambda.$$

Now, applying (a) of Theorem A.5.1, we obtain

$$\Omega(D) \operatorname*{Lim}_{n\to\infty} P_n = \operatorname*{Lim}_{n\to\infty} \Omega(D)P_n = \operatorname*{Lim}_{n\to\infty} R_n. \tag{A.5.4}$$

This contradiction to the assumption that not all $\{R_n\}$ converge to the same limit proves the existence of $\int_{\alpha}^{\beta}(\Omega F_{\lambda})\, d\lambda$.

As to the relation (A.5.3), it follows from (A.5.4), which holds for any sequence $\{R_n\}$ of Riemann sums converging to the integral on the right-hand side of (A.5.3.) ∎

6. Operational Calculus on $\mathscr{D}'_-$

Providing one defines, for every $f(t) \in \mathscr{K}_-(R)$ and $p \geqslant 0$, the operator $(D - r)^{-p}$ by

$$(D - r)^{-p} f(t) = e^{rt} \int_{+\infty}^{t} \frac{(t-\tau)^{p-1}}{(p-1)!} e^{-r\tau} f(\tau)\, d\tau,$$

and, for every $\varphi \in \mathscr{D}_+$,

$$(D - r)^{-p}\, \varphi(t) = e^{rt} \int_{-\infty}^{t} \frac{(t-\tau)^{p-1}}{(p-1)!} e^{-r\tau}\, \varphi(\tau)\, d\tau,$$

the operational calculus we have just obtained on $\mathscr{D}'_+$ goes over without any further change into a similar calculus of operators on $\mathscr{D}'_-$. There is no need to go into this any further [compare §II.A.11].

**7. $(D - r)^p$ on $\mathscr{D}'_+$, p noninteger

In § I.9, operators with real noninteger exponents were considered on the operand set $\mathscr{D}_-$. A similar extension of operator methods to $\mathscr{D}'_+$ is feasible.

If $f(t) \in \mathscr{K}_+(R)$ and $p > 0$, define

$$(D - r)^{-p} f(t) = \frac{e^{rt}}{\Gamma(p)} \int_{-\infty}^{t} (t-\tau)^{p-1}\, e^{-r\tau} f(\tau)\, d\tau. \tag{A.7.1}$$

This is a $\mathscr{K}_+(R)$ function also, and for every $\varphi \in \mathscr{D}_-$ satisfies

$$\langle (D - r)^{-p} f, \varphi\rangle = \langle f, (-1)^{-p}(D + r)^{-p}\varphi\rangle, \tag{A.7.2}$$

where $(-1)^p = e^{p\pi i}$ (i.e., we take $\log(-1) = \pi i$) and where for $\log(t - \tau)$ we take the principal branch,† i.e.,

$$(A.7.3) \qquad (t-\tau)^{p-1} = \begin{cases} e^{(p-1)\log(t-\tau)} & \text{if } t > \tau. \\ e^{(p-1)\log|t-\tau|}e^{(p-1)\pi i} & \text{if } t < \tau. \end{cases}$$

To prove (A.7.2) for $p \geqslant 1$, observe that the repeated integral (φ carried in $(-\infty), b]$ and f carried in $[a, +\infty)$; where we take $a < b$ since for $a > b$ the repeated integral vanishes)

$$\int_{-\infty}^{\infty} \varphi(t)\left[e^{rt}\int_{-\infty}^{t} \frac{(t-\tau)^{p-1}}{\Gamma(p)} e^{-r\tau} f(\tau)\,d\tau\right]dt$$

$$= \int_a^b \int_a^t \varphi(t)e^{rt}\frac{(t-\tau)^{p-1}}{\Gamma(p)} e^{-r\tau} f(\tau)\,d\tau\,dt$$

represents a double integral over the triangle ABC shown in Figure 5. Note that $t - \tau \geqslant 0$ in the inner integral.

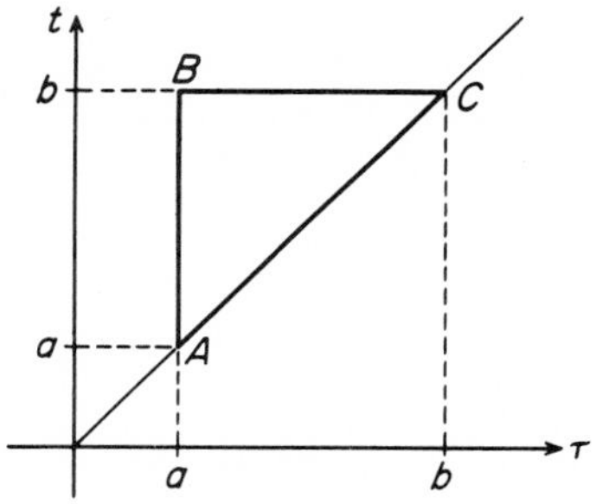

FIGURE 5

If the order of integration is reversed in the repeated integral expression of this double integral, as is permissible since the integrand is continuous throughout the triangle ABC, we find

$$\langle (D - r)^{-p} f, \varphi\rangle = \int_a^b f(\tau)e^{-r\tau}\left[\int_\tau^b e^{rt}\frac{(t-\tau)^{p-1}}{\Gamma(p)}\varphi(t)\,dt\right]d\tau$$

$$= (-1)^{-(p-1)}\int_a^b f(\tau)e^{-r\tau}\int_b^\tau \frac{(\tau - t)^{p-1}}{\Gamma(p)} e^{rt}\varphi(t)\,dt\,d\tau$$

$$= (-1)^{-p}\langle f, (D + r)^{-p}\varphi\rangle.$$

† For the handling of complex exponents of the logarithmic function with real or complex argument see any one of [1] [11] [19] [49] among others.

Here the inner integral in the second line has $\tau - t < 0$, so that choosing for the determination of $\log(\tau - t)$ its principal branch, i.e., using (A.7.3), we have

$$(\tau - t)^{p-1} = (t - \tau)^{p-1}(-1)^{p-1},$$

which, since $(-1)(-1)^{-(p-1)} = e^{[1-(p-1)]\pi i} = e^{-p\pi i} = (-1)^{-p}$, justifies the passage from the first to the second and third lines in the above string of equalities. Thus, for $p \geqslant 1$, (A.7.2) is proven. For $0 < p < 1$, the formal aspects of the proof do not differ from the above; however, because of the term $(t - \tau)^{p-1}$, the double integral is an improper integral of a standard kind for which the inversion of the order of integration can also be justified.

If $F \in \mathscr{D}'_+$ and $\{f_n\}$ is one of its defining sequences of $\mathscr{K}_+(R)$ functions, $(D - r)^{-p}F\ (p > 0)$ *is defined to be the g.f. determined by the sequence* $\{(D - r)^{-p}f_n\}$ [which, as a consequence of (A.7.2), is also fundamental].

For $p > 0$, noninteger, we define ($[p]$ = greatest integer $\leqslant p$)

$$(D - r)^{p}F = (D - r)^{[p]+1}(D - r)^{-[p]-1+p}F, \qquad \text{(A.7.4)}$$

which can be shown to be equal to $(D - r)^{-[p]-1+p}(D - r)^{[p]+1}F$. These indications will enable the interested reader to verify for himself that in all the operator identities of §§ A.1, A.2 above, the restriction to integer exponents can be relaxed to real exponents. The matter is not explored further here because it does not come into the mainstream of those ordinary and partial differential equations applications that we shall study in this volume.

B. THE INITIAL-VALUE PROBLEM FOR A DIFFERENTIAL EQUATION WITH CONSTANT COEFFICIENTS

The applications to be considered in the remaining portions of this chapter and in part A of the next chapter center on the solution of initial-value problems for linear differential equations with constant coefficients and for systems of such equations. Problems of this kind arise rather frequently in such diverse fields as physics, chemistry, and biology, and are particularly rife in all branches of engineering where they serve to describe complex assemblages of systems, picturesquely, if evasively, called "black boxes," but actually consisting of masses of electric circuitry or of mechanical linkages. The prevalence of these equations is largely due to the fact that they are the easiest differential equations to solve analytically, while still constituting tolerably accurate mathematical models of many physical facts.

The input to a black box is often taken to be an "impulsive" mechanical force or electrical voltage, e.g., a Dirac delta function. Since this is a generalized, not ordinary, function it is fitting that the corresponding differential equations be treated in terms of g.f.'s—this is so, as will be seen, especially for simultaneous D.E.'s.

1. Initial-Value Problem for D.E. with Constant Coefficients. Equation of Evolution

Let us now specialize the D.E. initial-value problem described in § II.B.2 by requiring the coefficients of the D.E. to be constants; also, let us modify it slightly by taking the initial values at $t = t_0$. The problem envisaged then takes the form:

Given: $f(t)$ defined and continuous in $(t_0, +\infty)$ except possibly at isolated points t_i where $f(t_i + 0)$, $f(t_i - 0)$ exist† *and differ; the real or complex constants $a_0, a_1, \ldots, a_p$; the real or complex constants $x_0, x_1, \ldots, x_{p-1}$. Find a function $x(t)$ (which, with its derivatives $dx/dt, \ldots, d^{p-1}x/dt^{p-1}$ is defined and continuous for $t > t_0$ while d^px/dt^p is continuous in every interval of continuity of $f(t)$ in $(t_0, +\infty)$) such that the equation*

$$a_0 \frac{d^p x}{dt^p} + a_1 \frac{d^{p-1}x}{dt^{p-1}} + \cdots + a_p x = f(t) \tag{B.1.1}$$

is satisfied in every interval of continuity of $f(t)$ in $(t_0, +\infty)$ and such that

$$x(t_0 + 0) = x_0, \quad x'(t_0 + 0) = x_1, \quad \ldots, \quad x^{(p-1)}(t_0 + 0) = x_{p-1}. \tag{B.1.2}$$

The equation (B.1.1) we shall usually write more briefly as

$$P\left(\frac{d}{dt}\right)x = f. \tag{B.1.1'}$$

The quantities $x_0, x_1, \ldots, x_{p-1}$ are called *initial values* of the solution $x(t)$.

Henceforth, this problem will be called the "*ordinary I.V. problem* for a linear D.E. with constant coefficients." Note that $f(t)$ is restricted in this formulation.

The existence and uniqueness of the solution to this problem can be derived from classical existence theorems on D.E.'s. We have, however, no need to invoke these here as we shall follow the path indicated in § II.B.2.

Borrowing a convenient, if overworked, expression, this approach can be described by saying that, before attacking the original problem (B.1.1, 2), we *enlarge to $\mathscr{D}'_+$ the "universe of discourse"* within which it is framed. (This is somewhat like the approach to the solution of an algebraic polynomial equation, where, even though the coefficients be real, one considers the equation in the "universe" of complex numbers.)

We have already seen how this is done when the initial values are given at $t_0 = 0$. For arbitrary $t_0 \in R$, the procedure is quite the same: $f(t)$ and $x(t)$

---

† At t_0 the existence of $f(t_0 + 0)$ alone is assumed.

are "continued by zero" in $(-\infty, t_0)$, i.e., one defines the $\mathscr{K}_+(R)$ functions

$$\text{(B.1.3)} \qquad F(t) = \begin{cases} 0 & \text{for } t < t_0 \\ f(t) & \text{for } t > t_0, \end{cases} \qquad X(t) = \begin{cases} 0 & \text{for } t < t_0 \\ x(t) & \text{for } t > t_0, \end{cases}$$

which, if $x(t)$ is a solution of the given problem, satisfy equation (B.1.1) at every point of continuity of $F(t)$.

Designating, as before, by $D^l X$ the g.f. derivative of order l of the g.f. defined by the function $X(t)$ and by $[D^l X]$ the g.f. defined by $\mathscr{K}_+(R)$ function $d^l(tX)/dt^l$, Theorem II.B.1.1 and its Corollary yield $(1 \leqslant l \leqslant p)$

$$DX = [DX] + x_0\delta(t - t_0)$$

$$\cdots\cdots\cdots\cdots\cdots\cdots\cdots\cdots\cdots\cdots\cdots\cdots$$

$$\text{(B.1.4)} \qquad D^l X = [D^l X] + x_0\delta^{(l-1)}(t - t_0) + x_1\delta^{(l-2)}(t - t_0) + \cdots + x_{l-1}\delta(t - t_0)$$

$$\cdots\cdots\cdots\cdots\cdots\cdots\cdots\cdots\cdots\cdots\cdots\cdots$$

$$D^p X = [D^p X] + x_0\delta^{(p-1)}(t - t_0) + x_1\delta^{(p-2)}(t - t_0) + \cdots + x_{p-1}\delta(t - t_0).$$

Following the argument of § II.B.2, we arrive at the conclusion that, if the solution $x(t)$ of problem (B.1.1, 2) above exists, then its continuation $X(t)$ is a $\mathscr{K}_+(R)$ function whose associated $\mathscr{D}'_+$ g.f. satisfies the equation

$$\text{(B.1.5)} \qquad \begin{aligned} a_0 D^p X + a_1 D^{p-1} X + \cdots + a_p X &= F + (a_0 x_{p-1} + a_1 x_{p-2} + \cdots + a_{p-1} x_0)\delta(t - t_0) \\ &\quad + (a_0 x_{p-2} + a_1 x_{p-3} + \cdots + a_{p-2} x_0)\delta'(t - t_0) + \cdots \\ &\quad + (a_0 x_{p-1-j} + a_1 x_{p-2-j} + \cdots + a_{p-1-j} x_0)\delta^{(j)}(t - t_0) \\ &\quad + \cdots + a_0 x_0 \delta^{(p-1)}(t - t_0). \end{aligned}$$

This equation, more conveniently written as

$$\text{(B.1.5')} \qquad P(D)X = F + B,^{\dagger}$$

we shall call the *equation of evolution* of the ordinary I.V. problem. This is because when in that problem $x(t)$ corresponds to a physical magnitude depending on the time, t, equation (B.1.5′), thanks to the presence of both the *forcing term*, F, and the *boundary term*, B, describes all by itself the evolution in time of the physical variable X as viewed in $\mathscr{D}'_+$ [i.e., through its "observation" with any test function $\varphi(t)$].

† B represents the sum of all the terms other than F on the right-hand side of (B.1.5).

The boundary term can also be expressed as

$$\begin{aligned}
\text{(B.1.6)} \qquad B = {} & x_0(a_0\delta^{(p-1)}(t - t_0) + a_1\delta^{(p-2)}(t - t_0) + \cdots \\
& + a_{p-2}\delta'(t - t_0) + a_{p-1}\delta(t - t_0)) \\
& + x_1(a_0\delta^{(p-2)}(t - t_0) + a_1\delta^{(p-3)}(t - t_0) + \cdots \\
& + a_{p-3}\delta'(t - t_0) + a_{p-2}\delta(t - t_0)) \\
& + \cdots \\
& + x_{p-2}(a_0\delta'(t - t_0) + a_1\delta(t - t_0)) \\
& + x_{p-1}a_0\delta(t - t_0).
\end{aligned}$$

In this form, the coefficients of the x_i are reminiscent of the successive steps in the computation of the value of a polynomial by synthetic division, for we have† (Doetsch [14])

(B.1.7)

$$\begin{aligned}
a_0\delta^{(p-1)}(t - t_0) + a_1\delta^{(p-2)}(t - t_0) + \cdots + a_{p-2}\delta'(t - t_0) + a_{p-1}\delta(t - t_0) \\
= [a_0D^{p-1} + a_1D^{p-2} + \cdots + a_{p-2}D + a_{p-1}]\delta(t - t_0) \\
= [(\cdots(((a_0D + a_1)D + a_2)D + a_3)D + \cdots)D + a_{p-1}]\delta(t - t_0).
\end{aligned}$$

In terms of finite differences, where we write, purely formally,

$$\Delta P(D) = \frac{P(D) - P(0)}{D}, \quad \Delta^2 P(D) = \Delta(\Delta P(D)), \ldots, \quad \Delta^p P(D) = a_0,$$

we get

$$\text{(B.1.8)} \qquad B = x_0\,\Delta P(D)\,\delta(t - t_0) + x_1\,\Delta^2 P(D)\,\delta(t - t_0) + \cdots + x_{p-1}\,\Delta^p P(D)\,\delta(t - t_0).$$

The equation of evolution is guaranteed, by Theorem A.3.1, to have in $\mathscr{D}'_+$ a solution and only one solution. It is explicitly given by

$$\text{(B.1.9)} \qquad X = P^{-1}(D)F + P^{-1}(D)B,$$

an expression which shows that the roles of the forcing term, F, and of the boundary term, B, are entirely analogous.

Though this does not, as yet, tell us whether the narrower original problem has a solution, the uniqueness of the g.f. X does guarantee that the function $x(t)$, if it exists, is the only solution of (B.1.1, 2). Therefore, to determine whether $x(t)$ actually exists, and has the ordinary continuity and differentiability properties stipulated in the original statement of the problem, we have only to examine the explicit form (B.1.9) of X. Let us do so.

---

† The reader familiar with the classical Laplace transform method of solving the problem (B.1.1, 2) [7] [14] [55], will notice the association between (B.1.5) and the Laplace image of the given problem. The transform method imposes on $f(t)$ the restriction $\int_{t_0}^{\infty} e^{-st} f(t)\,dt < \infty$ for some real s. (See Chapter VII.)

We begin with the observation that the g.f.

$$\text{(B.1.10)} \qquad X_B = P^{-1}(D)B = \frac{1}{a_0}(D - r_1)^{-p_1} \cdots (D - r_l)^{-p_l}B$$

is defined by a function, $X_B(t)$, that vanishes for $t < t_0$, is continuous, and has (ordinary) derivatives

$$\frac{d^iX_B}{dt^i} \qquad (i = 1, 2, \ldots, p)$$

that are continuous for $t \neq t_0$.

To confirm this, observe that, setting $G(t - t_0) = P^{-1}(D)\,\delta(t - t_0)$, it follows from (B.1.5) that

$$\text{(B.1.11)} \quad \begin{aligned} P^{-1}(D)B = {} & (a_0x_{p-1} + a_1x_{p-2} + \cdots + a_{p-1}x_0)G(t - t_0) \\ & + (a_0x_{p-2} + a_1x_{p-3} + \cdots + a_{p-2}x_0)DG(t - t_0) \\ & + \cdots \\ & + a_0x_0D^{p-1}G(t - t_0), \end{aligned}$$

and that, by the shift formula (A.2.14)

$$\text{(B.1.12)} \quad \begin{aligned} G(t - t_0) = {} & \frac{1}{a_0} e^{r_1t}D^{-p_1}(e^{-r_1t}e^{r_2t}D^{-p_2}(e^{-r_2t}e^{r_2t}D^{-p_3} \\ & \times (\cdots (e^{-r_{l-1}t}e^{r_lt}D^{-p_l}(e^{-r_lt}\,\delta(t - t_0))) \cdots))). \end{aligned}$$

This expression for $G(t - t_0)$ shows clearly that G *has the same ordinary continuity and differentiability properties as* $D^{-p}\delta(t - t_0) = D^{-p+1}H(t - t_0)$, i.e., $G(t - t_0)$ vanishes for $t \leqslant t_0$, is continuous, and has continuous ordinary derivatives $\dfrac{dG}{dt}, \ldots, \dfrac{d^{p-2}G}{dt^{p-2}}$ for $t \in R$, which vanish for $t \leqslant t_0$, while

$$\frac{d^{p-1}G}{dt^{p-1}}(t - t_0)$$

and all higher-order derivatives are continuous for $t \neq t_0$ and vanish for $t < t_0$.

Next let us verify that the function $X_B(t)$ and its ordinary derivatives $X_B'(t), \ldots, X_B^{(p-1)}(t)$ satisfy the relations

$$\text{(B.1.13)} \qquad X_B^{(i)}(t_0 + 0) = x_i \qquad (i = 0, 1, 2, \ldots, p - 1).$$

One way of doing this is to actually compute $X_B^{(i)}(t_0 + 0)$. A rather less tedious and more informative confirmation of (B.1.13) is achieved as follows: observe first that since the $X_B^{(i)}(t)$ $(i = 0, 1, 2, \ldots, p)$ vanish for $t < t_0$ and are continuous for $t > t_0$, we may apply Theorem II.B.1.1 and its Corollary, obtaining

$$\begin{aligned}(\text{B.1.14})\quad P(D)X_B = {} & a_0[D^pX_B] + a_1[D^{p-1}X_B] + \cdots + a_pX_B \\ & + (a_0X_B^{(p-1)}(t_0+0) + a_1X_B^{(p-2)}(t_0+0) + \cdots \\ & + a_{p-1}X_B(t_0+0))\,\delta(t-t_0) \\ & + (a_0X_B^{(p-2)}(t_0+0) + a_1X^{(p-3)}(t_0+0) + \cdots \\ & + a_{p-2}X_B(t_0+0))\,\delta'(t-t_0) \\ & + \cdots \\ & + a_0X_B(t_0+0)\,\delta^{(p-1)}(t-t_0),\end{aligned}$$

which we write

$$(\text{B.1.15})\qquad P(D)X_B = \left[P\left(\frac{d}{dt}\right)X_B(t)\right] + C,$$

where C is the sum

$$\begin{aligned}C = {} & (a_0X_B^{(p-1)}(t_0+0) + a_1X_B^{(p-2)}(t_0+0) + \cdots \\ & + a_{p-1}X_B(t_0+0))\,\delta(t-t_0) \\ & + (a_0X_B^{(p-2)}(t_0+0)\cdots \\ & + a_{p-2}X_B(t_0+0))\,\delta'(t-t_0) \\ & + \cdots \\ & + a_0X_B(t_0+0)\,\delta^{(p-1)}(t-t_0).\end{aligned}$$

By its very definition, X_B also satisfies the relation

$$(\text{B.1.16})\qquad P(D)X_B = B.$$

For any $\varphi \in \mathscr{D}_-$ that is carried in the half-line $(t_0, +\infty)$ we have, since only terms in the $\delta^{(j)}(t-t_0)$ occur in C,

$$\langle B, \varphi\rangle = \langle C, \varphi\rangle = 0;$$

but then it follows from the equality of the left-hand sides of (B.1.15) and (B.1.16) that for every such test function

$$(\text{B.1.17})\qquad \langle P(D)X_B, \varphi\rangle = \left\langle\left[P\left(\frac{d}{dt}\right)X_B(t)\right], \varphi\right\rangle = 0.$$

Since $P(d/dt)X_B(t)$ is a *continuous* function on $(t_0, +\infty)$, we are then guaranteed by reasoning as in Theorem II.A.7.1 that it vanishes identically on this half-line. We already know from the remarks following (B.1.12), that this $\mathscr{K}_+(R)$ function vanishes for $t < t_0$ and so can now assert that (B.1.15) may be rewritten as

$$(\text{B.1.15}')\qquad P(D)X_B = C.$$

This and (B.1.16) prove that

$$(\text{B.1.18})\qquad B = C.$$

Let $\varphi \in \mathscr{D}_-$ be such that $\varphi(t_0) \neq 0$, then

$$(t - t_0)^q \varphi(t) \in \mathscr{D}_-,$$

while

$$\left(\frac{d^l(t - t_0)^q \varphi(t)}{dt^l}\right)_{t=t_0} = 0 \qquad \text{for } l = 0, 1, \ldots, q - 1,$$

and

$$\left(\frac{d^q[(t - t_0)^q \varphi(t)]}{dt^q}\right)_{t=t_0} = q!\, \varphi(t_0).$$

Then, by (B.1.6) and the expression for C

$$\langle B, (t - t_0)^{p-1} \varphi(t)\rangle = a_0 x_0 (p - 1)!\, \varphi(t_0),$$
$$\langle C, (t - t_0)^{p-1} \varphi(t)\rangle = a_0 X_B(t_0 + 0)(p - 1)!\, \varphi(t_0),$$

and, therefore, in view of (B.1.18),

$$X_B(t_0 + 0) = x_{p-1}.$$

Taking the values of B and C at the functions

$$(t - t_0)^{p-2} \varphi(t), \quad (t - t_0)^{p-3} \varphi(t), \quad \ldots, \quad \varphi(t)$$

successively and applying (B.1.18) each time, we then obtain all the equalities (B.1.13). This concludes the proof of

Lemma B.1.1. *$X_B = P^{-1}(D)B$ is defined by a $\mathscr{K}_+(R)$ function $X_B(t)$ which vanishes for $t < t_0$ and whose restriction to $(t_0, +\infty)$ is a C^∞ function $X_B(t)$ that satisfies the equation*

(B.1.19) $$P\left(\frac{d}{dt}\right) X_B(t) = 0$$

for $t > t_0$ and takes on the initial values

(B.1.20)

$$X_B(t_0 + 0) = x_0, \quad X'_B(t_0 + 0) = x_1, \quad \ldots, \quad X_B^{(p-1)}(t_0 + 0) = x_{p-1}.$$

To complete the study of the relevance to the ordinary I.V. problem of the solution $X_B + X_F$ of its equation of evolution, let us turn to

(B.1.21) $$X_F = P^{-1}(D)F.$$

From the relation ($q > 0$, integer)

$$L(t) = (D - r)^{-q} F = e^{rt} \int_{t_0}^{t} \int_{t_0}^{\tau_q} \cdots \int_{t_0}^{\tau_2} e^{-r\tau_1} F(\tau_1)\, d\tau_1\, d\tau_2 \cdots d\tau_q,$$

where $F(t) \in \mathscr{K}_+(R)$ is carried in $(t_0, +\infty)$, and from the factored form of $P^{-1}(D)$, it immediately follows that $X_F(t)$ is continuous and vanishes for $t < t_0$, and that these same properties hold for the ordinary derivatives $X'_F(t), \ldots, X_F^{(p-1)}(t)$.

Also the ordinary derivative $X_F^{(p)}$ exists at every point of continuity of $F(t)$ and vanishes for $t < t_0$. Let us summarize this in a formal statement:

Lemma B.1.2. *If $F \in \mathscr{K}_+(R)$ is carried in $[t_0, +\infty)$, $X_F = P^{-1}(D)F$ is defined by a continuous function $X_F(t)$ which vanishes for $t < t_0$ and whose restriction to $(t_0, +\infty)$ is a function $X_F(t)$ whose ordinary derivatives $X_F'(t), \ldots, X_F^{(p-1)}(t)$ are continuous and whose ordinary derivative $X_F^{(p)}(t)$ is continuous at every point of continuity of $F(t)$. Furthermore, $X_F(t)$ satisfies, for $t > t_0$ and $t \neq t_i$ [where t_i $(i = 1, 2, \ldots)$ are the isolated singular points of $f(t)$] the equation*

$$P\left(\frac{d}{dt}\right)X_F(t) = F(t), \tag{B.1.22}$$

and takes on the initial values

$$X_F(t_0 + 0) = X_F'(t_0 + 0) = \cdots = X_F^{(p-1)}(t_0 + 0) = 0. \tag{B.1.23}$$

Combining relevant portions of the two lemmas above, we have

Theorem B.1.1. *The ordinary I.V. problem for a single linear D.E. with constant coefficients has one and only one solution. It is the function $x(t) = \mathring{x}_F(t) + x_B(t)$ which defines the unique g.f. solution, $X = X_F + X_B$, of the equation of evolution. $x_B(t)$ is the solution of the associated homogeneous equation $P(d/dt)x_B = 0$ with the initial values* (B.1.2) *while x_F is the solution of* (B.1.1) *with vanishing initial conditions.*

Remark 1. *Formulation of initial-value problem.* Frequently the initial-value problem for the equation (B.1.1) is stated as follows: given that (B.1.1) holds for $t \geqslant t_0$ and given the initial values

$$x(t_0) = x_0, \quad x'(t_0) = x_1, \quad \ldots, \quad x^{(p-1)}(t_0) = x_{p-1},$$

find the function $x(t)$.

In this formulation, it is understood that the derivatives at $t = 0$ are all right-hand derivatives.

The solution to this is instantly obtained from $X(t)$, as found above, simply by taking

$$x(t) = \begin{cases} X(t) & \text{for } t > t_0 \\ X(t_0 + 0) = x_0 & \text{for } t = t_0. \end{cases} \tag{B.1.24}$$

Indeed, by the Theorem of the Mean of differential calculus, there exists $\theta(h)(0 < \theta(h) < 1)$ such that

$$\frac{X(t_0 + h) - X(t_0 + 0)}{h} = X'(t_0 + \theta(h)h),$$

whence the right-hand derivative of $x(t)$, as defined for $t \geqslant t_0$ in (B.1.24), is

$$x'(0) = \lim_{\substack{h\to 0\\ h>0}} \frac{x(t_0 + h) - x(t_0)}{h}$$

$$= \lim_{\substack{h\to 0\\ h>0}} X'(t_0 + \theta(h)h) = X'(t_0 + 0) = x_1.$$

Since $X(t)$ is continuous and has continuous (ordinary) derivatives, as was seen earlier, repetition of this argument shows that the right-hand derivatives $x'(t_0)$, $x''(t_0), \ldots, x^{(p)}(t_0)$ all exist and satisfy the equation.

Remark 2. It is instructive to review some remarks of § 2 of Chapter 0 in the light of the mathematically valid operational calculus that we have developed.

The problem (2.1) (2.8) of Chapter 0 was stated in somewhat vague terms sufficient for heuristic purposes, but neglecting details that are essential to any mathematically proper consideration of the problem. In particular, the continuity properties of $f(t)$ were not specified; nor was the meaning of the symbol dx/dt at the points of discontinuity, if any, of $f(t)$. This is remedied by putting the problem in the form (B.1.1, 2): given $f(t)$, defined and continuous on $(0, +\infty)$ except possibly at isolated points t_i $(i = 1, 2, \ldots)$ where $f(t_i + 0)$, $f(t_i - 0)$ exist and $f(t_i + 0) \neq f(t_i - 0)$ (the set $\{t_i\}$ may be empty), find $x(t)$ continuous on $(0, +\infty)$ such that

(B.1.25) $$\frac{dx(t)}{dt} = f(t) \qquad (t > 0, t \neq t_i)$$

and such that

(B.1.26) $$x(+0) = x_0.$$

The equation of evolution of this problem is

(B.1.27) $$DX = F + x_0\,\delta(t).$$

In Chapter 0 this had been termed the "limit" of the sequence of problems (2.9) (2.10). Since the $\mathscr{K}_+(R)$ function associated with the piecewise continuous function $q_n(t)$ defined in (0.2.11) is $p_n(t)$ defined in the relation (II.A.2.1) and since $\operatorname{Lim}_{n\to\infty} p_n(t) = \delta(t)$, in the sense of convergence in $\mathscr{D}'_+$, the solution, X_n, of

(B.1.28) $$DX_n = F + p_n$$

has, by Theorem A.5.1, the property

$$\operatorname{Lim}_{n\to\infty} X_n = X.$$

In other words the solution, X, of the "limit" problem (B.1.27) is indeed the limit (in the $\mathscr{D}'_+$ sense) of the solutions X_n of the members of the sequence of problems (B.1.28). (Concerning the replacement of q_n by p_n see Remark 2 of § II.A.7.)

Remark 3. We have defined the "ordinary" I.V. problem as having its "forcing" term, $f(t)$, in $\mathscr{K}_+(R)$. This covers a multitude of physical situations while retaining the advantage of simplicity. Obviously, fewer restrictions on $f(t)$ are possible if the ordinary differential equation is interpreted in the appropriate sense [for instance, in some broad treatments [9] f is taken to be Lebesgue measurable and (ordinary) derivatives are taken to exist only "almost everywhere" in the sense of Lebesgue measure]. Such more general ordinary derivative relations on a half-line are equally amenable, and in quite the same manner, to submergence in $\mathscr{D}'_+$ in the form of equations of evolution exactly like (B.1.5).

Without going into that, we note that use of singular g.f.'s of the kind discussed in part C of Chapter II enables one to broaden the treatment of I.V. problems, as just given, to include forcing functions, such as $1/\sqrt{t}$, whose absolute values possess improper integrals on every finite interval. The most obvious modifications to the reasoning used here suffice to achieve this.

2. Example. The I.V. Problem for the D.E. of a Free Vibrating System

The most ubiquitous of all elementary D.E.'s in physical applications is the equation with real nonnegative constant coefficients

$$a\frac{d^2x}{dt^2} + b\frac{dx}{dt} + cx = f(t), \tag{B.2.1}$$

which describes the small oscillations of fundamental mechanical and electrical systems subject to an exterior disturbance represented by the function $f(t)$. In different applications, the terms in the equation are designated by different symbols appropriate to the physical problem under examination.

In all these applications, t represents the time and the equation (B.2.1) furnishes a mathematical description valid on some forward half-line of the t-axis [which we may as well take to be $(0, +\infty)$, since the general case $(t_0, +\infty)$ is reducible to this by changing the independent variable to $t - t_0$].

When the function $f(t)$ vanishes on this half-line, we shall speak of the system as being *free* (of external disturbances). This is the case that we now wish to examine.

Formulated in mathematically precise terms, the problem we consider is this: find the function $x(t)$ defined on $(0, +\infty)$ such that for $t > 0$

$$a\frac{d^2x}{dt^2} + b\frac{dx}{dt} + cx = 0 \qquad (a > 0;\ b, c \geqslant 0) \tag{B.2.2}$$

and

$$x(+0) = x_0, \qquad x'(+0) = x_1 \tag{B.2.3}$$

The solution procedure is entirely routine for this and any other I.V. problem for D.E.'s with constant coefficients. In view of the results of § B.1, it consists of *two steps*:

(i) find the g.f. equation of evolution for the given problem,

(ii) solve the equation of evolution by means of Theorems A.3.1 and A.3.2 and the operator identities on $\mathscr{D}'_+$.

As always, denote by $X(t)$ the "prolongation by zero" of $x(t)$ and use (B.2.3) and Theorem II.B.1.1 and its Corollary to get

$$DX = [DX] + x_0\,\delta(t),$$
$$D^2X = [D^2X] + x_1\,\delta(t) + x_0\,\delta'(t),$$

which leads to the equation of evolution

$$aD^2X + bDX + cX = (ax_1 + bx_0)\,\delta(t) + ax_0\,\delta'(t). \tag{B.2.4}$$

This completes step (i).

3. Explicit Solution of the Preceding Problem

Step (ii), the explicit solution of (B.2.4), depends on the factorization of the derivative polynomial $aD^2 + bD + c$. There are three basic cases:

$$b^2 - 4ac > 0, \qquad b^2 - 4ac = 0, \qquad b^2 - 4ac < 0.$$

(a) *Case* 1. $b^2 - 4ac > 0$. *Overdamping*

Then, writing

$$r_1 = -\frac{b}{2a} - \sqrt{\frac{b^2}{4a^2} - \frac{c}{a}}, \quad r_2 = -\frac{b}{2a} + \sqrt{\frac{b^2}{4a^2} - \frac{c}{a}}, \tag{B.3.1}$$

it follows from the assumed nonnegativity of a, b, c that $r_1 < 0$ and $r_2 < 0$ and equation (B.2.4) becomes

$$a(D - r_1)(D - r_2)X = (ax_1 + bx_0)\,\delta(t) + ax_0\,\delta'(t).$$

Decomposing into partial fractions, we have†

$$\frac{1}{(D - r_1)(D - r_2)} = \frac{1}{r_2 - r_1}\left(\frac{1}{D - r_2} - \frac{1}{D - r_1}\right) \tag{B.3.2}$$

and

(B.3.3)

$$X = \frac{1}{a(r_2 - r_1)}\left(\frac{1}{D - r_2} - \frac{1}{D - r_1}\right)((ax_1 + bx_0)\,\delta(t) + ax_0\,\delta'(t)).$$

The identity (A.4.10) or Table I of the Appendix could be used here. It is just as easy, though, to compute the right-hand side of (B.3.3) directly. For this, we first seek the explicit form of

$$G(t) = \frac{1}{a(r_2 - r_1)}\left(\frac{1}{D - r_2} - \frac{1}{D - r_1}\right)\delta(t). \tag{B.3.4}$$

† In part A, the inverse of $(D - r)^p$ was always denoted by $(D - r)^{-p}$ in order to stress its character as an operator. From now on, however, we shall find it convenient to use the notations $1/(D - r)^p$ and $(D - r)^{-p}$ interchangeably.

From $\alpha(t)\,\delta(t) = \alpha(0)\,\delta(t)$ ($\alpha(t) \in C^\infty(R)$), we have

$$\frac{1}{D - r_2}\,\delta(t) = e^{r_2 t} D^{-1}(e^{-r_2 t}\,\delta(t)) = e^{r_2 t} D^{-1}\,\delta(t) = e^{r_2 t}\,H(t),$$

whence

$$G(t) = \frac{H(t)}{a(r_2 - r_1)}(e^{r_2 t} - e^{r_1 t}). \tag{B.3.4}$$

But then (B.3.3) and the algebra of operators on $\mathscr{D}'_+$ give (compare with (B.1.11))

$$X = (ax_1 + bx_0)\,G(t) + ax_0 DG(t). \tag{B.3.5}$$

By Leibniz' formula,

$$\begin{aligned} D\,G(t) &= \frac{1}{a(r_2 - r_1)}[(e^{r_2 t} - e^{r_1 t})\,\delta(t) + (r_2 e^{r_2 t} - r_1 e^{r_1 t})\,H(t)] \\ &= \frac{H(t)}{a(r_2 - r_1)}(r_2 e^{r_2 t} - r_1 e^{r_1 t}). \end{aligned}$$

The g.f. X is then defined by the $\mathscr{K}_+(R)$ function

$$X(t) = \frac{H(t)}{a(r_2 - r_1)} \cdot [(ax_1 + bx_0 + ax_0 r_2)e^{r_2 t} - (ax_1 + bx_0 + ax_0 r_1)e^{r_1 t}], \tag{B.3.6}$$

which can also be expressed in terms of hyperbolic functions. As $t \to \infty$, $X(t) \to 0$ as a function of t because $r_1, r_2 < 0$. For this reason, the corresponding physical system is said to be *overdamped*—it does not oscillate at all.

(b) *Case* 2. $b^2 - 4ac = 0$. *Critical damping*
The operator $aD^2 + bD + c$ becomes, on putting $r = -b/2a$,

$$a(D - r)^{-2},$$

and in this case

$$G(t) = \frac{1}{a}(D - r)^{-2}\,\delta(t). \tag{B.3.7}$$

From the shift relation follows

$$(D - r)^{-2}\,\delta(t) = e^{rt} D^{-2}(e^{-rt}\,\delta(t)) = e^{rt} D^{-2}\,\delta(t) = e^{rt} t\,H(t)$$

Then

$$G(t) = \frac{1}{a}\,e^{rt} t\,H(t)$$

and

$$D\,G(t) = \frac{1}{a}\,e^{rt}t\,\delta(t) + \frac{e^{rt}}{a}(rt+1)\,H(t)$$
$$= \frac{e^{rt}}{a}\,(rt+1)\,H(t),$$

so that X is the $\mathscr{K}_+(R)$ function

$$X(t) = (ax_1 + bx_0)\,G(t) + ax_0 D\,G(t)$$
$$= \frac{e^{rt}\,H(t)}{a}\,[(ax_1 + bx_0)t + ax_0(rt+1)],$$

(B.3.8) $$X(t) = e^{-(b/2a)t}H(t)\left(x_1 + \frac{b}{2a}\,x_0\right)t + x_0$$

Here $\lim_{t\to\infty} X(t) = 0$ providing $b/a > 0$. The physical system is said to be critically damped; it does not oscillate. If $b = 0$, then $c = 0$ and $X(t)$ is a linear function of t.

(c) *Case* 3. $b^2 - 4ac < 0$. *Underdamping*

For this, we have only to review Case 1 with the modification that r_1, r_2, as given by (B.3.1) are conjugate complex numbers,

$$r_1 = \alpha - i\omega, \quad r_2 = \alpha + i\omega \quad \left(\alpha = -\frac{b}{2a},\ \omega = \frac{1}{2a}\sqrt{4ac - b^2}\right).$$

Thus, we obtain from (B.3.4)

(B.3.9) $$G(t) = \frac{H(t)e^{\alpha t}}{2i\omega a}(e^{i\omega t} - e^{-i\omega t}) = \frac{H(t)e^{\alpha t}}{\omega a}\sin\omega t,$$

whence

$$D\,G(t) = \frac{e^{\alpha t}\sin\omega t}{\omega a}\,\delta(t) + \frac{H(t)e^{\alpha t}}{\omega a}\,[\alpha\sin\omega t + \omega\cos\omega t]$$
$$= \frac{e^{\alpha t}\,H(t)}{a\omega}\,(\alpha\sin\omega t + \omega\cos\omega t).$$

Finally, using $\alpha = -b/2a$,

(B.3.10) $$X(t) = \frac{e^{-(b/2a)t}H(t)}{a\omega}\left[\left(ax_1 + \frac{b}{2}\,x_0\right)\sin\omega t + ax_0\omega\cos\omega t\right].$$

Choosing ϕ so that

$$\cos\phi = \frac{ax_1 + (b/2)x_0}{\sqrt{(ax_1 + (b/2)x_0)^2 + a^2x_0^2\omega^2}},$$

$$\sin\phi = \frac{ax_0\omega}{\sqrt{(ax_1 + (b/2)x_0)^2 + a^2x_0^2\omega^2}}$$

the solution can be written in the form (A = constant)

$$X(t) = Ae^{-(b/2a)t}\cos(\omega t - \phi) \tag{B.3.11}$$

whose graph is given in Figure 6.

If $b = 0$, the system is called undamped; $X(t)$ is a periodic function for $t > 0$ and represents a steady oscillation. The quantity

$$\frac{\omega_n}{2\pi} = \frac{1}{2\pi}\sqrt{\frac{c}{a}} \tag{B.3.12}$$

is called the *natural frequency* of the undamped system.

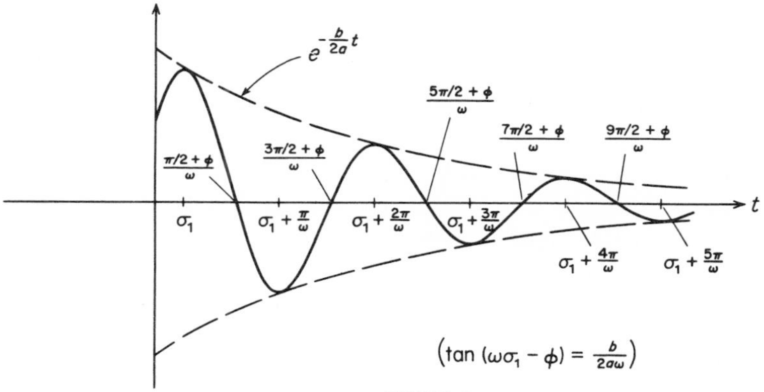

FIGURE 6

If $b > 0$, the system is underdamped; $X(t)$, although not periodic, has zeros on the half-line $(0, +\infty)$ that are equally spaced π/ω apart and $\lim_{t\to\infty} X(t) = 0$. The quantity

$$\frac{\omega}{2\pi} = \frac{1}{2\pi}\sqrt{\frac{c}{a} - \frac{b^2}{4a}} \tag{B.3.13}$$

is called the pseudo-frequency of the system. Observe that it is *smaller than the natural frequency* of the same system without damping.

Remark. The procedure, followed in the above examples, of first finding the function $G(t) = P^{-1}(D)\,\delta(t)$, and then obtaining the solution, $X(t)$, from this function by combining its derivatives of orders $0, 1, \ldots, p-1$, each affected with coefficients depending on the initial values $x_0, x_1, \ldots, x_{p-1}$, *provides a partial check on the accuracy of computations* in the solution of such problems. Indeed, we saw apropos (B.1.12) that $G(t)$, $D\,G(t), \ldots, D^{p-1}G(t)$ are all $\mathscr{K}_+(R)$ functions and so contain no terms in $\delta, \delta', \ldots, \delta^{(p)}$. Since such impulse-type g.f.'s arise in the individual terms of each of the g.f.'s $DG, \ldots, D^{p-1}G$ [for instance, in the relation preceding (B.3.6), there occurs $e^{r_2 t}\,\delta(t) - e^{r_1 t}\,\delta(t)$] they *must cancel each other out*

$$[e^{r_2 t}\,\delta(t) - e^{r_1 t}\,\delta(t) = \delta(t) - \delta(t) = 0].$$

If then, in the course of the computation of a solution, such cancelation does not take place, this indicates a computational error which must then be removed before continuing.

4. I.V. Problem for a Forced Vibrating System

It is a basic feature of the $\mathscr{D}'_+$ version of ordinary initial-value problems that the initial values and the forcing term are on a par in the equation of evolution, insofar as its solution is simply the sum of $P^{-1}(D)B$ and $P^{-1}(D)F$.

In some of the physical systems just considered, the effect of the initial values rapidly dies out [$X(t)$ tends to zero rapidly as $t \to +\infty$ if b is large], while in others it persists. The reactions of such systems to sustained exterior excitation may, therefore, be expected to be characterized by their behavior as free systems.

Representing such excitation by the $\mathscr{K}_+(R)$ function $f(t)$, carried in $[0, +\infty)$, and denoting by $F(t)$ its "continuation by zero", we have as the equation of evolution for such a system:

(B.4.1) $$(aD^2 + bD + c)X = (ax_1 + bx_0)\,\delta(t) + ax_0\,\delta'(t) + F.$$

The explicit form of the contribution $X_F = (aD^2 + bD + c)^{-1}F$ is easily found with the aid of the partial fraction decompositions used in the last section and the identities of § A.4.

Case 1. $b^2 - 4ac > 0$. *Overdamping*

(B.4.2) $$X_F(t) = \frac{1}{\sqrt{b^2 - 4ac}}\left(\frac{1}{D - r_2} - \frac{1}{D - r_1}\right)F$$
$$= \frac{H(t)}{\sqrt{b^2 - 4ac}}\left[\int_0^t e^{r_2(t-\tau)} f(\tau)\,d\tau - \int_0^t e^{r_1(t-\tau)} f(\tau)\,d\tau\right].$$

Case 2. $b^2 - 4ac = 0$. *Critical damping*

(B.4.3) $$X_F(t) = \frac{1}{a}\left(D - \frac{b}{2a}\right)^{-2} F = \frac{H(t)}{a}\int_0^t (t - \tau)e^{-(b/2a)(t-\tau)} f(\tau)\,d\tau.$$

Case 3. $b^2 - 4ac < 0$. *Underdamping*

(B.4.4) $$X_F(t) = \frac{1}{2i\omega a}\left(\frac{1}{D - \alpha - i\omega} - \frac{1}{D - \alpha + i\omega}\right)F$$
$$= \frac{H(t)}{\omega a}\int_0^t e^{-(b/2a)(t-\tau)} \sin \omega(t - \tau)\, f(\tau)\,d\tau$$

where $\omega = \sqrt{4ac - b^2}/2a$, this last step being obtained from (A.4.7).

The sum of $X_F(t)$ and the corresponding expression for

$$(aD^2 + bD + C)^{-1}[(ax_1 + bx_0)\,\delta(t) + ax_0\,\delta'(t)]$$

from the previous section gives the explicit solution of the initial-value problem for a vibrating system under forced motion.

The technical analysis of vibrating systems makes particular use of the effect of forcing terms of the form

(B.4.5) $$F_1(t) = H(t)\sin\beta t,\ F_2(t) = H(t)\cos\beta t.$$

In the underdamped case, this gives

$$X_{F_1}(t) = \frac{H(t)}{\omega a}\int_0^t e^{-(b/2a)(t-\tau)}\sin\omega(t-\tau)\sin\beta\tau\,d\tau.$$

If the period $2\pi/\beta$ of the forcing term equals the pseudo-period $2\pi/\omega$ of the system, this becomes

(B.4.6)

$$\begin{aligned} X_{F_1}(t) &= \frac{H(t)}{\omega}\int_0^t e^{-(b/2a)(t-\tau)}\sin\omega(t-\tau)\sin\omega\tau\,d\tau \\ &= \frac{H(t)}{2\omega}\int_0^t e^{-(b/2a)(t-\tau)}\cos\omega(t-2\tau)\,d\tau - \frac{H(t)}{2\omega}\int_0^t e^{-(b/2a)(t-\tau)}\cos\omega t\,d\tau \\ &= \frac{H(t)}{2\omega}\int_0^t e^{-(b/2a)(t-\tau)}\cos\omega(t-2\tau)\,d\tau + \frac{aH(t)}{b\omega}(1 - e^{-(b/2a)t})\cos\omega t. \end{aligned}$$

So long as $b > 0$, this quantity remains finite when $t \to +\infty$. If, however, the underdamped system contains no friction ($b = 0$), and the natural frequency $\dfrac{\omega_n}{2\pi} = \dfrac{1}{2\pi}\sqrt{\dfrac{c}{a}}$ and the driving frequency $\dfrac{\beta}{2\pi}$ coincide, we get

(B.4.7) $$\begin{aligned} X_{F_1}(t) &= \frac{H(t)}{\omega_n}\int_0^t \sin\omega_n(t-\tau)\sin\omega_n\tau\,d\tau \\ &= \frac{H(t)}{2\omega_n}\int_0^t \cos\omega_n(t-2\tau)\,d\tau - \frac{H(t)}{2\omega_n}\int_0^t \cos\omega_n t\,d\tau \\ &= \frac{H(t)}{4\omega_n^2}\sin\omega_n t - \frac{H(t)}{2\omega_n}t\cos\omega_n t. \end{aligned}$$

In this case, $X_{F_1}(t)$ is not bounded as t increases; the system and the driving force are in *resonance*.

Remark. The restriction $a > 0$, $b \geqslant 0$, $c \geqslant 0$ on the coefficients of equat ions (B.2.4) and (B.4.1) was made in §§ 3, 4 merely because this happens to be the most prevalent case in physical applications. Note, however, that the computational procedures followed in these two sections hold just as well with any real or complex a, b, c.

There exist physical situations where $b < 0$, and also $c < 0$, and the solution formulae for X and X_F given here apply to them as well. In such situations there is no damping, since, the ratio $-b/2a$ being positive, the factor $e^{-(b/2a)t}$ increases rapidly to $+\infty$ as $t \to +\infty$. The physical system is then said to be *unstable*.

Remark. The examples of §§ 3, 4 above illustrate the usefulness of the operational calculus as a practical way of solving I.V. problems. All the tools required for the solution of such problems have been provided and the reader should now be able to successfully tackle the exercises on this topic given at the end of the chapter.

It should be realized that a solution procedure, however practical it may be, does not in itself necessarily furnish the fullest insight into a class of problems. For this reason, we shall devote further space (part C of this chapter) to the I.V. problem for a D.E. with constant coefficients. There we shall consider a device, the Green's function, whose use in many ways simplifies the computation of solutions. Because of this and its intuitive appeal the solution procedure employing the Green's function is advocated in § C.4. Nonetheless, the student in a rush can, after reading § 5 below, go directly to Chapter IV.

5. Infinite Series Solutions of I.V. Problems

Theorem A.5.1 makes it very easy to solve initial-value problems whose equations of evolution contain a forcing term F which is a convergent series in $\mathscr{D}'_+$. This is illustrated in the following example, which represents a situation of physical relevance, where the input to the system is itself a generalized function that is not defined by an ordinary function. Such cases present particularly natural applications of $\mathscr{D}'_+$ theory.

Example. An underdamped vibrating system initially at rest receives a succession of equally spaced impulsive inputs

$$\delta(t - \xi),\ \delta(t - \xi - T), \ldots, \delta(t - \xi - nT), \ldots$$

starting at $t = \xi$. Determine the response of the system.

The equation of evolution for this problem is

$$(aD^2 + bD + c)X = \sum_{l=0}^{\infty} \delta(t - lT - \xi). \tag{B.5.1}$$

The system being underdamped let us write, as in Case 3 of the last two sections,

$$P^{-1}(D) = (aD^2 + bD + c)^{-1} = \frac{1}{a}\left(\frac{1}{D - \alpha - i\omega} - \frac{1}{D - \alpha + i\omega}\right)$$

with

$$\alpha = -\frac{b}{2a}, \qquad \omega = \sqrt{\frac{c}{a} - \frac{b^2}{4a^2}}\,.$$

To get $P^{-1}(D)\,\delta(t - lT - \xi)$, we refer to (A.4.10):

$$\text{(B.5.2)}\qquad \frac{1}{a2i\omega}\left(\frac{1}{D-\alpha-i\omega}-\frac{1}{D-\alpha+i\omega}\right)\delta(t-lT-\xi)$$
$$= e^{-(b/2a)(t-\xi-lT)}\,\frac{\sin\omega(t-lT-\xi)}{a\omega}\,H(t-lT-\xi).$$

Applying Theorem A.5.1, we have directly

$$\text{(B.5.3)}\qquad X(t) = \sum_{l=0}^{\infty} e^{-(b/2a)(t-\xi-lT)}\,\frac{\sin\omega(t-\xi-lT)}{a\omega}\,H(t-\xi-lT).$$

If N is a nonnegative integer and t is in the open interval $(\xi + NT, \xi + (N+1)T)$, the only nonzero terms in the above series correspond to $l = 0, 1, 2, \ldots, N$. For such t (B.5.3) can therefore be written in the form

$$\text{(B.5.4)}\qquad X(t) = \frac{1}{a\omega}\,e^{-(b/2a)(t-\xi)}H(t-\xi)\sum_{l=0}^{N} e^{+lT(b/2a)}\sin\omega(t-\xi-lT).$$

If $b = 0$, so that there is no damping, retain the condition $b^2 - 4ac < 0$ so $\omega = \sqrt{c/a}$; the solution is, for $\xi + NT < t < \xi + (N+1)T$,

$$\text{(B.5.5)}\qquad X(t) = \frac{1}{\sqrt{ac}}\,H(t-\xi)\sum_{l=0}^{N}\sin\sqrt{\frac{c}{a}}\,(t-\xi-lT).$$

Let us then consider the case where the period T of the forcing term and the natural period $2\pi\sqrt{a/c}$ of the vibrating system are related by

$$T\sqrt{\frac{c}{a}} = 2\pi q \qquad (\text{integer } q > 0).$$

Then (B.5.5) becomes $(\xi + NT < t < \xi + (N+1)T)$

$$\text{(B.5.6)}\qquad X(t) = \frac{1}{\sqrt{ac}}\,H(t-\xi)(N+1)\sin\sqrt{\frac{c}{a}}\,(t-\xi).$$

$X(t)$ is *not* bounded as t increases. Thus, when the frequency *of repetition*, $\nu = 1/T$, of the impulses equals or is a submultiple of the natural frequency $(1/2\pi)\sqrt{c/a}$ of the system, there occurs an unbounded increase with time of the response $X(t)$.

In the case of a sinusoidal forcing term this occurs only when the frequencies are equal [cf. (B.4.7)].

*C. CONVOLUTION IN $\mathscr{D}'_+$

1. Green's Function—Intuitive and Physical Basis

The Green's function of a D.E. initial-value problem, also called the impulsive response function by engineers, is a kind of "unit solution" associated with the D.E. From this the solution of any initial-value problem, with any given forcing term, concerning this equation is obtained by an operation called convolution, which has some of the properties of ordinary multiplication.

To make these ideas clear, we start by treating a particular case. Take the I.V. problem (B.1.1, 2) but with the following additional hypotheses: $t_0 = 0$; $f(t)$ continuous for $t > 0$ and $f(+0)$ exists; the initial values are

$$x(+0) = x'(+0) = \cdots = x^{(p-1)}(+0) = 0.$$

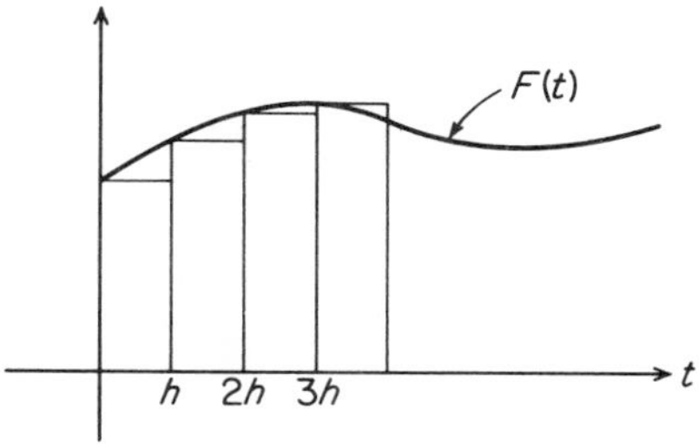

FIGURE 7

Also, it will be suggestive to think of the variable t as representing time.

The equation of evolution is then, with the usual definition of $X_F(t)$, $F(t)$, as prolongations of $x(t)$, $f(t)$,

$$P(D)\, X_F(t) = F(t). \tag{C.1.1}$$

While we already know how to solve this problem, we shall find it instructive, as well as helpful for practical solution purposes, to re-examine it from a viewpoint that is both physical and intuitive.

Given some small time interval h, the value of $F(t)$ in each of the intervals $(0, h)$, $(h, 2h)$, ... is approximable by a constant, say $f(+0)$, $f(h)$, ..., $f(\nu h)$, ... If $q_h(t)$ is the unit rectangular pulse function

$$q_h(t) = \begin{cases} 0 & \text{if } t \leqslant 0 \\ \dfrac{1}{h} & \text{if } 0 < t \leqslant h \\ 0 & \text{if } h < t, \end{cases} \tag{C.1.2}$$

the following sum of pulses then constitutes an approximation to $F(t)$ (Figure 7):

$$A_h(t) = \sum_{\nu=0}^{\infty} F(\nu h) q_h(t - \nu h) h. \tag{C.1.3}$$

The series on the right converges because, for any given t, all its terms are zero except the one with $\nu h < t \leqslant (\nu + 1)h$; it equals $F(\nu h)\, q_h(t - \nu h)h = f(\nu h)$. $A_h(t)$ is an approximation to $F(t)$ in the sense that, for every $t > 0$,

$$\lim_{h \to 0} A_h(t) = F(t). \tag{C.1.4}$$

Furthermore, it is easily seen that in every finite interval $(0, b]$ this convergence is uniform.† Therefore, by a trivial modification of Theorem II.B.6.1,

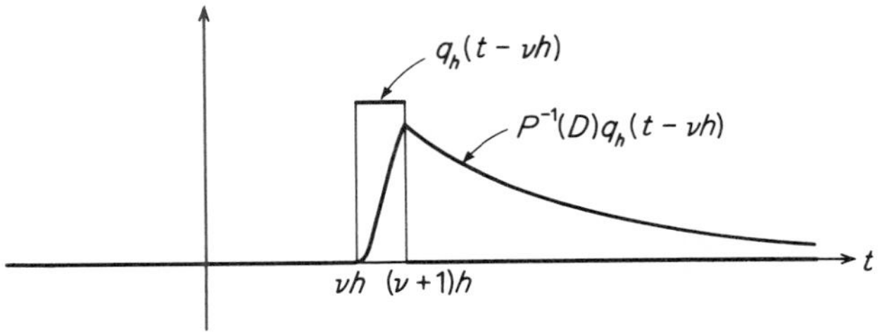

FIGURE 8

$$\operatorname*{Lim}_{h \to 0} A_h = F, \tag{C.1.5}$$

so that, by Theorem A.5.1,

$$X_F(t) = P^{-1}(D)F(t) = \operatorname*{Lim}_{h \to 0} P^{-1}(D)A_h(t). \tag{C.1.6}$$

For the sake of pictorial simplicity, let us momentarily consider $P(D) = D + 2$. Figure 8 then exhibits the graphs of $q_h(t - \nu h)$ and of $(D + 2)^{-1}$ $q_h(t - \nu h)$, which is the function

$$y_h(t - \nu h) = \begin{cases} H(t - \nu h) \displaystyle\int_{\nu h}^{t} e^{-2(t-\tau)}\, d\tau & \text{if } t < (\nu + 1)h \\ H(t - \nu h) \dfrac{(e^{2h} - 1)}{2}\, e^{-2(t-\nu h)} & \text{if } t \geqslant (\nu + 1)h. \end{cases}$$

This diagram is representative of the general situation, which, physically,

---

† The function

$$\bar{f}(t) = \begin{cases} f(t) & \text{if } t > 0 \\ f(+0) & \text{if } t = 0 \end{cases}$$

is continuous in the closed interval $[0, b]$ and, therefore, uniformly continuous there. Consequently, to every $\varepsilon > 0$ corresponds $\eta > 0$ such that for all $t \in [0, b]$

$$|h| < \eta \Rightarrow |\bar{f}(t) - A_h(t)| < \varepsilon.$$

Also

$$F(t) = A_h(t) = 0 \qquad \text{for } t < 0.$$

is this: if, instead of $F(t)$, there is applied to the system the forcing term $A_h(t)$, the νth term of $A_h(t)$, $F(\nu h)\, q_h(t-\nu h)h$, has no effect on the system until the instant νh, after which it provokes the response

(C.1.7) $$hF(\nu h)\, y_h(t-\nu h) = hF(\nu h)\, P^{-1}(D)\, q_h(t-\nu h).$$

Consequently, the response of the system at any $t > 0$ is simply the algebraic sum,

(C.1.8) $$\sum_{\nu=0}^{n} hF(\nu h) y_h(t-\nu h) = P^{-1}(D) A_h(t)$$

$$\left(n = \left[\frac{t}{h}\right] = \text{greatest integer} \leqslant \frac{t}{h}\right),$$

of the values at t of the response functions due to all the pulses that entered the system *prior to the instant t*. Note that $A_h(t)$ can also be written in the form

(C.1.3′) $$A_h(t) = \sum_{\nu=0}^{n} hF(\nu h) q_h(t-\nu h).$$

This sum and that of (C.1.8) resemble Riemann sums for integrals, so that one is tempted to write

$$A_h(t) \approx \int_0^t F(\tau) q_h(t-\tau)\, d\tau = \int_{-\infty}^{\infty} q_h(t-\tau) F(\tau)\, d\tau,$$

$$P^{-1}(D) A_h(t) \approx \int_0^t F(\tau) y_h(t-\tau)\, d\tau = \int_{-\infty}^{\infty} F(\tau) y_h(t-\tau)\, d\tau.$$

One is further tempted to conclude that

(C.1.9) $$F(t) = \operatorname*{Lim}_{h\to 0} \int_{-\infty}^{\infty} q_h(t-\tau) F(\tau)\, d\tau,$$

(C.1.10) $$X_F(t) = P^{-1}(D) F = \operatorname*{Lim}_{h\to 0} \int_{-\infty}^{\infty} y_h(t-\tau) F(\tau)\, d\tau.$$

If these manipulations were justified, and if in the last integral the Lim and integration symbols could be exchanged, there would result

(C.1.11) $$X_F(t) = \int_{-\infty}^{\infty} G(t-\tau) F(\tau)\, d\tau,$$

where

(C.1.12) $$G(t-\tau) = P^{-1}(D) \operatorname*{Lim}_{h\to 0} q_h(t-\tau) = P^{-1}(D)\, \delta(t-\tau).$$

It so happens that not only can all this be put on a mathematically sound basis, but the continuity hypothesis on F can be relaxed to the simple demand that $F \in \mathscr{D}'_+$.

2. Convolution of $\mathscr{K}_+(R)$ Functions

The integral in (C.1.11) defines the so-called convolution product of G and F. In this section we study the properties of convolutions of $\mathscr{K}_+(R)$ functions as a preliminary to a substantiation of the intuitive observations of § 1 to be given in § 3.

Let $f(t)$, $g(t) \in \mathscr{K}_+(R)$. The convolution product of these two functions is a function of t denoted by $f * g$, $f(t) * g(t)$, or $(f * g)(t)$, whose values are given by

$$(f * g)(t) = \int_{-\infty}^{\infty} f(t-\tau)g(\tau)\, d\tau. \tag{C.2.1}$$

If $[a_f, +\infty)$ and $[a_g, +\infty)$ are carrier half-lines of $f(t)$ and $g(t)$, respectively, the integral in (C.2.1) can, by means of simple changes of the variable of integration, be transformed into

$$(f * g)(t) = \int_{-\infty}^{\infty} f(t-\tau)g(\tau)\, d\tau = \int_{a_g}^{t-a_f} f(t-\tau)g(\tau)\, d\tau$$
$$= \int_{0}^{t-a_f-a_g} f(t-\tau-a_g)g(\tau+a_g)\, d\tau. \tag{C.2.2}$$

Similarly, one obtains

$$(g * f)(t) = \int_{-\infty}^{\infty} f(\tau)g(t-\tau)\, d\tau = \int_{a_f}^{t-a_g} f(\tau)g(t-\tau)\, d\tau$$
$$= \int_{0}^{t-a_f-a_g} f(\tau+a_f)g(t-\tau-a_f)\, d\tau, \tag{C.2.3}$$

which brings out the fact that the integrals involved are simply integrals of $\mathscr{K}_+(R)$ functions over intervals of finite length and are therefore well defined. It also follows from these expressions that $(f * g)(t)$ and $(g * f)(t)$ vanish for $t < a_f + a_g$. Figure 9 illustrates the convolution of the particular functions $f(t) = H(t+1)$, $g(t) = e^{-t}H(t)$.

The convolution product $c(t) = (f * g)(t)$ is a continuous function of t on R. Let us prove this in the particular case where one of the functions, f say, is a $C(R)$ function. Using (C.2.2) and taking $h \in R$,

$$c(t+h) - c(t) = \int_{a_g}^{t-a_f} [f(t+h-\tau) - f(t-\tau)]g(\tau)\, d\tau$$
$$+ \int_{t-a_f}^{t+h-a_f} f(t+h-\tau)g(\tau)\, d\tau. \tag{C.2.4}$$

The function f, being continuous on R, is uniformly continuous on every finite closed interval. Consequently to every $\varepsilon > 0$ corresponds $\eta > 0$, such that $|h| < \eta$ ensures

$$|f(t+h-\tau) - f(t-\tau)| < \varepsilon \qquad \text{for } \tau \in [a_g, t-a_f],$$

and therefore also, by (C.2.4),

$$|c(t+h)-c(t)| < \varepsilon \int_{a_g}^{t-a_f} |g(\tau)|\, d\tau + |h|\, M,$$

where M is an upper bound, for $|h| < \eta$, of the modulus $|f(t+h-\tau)\, g(\tau)|$ of the integrand in the second integral on the right in (C.2.4). From this it easily follows that $c(t)$ is continuous for all real t. It is therefore a $\mathscr{K}_+(R)$ function carried in the half-line $[a_f + a_g, +\infty)$. (The case $f, g \in \mathscr{K}_+(R)$ is left to Exercises 26, 27.)

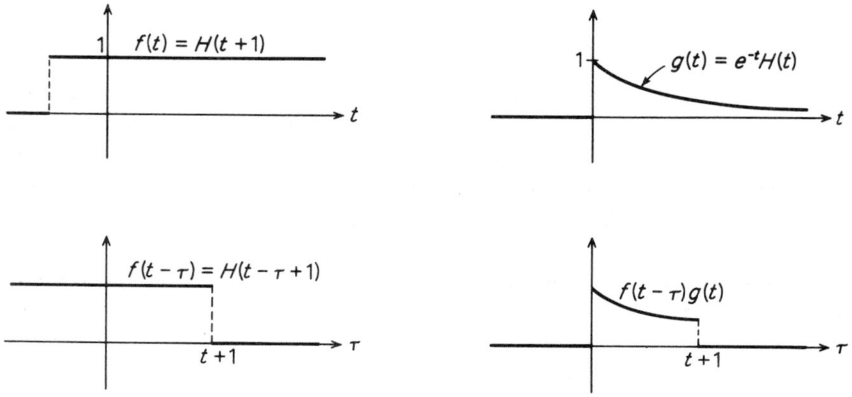

FIGURE 9

One can go further. Suppose that $f(t) \in C^1(R)$; then $f * g \in C^1(R)$ and

(C.2.5) $$\frac{d}{dt}(f * g) = f' * g.$$

To prove it, write

(C.2.6) $$\frac{(c+h)-c(t)}{h} = \int_{a_g}^{t-a_f} \frac{f(t+h-\tau)-f(t-\tau)}{h}\, g(\tau)\, d\tau + \frac{1}{h}\int_{t-a_f}^{t+h-a_f} f(t+h-\tau) g(\tau)\, d\tau.$$

From here on, we assume f to be real-valued. Modifications required for complex-valued f are obvious. By the Theorem of the Mean of differential calculus, given h and t there corresponds to every τ the quantity $\theta(\tau)$ with $0 < \theta(\tau) < 1$ such that

$$\frac{f(t+h-\tau)-f(t-\tau)}{h} = f'(t+\theta(\tau)h-\tau)$$
$$= f'(t-\tau) + [f'(t+\theta h-\tau) - f'(t-\tau)].$$

Since df/dt is continuous, it is uniformly continuous in every closed finite interval and to every $\varepsilon > 0$ corresponds $\eta > 0$, independent of τ in the interval of integration in (C.2.6), such that $|h| < \eta$ (which makes $|\theta h| < \eta$) entails $|f'(t + \theta h - \tau) - f'(t - \tau)| < \varepsilon$, and consequently

$$\left| \frac{f(t+h-\tau) - f(t-\tau)}{h} - f'(t-\tau) \right| < \varepsilon.$$

From this it follows by a simple argument that the first term on the right in (C.2.6) has, as $h \to 0$, the limit

$$\int_{a_g}^{t-a_f} f'(t-\tau)g(\tau)\, d\tau.$$

From the Theorem of the Mean of integral calculus and the continuity of $f(t)$†, it follows that the second term on the right in (C.2.6) approaches $f(a_f)\, g(t - a_f \pm 0)$ ($+0$ if $h > 0$, -0 if $h < 0$). But $f(a_f) = 0$, since $f(t)$ is by hypothesis continuous on R, and the proof of (C.2.5) is complete. If $f \in C^p(R)$, this result can be applied repeatedly so that we have

Theorem C.2.1. *The convolution $f * g$ of two $\mathscr{K}_+(R)$ functions, $f(t)$ and $g(t)$ carried in $[a_f, +\infty)$ and $[a_g, +\infty)$ respectively, is continuous on R and is carried in $[a_f + a_g, +\infty)$. If $f(t) \in C^p(R)$ and $g(t) \in \mathscr{K}_+(R)$, the convolution $(f * g)(t) \in C^p(R)$ and satisfies*

$$(f(t) * g(t))^{(p)} = f^{(p)}(t) * g(t). \tag{C.2.7}$$

Theorem C.2.2. *Whenever $f(t)$, $g(t)$, $h(t) \in \mathscr{K}_+(R)$, the following identities hold:*

$$\begin{aligned} &\text{(a) } f * g = g * f; \\ &\text{(b) } f * (g + h) = f * g + f * h; \\ &\text{(c) } h * (f * g) = (h * f) * g. \end{aligned} \tag{C.2.8}$$

(*The convolution of $\mathscr{K}_+(R)$ functions is a commutative, distributive, and associative operation.*)

Proof. (a) follows, for example, from a change of variables in the integral on the right in (C.2.2) from τ to $u = t - \tau - a_f - a_g$, which gives

$$\int_0^{t-a_f-a_g} f(t - \tau - a_g)g(\tau + a_g)\, d\tau = \int_0^{t-a_f-a_g} f(u + a_f)g(t - u - a_f)\, du.$$

This equals the integral on the right in (C.2.3).

---

† h can always be taken small enough for $g(\tau)$ to be continuous when τ is in the open interval $(t - a_f,\ t + h - a_p)$.

(b) is an immediate consequence of the properties of integrals. To prove (c) observe that f, g, h, being carried in $[a_f, +\infty)$, $[a_g, +\infty)$, $[a_h, +\infty)$, $f * g$ is carried in $[a_f + a_g, +\infty)$ and $((f * g) * h)(t)$ in $[a_f + a_g + a_h, +\infty)$, so we need only consider its value for $t > a_f + a_g + a_h$. Furthermore, by (C.2.2),

$$((f * g) * h)(t) = \int_{a_h}^{t-a_f-a_g} h(y) \int_{a_g}^{(t-y)-a_f} f[(t-y)-x]g(x)\,dx\,dy.$$

This is a repeated integral corresponding to a double integral over the triangle ABC of Figure 10 whose hypotenuse is a segment of the line $y = -x + t - a_f$ in the (x, y) plane.

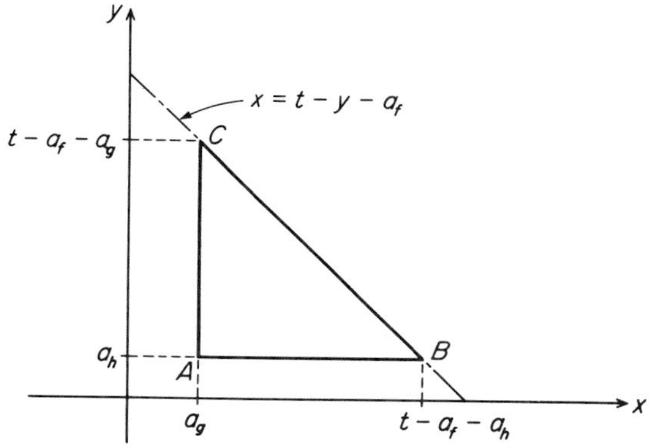

FIGURE 10

The integrand being piecewise continuous, this double integral can also be computed by repeated integration with the order of integration inverted, which gives

$$((f * g) * h)(t) = \int_{a_g}^{t-a_f-a_h} g(x) \int_{a_h}^{(t-x)-a_f} f[(t-x)-y]h(y)\,dy\,dx.$$

The right-hand side, since $f * h$ is carried in $[a_f + a_h, +\infty)$, is seen, in accord with (C.2.2), to be $(f * h) * g$. Use of the commutativity property now yields (C.2.8c). ∎

Example 1. $H(t - h) * H(t - k)\ (h \leqslant k)$.

$$H(t-h) * H(t-k) = \int_{-\infty}^{\infty} H(t-h-\tau)H(\tau-k)\,d\tau$$

$$= \begin{cases} 0 & \text{if } t \leqslant h+k \\ \int_k^{t-h} d\tau = t-h-k & \text{if } t > h+k \end{cases}.$$

Except at the point $t = h + k$, this equals the function

$$(t - h - k)H(t - h - k),$$

so both define the same g.f. and we may write the g.f. equality

$$H(t - h) * H(t - k) = (t - h - k)H(t - h - k). \tag{C.2.9}$$

Example 2. $H(t - h) * H(t - h) * \cdots * H(t - h) = [H(t - h)]^{*n}$. By (C.2.9) $[H(t - h)]^{*2} = (t - 2h)H(t - 2h)$, from which follows the g.f. equality

$$[H(t - h)]^{*3} = \begin{Bmatrix} 0 & \text{if } t \leqslant 3h \\ \dfrac{(t - 3h)^2}{2!} & \text{if } 3h < t \end{Bmatrix} = \frac{(t - 3h)^2}{2!} H(t - 3h).$$

A simple induction proves

$$[H(t - h)]^{*n} = \frac{(t - nh)^{n-1}}{(n - 1)!} H(t - nh). \tag{C.2.10}$$

A particular case of interest is the relation

$$[H(t)]^{*n} = \frac{t^{n-1}}{(n - 1)!} H(t) = D^{-n+1}H(t). \tag{C.2.11}$$

Example 3. For any $F(t) \in \mathscr{K}_+(R)$ and integer $p > 0$ mathematical induction also leads to the important relation:

$$D^{-p}F(t) = [H(t)]^{*p} * F(t). \tag{C.2.12}$$

Theorem C.2.3. *If $f(t), g(t) \in \mathscr{K}_+(R)$ then for any integer $p > 0$ there holds the relation*

$$D^{-p}(f * g) = (D^{-p}f) * g = f * (D^{-p}g). \tag{C.2.13}$$

Proof. Follows from (C.2.8c) and (C.2.12). ∎

Theorem C.2.4. *If $f(t), g(t) \in \mathscr{K}_+(R)$ and r is a complex scalar, there holds the relation*

$$(e^{rt} f(t)) * (e^{rt} g(t)) = e^{rt}(f * g). \tag{C.2.14}$$

Proof. Obvious from the definition of convolution. ∎

Theorem C.2.5. *If $f(t) \in \mathscr{K}_+(R)$ and $P(D)$ is a derivative polynomial on $\mathscr{D}'_+$, then*

$$P^{-1}(D)f(t) = (P^{-1}(D)\, \delta(t)) * f(t), \tag{C.2.15}$$

$$P^{-1}(D)f(t) = \frac{1}{a_0} [e^{r_1 t}H(t)]^{*p_1} * \cdots * [e^{r_l t}H(t)]^{*p_l} * f(t). \tag{C.2.15$'$}$$

Proof. Start with $P(D) = (D - r_i)$. Then

$$P^{-1}(D)\,\delta(t) = e^{r_i t}D^{-1}(e^{-r_i t}\,\delta(t))$$
$$= e^{r_i t}D^{-1}\,\delta(t) = e^{r_i t}H(t),$$

and

$$(e^{r_i t}H(t)) * f(t) = \int_{-\infty}^{t} e^{r_i(t-\tau)}\,H(t-\tau)f(\tau)\,d\tau. \tag{C.2.16}$$

This is equal to

$$(D - r_i)^{-1}f(t) = e^{r_i t}D^{-1}(e^{-r_i t}f(t)) = e^{r_i t}\int_{-\infty}^{t} e^{-r_i \tau}f(\tau)\,d\tau. \tag{C.2.17}$$

For the general case,

$$P^{-1}(D) = \frac{1}{a_0}(D - r_1)^{-p_1}\cdots(D - r_l)^{p_l},$$

we have only to make repeated use of the equivalence of (C.2.16) and (C.2.17) to obtain (C.2.15) and (C.2.15′). ∎

3. The Green's Function. Mathematical Basis

The heuristic arguments of § C.1 above can be put on a mathematically solid footing if one appeals to the theory of convergence in $\mathscr{D}_+'$ to justify each of the limit processes employed there in purely formal fashion. This is not the path we shall follow here. It seems preferable to spare ourselves the slight tedium of ε, η arguments by verifying more directly the truth of relation (C.1.11) and the role of the Green's function as a "unit solution" of the I.V. problem (B.1.1, 2).

Definition C.3.1. *The Green's function of the I.V. problem* (B.1.1, 2) *is the function of t defined by*

$$G(t-\tau) = P^{-1}(D)\,\delta(t-\tau). \tag{C.3.1}$$

Fundamental Theorem C.3.1. *The unique solution in* $\mathscr{D}_+'$ *of the equation of evolution* (B.1.5) *of the I.V. problem* (B.1.1, 2) *is obtained from the Green's function of this problem as*

$$X(t) = X_F(t) + X_B(t), \tag{C.3.2}$$

where

$$X_F(t) = \int_{-\infty}^{\infty} G(t-\tau)F(\tau)\,d\tau = G(t) * F(t) \tag{C.3.3}$$

and

$$\begin{aligned} X_B(t) = {} & (a_0x_{p-1} + a_1x_{p-2} + \cdots + a_{p-1}x_0)G(t) \\ & + (a_0x_{p-2} + a_1x_{p-3} + \cdots + a_{p-2}x_0)DG(t) \\ & + \cdots \\ & + a_0x_0D^{p-1}G(t). \end{aligned} \tag{C.3.4}$$

The function $x(t)$, which coincides with $X(t)$ for $t > t_0$, is the unique solution (in the ordinary sense) of (B.1.1, 2).

Proof. In § B.1, it was proved that

$$X = X_F + X_B,$$

where

(C.3.5) $$X_F(t) = P^{-1}(D)\, F(t)$$

and also

(C.3.6) $$X_B(t) = P^{-1}(D)B.$$

That this last relation is equivalent to (C.3.4) was shown in (B.1.11). As to (C.3.5), it is equivalent to (C.3.3) because of Theorem C.2.5. That $x(t)$, the restriction of $X(t)$ to $t > t_0$, is the unique ordinary solution of (B.1.1, 2), we already know from § B.1. ∎

Remark. The concept of the Green's function is of both theoretical and practical interest. In the examples of actual solutions in § B.3 above, we have already used it (without naming it) in computing X_B, the contribution to X of the boundary terms of the equation of evolution. Now we see that X_F also can be obtained from $G(t)$. While the Green's function is not necessary for this purpose, it is very convenient and will be therefore employed in actual computations, as exemplified in the following section and part A of Chapter IV. A table of such Green's functions is provided in the Appendix.

4. Resumé of the Operational Method—Example

By way of summarizing this method and exhibiting its practical aspects, let us treat a final example of ordinary I.V. problem.

Example. Given $f(t)$ carried in $(0, +\infty)$ and continuous, except at isolated points t_i where $f(t_i + 0), f(t_i - 0)$ exist and differ, find $x(t)$ such that

(C.4.1) $$12\frac{d^3x}{dt^3} - 8\frac{d^2x}{dt^2} - 3\frac{dx}{dt} + 2x = f(t)$$

$(t > 0,\ t \neq t_i\ (i = 1, 2, \ldots))$ ($\{t_i\}$ may be empty), and

(C.4.2) $$x(+0) = x_0, \quad x'(+0) = x_1, \quad x''(+0) = x_2.$$

This problem is a generalization of the example of § 7, Chapter I. There we performed simple computations which easily carry over to the present problem, as we now verify in successive steps:

Step 1. *Obtain the equation of evolution of* (C.4.1, 2). The "prolongations by zero" $X(t)$ and $F(t)$ satisfy (§ II.B.2, § III.B.2)

(C.4.3)
$$\begin{aligned} DX &= [DX] + x_0\, \delta(t), \\ D^2X &= [D^2X] + x_0\, \delta'(t) + x_1\, \delta(t), \\ D^3X &= [D^3X] + x_0\, \delta''(t) + x_1\, \delta'(t) + x_2\, \delta(t). \end{aligned}$$

The equation (C.4.1) in g.f. terms leads to

$$12[D^3X] - 8[D^2X] - 3[DX] + 2X = F, \tag{C.4.4}$$

and substituting in this from (C.4.3), we find

$$\begin{aligned}(12D^3 - 8D^2 - 3D + 2)X &= F + (12x_2 - 8x_1 - 3x_0)\,\delta(t) \\ &\quad + (12x_1 - 8x_0)\,\delta'(t) + 12x_0\,\delta''(t) \\ &= F + B.\end{aligned} \tag{C.4.5}$$

This is the equation of evolution.

Step 2. *Find the Green's function.* This amounts to solving the g.f. equation

$$(12D^3 - 8D^2 - 3D + 2)\,G(t) = \delta(t). \tag{C.4.6}$$

As in § I.7, we have

$$12D^3 - 8D^2 - 3D + 2 = 12(D - \tfrac{1}{2})(D + \tfrac{1}{2})(D - \tfrac{2}{3}),$$

where D is now the derivative operator on $\mathscr{D}'_+$ instead of on $\mathscr{D}_-$. The calculations of § I.7 can now be copied directly, but with the understanding that the operand space is $\mathscr{D}'_+$, and yield† (Table I, Appendix)

$$G(t) = -\frac{1}{2}\left(D - \frac{1}{2}\right)^{-1}\delta(t) + \frac{1}{14}\left(D + \frac{1}{2}\right)^{-1}\delta(t) + \frac{3}{7}\left(D - \frac{2}{3}\right)^{-1}\delta(t)$$

$$G(t) = -\frac{e^{t/2}}{2}H(t) + \frac{e^{-t/2}}{14}H(t) + \frac{3e^{2t/3}}{7}H(t). \tag{C.4.7}$$

Step 3. *Compute the solution X of the equation of evolution from G(t).* The solution of (C.4.5) is by (C.3.2)

$$X(t) = X_F(t) + X_B(t), \tag{C.4.8}$$

in which, by (C.3.3),

$$\begin{aligned}X_F(t) &= \int_{-\infty}^{\infty} G(t - \tau)F(\tau)\,d\tau \\ &= \int_0^t \left(-\frac{1}{2}e^{(t-\tau)/2} + \frac{1}{14}e^{(-t+\tau)/2} + \frac{3}{7}e^{2(t-\tau)/3}\right)F(\tau)\,d\tau,\end{aligned} \tag{C.4.9}$$

and, by (C.3.4) and the right-hand side of (C.4.5),

$$X_B(t) = (12x_2 - 8x_1 - 3x_0)G(t) + (12x_1 - 8x_0)DG(t) + 12x_0D^2G(t). \tag{C.4.10}$$

† Notice that instead of the form

$$G(t) = \frac{1}{a_0}[e^{-r_1t}\,H(t)]^{*p_1} * \cdots * [e^{-r_lt}\,H(t)]^{*p_l}$$

given in Theorem C.2.5 it is the partial fraction expansion of $P^{-1}(D)$ that we use for the explicit determination of $G(t)$ (just as was done in § B.3). This makes the actual computations more tractable.

The Leibniz theorem for g.f. derivatives applied to each term in (C.4.7) furnishes the expressions

$$DG(t) = \left(-\frac{e^{t/2}}{2} + \frac{e^{-t/2}}{14} + \frac{3e^{2t/3}}{7}\right)\delta(t) + \left(-\frac{e^{t/2}}{4} - \frac{e^{-t/2}}{28} + \frac{2e^{2t/3}}{7}\right)H(t)$$

$$= \left(-\frac{1}{2} + \frac{1}{14} + \frac{3}{7}\right)\delta(t) + \left(-\frac{e^{t/2}}{4} - \frac{e^{-t/2}}{28} + \frac{2e^{2t/3}}{7}\right)H(t)$$

$$= \left(-\frac{e^{t/2}}{4} - \frac{e^{-t/2}}{28} + \frac{2e^{2t/3}}{7}\right)H(t),$$

$$D^2G(t) = +\left(-\frac{e^{t/2}}{4} - \frac{e^{-t/2}}{28} + \frac{2e^{2t/3}}{7}\right)\delta(t) + \left(-\frac{e^{t/2}}{8} + \frac{e^{-t/2}}{56} + \frac{4e^{2t/3}}{21}\right)H(t)$$

$$= \left(-\frac{e^{t/2}}{4} + \frac{e^{-t/2}}{56} + \frac{4e^{2t/3}}{21}\right)H(t).$$

These are substituted in (C.4.10)

If the problem is particularized by taking

(C.4.11) $$x_0 = 3, \qquad x_1 = 2, \qquad x_2 = \frac{25}{12},$$

substitution of these values in (C.4.10) and (C.4.8) leaves us with

(C.4.12) $$X(t) = \left(-\frac{9}{2}e^{t/2} + \frac{9}{14}e^{-t/2} + \frac{48}{7}e^{2t/3}\right)H(t)$$

$$+ \int_0^t \left(\frac{3}{7}e^{2(t-\tau)/3} + \frac{1}{14}e^{(-t+\tau)/2} - \frac{1}{2}e^{(t-\tau)/2}\right)F(\tau)\,d\tau.$$

The function $x(t)$, which is the unique solution of problem (C.4.1) (C.4.2) (C.4.11), is therefore the function defined for $t > 0$, whose value is

(C.4.13) $$x(t) = -\frac{9}{2}e^{t/2} + \frac{9}{14}e^{-t/2} + \frac{48}{7}e^{2t/3}$$

$$+ \int_0^t \left[\frac{3}{7}e^{2(t-\tau)/3} + \frac{1}{14}e^{(-t+\tau)/2} - \frac{1}{2}e^{(t-\tau)/2}\right]f(\tau)\,d\tau.$$

5. Convolution in $\mathscr{D}'_+$

The convolution product can be defined for any two elements of $\mathscr{D}'_+$ (Chapter V). Here we shall consider it only for certain g.f.'s. Those which are of "finite K-order" (Definition C.5.1 below). The main point of this extended concept of convolution is that it provides a new outlook on expressions of the form

(C.5.1) $$\Omega(D)F \qquad (F \in \mathscr{D}'_+ \text{ and of finite } K\text{-order}),$$

where Ω is a rational operator in D: they can be written as convolution products

(C.5.1′) $$\Omega(\delta) * F,$$

where $\Omega(\delta)$ is a g.f. of class $\mathscr{D}'_+$ equal to $\Omega(D)\ \delta(t)$. Here we shall exploit this result only in §§ IV.6, IV.7, below, to simplify certain computations. Other implications of this result, e.g., that it makes many differential equations particular types of convolution equations, will not be dwelt upon. (See vol. II of [43]).

Definition C.5.1. *$F \in \mathscr{D}'_+$ is of finite K-order*† *if and only if there exists an integer $l \geqslant 0$, such that $D^{-l}F \in \mathscr{K}_+(R)$. The smallest $l \geqslant 0$ for which this holds is the K-order of F.*

G.f.'s of class $\mathscr{D}'_+$ that arise in physical applications are of finite K-order and it is for these that convolution will be defined in the present section. The convolution of arbitrary g.f.'s of class $\mathscr{D}'_+$ is considered in Chapter V.

Definition C.5.2. *If $F \in \mathscr{D}'_+$ is of finite K-order l and $G \in \mathscr{D}'_+$ is of finite K-order m, the convolution product $F * G$ is the g.f. of class $\mathscr{D}'_+$ defined by*

(C.5.2) $$F * G = D^{l+m}(D^{-l}F * D^{-m}G).$$

(Throughout the rest of this section, all $\mathscr{D}'_+$ g.f.'s considered are assumed to be of finite K-order. Actually, though, all relations and theorems remain valid when this restriction is lifted.)

In consequence of (C.5.2), $F * G$ is also of finite K-order, so that, if $E \in \mathscr{D}'_+$ is of finite order, the convolution $E * (F * G)$ is also defined.

An immediate consequence of this definition and of Theorem C.2.2 is the commutativity, distributivity, and associativity of the convolution of $\mathscr{D}'_+$ g.f.'s of finite order as expressed by

(C.5.3) $$\begin{aligned} F * G &= G * F, \\ E * (F + G) &= E * F + E * G, \\ E * (F * G) &= (E * F) * G. \end{aligned}$$

It is left as an exercise for the reader to apply Theorems C.2.1 and C.2.3 and the above definition to prove

Theorem C.5.1. *Given $F, G \in \mathscr{D}'_+$, both of finite K-order, and p an arbitrary integer (> 0, 0, or < 0), there holds the identity*

(C.5.4) $$D^p(F * G) = D^pF * G = F * D^pG.$$

† Such g.f.'s were mentioned in Example 2, § II.B.5.

Example 1. $\delta(t - h) * F(t)$. We begin with the particular case $F(t) \in \mathscr{K}_+(R)$. Then, by (C.5.2) and the equality $D^{-1}\,\delta(t - h) = H(t - h)$, we have

$$\begin{aligned}\delta(t - h) * F(t) &= D(H(t - h) * F(t)) \\ &= D\Big(\int_{-\infty}^{t-h} F(\tau)\,d\tau\Big).\end{aligned}$$

Since $\int_{-\infty}^{t-h} F(\tau)\,d\tau$ is a continuous $\mathscr{K}_+(R)$ function, its g.f. derivative is, by Theorem II.B.1.1, the g.f. defined by the $\mathscr{K}_+(R)$ function associated with the ordinary derivative

$$\frac{d}{dt}\int_{-\infty}^{t-h} F(\tau)\,d\tau = F(t - h).$$

This proves that

(C.5.5) $$\delta(t - h) * F(t) = F(t - h)$$

in this particular case. That (C.5.5) holds for any $F \in \mathscr{D}'_+$ of finite order, l, results from (C.5.2) and the fact that $D^l G(t) = F(t)$ ($G = D^{-l}F \in \mathscr{K}_+(R)$) entails $D^l G(t - h) = F(t - h)$.

As particular cases of (C.5.5), note the relations

(C.5.6) $$\delta(t - h) * \delta^{(p)}(t - k) = \delta^{(p)}(t - k - h).$$

(C.5.7) $$\delta(t) * F(t) = F(t).$$

Example 2. $\delta^{(p)}(t - h) * F(t)$. From Theorem C.5.1 and relation (C.5.5), there follows, for any $F(t) \in \mathscr{D}'_+$ of finite K-order,

(C.5.8) $$\delta^{(p)}(t - h) * F = D^p(\delta(t - h) * F(t)) = D^p F(t - h),$$

important particular cases of which are

(C.5.9) $$\delta^{(p)}(t) * F(t) = D^p F(t),$$

(C.5.10) $$\delta^{(p)}(t) * \delta^{(q)}(t) = \delta^{(p+q)}(t).$$

Designating by l the K-order of $F \in \mathscr{D}'_+$, so that

$$D^{-l}F(t) \in \mathscr{K}_+(R),$$

we find, with the aid of (C.2.12),

$$[H(t)]^{*p} * F(t) = D^l([H(t)]^{*p} * D^{-l}F(t)) = D^l D^{-p} D^{-l} F(t).$$

Thus (C.2.12) carries over to g.f.'s of finite K-order:

(C.5.11) $$[H(t)]^{*p} * F(t) = D^{-p}F(t).$$

Similarly, one finds for integer $p \geqslant 1$

(C.5.12) $$(D - r)^{-p}F = [e^{rt}H(t)]^{*p} * F.$$

Taking $F(t) = \delta(t)$ and using (C.5.7) this becomes

(C.5.13) $$(D - r)^{-p}\,\delta(t) = [e^{rt}H(t)]^{*p} \qquad (\text{integer } p \geqslant 1).$$

Combining (C.5.12) and (C.5.13) we see that

(C.5.14) $$(D - r)^{-p}F(t) = [(D - r)^{-p}\,\delta(t)] * F(t) \qquad (\text{integer } p \geqslant 1).$$

This brings us to the result announced at the beginning of this section, and which is an extension of Theorem C.2.5:

Theorem C.5.1. *If $\Omega(D)$ is a rational operator (i.e., $\Omega(D) = A(D)B^{-1}(D)$; A, B derivative polynomials of degrees m, n respectively), and if $F \in \mathscr{D}'_+$ is of finite K-order, there holds the identity*

(C.5.15) $$\Omega(D)\,F(t) = [\Omega(D)\,\delta(t)] * F(t).$$

The g.f. $\Omega(\delta) = \Omega(D)\,\delta(t)$ has these properties: (a) if $n \geqslant m + 2$ it is a $C^{n-m-2}(R) \cap \mathscr{K}_+^{n-m-1}(R)$ function; (b) if $n < m + 2$ it is a g.f. of K-order $m - n + 1$.

Proof. The polynomial $B(D)$ can be factored:

$$B(D) = b_0(D - r_1)^{n_1} \cdots (D - r_l)^{n_l}$$

and it follows from (C.5.14) that

$$B^{-1}(D)\,F(t) = [B^{-1}(D)\,\delta(t)] * F(t).$$

Applying to both sides the polynomial $A(D) = a_0D^m + a_1D^{m-1} + \cdots + a_m$ and using (C.5.4) we obtain

$$A(D)B^{-1}(D)\,F(t) = [A(D)B^{-1}(D)\,\delta(t)] * F(t),$$

which is more briefly written in the form (C.5.15).

From (C.5.12) it follows that $B^{-1}(D)\,H(t)$ involves $n_1 + n_2 + \cdots + n_l = n$ successive integrations, and so, like $D^{-n}\,H(t)$, is a $C^{n-1}(R)$ function with an ordinary derivative of order n that has a jump at $t = 0$ and belongs to $\mathscr{K}_+(R)$. Consequently

$$B^{-1}(D)\,\delta(t) \in C^{n-2}(R) \cap \mathscr{K}_+^{n-1}(R).$$

The highest-order derivative in $A(D)$ being D^m, the conclusions concerning the order of $\Omega(\delta)$ easily follow. ∎

Remark. (1) The *K*-order of $\Omega(\delta)$ is that of $D^{m-n}\,\delta(t)$.

(2) The practical computation of $\Omega(\delta)$ is usually done by decomposing $\Omega(D)$ into partial fractions.

(3) (C.5.15) is true for any $F \in \mathscr{D}'_+$ (the proof of this statement requires the results of Chapter V.)

EXERCISES

Part A

(Answers to many of these problems are given in Table I of the Appendix.)

1. Find $(D - r_1)^{-1}(D - r_2)^{-1}(D - r_3)^{-1}\,\delta(t)$ (r_1, r_2, r_3 distinct).

2. Find $(D - r_1)^{-2}(D - r_2)^{-1}\,\delta(t)$ ($r_1 \neq r_2$).

3. Find $(D^2 + r^2)^{-2}\,\delta(t)$ (r real).

4. Find $(D^2 + r_1^2)^{-1}(D^2 + r_2^2)^{-1}\,\delta(t)$ ($r_1 \neq r_2$, $r_1, r_2 \in R$).

5. Find $(D - r_1)^{-1}(D - r_2)^{-1} \cdots (D - r_p)^{-1}\,\delta(t)$ when the r_j are distinct.

6. The operator $(D - r)^{-1}$ depends on the parameter r. Formal differentiation gives

$$\frac{\partial^k}{\partial r^k}(D - r)^{-1} = k!\,(D - r)^{-k-1}.$$

(a) Verify that

$$[(D - r)^{-k-1}]\delta(t) = \frac{1}{k!}\frac{\partial^k}{\partial r^k}[(D - r)^{-1}\,\delta(t)],$$

where the derivative on the right is the parametric derivative of a $\mathscr{D}'_+$ g.f.

(b) prove that, as a consequence of (a),

$$(D - r_1)^{-k}(D - r_2)^{-1} \cdots (D - r_p)^{-1}\,\delta(t)$$

$$= \frac{1}{(k-1)!}\frac{\partial^{k-1}}{\partial r_1^{k-1}}[(D - r_1)^{-1}(D - r_2)^{-1}(D - r_p)^{-1}\,\delta(t)].$$

[Note that, given any derivative polynomial $P(D)$, the g.f. $P^{-1}(D)\,\delta(t)$ is, thanks to (b), very easily obtained by parametric differentiation from the result of Exercise 5. The student unfamiliar with functions of a complex variable should confine his treatment of this exercise to the case where r, r_1 are real.]

7. Let $F \in \mathscr{D}'_+$ be of the form $F = D^m G$, $G \in \mathscr{K}_+(R)$, integer $m \geqslant 0$. Carry out Exercise 6 with $F(t)$ in place of $\delta(t)$.

***8.** Use the result of Exercise 7 to find $D^{-p}t_+^\lambda$ and $(D - r)^{-p}t_+^\lambda$ (integer $p > 0$, real $\lambda \neq -1, -2, \ldots$; t_+^λ defined in § II.C.2).

***9.** Find $(D - r)^{-p}t_+^\lambda \log t$ (§ II.C.4) for integer $p > 0$, real $\lambda \neq -1, -2, \ldots$.

***10.** Show that

$$D^p \frac{t_+^{\lambda-1}}{\Gamma(\lambda)} = \frac{t_+^{\lambda+p-1}}{\Gamma(\lambda + p)}$$

for integer p, real λ (§ II.C.3).

****11.** Let a, $b > 0$, $c \in R$. Show that $(aD^2 + bD + c)^{-1}\,\delta(t)$ converges to $(bD + c)^{-1}\,\delta(t)$ in $\mathscr{D}'_+$ when a tends to zero. Is this true if $a \cdot b < 0$?

****12.** Given $F \in \mathscr{D}'_+$ of finite K-order (i.e., $F = D^q G$, integer $q \geqslant 0$, $G(t) \in \mathscr{K}_+(R)$), prove that

$$(D - r)^{-1}F(t) = \sum_{n=0}^{\infty} r^n D^{-n-1}F \qquad \text{(convergence in } \mathscr{D}'_+).$$

Compare the application of this result to $F = t_+^\lambda$ with the result of the second part of Exercise 8 (when $p = 1$).

Part B

Exercises 13–19 describe ordinary I.V. problems for $x(t)$, $t > 0$. Unless otherwise specified,

$$x_0 = x(+0), \ldots, x_{p-1} = x^{(p-1)}(+0)$$

are arbitrary. $f(t)$ is piecewise continuous for $t > 0$, and $f(+0)$ exists by hypothesis. In each case, find the g.f. equation of evolution, solve it operationally, and check that this yields a solution to the given ordinary I.V. problem. (Observe that the result of Exercise 7 reduces the computational labor in solving some of these problems.)

13. $\dfrac{d^3x}{dt^3} + x = 0$. $x_0 = 1$, $x_1 = x_2 = 0$; $x_0 = 0$, $x_1 = -1$, $x_2 = 0$; $x_0 = x_1 = 0$, $x_1 = 1$.

14. $\dfrac{d^4x}{dt^4} + 5\dfrac{d^2x}{dt^2} + 4x = f(t)$, $x_0 = x_2 = 0$, $x_1 = x_3 = 1$ (see Exercise I.15).

15. $\dfrac{d^4x}{dt^4} + 4\dfrac{d^2x}{dt^2} + 4x = f(t)$ (see Exercise I.16).

16. $\dfrac{d^3x}{dt^3} + 2\dfrac{dx}{dt} = f(t)$ (see Exercise I.17).

17. $\dfrac{d^4x}{dt^4} - \dfrac{d^3x}{dt^3} + 4\dfrac{d^2x}{dt^2} - 4\dfrac{dx}{dt} = f(t)$ (see Exercise I.18).

18. $\dfrac{d^4x}{dt^4} + 3\dfrac{d^3x}{dt^3} + \dfrac{d^2x}{dt^2} - 5\dfrac{dx}{dt} = f(t)$, $x_0 = 1$, $x_1 = x_2 = x_3 = 0$ (see Exercise I.19).

***19.** $\dfrac{d^3x}{dt^3} + 3\dfrac{d^2x}{dt^2} + 4\dfrac{dx}{dt} + 2x = t^{1/2}\log t$ $(t > 0)$, $x_0 = x_1 = x_2 = 0$.

20. L, C, R are positive constants. Use the operational algebra on $\mathscr{D}'_+$ to find a function $i(t) \in C^1[0, +\infty)$ such that

$$L\frac{di}{dt} + Ri + \frac{1}{C}\int_0^t i(\tau)\,d\tau = \cos t \qquad \text{for } t > 0$$

and having $i(0) = 2$. Show that the solution is unique.

***21.** If the conditions $i(0) = 2$ and $i'(0) = 0$ are imposed on $i(t)$ in Exercise 20, show that there does not exist a $C^1[0, +\infty)$ solution. Replacing the definite integral in the differential equation by the operator D^{-1} leads to a natural extension of the problem in the form

$$LDI + RI + \frac{1}{C} D^{-1}I = H(t)\cos t + F(t)$$

where $F \in \mathscr{D}'_+$ and $I(t) = C(1 - 2R)\ \delta(t) + J(t)$ with $J \in \mathscr{K}_+(R)$. (a) Find F. (b) Solve for $Q = D^{-1}I$. (c) Find $J(+0)$, $J'(+0)$. (The student of engineering or physics is advised to work out the details of the interpretation of this problem in terms of a series electric circuit consisting of an inductance L, a resistance R, and a capacity C, to which is applied, from $t = 0$ on, the e.m.f. $\cos t$, the capacitor having a nonzero initial charge. Such "switching" problems arise in numerous practical cases. For examples, see [7] [39] [52] among others.)

***22.** A $\mathscr{K}_+(R)$ function $F(t)$ carried in $[0, +\infty)$ is forward periodic with period $2L$ if $F(t + 2nL) = F(t)$ at all points of continuity $t > 0$ and for all positive integers n. With every such function is associated a series with partial sums

$$\frac{a_0}{2} + \sum_{n=1}^{N} \left(a_n \cos n\frac{\pi}{L}t + b_n \sin n\frac{\pi}{L}t\right) = T_N(t)$$

such that for every finite interval $[a, b]$

$$\lim_{N\to\infty} \int_a^b |F(t) - H(t)T_N(t)|^2\, dt = 0.$$

(This will be seen in Chapter VIII, Exercises.) Recalling Theorems II.B.6.2 and III.A.5.1, deduce from this a useful infinite series representation for $X \in \mathscr{D}'_+$, the solution of $P(D)X = F$ where $P(D)$ is a derivative polynomial and $F \in \mathscr{K}'_+$ is forward periodic.

***23.** Apply the result of Exercise 22 to get a series representation (convergent in $\mathscr{D}'_+$) for the solution of the ordinary I.V. problem

$$\frac{d^2x}{dt^2} + 3\frac{dx}{dt} + 2x = f(t) \quad (t > 0) \qquad x(+0) = x'(+0) = 0$$

where

$$f(t) = \begin{cases} +1 & \text{for } 0 < t < \pi \\ -1 & \text{for } \pi < t < 2\pi \end{cases}$$

and is forward periodic with period 2π. (The coefficients in the partial sums $T_N(t)$ are then given by

$$a_n = 0\ (n = 0, 1, 2, \ldots) \quad \text{and} \quad b_n = \begin{cases} 0 & \text{if } n \text{ is even} \\ \dfrac{4}{\pi n} & \text{if } n \text{ is odd.)} \end{cases}$$

24.
$$\frac{d^2x}{dt^2} + [3 + 2H(t-1)]\frac{dx}{dt} + [2 + 2H(t-1)]x = 0 \text{ for } t > 0.$$

Find a $C^1(0, +\infty)$ function $x(t)$ that satisfies this equation when $t > 0$ and $t \neq 1$ and which has $x(+0) = 1$, $x'(+0) = 1$.

25. Find the function $y(x)$ which satisfies

$$x^2 \frac{d^2y}{dx^2} + 4x \frac{dy}{dx} + 3 \frac{dy}{dx} = f(x)$$

for $x > 1$, where $f(x)$ is piecewise continuous and where $y(+1) = y_0$, $y'(+1) = y_1$. [*Hint:* Take $x = e^t$, $t = \log x$. This transforms the equation into a constant coefficient equation in the independent variable t.]

***Sections C.1 C.2 C.3**

26. Prove by a direct argument that

$$f, g \in \mathscr{K}_+(R) \Rightarrow f * g \in C(R).$$

27. Prove the result of Exercise 26 by using the decomposition of Exercise II.1.

28. For integer $p > 0$,

$$[e^{rt}H(t)]^{*p} = e^{rt}F(t)H(t)$$

with $F(t) \in C(R)$. Find $F(t)$.

***Section C.4**

29. Use the Green's function method to do Exercise 15.

30. Do Exercise 15 as follows:

(a) observe that the equation of evolution is

$$(D^2 + 2)^2 X = F + B;$$

(b) observe that this equation is of the form

$$(D - r_1)^2(D - r_2)^2 X = F + B,$$

where $r_1 = i\sqrt{2}$, $r_2 = -i\sqrt{2}$;

(c) find $(D - r_1)^{-1}(D - r_2)^{-1}\,\delta(t) = A(t, r_1, r_2)$ by partial fraction expansion, and use Exercise 6 to get

$$(D - r_1)^{-2}(D - r_2)^{-2}\,\delta(t) = B(t, r_1, r_2)$$

from this;

(d) note that taking $r_1 = i\sqrt{2}$, $r_2 = -i\sqrt{2}$ in $B(t, r_1, r_2)$ gives the Green's function of Exercise 15;

(e) from this Green's function, obtain the explicit solution of that exercise.

31. Use the Green's function method to do Exercise 16.

32. Use the Green's function method to do Exercise 17.

33. Use the Green's function method to do Exercise 18.

34. Use the Green's function method to do Exercise 19.

***Section C.5**

35. Show that for $f(t) \in \mathscr{K}_+$, $\varphi(t) \in \mathscr{D}_-$

$$\langle f(t), \varphi(t) \rangle = (f(t) * \varphi(-t))\,(0).$$

36. Extend Definition II.A.5.1 (c) to define the product $\alpha(t)\,F(t)$ when $\alpha(t) \in C^k(R)$ and $F(t) \in \mathscr{D}'_+$ is of finite K-order k. Observe that as a result

$$\alpha(t)\,\delta(t-h) = \alpha(h)\,\delta(t-h)$$

whenever $\alpha(t) \in C(R)$ and determine to what extent the differentiability conditions on $\alpha(t)$ in the identity (II.B.3.9) can be relaxed.

37. Given $\alpha,\ \beta \in R$, show that the parametric integral

$$\int_\alpha^\beta \delta'(t-\lambda)\,d\lambda$$

exists and equals

$$\delta'(t) * [H(t-\alpha) - H(t-\beta)].$$

Extend to $\delta^{(k)}(t)$ (integer $k \geqslant 0$).

38. $\alpha \in C^1(R), f \in \mathscr{K}_+(R)$. Show that, when f is continuous at t,

$$\frac{d}{dt}\int_0^t \alpha(t-\tau)\,f(\tau)\,d\tau = \alpha(0)\,f(t) + \int_0^t \alpha'(t-\tau)\,f(\tau)\,d\tau.$$

39. Show that if $F,\ G \in \mathscr{D}'_+$ are of finite K-order, there holds the identity

$$e^{rt}(F * G) = (e^{rt}F) * (e^{rt}G);$$

apply this to $(e^{rt}\delta') * (e^{rt}H)$.

40. $F,\ G \in \mathscr{D}'_+$ are of finite K-order. Show that

$$t(F * G) = (tF) * G + F * (tG).$$

****41.** $F \in \mathscr{D}'_+$ is of finite K-order. $\lambda \in R$. Prove that

$$\frac{t_+^{\lambda-1}}{\Gamma(\lambda)} * F = D^\lambda F.$$

42. $F,\ G \in \mathscr{K}_+(R)$. $\varphi \in \mathscr{D}_-$. Prove that

$$\int_{-\infty}^{\infty} \varphi(t)\left(\int_{-\infty}^{\infty} F(t-\tau)\,G(\tau)\,d\tau\right)dt = \int_{-\infty}^{\infty} F(t)\left(\int_{-\infty}^{\infty} G(\tau)\,\varphi(t+\tau)\,d\tau\right)dt.$$

In the notation of g.f. values, this is written as

$$\langle F(t) * G(t), \varphi(t)\rangle = \langle F(t), \langle G(\tau), \varphi(t+\tau)\rangle\rangle,$$

where t in $\langle G(\tau), \varphi(t+\tau)\rangle$ is a parameter.

43. Given (a) $G \in \mathscr{D}'_+$ of finite K-order, (b) the sequence $\{F_n\}$ of $\mathscr{D}'_+$ g.f.'s all of finite K-order $\leqslant k$ and carried in the half-line $[a, +\infty)$, (c) there exists $F \in \mathscr{D}'_+$ of finite K-order k with $\operatorname{Lim}_{n\to\infty} F_n = F$. Prove that

$$\operatorname*{Lim}_{n\to\infty} F_n * G = F * G$$

(use Exercise 42). Note that in view of the relations (C.5.9) (C.5.10), this result constitutes a generalization of Theorem A.5.1.

CHAPTER IV

SYSTEMS OF DIFFERENTIAL EQUATIONS—OTHER APPLICATIONS

A. OPERATIONAL SOLUTION OF SIMULTANEOUS DIFFERENTIAL EQUATIONS

The simplicity of the algebra of operators on $\mathscr{D}'_+$ reduces the actual solution of systems of simultaneous linear differential equations with constant coefficients to an elementary and practical routine which is merely the operator version of the procedure for solving simultaneous linear algebraic equations by everyday algebra.

Existence and uniqueness properties of solutions of initial-value problems for such simultaneous differential equations can be obtained from the operational method of solution, as they were for individual equations in the preceding chapter. A broader variety of situations, however, occurs: while an ordinary I.V. problem which refers to a single differential equation always has a solution in $\mathscr{K}_+(R)$, such is no longer the case for a system of several differential equations, which may very well have a solution in $\mathscr{D}'_+$ without having one in $\mathscr{K}_+(R)$. Systems of equations for which this last event happens are called nonnormal; such systems, besides being of mathematical interest, are physically relevant, as will be illustrated with an example.

To save effort, general existence and uniqueness theorems are not given here. Instead, stress is laid on the operational method which automatically provides relevant existence and uniqueness properties for any specific system of equations to which it is applied.

1. Example of I.V. Problem for Simultaneous D.E.'s

If a particle of mass m is projected at $t = 0$ from a point C on the surface of the earth which we take here to be at latitude $\lambda \neq \pm 90°$ (C is neither the North nor the South pole), and if the subsequent motion of this particle is observed in a coordinate system whose origin is C, whose x and y axes are tangents to the spherical earth at C, directed southwards and eastwards respectively, and whose z axis is along the direction of the gravitational force at C and directed upwards, the equations of motion of the particle for $t > 0$ are [30]

$$\begin{aligned} m\frac{d^2x}{dt^2} - 2m\omega\sin\lambda\frac{dy}{dt} &= 0, \\ m\frac{d^2y}{dt^2} + 2m\omega\sin\lambda\frac{dx}{dt} + 2m\omega\cos\lambda\frac{dz}{dt} &= 0, \\ m\frac{d^2z}{dt^2} - 2m\omega\cos\lambda\frac{dy}{dt} &= -mg, \end{aligned} \tag{A.1.1}$$

with the initial conditions

$$\begin{aligned} &x(+0) = y(+0) = z(+0) = 0, \\ &x'(+0) = x_1, \quad y'(+0) = y_1, \quad z'(+0) = z_1, \end{aligned} \tag{A.1.2}$$

indicating that the particle is launched from the origin with initial velocity components x_1, y_1, z_1. Here ω designates the magnitude of the earth's angular velocity about its axis.

The system (A.1.1) may be written in the form

$$\begin{aligned} \frac{d^2x}{dt^2} \qquad - a\frac{dy}{dt} \qquad &= 0, \\ a\frac{dx}{dt} + \frac{d^2y}{dt^2} \qquad + b\frac{dz}{dt} &= 0, \\ - b\frac{dy}{dt} + \frac{d^2z}{dt^2} \qquad &= -g, \end{aligned} \tag{A.1.1$'$}$$

which is satisfied for $t > 0$.

As here stated, the problem involves functions of t. We begin by enlarging it into a problem relating g.f.'s of class $\mathscr{D}'_+$, i.e., into a *system of simultaneous equations of evolution*, by the usual device of defining the "prolongations by zero":

$$\begin{aligned} &X(t) = \begin{cases} 0 & \text{for } t < 0 \\ x(t) & \text{for } t > 0, \end{cases} \qquad Y(t) = \begin{cases} 0 & \text{for } t < 0 \\ y(t) & \text{for } t > 0, \end{cases} \\ &Z(t) = \begin{cases} 0 & \text{for } t < 0 \\ z(t) & \text{for } t > 0. \end{cases} \end{aligned} \tag{A.1.3}$$

Replacing $x(t)$, $y(t)$, $z(t)$ by $X(t)$, $Y(t)$, $Z(t)$ respectively in (A.1.1$'$), and g by the $\mathscr{K}_+(R)$ function $g\,H(t)$, we obtain a system of equations that is satisfied for all real $t \neq 0$. This system we shall call (A.1.1$''$), but do not bother to copy down because of its resemblance to (A.1.1$'$).

The $\mathscr{D}'_+$ g.f.'s X, Y, Z, their g.f. derivatives of orders one and two, and the g.f.'s $[D^2X]$, $[DX], \ldots, [DZ]$ defined by the $\mathscr{K}_+(R)$ functions $\dfrac{d^2X(t)}{dt^2}$, $\dfrac{d\,X(t)}{dt}, \ldots, \dfrac{d\,Z(t)}{dt}$ respectively are related, according to Theorem II.B.1.1 and its Corollary, as follows:

$$DX = [DX], \qquad DY = [DY], \qquad DZ = [DZ] \tag{A.1.4}$$

$$\begin{aligned} D^2X &= [D^2X] + x_1\,\delta(t),\\ D^2Y &= [D^2Y] + y_1\,\delta(t),\\ D^2Z &= [D^2Z] + z_1\,\delta(t). \end{aligned} \tag{A.1.5}$$

The [ ] terms correspond to the ordinary derivative terms on the left in (A.1.1″) so that substituting from (A.1.4) (A.1.5) in (A.1.1″) yields

$$\begin{aligned} D^2X - aDY \qquad\quad &= x_1\,\delta(t),\\ aDX + D^2Y + bDZ &= y_1\,\delta(t),\\ -\,bDY + D^2Z &= -g\,H(t) + z_1\,\delta(t). \end{aligned} \tag{A.1.6}$$

This is the system of equations of evolution of problem (A.1.1, 2); it has been derived on the assumption that the latter problem has solutions in $\mathscr{K}_+(R)$. Any solution of the original problem, therefore, determines a solution of (A.1.6). Just as in the preceding chapter, we shall solve the equations of evolution by operational calculus and then verify that this solution also satisfies the original problem. The manner in which this is done for the present example is typical of the general procedure to be examined in more detail in § 3 below. It amounts simply to an operational calculus extension of the familiar determinant procedure of linear algebra.

Since the operators D^p on $\mathscr{D}'_+$ submit to algebraic manipulations that are carbon copies of the manipulations of ordinary algebra, we can define determinants with such operator elements in the obvious way and call

$$\Delta(D) = \begin{vmatrix} D^2 & -aD & 0 \\ aD & D^2 & bD \\ 0 & -bD & D^2 \end{vmatrix} = \begin{vmatrix} c_{11}(D) & c_{12}(D) & c_{13}(D) \\ c_{21}(D) & c_{22}(D) & c_{23}(D) \\ c_{31}(D) & c_{32}(D) & c_{33}(D) \end{vmatrix} \tag{A.1.7}$$

the determinant of the coefficients in (A.1.6). With all mathematical rigor, we can expand $\Delta(D)$ in any one of the classical ways (e.g., in terms of the first row), obtaining

$$\begin{aligned} \Delta(D) &= D^2 \begin{vmatrix} D^2 & bD \\ -bD & D^2 \end{vmatrix} + aD \begin{vmatrix} aD & bD \\ 0 & D^2 \end{vmatrix}\\ &= D^2(D^4 + b^2D^2) + a^2D^4, \end{aligned}$$

$$\Delta(D) = D^4(D^2 + a^2 + b^2). \tag{A.1.7′}$$

In (A.1.6), apply to both sides of the first equation the cofactor,

$$C_{11} = \begin{vmatrix} D^2 & bD \\ -bD & D^2 \end{vmatrix} = D^2(D^2 + b^2),$$

of $c_{11}(D)$ in $\Delta(D)$; to both sides of the second equation the cofactor,

$$C_{21} = (-1)\begin{vmatrix} -aD & 0 \\ -bD & D^2 \end{vmatrix} = aD^3,$$

of $c_{21}(D)$; and to both sides of the third equation the cofactor,

$$C_{31} = \begin{vmatrix} -aD & 0 \\ D^2 & bD \end{vmatrix} = -abD^2,$$

of $c_{31}(D)$. On adding the transformed equations term by term, we end up with

(A.1.8) $$\begin{aligned}(c_{11}C_{11} + c_{21}C_{21} + c_{31}C_{31})X + (c_{12}C_{11} + c_{22}C_{21} + c_{32}C_{31})Y \\ + (c_{13}C_{11} + c_{23}C_{21} + c_{33}C_{31})Z \\ = C_{11}x_1\,\delta(t) + C_{21}y_1\,\delta(t) + C_{31}(-g\,H(t) + z_1\,\delta(t)).\end{aligned}$$

This can be written in terms of determinants, as

(A.1.9) $$\Delta(D)X + \begin{vmatrix} c_{12} & c_{12} & c_{13} \\ c_{22} & c_{22} & c_{23} \\ c_{32} & c_{32} & c_{33} \end{vmatrix} Y + \begin{vmatrix} c_{13} & c_{12} & c_{13} \\ c_{23} & c_{22} & c_{23} \\ c_{33} & c_{32} & c_{33} \end{vmatrix} Z$$

$$= \begin{vmatrix} x_1\,\delta(t) & c_{12} & c_{13} \\ y_1\,\delta(t) & c_{22} & c_{23} \\ -g\,H(t) + z_1\,\delta(t) & c_{32} & c_{33} \end{vmatrix} = \Delta_1,$$

providing that in the determinant on the right-hand side it is understood that in every term of its expansion the operators in D are applied to the g.f. terms [i.e., as on the right in (A.1.8)]. It suffices to expand the operator determinant coefficients of X, Y, and Z in (A.1.9) in terms of the elements of their first columns to see that these coefficients are identical to those in (A.1.8). The coefficients of Y and Z are identically zero operators on $\mathscr{D}'_+$. Indeed, each has two identical columns (if the c_{ij} are scalars, this is a classical property of determinants; however, even though the c_{ij} are derivative polynomials, it is clear that since their algebraic properties are the same as those of real numbers, the proofs of the classical properties of numerical determinants carry over verbatim to those with operator elements). Thus, X satisfies the g.f. equation

(A.1.10a) $$\Delta(D)X = \Delta_1.$$

In quite the same way, one finds

(A.1.10b) $$\Delta(D)Y = \Delta_2,$$

(A.1.10c) $$\Delta(D)Z = \Delta_3,$$

re

(A.1.11)
$$\Delta_2 = \begin{vmatrix} c_{11} & x_1\,\delta(t) & c_{13} \\ c_{21} & y_1\,\delta(t) & c_{23} \\ c_{31} & (-g\,H(t) + z_1\,\delta(t)) & c_{33} \end{vmatrix},$$

$$\Delta_3 = \begin{vmatrix} c_{11} & c_{12} & x_1\,\delta(t) \\ c_{21} & c_{22} & y_1\,\delta(t) \\ c_{31} & c_{32} & (-g\,H(t) + z_1\,\delta(t)) \end{vmatrix}.$$

We have in (A.1.10a, b, c) an operational calculus version of the well-known Cramer's rule of linear algebra; the solution of the system of equations of evolution follows:

(A.1.12) $$X = \Delta^{-1}(D)\Delta_1, \quad Y = \Delta^{-1}(D)\Delta_2, \quad Z = \Delta^{-1}(D)\Delta_3,$$

where

(A.1.13)
$$\Delta_1 = D^2[(D^2 + b^2)x_1\,\delta(t) + aDy_1\,\delta(t) - ab(-g\,H(t) + z_1\,\delta(t))],$$
$$\Delta_2 = D^3[Dy_1\,\delta(t) - ax_1\,\delta(t) - b(-g\,H(t) + z_1\,\delta(t))],$$
$$\Delta_3 = D^2[(D^2 + a^2)(-g\,H(t) + z_1\,\delta(t)) - abx_1\,\delta(t) + bDy_1\,\delta(t)].$$

From (A.1.7′) results, by partial fraction expansion,

(A.1.14) $$D^2\Delta^{-1}(D)$$
$$= D^{-2}(D^2 + a^2 + b^2)^{-1}$$
$$= \frac{1}{a^2 + b^2}\left[\frac{1}{D^2} + \frac{1}{2i\sqrt{a^2 + b^2}}\left(\frac{1}{D + i\sqrt{a^2 + b^2}} - \frac{1}{D - i\sqrt{a^2 + b^2}}\right)\right],$$

so that, with the help of (III.A.4.2) and (III.A.4.10), or Table I of the Appendix, we obtain the function $J(t)$:

(A.1.15) $$J(t) = D^2\Delta^{-1}(D)\,\delta(t)$$
$$= \frac{1}{a^2 + b^2}\left[t\,H(t) - \frac{H(t)}{\sqrt{a^2 + b^2}}\sin(t\sqrt{a^2 + b^2})\right].$$

It is now easy to find X, Y, Z from this, (A.1.12), and (A.1.13):

(A.1.16)
$$X(t) = [x_1D^2 + ay_1D + b(x_1b - az_1) + abgD^{-1}]J,$$
$$Y(t) = [y_1D^2 - (ax_1 + bz_1)D + bg]J,$$
$$Z(t) = [z_1D^2 + (by_1 - g)D + a(az_1 - bx_1) - a^2gD^{-1}]J.$$

In these expressions, there appear

$$DJ(t) = \frac{H(t)}{a^2 + b^2}\,(1 - \cos t\sqrt{a^2 + b^2}),$$

$$D^2J(t) = \frac{H(t)}{\sqrt{a^2 + b^2}} \sin t\sqrt{a^2 + b^2},$$

$$D^{-1}J(t) = \frac{H(t)}{a^2 + b^2}\left(\frac{t^2}{2} + \frac{\cos t\sqrt{a^2 + b^2} - 1}{a^2 + b^2}\right),$$

which on substitution in (A.1.16) and replacement of a, b by their original representation in terms of ω, λ gives the solution

$$X(t) = \frac{H(t)}{4\omega^2}\Big\{\sin \lambda(2x_1\omega \sin \lambda + z_1) \sin 2\omega t + \left(2\omega \sin \lambda y_1 - g\frac{\sin 2\lambda}{2}\right)(1 - \cos 2\omega t) + 4\omega^2 \cos \lambda\,(x_1 \cos \lambda - z_1 \sin \lambda)t + t^2\omega^2 g \sin 2\lambda\Big\},$$

$$Y(t) = \frac{H(t)}{4\omega^2}\Big\{(2\omega y_1 - g \cos \lambda) \sin 2\omega t - 2\omega(x_1 \sin \lambda + z_1 \cos \lambda)(1 - \cos 2\omega t) + 2\omega g t \cos \lambda\Big\}, \tag{A.1.17}$$

$$Z(t) = \frac{H(t)}{4\omega^2}\Big\{2\omega \cos \lambda\,(z_1 \cos \lambda + x_1 \sin \lambda) \sin 2\omega t + 2\omega \cos \lambda\,(y_1 - g \cos^2 \lambda)(1 - \cos 2\omega t) + 4\omega^2 t \sin \lambda\,(z_1 \sin \lambda - x_1 \cos \lambda) - 2\omega^2 g t \sin^2 \lambda\Big\}.$$

These are the unique g.f. solutions of the system of equations of evolution (A.1.6) and are defined by $\mathscr{K}_+(R)$ functions whose restrictions to $t > 0$ furnish the unique solution $x(t)$, $y(t)$, $z(t)$ of the problem (A.1.1, 2) originally formulated.

2. The System of Equations of Evolution

The linear system form of problem (III.B.1, 2) is this: given $f_1(t), f_2(t), \ldots, f_m(t)$, m complex-valued functions, each defined and continuous in $(t_0, +\infty)$ except possibly at isolated points† t_{m_i}, where $f(t_{m_i} + 0)$, $f(t_{m_i} - 0)$ exist and

† At t_0 only the right-hand limits $f_i(t_0 + 0)$ are assumed to exist.

differ, find functions $x_1(t), x_2(t), \ldots, x_m(t)$ such that the ordinary differential equations

$$
\begin{aligned}
&c_{11}\left(\frac{d}{dt}\right)x_1(t) + c_{12}\left(\frac{d}{dt}\right)x_2(t) + \cdots + c_{1m}\left(\frac{d}{dt}\right)x_m(t) = f_1(t),\\
&\ldots\ldots\ldots\ldots\ldots\ldots\ldots\ldots\ldots\ldots\ldots\ldots\ldots\ldots\ldots\ldots\ldots\ldots\\
&c_{m1}\left(\frac{d}{dt}\right)x_1(t) + c_{m2}\left(\frac{d}{dt}\right)x_2(t) + \cdots + c_{mm}\left(\frac{d}{dt}\right)x_m(t) = f_m(t)
\end{aligned} \tag{A.2.1}
$$

are satisfied for $t > t_0$ at every common point of continuity of $f_1(t), \ldots, f_m(t)$. The coefficients are polynomials of the form

$$
c_{ij}\left(\frac{d}{dt}\right) = a_{ij}^0 \frac{d^N}{dt^N} + a_{ij}^1 \frac{d^{N-1}}{dt^{N-1}} + \cdots + a_{ij}^N \quad (i, j = 1, 2, \ldots, m), \tag{A.2.2}
$$

where the a_{ij}^k are real or complex constants and differentiation is understood to be in the ordinary sense.

A further restriction imposed on the unknowns $x_j(t)$ in this problem is that they satisfy the set of initial conditions

$$
\begin{aligned}
&x_j(t_0 + 0) = x_j^0, \qquad x_j'(t_0 + 0) = x_j^1, \ldots,\\
&\qquad x_j^{(N_j-1)}(t_0 + 0) = x_j^{N_j-1} \qquad (j = 1, 2, \ldots, m),
\end{aligned} \tag{A.2.3}
$$

where N_j indicates the highest-order derivative of x_j that appears in the system (A.2.1). Finally we require that $x_j(t), x_j'(t), \ldots, x_j^{(N_j-1)}(t)$ be continuous on $(t_0, +\infty)$ and that $x_j^{(N_j)}(t)$ be piecewise continuous there.

Whether this problem, which we shall call the ordinary I.V. problem for a system of linear D.E.'s with constant coefficients, has a solution and, if so, under what conditions, is a question which we approach in the same spirit as in the preceding example and in part B of Chapter III: we enlarge to $\mathscr{D}'_+$ the setting in which it is formulated.

The "continuation by zero" of $x_j(t)$ $(j = 1, 2, \ldots, m)$,

$$
X_j(t) = \begin{cases} 0 & \text{for } t < t_0 \\ x_j(t) & \text{for } t > t_0, \end{cases} \tag{A.2.4}
$$

defines a $\mathscr{K}_+(R)$ function for which Theorem II.B.1.1, its Corollary, and (A.2.3) furnish the identities

$$
\begin{aligned}
DX_j &= [DX_j] + x_j^0\,\delta(t - t_0),\\
D^2X_j &= [D^2X_j] + x_j^0\,\delta'(t - t_0) + x_j^1\,\delta(t - t_0),\\
&\ldots\ldots\ldots\ldots\ldots\ldots\ldots\ldots\ldots\ldots\ldots\ldots\\
D^{N_j}X_j &= [D^{N_j}X_j] + x_j^0\,\delta^{(N_j-1)}(t - t_0) + x_j^1\,\delta^{(N_j-2)}(t - t_0)\\
&\quad + \cdots + x_j^{N_j-1}\,\delta(t - t_0),
\end{aligned} \tag{A.2.5}
$$

in which D^lX_j is a g.f. derivative and $[D^lX_j]$ is the g.f. defined by the $\mathscr{K}_+$ function associated with the ordinary derivative $d^lX_j(t)/dt^l$.

Substituting in (A.2.1) the "continuation by zero,"

$$F_j(t) = \begin{cases} 0 & \text{for } t < t_0 \\ f_j(t) & \text{for } t > t_0 \end{cases} \qquad (j = 1, 2, \ldots, m) \tag{A.2.6}$$

for $f_j(t)$ and the g.f.'s $[D^l X_j]$ for $d^l x_j/dt^l$ gives a system of g.f. equations which must be satisfied if (A.2.1) holds and which, because of (A.2.5), takes the form

$$\begin{aligned} c_{11}(D)X_1 + c_{12}(D)X_2 + \cdots + c_{1m}(D)X_m &= F_1 + B_1, \\ \cdots\cdots\cdots\cdots\cdots\cdots\cdots\cdots\cdots\cdots\cdots\cdots \\ c_{m1}(D)X_1 + c_{m2}(D)X_2 + \cdots + c_{mm}(D)X_m &= F_m + B_m. \end{aligned} \tag{A.2.7}$$

Here the $c_{ij}(D)$ are the derivative polynomials obtained by replacing d/dt with the operator D on $\mathscr{D}'_+$ and the $B_j (j = 1, 2, \ldots, m)$ are the "boundary" terms consisting of linear combinations of $\delta(t - t_0)$, $\delta'(t - t_0), \ldots,$ $\delta^{(N-1)}(t - t_0)$, whose coefficients contain initial values x_j^l from (A.2.3). There is no need for us to set down the explicit formulae for the B_j; they are ungainly in this general case†, and, in any specific problem, it is just as convenient to compute these boundary terms anew, just as was done in the example of § A.1 above.

The system (A.2.7) is called the *system of equations of evolution* of problem (A.2.1, 3). It is essential to realize that when we defined the $\mathscr{K}_+^{N_j}(R)$ functions $X_j(t)$, we were, in fact, assuming that there exist functions $x_j(t)$ $(j = 1, 2, \ldots,$ $m)$ constituting a solution of (A.2.1, 3), and so continuable by zero for $t < t_0$. The g.f.'s X_j then must be solutions of (A.2.7).

The system (A.2.7), however, is a set of equations in its own right which relates elements X_j, $F_j + B_j$ of $\mathscr{D}'_+$, and which, for all we know at this stage, may very well have solutions $X_j \in \mathscr{D}'_+$ $(j = 1, 2, \ldots, m)$ that are not defined by $\mathscr{K}_+(R)$ functions sufficiently often differentiable in the sense of ordinary calculus. In contradistinction to the case of a single equation, there are several possible outcomes:

(a) (A.2.7) has no solution; therefore, (A.2.1, 3) has no solution either.

(b) (A.2.7) has a unique solution and it is a solution of (A.2.1, 3) [and therefore the unique solution of (A.2.1, 3)]; the system (A.2.1) is called *normal* in this case.

(c) (A.2.7) has a unique solution, but it lacks the continuity and differentiability properties for a solution of (A.2.1, 3) and satisfies the initial conditions only in special cases; therefore, the latter has no solution. In this case (A.2.1) is called a *nonnormal system.*

(d) (A.2.7) has more than one solution; then either they are all solutions of (A.2,1. 3) or else the latter has no solution.

---

† Unless one uses matrix notation (Exercise 13).

Of these cases, the most prevalent in applications with a physical context are *b* and *c*.

Our attitude in regard to these questions will be this: whenever we are confronted with a specific problem of the type (A.2.1, 3), we explicitly solve its associated system of evolution and then determine by ordinary substitution whether it is also a solution of the original problem. In justification of this pedestrian outlook, there is the fact that a general theory with devices for the a priori diagnosis of cases (a), (b), (c), or (d) requires more space and use of matrix theory than seems worthwhile here. The interested reader is referred to [3s]. Besides this, there is the fact (§ 6 below) that there are grounds for considering the system of evolution to be a more correct formulation of a physical situation than is (A.2.1, 3) anyway.

The system of evolution is more conveniently written as a *matrix equation of evolution*

(A.2.8) $$P(D)X = F + B,$$

where

(A.2.9) $$P(D) = \begin{pmatrix} c_{11}(D) & \cdots & c_{1m}(D) \\ \cdot & & \cdot \\ \cdot & & \cdot \\ \cdot & & \cdot \\ c_{m1}(D) & \cdots & c_{mm}(D) \end{pmatrix},$$

$$X = \begin{pmatrix} X_1 \\ X_2 \\ \cdot \\ \cdot \\ \cdot \\ X_m \end{pmatrix}, \qquad F + B = \begin{pmatrix} F_1 \\ F_1 \\ \cdot \\ \cdot \\ \cdot \\ F_m \end{pmatrix} + \begin{pmatrix} B_1 \\ B_2 \\ \cdot \\ \cdot \\ \cdot \\ B_m \end{pmatrix}.$$

3. Operational Form of Cramer's Rule

In § 1 above, we used an extension to operators on $\mathscr{D}'_+$ of the theory of determinants of order 3 of elementary algebra to solve the system (A.1.6). We shall now consider a more general situation which includes that example as a particular case.

Let $c_{ij}(i, j = 1, 2, \ldots, m)$ be a rational operator in D and expand

$$\begin{vmatrix} c_{11}(D) & \cdots & c_{1m}(D) \\ \cdot & & \cdot \\ \cdot & & \cdot \\ \cdot & & \cdot \\ c_{m1}(D) & \cdots & c_{mm}(D) \end{vmatrix} = \Delta(D)$$

into a sum

$$\Delta(D) = \Sigma\, (-1)^{\omega_{j_1 \cdots j_m}} c_{1j_1}(D)\, c_{2j_2}(D) \cdots c_{mj_m}(D)$$

exactly as if the c_{ij} were numerical elements of an ordinary determinant of order m (i.e., Σ is over the sum of all the possible $m!$ permutations of the integers $1, 2, \ldots, m$ and $\omega_{j_1 \cdots j_m}$ is the parity of the particular permutation $(j_1, j_2, \ldots, j_m)$ of these integers). The operator determinant thus defined is a rational operator in D on $\mathscr{D}'_+$. Such a determinant has properties analogous to those of ordinary determinants:

(i) if its rows and columns are interchanged, the determinant $\Delta(D)$ is unchanged;

(ii) if two rows (or two columns) are interchanged the resulting determinant equals $-\Delta(D)$;

(iii) if the elements of one row (or column) are multiplied by the same rational operator $\Omega(D)$ (which may be a scalar, k) the resulting determinant equals $\Omega(D)\,\Delta(D)$;

(iv) if corresponding elements of two rows (or columns) are equal, or have a ratio equal to a fixed rational operator $\Omega(D)$, then $\Delta(D) = 0$;

(v) if for a given integer $i(1 \leqslant i \leqslant m)$

$$c_{ij}(D) = c'_{ij}(D) + c''_{ij}(D) \qquad (j = 1, 2, \ldots, m)$$

then $\Delta(D) = \Delta'(D) + \Delta''(D)$, where $\Delta'(D)$ is the determinant obtained when the ith row of $\Delta(D)$ is replaced by $c'_{i1}(D), c'_{i2}(D), \ldots, c'_{im}(D)$ and $\Delta''(D)$ is $\Delta(D)$ with the ith row replaced by $c''_{i1}(D), c''_{i2}(D), \ldots, c''_{im}(D)$. (Analogous property with roles of i and j interchanged and jth column instead of ith row.)

The determinant $M_{ij}(D)$ of order $(m - 1)$ obtained by crossing out the ith row and jth column in the array (matrix) for $\Delta(D)$ is called the minor of the element c_{ij}, and $C_{ij}(D) = (-1)^{i+j} M_{ij}(D)$ is called the cofactor of this element. There then hold, as in the case of numerical determinants, the Laplace formulae for the expansion of $\Delta(D)$ in the elements of the ith row or jth column:

(A.3.3)
$$\Delta(D) = \sum_{i=1}^{m} c_{ij}(D)\, C_{ij}(D),$$

(A.3.3′)
$$\Delta(D) = \sum_{j=1}^{m} c_{ij}(D)\, C_{ij}(D).$$

These relations, in conjunction with property (iv) [where we take $\Omega(D) = I$, the identity operator], lead, as in the case of numerical determinants, to the identities

(A.3.4)
$$\sum_{i=1}^{m} c_{ik}(D)\, C_{ij}(D) = 0 \qquad (k \neq j),$$

(A.3.4′)
$$\sum_{j=1}^{m} c_{ij}(D)\, C_{kj}(D) = 0 \qquad (k \neq i).$$

There is no point in our going through the proofs of all these properties of operator determinants here. They consist in no more than the mechanical transcription of the classical proofs for numerical determinants (see [2], for instance), which is made possible by the fact that the algebra of rational operators in D is analogous to the algebra of real numbers (in technical terms: the rational operators in D form an algebraic *field*).

Thanks to the analogy between the operator determinants and ordinary numerical determinants, systems of differential equations in $\mathscr{D}'_+$ can be handled in quite the same way as are simultaneous linear algebraic equations, as the example in § 1 indicates.

Consider the system of m equations in m unknowns $X_1, X_2, \ldots, X_m$ ($\in \mathscr{D}'_+$) where $Y_1, \ldots, Y_m$ are m given members of $\mathscr{D}'_+$ and the $c_{ij}(D)$ ($i, j = 1, \ldots, m$) are rational operators in D:

(A.3.5)
$$\begin{aligned} c_{11}(D)X_1 + c_{12}(D)X_2 + \cdots + c_{1m}(D)X_m &= Y_1, \\ \cdots\cdots\cdots\cdots\cdots\cdots\cdots\cdots\cdots \\ c_{m1}(D)X_1 + c_{m2}(D)X_2 + \cdots + c_{mm}(D)X_m &= Y_m. \end{aligned}$$

First assume that this system has a solution $X_1, \ldots, X_m$ and let j be any integer, such that $1 \leqslant j \leqslant m$; we can then apply to each side of the first equation the operator $C_{1j}(D)$ [the cofactor of $c_{1j}(D)$]; to both sides of the second equation, the operator $C_{2j}(D); \ldots$; to both sides of the mth equation, the operator $C_{mj}(D)$. Adding the transformed equations term by term and using the identities (A.3.3′) (A.3.4′) then leaves us with

(A.3.6)
$$\Delta(D)X_j = \sum_{i=1}^{m} C_{ij}(D)Y_i \qquad (j = 1, 2, \ldots, m).$$

The right-hand side of (A.3.6) we designate by $\Delta_j(D)$. It is the Laplace expansion in terms of its jth column of the mixed determinant

(A.3.7)
$$\Delta_j(D) = \begin{vmatrix} c_{11}(D) & \cdots & c_{1j-1}(D) & Y_1 & c_{1j+1}(D) & \cdots & c_{1m}(D) \\ c_{21}(D) & \cdots & c_{2j-1}(D) & Y_2 & c_{2j+1}(D) & \cdots & c_{2m}(D) \\ \cdots & \cdots & \cdots & \cdots & \cdots & \cdots & \cdots \\ c_{m1}(D) & \cdots & c_{mj-1}(D) & Y_m & c_{mj+1}(D) & \cdots & c_{mm}(D) \end{vmatrix},$$

providing we adopt the convention that in every term of the formal expansion of this determinant the operators are all written, as in (A.3.6), in front of the g.f. term.†

The resulting set of m identities ($j = 1, 2, \ldots, m$)

(A.3.6′)
$$\Delta(D)X_j = \Delta_j(D),$$

† It will be noted that if one uses the commutative convolution product defined in § III.C.5 and the identity (III.C.5.15), such precautions in the description of "mixed" determinants are unnecessary. Both "pure" operator and "mixed" determinants can then be viewed simply as consisting entirely of elements of $\mathscr{D}'_+$.

since it was obtained on the assumption that (A.3.5) has a solution, expresses the fact that, if $\Delta(D) \neq 0$ and if the system (A.3.5) has a solution, this solution is unique and is given explicitly by

$$X_j = \Delta^{-1}(D)\,\Delta_j(D). \tag{A.3.8}$$

When $\Delta(D) \neq 0$, it has a two-sided inverse $\Delta^{-1}(D)$ by Theorem III.A.3.1; it is then easily verified by substitution that the g.f.'s defined by

$$X_j = \Delta^{-1}(D)\,\Delta_j(D)$$

are effectively solutions of (A.3.5). Thus, we can conclude that *if* $\Delta(D) \neq 0$, *the system* (A.3.5) *has a solution whose components are* $\mathscr{D}'_+$ *g.f.'s*, and *this solution is unique and given by* (A.3.8). This is Cramer's rule in operator form.

If the system (A.3.5) is written more compactly as the matrix equation:

$$\begin{pmatrix} c_{11}(D) & \cdots & c_{1m}(D) \\ \cdot & \cdots & \cdot \\ c_{m1}(D) & \cdots & c_{mm}(D) \end{pmatrix} \begin{pmatrix} X_1 \\ X_2 \\ \cdot \\ \cdot \\ \cdot \\ X_m \end{pmatrix} = \begin{pmatrix} Y_1 \\ Y_2 \\ \cdot \\ \cdot \\ \cdot \\ Y_m \end{pmatrix}, \tag{A.3.9}$$

$$C(D)X = Y, \tag{A.3.9$'$}$$

the identities (A.3.8) enable us to express its solution with the matrix relation

$$X = C^{-1}(D)\,Y, \tag{A.3.10}$$

where the inverse operator matrix $C^{-1}(D)$ is

$$C^{-1}(D) = \begin{pmatrix} \Delta^{-1}(D)C_{11}(D) & \Delta^{-1}(D)C_{21}(D) & \cdots & \Delta^{-1}(D)C_{m1}(D) \\ \Delta^{-1}(D)C_{12}(D) & \Delta^{-1}(D)C_{22}(D) & \cdots & \Delta^{-1}(D)C_{m2}(D) \\ \cdot & & & \\ \cdot & & & \\ \cdot & & & \\ \Delta^{-1}(D)C_{1m}(D) & \Delta^{-1}(D)C_{2m}(D) & \cdots & \Delta^{-1}(D)C_{mm}(D) \end{pmatrix}. \tag{A.3.11}$$

Thus the formal form for the inverses of operator matrices is quite the same as that for numerical ones.

Remark 1. In applications, one often requires an explicit representation for only some of the unknowns X_j. Cramer's rule (A.3.8) is well adapted to such problems. Note, furthermore, that this rule has been derived here not just for differential equations but also for a large class of integro-differential equations, since we do not demand that the $c_{ij}(D)$ be polynomials but merely rational expressions in D.

Remark 2. If $\Delta(D) = 0$, or if the number of equations differs from the number of unknowns, the discussion above must be modified. The parallelism of the resulting theory with the ordinary algebraic theory of linear equations is very close. As in the classical theory, these matters can be approached by the Gauss triangularization procedure, which leads to natural extensions to operators for such concepts as the rank of a matrix and linear independence of operators, but is computationally less attractive than its numerical version. We shall not go into these questions here, especially since in classical physical applications, such as those of electric circuit theory, the occurrence of these particular cases is relatively infrequent.

4. The Chió Method for Computing Determinants

The use of Cramer's rule requires the computation of determinants; for this, we have an algorithm due to Chió, which we describe here because of its computational utility [53].

Consider the determinant

$$\Delta = \begin{vmatrix} c_{11} & c_{12} & c_{13} & c_{14} \\ c_{21} & c_{22} & c_{23} & c_{24} \\ c_{31} & c_{32} & c_{33} & c_{34} \\ c_{41} & c_{42} & c_{43} & c_{44} \end{vmatrix} \tag{A.4.1}$$

and suppose some element, say c_{23}, is 1 (otherwise factor out a nonzero term from some column or row to get an element equal to 1); this element is called the *pivotal element*. By property (iii)

$$\Delta = c_{21}^{-1}(D)\, c_{22}^{-1}(D)\, c_{24}^{-1}(D) \begin{vmatrix} c_{11}c_{21}^{-1} & c_{12}c_{22}^{-1} & c_{13} & c_{14}c_{24}^{-1} \\ 1 & 1 & 1 & 1 \\ c_{31}c_{21}^{-1} & c_{32}c_{22}^{-1} & c_{33} & c_{34}c_{24}^{-1} \\ c_{41}c_{21}^{-1} & c_{42}c_{22}^{-1} & c_{43} & c_{44}c_{24}^{-1} \end{vmatrix} \tag{A.4.2}$$

[if some element c_{2j} of the second row of Δ is zero, we leave the jth column in its original form and there is no factor c_{2j}^{-1} in (A.4.2)].

Subtract corresponding terms in the third column from those of every other column whose second-row element does not vanish, so that by property (iv) we have

$$\Delta = c_{21}^{-1}c_{22}^{-1}c_{24}^{-1} \begin{vmatrix} c_{11}c_{21}^{-1} - c_{13} & c_{12}c_{22}^{-1} - c_{13} & c_{13} & c_{14}c_{24}^{-1} - c_{13} \\ 0 & 0 & 1 & 0 \\ c_{31}c_{21}^{-1} - c_{33} & c_{32}c_{22}^{-1} - c_{33} & c_{33} & c_{34}c_{24}^{-1} - c_{33} \\ c_{41}c_{21}^{-1} - c_{43} & c_{42}c_{22}^{-1} - c_{43} & c_{43} & c_{44}c_{24}^{-1} - c_{43} \end{vmatrix},$$

and, on expanding in terms of elements of the second row,

$$\Delta = (-1)^{2+3} c_{21}^{-1} c_{22}^{-1} c_{24}^{-1} \begin{vmatrix} c_{11}c_{21}^{-1} - c_{13} & c_{12}c_{22}^{-1} - c_{13} & c_{14}c_{24}^{-1} - c_{13} \\ c_{31}c_{21}^{-1} - c_{33} & c_{32}c_{22}^{-1} - c_{33} & c_{34}c_{24}^{-1} - c_{33} \\ c_{41}c_{21}^{-1} - c_{43} & c_{42}c_{22}^{-1} - c_{43} & c_{44}c_{24}^{-1} - c_{43} \end{vmatrix},$$

$$\text{(A.4.3)} \qquad \Delta = (-1)^{2+3} \begin{vmatrix} c_{11} - c_{13}c_{21} & c_{12} - c_{13}c_{22} & c_{14} - c_{13}c_{24} \\ c_{31} - c_{33}c_{21} & c_{32} - c_{33}c_{22} & c_{34} - c_{33}c_{24} \\ c_{41} - c_{43}c_{21} & c_{42} - c_{43}c_{22} & c_{44} - c_{43}c_{24} \end{vmatrix}.$$

Thus the computation of Δ has been reduced to that of a determinant of order 3. The steps of the Chió algorithm simply consist in obtaining the form (A.4.3) directly from (A.4.1). For this, draw a vertical line V and a horizontal line H through the pivotal element $c_{23} = 1$ in (A.4.1) (Figure 11).

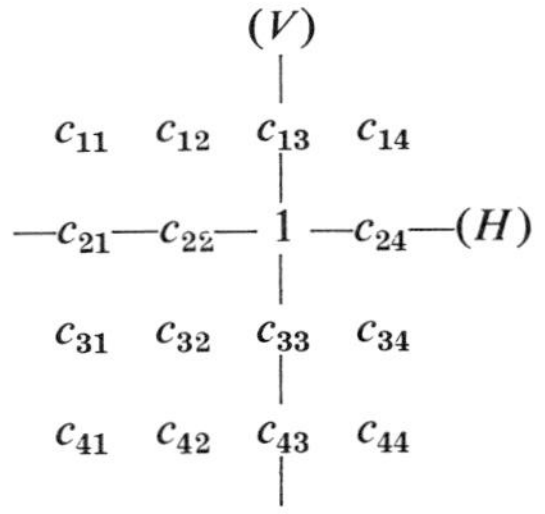

FIGURE 11

The reduced determinant has its elements located in the positions outside these two lines. Each one is obtained by subtracting from the corresponding element in Δ the product of the two elements in Δ that lie at the feet of the perpendiculars dropped from this element onto H and V. For example c_{32} is replaced by $c_{32} - c_{22}c_{33}$, the feet of the perpendiculars from c_{32} being c_{22} and c_{33}. Finally, the determinant resulting from this rearrangement is multiplied by $(-1)^{r+s}$, where r and s are the row and column index of the pivotal element ($r = 2$, $s = 3$ in the present example).

When this procedure is applied to a determinant of order n, it reduces it to one of order $n - 1$, to which the procedure is in turn applied . . . and so on until we have a determinant of order two whose explicit expansion we immediately obtain. The computations are lightened if, in each intermediate determinant, elements in the row of the pivotal element are reduced to zero by appropriate linear combinations of columns when possible.

The simplicity of this algorithm makes it easy to apply. It has other features that recommend it, in that it provides computational checks at successive steps. For a discussion of these, the reader is referred to [53].

5. I.V. Problem for Normal Systems

Let us return now to the I.V. problem (A.2.1, 3) where N is the highest order derivative appearing in the equations. The systems (A.2.1) and (A.2.7) are said to be *normal* if the operator determinant $\Delta(D)$ of the coefficients,

$$\Delta(D) = \begin{vmatrix} c_{11}(D) & \cdots & c_{1m}(D) \\ c_{m1}(D) & \cdots & c_{mm}(D) \end{vmatrix}, \tag{A.5.1}$$

is a polynomial of degree $M \cdot N$ in D. It is easily shown with the aid of property (v) that for this to be so, it is necessary and sufficient that the numerical determinant

$$\begin{vmatrix} a^0_{11} & a^0_{12} & \cdots & a^0_{1m} \\ a^0_{m1} & a^0_{m2} & \cdots & a^0_{mm} \end{vmatrix} \tag{A.5.2}$$

[whose elements are, in view of (A.2.2), the coefficients of D^N in (A.2.7)] be different from zero. In these circumstances, the cofactor $C_{ij}(D)$ of every $c_{ij}(D)$ in $\Delta(D)$ is a polynomial in D of degree not exceeding $(m - 1)N$. By Cramer's rule, the system of evolution (A.2.7) has a unique $\mathscr{D}'_+$ solution given by

$$X_j = \sum_{i=1}^{m} \Delta^{-1}(D)\, C_{ij}(D)(F_i + B_i) \qquad (j = 1, 2, \ldots, m), \tag{A.5.3}$$

and, since each of the operators $\Delta^{-1}(D)\, C_{ij}(D)$ is of degree $-N$ or lower in D, each term $\Delta^{-1}C_{ij}F_i$ is a g.f. which, because $F_i \in \mathscr{K}_+$, involves N integrations so that it is a function that is continuous for all real t, vanishes for $t < t_0$ and has ordinary derivatives of order up to $N - 1$ with the same properties, while its ordinary derivative of order N exists and is continuous at all points of continuity of $F_i(t)$. As to the terms

$$\Delta^{-1}C_{ij}\, \delta^{(k)}(t - t_0) \qquad (k = 1, 2, \ldots, N - 1),$$

of which $\Delta^{-1}C_{ij}B_i$ is a linear combination, they are g.f.'s defined by $\mathscr{K}_+(R)$ functions which are continuous and infinitely differentiable for all $t \neq t_0$.

The analogy with the I.V. problem for a single differential equation is complete: each $X_j = X_{jF} + X_{jB}$ and the

$$X_{jF}(t) = \sum_{i=1}^{m} \Delta^{-1}C_{ij}F_i(t) \tag{A.5.4}$$

define the solution to (A.2.1) with vanishing initial values, while the

$$X_{jB}(t) = \sum_{i=1}^{m} \Delta^{-1}C_{ij}B_i \tag{A.5.5}$$

define the solution of the homogeneous system associated with (A.2.1) [i.e., with $f_j(t) = 0$; $j = 1, 2, \ldots, m$] but taking on the given arbitrary initial values (A.2.3). That this last statement is correct can be proved by a matrix version of the argument used for Lemma III.B.1.1. We shall not go through with this here because it can be verified whenever one is solving a specific problem of type (A.2.1, 3). It then becomes part of the routine check that should always follow the solution of such problems.

The system (A.1.1) is an example of a normal system. This is shown by (A.1.7′), which gives the degree of $\Delta(D)$ as 6, or by observing that the determinant of the coefficients of the terms D^2X, D^2Y, D^2Z in the system of evolution (A.1.6),

$$\begin{vmatrix} 1 & 0 & 0 \\ 0 & 1 & 0 \\ 0 & 0 & 1 \end{vmatrix} = 1,$$

which differs from zero.

*6. Computational Considerations

With the procedures so far described in this chapter it is possible to solve the ordinary I.V. problem for n simultaneous differential equations in n unknowns, when it has a solution. However, some advantage is to be found in applying the results of § III.C.5, and we shall do so in the examples treated in this and the next section. The reader who omitted part C of Chapter III should also omit §§ IV.A.6, IV.A.7, IV.A.8; he will still be able to do most of the proposed exercises without them.

The identity (C.5.15) of Chapter III is a valuable tool for practical computations. Thus, in the explicit evaluation of X_j for some given j, by means of the expressions (A.5.4) and (A.5.5) above, it is usually helpful to first determine (conveniently with the aid of partial fraction expansions of the rational operators in D)

(A.6.1) $$G_{ij}(t) = \Delta^{-1}(D)\, C_{ij}(D)\, \delta(t).$$

The identity (III.C.5.15) is applicable, yielding for any $F_i(t) \in \mathscr{D}'_+$ of finite K-order†,

(A.6.2) $$\Delta^{-1}(D)\, C_{ij}(D)\, F_i(t) = G_{ij}(t) * F_i(t)$$

i.e., in view of (A.5.4),

(A.6.3) $$X_{jF}(t) = \sum_{i=1}^{m} G_{ij}(t) * F_i(t).$$

---

† Actually this holds for any $F \in \mathscr{D}'_+$. Here we state it only for finite K-order g.f.'s, as the truth of (III.C.5.15) without this restriction is established only later (§ V.B.4).

As to $X_{jB}(t)$ given in (A.5.5), since the boundary terms B_i result from the application of derivative polynomials to $\delta(t - t_0)$, it is obtained by applying these derivative polynomials to the $G_{ij}(t)$ $(i = 1, 2, \ldots, m)$.

In illustration of these indications, we may consider the following

Example. Given $f(t)$ defined and continuous for $t > 0$ [except possibly at isolated points t_i where $f(t_i + 0), f(t_i - 0)$ exist† and differ find the explicit formula for $x_3(t)$ when $x_1(t)$, $x_2(t)$, $x_3(t)$ satisfy at every point of continuity of $f(t)$ the system

$$\begin{aligned} \frac{d^2x_1}{dt^2} - \frac{dx_2}{dt} \qquad\quad &= f(t), \\ -\frac{dx_1}{dt} + \frac{d^2x_2}{dt^2} \qquad\quad &= 0, \\ x_2 + \frac{d^2x_3}{dt^2} &= 0, \end{aligned} \tag{A.6.4}$$

and assume the initial values

$$\text{(a)}\ \begin{matrix} x_1(+0) = 0, \\ x_1'(+0) = 0, \end{matrix} \qquad \text{(b)}\ \begin{matrix} x_2(+0) = 0, \\ x_2'(+0) = -1, \end{matrix} \qquad \text{(c)}\ \begin{matrix} x_3(+0) = 2, \\ x_3'(+0) = 3. \end{matrix} \tag{A.6.5}$$

Solution. (a) *Step* 1. *Find the system of evolution.* In the usual notation, using (A.6.5),

$$\begin{aligned} DX_1 &= [DX_1], & D^2X_1 &= [D^2X_1], \\ DX_2 &= [DX_2], & D^2X_2 &= [D^2X_2] - \delta(t), \\ DX_3 &= [DX_3] + 2\,\delta(t), & D^2X_3 &= [D^2X_3] + 2\,\delta'(t) + 3\,\delta(t). \end{aligned}$$

Therefore, the system of evolution is

$$\begin{aligned} D^2X_1 - DX_2 \qquad\quad &= F, \\ -DX_1 + D^2X_2 \qquad\quad &= -\delta(t), \\ X_2 + D^2X_3 &= 3\,\delta(t) + 2\,\delta'(t). \end{aligned} \tag{A.6.6}$$

(b) *Step* 2. *Solution of system of evolution for* X_3. The determinant of the coefficients of D^2 in (A.6.6) is

$$\begin{vmatrix} 1 & 0 & 0 \\ 0 & 1 & 0 \\ 0 & 0 & 1 \end{vmatrix} = 1.$$

This means that $\Delta^{-1}(D)$ is of degree $3 \cdot 2 = 6$, i.e., the system is normal.

† At $t_0 = 0$ only $f(+0)$ is required to exist.

Adopting the notation of §§ 3, 5 above, write

$$\Delta(D) = \begin{vmatrix} D^2 & -D & 0 \\ -D & D^2 & 0 \\ 0 & 1 & D^2 \end{vmatrix} = D^4(D-1)(D+1). \tag{A.6.7}$$

To find X_3, we require the cofactors

$$C_{13} = (-1)^{1+3}\begin{vmatrix} -D & +D^2 \\ 0 & 1 \end{vmatrix} = -D,$$

$$C_{23} = (-1)^{2+3}\begin{vmatrix} +D^2 & -D \\ 0 & 1 \end{vmatrix} = -D^2,$$

$$C_{33} = (-1)^{3+3}\begin{vmatrix} +D^2 & -D \\ -D & D^2 \end{vmatrix} = D^2(D^2-1),$$

whence

$$G_{13}(t) = \Delta^{-1}C_{13}\,\delta(t) = -D^{-3}(D-1)^{-1}(D+1)^{-1}\,\delta(t),$$
$$G_{23}(t) = \Delta^{-1}C_{23}\,\delta(t) = -D^{-2}(D-1)^{-1}(D+1)^{-1}\,\delta(t),$$
$$G_{33}(t) = \Delta^{-1}C_{33}\,\delta(t) = +D^{-2}\,\delta(t).$$

Expanding in partial fractions, we find

$$G_{13}(t) = \left[\frac{1}{D^3} + \frac{1}{D} - \frac{1}{2(D-1)} - \frac{1}{2(D+1)}\right]\delta(t) = \left[\frac{t^2}{2!} + 1 - \cosh t\right] H(t),$$

$$G_{23}(t) = DG_{13}(t) = (t - \sinh t)\, H(t), \tag{A.6.8}$$

$$G_{33}(t) = t\, H(t).$$

(c) *Step* 3. *Discussion of the solution. Relevance to original problem.* The $\mathscr{K}_+(R)$ functions $G_{ij}(t)$, thanks to (III.C.5.15), Cramer's rule, and property (v) of determinants give, on expanding Δ_3 in terms of its third column in the equality

$$X_3(t) = \Delta^{-1}(D)\begin{vmatrix} D^2 & -D & F(t) \\ -D & D^2 & -\delta(t) \\ 0 & 1 & 3\,\delta(t) + 2\,\delta'(t) \end{vmatrix} = \Delta^{-1}\Delta_3,$$

the explicit result:

$$X_3(t) = \int_{-\infty}^{\infty} G_{13}(t-\tau)\, F(\tau)\, d\tau - (t - \sinh t)\, H(t) + (3 + 2D)(t\, H(t))$$

$$= \int_0^t \left[\frac{(t-\tau)^2}{2!} + 1 - \cosh(t-\tau)\right] F(\tau)\, d\tau + 2(t+1)\, H(t) + H(t) \sinh t.$$

This is a $\mathscr{K}_+(R)$ function for which it is easily verified that $X_3(+0) = 2$ and $DX_3(+0) = 3$ so that its restriction to $t > 0$, the function $x_3(t)$, satisfies (A.6.5c) and is a $C^1(0, +\infty)$ function with ordinary second derivative continuous at the points of continuity of $F(t)$.

The g.f.'s $X_1(t)$, $X_2(t)$ are found by similar procedures. In the present instance, we do not require the explicit form of the two g.f.'s. We do, however, need to ascertain that an ordinary function solution $x_1(t)$, $x_2(t)$, $x_3(t)$ exists. The statement has been made earlier (though without proof) that the normality of a system ensures this. If we do not wish to rely on this unproved general statement, we may still verify it in the present case by carrying out only partially the explicit computation of X_2 and X_3. Let us do so:

$$X_1 = \Delta^{-1}\begin{vmatrix} F & -D & 0 \\ -\delta & D^2 & 0 \\ 3\delta + 2\delta' & 1 & D^2 \end{vmatrix} = \Delta^{-1}D^4F - \Delta^{-1}D^3\delta,$$

$$X_2 = \Delta^{-1}\begin{vmatrix} D^2 & F & 0 \\ -D & -\delta & 0 \\ 0 & 3\delta + 2\delta' & D^2 \end{vmatrix} = +\Delta^{-1}D^3F - \Delta^{-1}D^4\delta.$$

Since Δ is of degree 6 in D, the shift formula shows that $\Delta^{-1}D^4F$ involves two integrations and $\Delta^{-1}D^3F$ involves three integrations over the interval $(0, t)$. They result then in $C^1(R)$ functions with ordinary second derivatives in $\mathscr{K}_+(R)$ and which, with their first derivatives, vanish as $t \to +0$.

Except at $t = 0$, both $\Delta^{-1}D^3\delta$ and $\Delta^{-1}D^4\delta$ have ordinary derivatives of every order. The shift formula with $D\,H(t) = \delta(t)$ substituted in these expressions easily shows that the corresponding functions of t satisfy (A.6.5a) and (A.6.5b). We see, therefore, without further rational fraction expansions and involved calculations, that $x_1(t)$, $x_2(t)$, $x_3(t)$ with the requisite properties exist. The problem, as stated, is thereby solved.

Remark. It will now be apparent to the reader that the solution of I.V. problems for simultaneous equations, though entirely straightforward—and elementary, in fact—is not always instantaneous. Fortunately, in many applications of physical relevance, as in the above example, only some of the components of the solution vector need be determined explicitly. This, incidentally, is partly why in this text so little attention is given to the matrix formulation and solution of simultaneous D.E. problems. In any case, the reader who is conversant with elementary matrix algebra will find it easy enough to recast the account of part A of this chapter in the language of matrices.

*7. I.V. Problem for a Nonnormal System

The electric circuit depicted in Figure 12 and consisting of a transformer with mutual induction coefficient M, whose primary and secondary circuits contain the indicated elements, is described by the system of differential equations

$$\text{(A.7.1)} \qquad \begin{aligned} L_1\frac{d^2q_1}{dt^2} + \frac{1}{C_1}q_1 + M\frac{d^2q_2}{dt^2} \qquad\qquad &= e_1(t), \\ M\frac{d^2q_1}{dt^2} \qquad\qquad + L_2\frac{d^2q_2}{dt^2} + \frac{1}{C_2}q_2 &= 0, \end{aligned}$$

where $q_1(t)$, $q_2(t)$ are the charges on the capacitors C_1 and C_2, respectively, and L_1, L_2 are the self-inductances of the transformer windings. $e_1(t)$ is the electromotive force applied to the primary circuit.

If the system is in operation after some instant, which it is convenient to take as $t = 0$, and $e_1(t)$ is continuous for $t > 0$, except at isolated points, these ordinary differential equations are satisfied at all $t > 0$ where the driving term $e_1(t)$ is continuous. Its behavior at any such instant t should then be predictable if we know the initial values

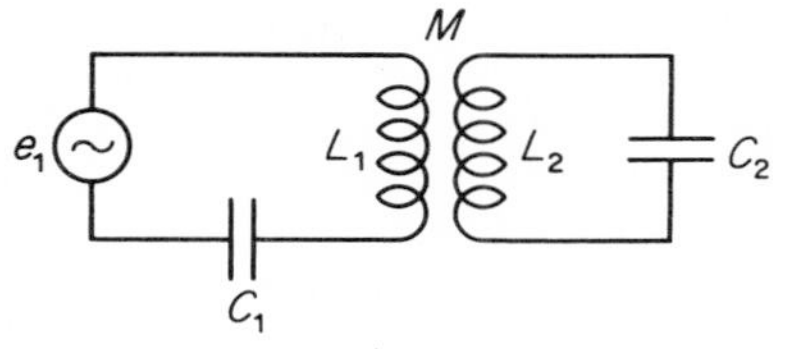

FIGURE 12

$$\text{(A.7.2)} \qquad \begin{aligned} q_1(+0) &= q_1^0, & q_1'(+0) &= q_1^1, \\ q_2(+0) &= q_2^0, & q_2'(+0) &= q_2^1. \end{aligned}$$

The usual procedure will again be followed: on the assumption that continuous $q_1(t)$, $q_2(t)$ exist and have continuous first and piecewise continuous second (ordinary) derivatives, a pair of equations of evolution is first obtained for the $\mathscr{D}'_+$ g.f.'s $E_1(t)$, $Q_1(t)$, $Q_2(t)$ defined by the continuations by zero of $e_1(t)$, $q_1(t)$, $q_2(t)$. Next, these equations are solved operationally. As a third, and final, step of this procedure these solutions are examined to see if they correspond to functions with the properties assumed for $q_1(t)$ and $q_2(t)$.

The system of evolution here is

$$\text{(A.7.3)} \qquad \begin{aligned} \left(L_1 D^2 + \frac{1}{C_1}\right) Q_1 + M D^2 Q_2 &= E_2 + (L_1 q_1^0 + M q_2^0)\,\delta'(t) \\ &\quad + (L_1 q_1^1 + M q_2^1)\,\delta(t), \\ M D^2 Q_1 + \left(L_2 D^2 + \frac{1}{C_2}\right) Q_2 &= (M q_1^0 + L_2 q_2^0)\,\delta'(t) \\ &\quad + (M q_1^1 + L_2 q_2^1)\,\delta(t), \end{aligned}$$

and has for the operator determinant of its coefficients

$$\text{(A.7.4)} \qquad \Delta(D) = \begin{vmatrix} \left(L_1 D^2 + \dfrac{1}{C_1}\right) & M D^2 \\ M D^2 & \left(L_2 D^2 + \dfrac{1}{C_2}\right) \end{vmatrix}.$$

If $L_1 L_2 \neq M^2$, this is a polynomial of degree 4 in D and the system is normal, the problem (A.7.1, 2) has a unique solution whose components $q_1(t)$ and $q_2(t)$ have continuous second derivatives for $t > 0$.

If $L_1 L_2 = M^2$, however (the primary and secondary circuits of the transformer are then said to be perfectly coupled), the system is not normal, for

$$\text{(A.7.5)} \qquad \Delta(D) = \left(\frac{L_1}{C_2} + \frac{L_2}{C_1}\right) D^2 + \frac{1}{C_1 C_2}$$

is only of degree 2 in D.

This is the case we wish to consider (compare Doetsch [14, vol. II, p. 318]). To do so with general parameters L_1, L_2, M, C_1, C_2 leads to formulae for the solution whose ungainliness in no way adds to the establishment of the points of principle that interest us. Let us therefore lighten the computational chore by taking the following numerical values

$$L_1 = 1, \qquad L_2 = \tfrac{1}{4}, \qquad M = \sqrt{L_1 L_2} = \tfrac{1}{2},$$
$$C_1 = \tfrac{1}{2}, \qquad C_2 = 2,$$

so that the system of evolution becomes

$$\text{(A.7.6)} \quad \begin{aligned} (D^2+2)Q_1 + \tfrac{1}{2}D^2Q_2 &= E_2 + (q_1^0 + \tfrac{1}{2}q_2^0)\,\delta'(t) + (q_1^1 + \tfrac{1}{2}q_2^1)\,\delta(t), \\ \tfrac{1}{2}D^2Q_1 + (\tfrac{1}{4}D^2 + \tfrac{1}{2})Q_2 &= (\tfrac{1}{2}q_1^0 + \tfrac{1}{4}q_2^0)\,\delta'(t) + (\tfrac{1}{2}q_1^1 + \tfrac{1}{4}q_2^1)\,\delta(t), \end{aligned}$$

with the determinant of coefficients

$$\text{(A.7.7)} \qquad \Delta(D) = D^2 + 1.$$

In solving (A.7.6), let us follow the practice, instituted in Chapter III for single equations and pursued in § 5 above, of separately evaluating, by means of Cramer's rule, the contributions of the driving term $\begin{pmatrix} E_2 \\ 0 \end{pmatrix}$ and of the boundary term.

The driving-term contribution is

$$\text{(A.7.8)} \quad Q_{1F} = \Delta^{-1}(D)\begin{vmatrix} E_2 & \tfrac{1}{2}D^2 \\ 0 & (\tfrac{1}{4}D^2 + \tfrac{1}{2}) \end{vmatrix}, \qquad Q_{2F} = \Delta^{-1}(D)\begin{vmatrix} D^2+2 & E_2 \\ \tfrac{1}{2}D^2 & 0 \end{vmatrix},$$

while the boundary terms on the right in (A.7.6) give

$$\text{(A.7.9)} \quad \begin{aligned} Q_{1B} &= \Delta^{-1}(D)\begin{vmatrix} [(q_1^0 + \tfrac{1}{2}q_2^0)D + (q_1^1 + \tfrac{1}{2}q_2^1)]\,\delta(t) & \tfrac{1}{2}D^2 \\ \tfrac{1}{2}[(q_1^0 + \tfrac{1}{2}q_2^0)D + (q_1^1 + \tfrac{1}{2}q_2^1)]\,\delta(t) & (\tfrac{1}{4}D^2 + \tfrac{1}{2}) \end{vmatrix}, \\ Q_{2B} &= \Delta^{-1}(D)\begin{vmatrix} D^2+2 & [(q_1^0 + \tfrac{1}{2}q_2^0)D + (q_1^1 + \tfrac{1}{2}q_2^1)]\,\delta(t) \\ \tfrac{1}{2}D^2 & \tfrac{1}{2}[(q_1^0 + \tfrac{1}{2}q_2^0)D + (q_1^1 + \tfrac{1}{2}q_2^1)]\,\delta(t) \end{vmatrix}, \end{aligned}$$

and the solution of (A.7.6) is

$$\text{(A.7.10)} \qquad Q_1 = Q_{1F} + Q_{1B}, \qquad Q_2 = Q_{2F} + Q_{2B}.$$

The explicit form of each term involved in the expansion of (A.7.9) we shall obtain by means of functions $G_{ij}(t)$ like those defined in § 6:

$$\text{(A.7.11)} \quad \begin{aligned} G_{11}(t) &= \Delta^{-1}(D)\tfrac{1}{2}(\tfrac{1}{2}D^2 + 1)\,\delta(t) = \tfrac{1}{2}(D^2+1)^{-1}(\tfrac{1}{2}D^2 + 1)\,\delta(t), \\ G_{21}(t) &= -(D^2+1)^{-1}\tfrac{1}{2}D^2\,\delta(t), \\ G_{12}(t) &= -(D^2+1)^{-1}\tfrac{1}{2}D^2\,\delta(t), \\ G_{22}(t) &= (D^2+1)^{-1}(D^2+2)\,\delta(t). \end{aligned}$$

These can be computed by first decomposing each of the operators on the right into partial fractions or, alternatively, from (cf. § III.A.4 or Table I, Appendix)

$$(D^2 + 1)^{-1}\,\delta(t) = H(t)\sin t, \tag{A.7.12}$$

by applying the derivative polynomials appearing in the numerators of (A.7.11). Since, by the Leibniz rule for generalized derivatives,

$$\begin{aligned} D^2\, H(t)\sin t &= D(\sin t\,\delta(t) + H(t)\cos t) = D[H(t)\cos t] \\ &= \delta(t) - H(t)\sin t, \end{aligned}$$

we find

$$\begin{aligned} G_{11}(t) &= \tfrac{1}{4}(\delta(t) + H(t)\sin t), \\ G_{21}(t) &= -\tfrac{1}{2}(\delta(t) - H(t)\sin t), \\ G_{12}(t) &= -\tfrac{1}{2}(\delta(t) - H(t)\sin t), \\ G_{22}(t) &= \delta(t) + H(t)\sin t. \end{aligned} \tag{A.7.11'}$$

Then, expanding in (A.7.9), there results

$$\begin{aligned} Q_{1B}(t) &= [(q_1^0 + \tfrac{1}{2}q_2^0)D + (q_1^1 + \tfrac{1}{2}q_2^1)]G_{11}(t) \\ &\quad + \tfrac{1}{2}[(q_1^0 + \tfrac{1}{2}q_2^0)D + (q_1^1 + \tfrac{1}{2}q_2^1)]G_{21}(t) \\ &= \tfrac{1}{2}(q_1^0 + \tfrac{1}{2}q_2^0)\,H(t)\cos t + \tfrac{1}{2}(q_1^1 + \tfrac{1}{2}q_2^1)\,H(t)\sin t, \\ Q_{2B}(t) &= [(q_1^0 + \tfrac{1}{2}q_2^0)D + (q_1^1 + \tfrac{1}{2}q_2^1)]\,G_{12}(t) \\ &\quad + \tfrac{1}{2}[(q_1^0 + \tfrac{1}{2}q_2^0)D + (q_1^1 + \tfrac{1}{2}q_2^1)]\,G_{22}(t) \\ &= (q_1^0 + \tfrac{1}{2}q_2^0)\,H(t)\cos t + (q_1^1 + \tfrac{1}{2}q_2^1)\,H(t)\sin t. \end{aligned} \tag{A.7.13}$$

Note that this gives

$$\begin{aligned} Q_{1B}(+0) &= \tfrac{1}{2}(q_1^0 + \tfrac{1}{2}q_2^0), \qquad Q_{2B}(+0) = q_1^0 + \tfrac{1}{2}q_2^0, \\ Q'_{1B}(+0) &= \tfrac{1}{2}(q_1^1 + \tfrac{1}{2}q_2^1), \qquad Q^1_{2B}(+0) = q_1^1 + \tfrac{1}{2}q_2^1. \end{aligned} \tag{A.7.14}$$

From (A.7.12) and (III.C.5.15) we find

$$(D^2 + 1)^{-1}\,E_1(t) = \int_0^t \sin(t - \tau)\,E_1(\tau)\,d\tau, \tag{A.7.15}$$

and, substituting in (A.7.8),

$$Q_{1F}(t) = (\tfrac{1}{4}D^2 + \tfrac{1}{2})\int_0^t \sin(t - \tau)\,E_1(\tau)\,d\tau,$$

$$Q_{2F}(t) = -\tfrac{1}{2}D^2\int_0^t \sin(t - \tau)\,E_1(\tau)\,d\tau.$$

This, in view of the relation (cf. Exercise III.38)

$$D\int_0^t \alpha(t - \tau)\,E_1(\tau)\,d\tau = \alpha(0)\,E_1(t) + \int_0^t \alpha'(t - \tau)\,E_1(\tau)\,d\tau,$$

valid for $\alpha(\tau) \in C^1(R)$ at every point, t, where E_1 is continuous, gives

$$(A.7.16)\qquad \begin{aligned} Q_{1F}(t) &= \tfrac{1}{4}\Big[E_1(t) + \int_0^t \sin(t-\tau)\,E_1(\tau)\,d\tau\Big],\\ Q_{2F}(t) &= -\tfrac{1}{2}\Big[E_1(t) - \int_0^t \sin(t-\tau)\,E_1(\tau)\,d\tau\Big], \end{aligned}$$

and

$$(A.7.17)\qquad \begin{aligned} Q_{1F}(+0) &= \tfrac{1}{4}E_1(+0), \qquad & Q_{2F}(+0) &= -\tfrac{1}{2}E_1(+0),\\ Q'_{1F}(+0) &= \tfrac{1}{4}E'_1(+0), \qquad & Q'_{2F}(+0) &= -\tfrac{1}{2}E'_1(+0). \end{aligned}$$

The substitution of (A.7.13) and (A.7.16) into (A.7.10), which we do not bother to write out, concludes the solution of the system of evolution (A.7.6) and, therefore, of the first two steps of the solution of the ordinary I.V. problem

$$(A.7.18)\qquad \begin{aligned} &\frac{d^2q_1}{dt^2} + 2q_1 + \frac{1}{2}\frac{d^2q_2}{dt^2} = e_1(t),\\ &\frac{1}{2}\frac{d^2q_1}{dt^2} + \frac{1}{4}\frac{d^2q_2}{dt^2} + \frac{1}{2}q_2 = 0, \end{aligned}$$

$$(A.7.19)\qquad \begin{aligned} q_1(+0) &= q_1^0, \qquad & q'_1(+0) &= q_1^1,\\ q_2(+0) &= q_2^0, \qquad & q'_2(+0) &= q_2^1. \end{aligned}$$

It is in the *third and final step* of the solution of this problem that the effects of the nonnormality of the system make themselves felt. Consider $Q_1(t)$ and $Q_2(t)$ on the half-line $(0, +\infty)$. By (A.7.16), they contain the terms $\frac{1}{4}e_1(t)$ and $\frac{1}{2}e_1(t)$ respectively, and therefore possess ordinary second derivatives d^2q_1/dt^2, d^2q_2/dt^2 only at those points where $e_1(t)$ is itself twice differentiable in the ordinary sense; at such points, the system (A.7.18) is always satisfied by $Q_1(t)$, $Q_2(t)$. Thus, *it is necessary to put on $e_1(t)$ a stronger restriction than the one originally made and which amounted to continuity except at isolated points*; instead, one may demand, for instance, that e_1 and de_1/dt be continuous and that d^2e_1/dt^2 be piecewise continuous.

But even if we add to the statement of the original problem this supplementary hypothesis we still do not automatically have a solution since, by (A.7.10) (A.7.14) (A.7.17),

$$(A.7.20)\qquad \begin{aligned} Q_1(+0) &= \tfrac{1}{2}q_1^0 + \tfrac{1}{4}q_2^0 + \tfrac{1}{4}e_1(+0),\\ Q_2(+0) &= q_1^0 + \tfrac{1}{2}q_2^0 - \tfrac{1}{2}e_1(+0),\\ Q'_1(+0) &= \tfrac{1}{2}q_1^1 + \tfrac{1}{4}q_2^1 + \tfrac{1}{4}e'_1(+0),\\ Q'_2(+0) &= q_1^1 + \tfrac{1}{2}q_2^1 - \tfrac{1}{2}e'_1(+0). \end{aligned}$$

Thus, we have as a *further necessary condition* for the original *ordinary* I.V. problem to have a solution that the *given initial values* (A.7.19) *may not be arbitrary* but must be related to $e_1(+0)$ and $e_1'(+0)$ through the equalities (called *compatibility relations*)

$$\text{(A.7.21)}\qquad \begin{aligned} Q_1(+0) &= q_1^0, \qquad & Q_2(+0) &= q_2^0,\\ Q_1'(+0) &= q_1', \qquad & Q_2'(+0) &= q_2', \end{aligned}$$

in which the left-hand sides are given by (A.7.20).

8. Mathematical and Physical Aspects of Nonnormal Systems

Should $e_1(t)$ have a piecewise continuous ordinary second derivative then, regardless of the initial values (A.7.19) chosen, we have just seen that the functions $Q_1(t)$, $Q_2(t)$ obtained are, for $t > 0$, solutions, in the ordinary sense, of the differential equations (A.7.18). As t approaches zero from the right, however, these functions and their derivatives tend to the initial values (A.7.20) which do not coincide, except in particular cases, with the initial values originally given.

Thus, when the compatibility relations (A.7.21) are *not* satisfied, what happens is this: the problem (A.7.18, 19) does *not* have a solution; nonetheless, applying to it the routine of our operational method yields a pair of functions Q_1, Q_2 that constitutes a solution to an I.V. problem for the *same* pair of differential *equations* but with *different* (and compatible) *initial values.*

There is nothing paradoxical about this outcome. Its explanation lies in the fact that many different I.V. problems for the same nonnormal system of ordinary differential equations lead to the same pair of equations of evolution: examination of the coefficients of $\delta(t)$ and $\delta'(t)$ on the right-hand sides of the equations of evolution reveals that two different sets of initial values, say $q_1^0, q_2^0, q_1^1, q_2^1$ on the one hand, and $x_1^0, x_2^0, x_1^1, x_2^1$ on the other, both lead to the very same system of evolution (A.7.6) so long as

$$\text{(A.8.1)}\qquad q_1^0 + \tfrac{1}{2}q_2^0 = x_1^0 + \tfrac{1}{2}x_2^0 \quad\text{and}\quad q_1^1 + \tfrac{1}{2}q_2^1 = x_1^1 + \tfrac{1}{2}x_2^1.$$

In particular, substitution immediately shows that these equalities hold for any choice whatever of the values of $q_1^0, q_2^0, q_1^1, q_2^1$, if we take $x_1^0 = Q_1(+0)$, $x_2^0 = Q_2(+0)$, $x_1^1 = Q_1'(+0)$, $x_2^1 = Q_2'(+0)$, with the values given by (A.7.20).

Physically, such nonnormal systems provide further evidence of the advantage of using generalized rather than ordinary functions to represent physical variables. Indeed, if (as we have until now done for "ordinary" I.V. problems) one lives in a "universe" of $\mathscr{K}_+(R)$ functions and their associated g.f.'s, it suddenly turns out that for some electric circuits the applied voltages have to be more than just $\mathscr{K}_+(R)$: if one wishes to describe the behavior of an ideal electrical transformer circuit with perfect coupling in terms of ordinary functions, it becomes necessary, in this "universe," to restrict consideration to applied voltages $e_1(t)$ having ordinary derivatives de_1/dt, d^2e_1/dt^2 at sufficiently many points (to ensure this, we used piecewise continuity above, but other conditions are possible if mathematically sophisticated concepts from the theory of functions of a real variable are used, which it is difficult, observationally, to verify).

Obviously, this is most repugnant from the physical point of view as it constitutes an artificial restriction. While it is sensible to limit the effective magnitude of $e_1(t)$ to avoid melting any wires [in which case, the differential equations (A.7.18) no longer describe the situation], to say that some transformers can be connected only to generators of sufficiently differentiable voltages, while others may be excited by nondifferentiable ones as well, smacks of a confusion between cause and effect.

Describing the physical system with the g.f. equations (A.7.6) removes such limitations. Providing we accept g.f.'s of class $\mathscr{D}'_+$, Q_1 and Q_2, as depicting electric charges, the same $\mathscr{K}_+(R)$ inputs, *as well as more general* $\mathscr{D}'_+$ *inputs*, can be handled regardless of the particular coupling coefficient of the circuit. This example is merely one illustration of the nonnormal systems of equations that occur in physical applications [7] [14].

B. OTHER APPLICATIONS OF THE OPERATIONAL CALCULUS IN $\mathscr{D}'_+$

Some further applications and extensions of the algebra of operators on $\mathscr{D}'_+$ are described in this second portion of Chapter IV. Each topic is discussed quite briefly and in terms of one or two specific examples which should suffice to make plain how other problems in these categories can be tackled.

1. Boundary-value Problems for Linear D.E.'s with Constant Coefficients

A simple example illustrates the manner in which the operational procedure of Chapter III can be applied to certain boundary-value problems. Questions of existence and uniqueness are left aside here.

Example. Find $x(t)$ such that

(B.1.1) $$\frac{d^2x}{dt^2} = \gamma^2 x \quad (0 < t, \qquad \gamma > 0)$$

given the boundary values

(B.1.2) $$x(+0) = \alpha, \qquad \lim_{t\to+\infty} x(t) = 0.$$

We reduce this to an ordinary initial-value problem with the initial values

(B.1.3) $$x(+0) = \alpha, \qquad x'(+0) = x_1,$$

where x_1 is treated as a variable parameter whose value is adjusted so as to give $\lim_{t\to+\infty} x(t) = 0$.

The equation of evolution of this I.V. problem is

(B.1.4) $$(D^2 - \gamma^2)X = \alpha\, \delta'(t) + x_1\, \delta(t).$$

We know (Chapter III) that its solution is obtained from

$$(D^2 - \gamma^2)^{-1}\, \delta(t) = \frac{1}{2\gamma}\,[(D - \gamma)^{-1} - (D + \gamma)^{-1}]\, \delta(t)$$

$$= \frac{1}{2\gamma}\,(e^{\gamma t} - e^{-\gamma t})H(t)$$

as

$$X(t) = \alpha D\left[\frac{e^{\gamma t} - e^{-\gamma t}}{2\gamma}\, H(t)\right] + x_1\, \frac{e^{\gamma t} - e^{-\gamma t}}{2\gamma}\, H(t)$$

$$= \alpha\, \frac{e^{\gamma t} + e^{-\gamma t}}{2}\, H(t) + x_1\, \frac{e^{\gamma t} - e^{-\gamma t}}{2\gamma}\, H(t),$$

which we write

(B.1.5) $$X(t) = \frac{1}{2}\left(\alpha + \frac{x_1}{\gamma}\right) e^{\gamma t}\, H(t) + \frac{1}{2}\left(\alpha - \frac{x_1}{\gamma}\right) e^{-\gamma t}\, H(t).$$

This is a $\mathscr{K}_+(R)$ function, and the question whether $\lim_{t\to+\infty} X(t)$ exists therefore makes sense. In particular, we can choose $x_1 = -\alpha\gamma$ so that only the second term in (B.1.5) does not vanish identically and, as $\gamma > 0$, $\lim_{t\to+\infty} X(t) = 0$. The solution to the boundary-value problem is the restriction of $X(t)$ to the domain $(0, +\infty)$, i.e.,

(B.1.6) $$x(t) = \alpha e^{-\gamma t} \qquad (t > 0).$$

This boundary-value problem, like many others, arises in the course of the solution of some partial differential equations (§§ VII.11 and VII.13).

*2. Integro-differential Equations of Convolution Type

A number of the physically motivated differential equation problems of Chapters III and IV stem from integro-differential equations, i.e., equations in which both derivatives and integrals of the unknown functions appear. For instance, the equation

$$L\frac{di}{dt} + Ri + \frac{1}{C}\int_0^t i(\tau)\, d\tau = e(t) \qquad (t > 0)$$

of electric circuit theory becomes, on taking $x(t) = \int_0^t i(\tau)\, d\tau$, the differential equation

$$L\frac{d^2x}{dt^2} + R\,\frac{dx}{dt} + \frac{x}{C} = e,$$

which, given appropriate initial conditions, we have solved by the operational method.

There is another type of integro-differential equation which, after some preliminary transformations, can be brought to the form

$$A(D)B^{-1}(D)X = F \qquad (A,\ B \text{ polynomials in } D)$$

so that it can be solved by the direct operational method. This is the convolution equation

$$\text{(B.2.1)} \qquad x(t) = f(t) + \int_0^t k(t-\tau)\left[P\left(\frac{d}{d\tau}\right)x(\tau)\right] d\tau \qquad (t > 0),$$

where $P(d/dt)$ is a polynomial of degree n in the ordinary differentiation operator d/dt, and where $k(t)$ is an exponential polynomial

$$\text{(B.2.2)} \qquad k(t) = \sum_{\substack{l=1\\m=1}}^{L,M} c_{lm}\, t^{l-1}e^{\gamma_m t} \qquad (c_{lm}, \gamma_m \in C),$$

and where $f(t)$ is continuous on $[0, +\infty)$.

No attempt will be made here to go into the theory of such equations. We shall merely seek a computational procedure applicable under appropriate hypotheses.

Specifically, we look for solutions (if they exist) such that $x(t)$, $x'(t)$, . . . , $x^{(n-1)}(t)$ are all continuous on $[0, +\infty)$ while $x^{(n)}(t)$ is piecewise continuous on $[0, +\infty)$.† Assuming such a solution to exist, set

$$\text{(B.2.3)} \qquad \begin{aligned} X(t) &= \begin{cases} 0 & \text{if } t < 0 \\ x(t) & \text{if } t > 0, \end{cases} \\ F(t) &= \begin{cases} 0 & \text{if } t < 0 \\ f(t) & \text{if } t > 0, \end{cases} \\ K(t) &= k(t)\, H(t). \end{aligned}$$

These functions then satisfy the convolution equation

(B.2.4)

$$X(t) = F(t) + \int_0^t k(t-\tau)\left[P\left(\frac{d}{d\tau}\right)X(\tau)\right] d\tau = F(t) + K(t) * P\left(\frac{d}{dt}\right)X(t),$$

for all real $t \neq 0$.

In view of the continuity assumptions on $x, x', \ldots, x^{(n-1)}, x^{(n)}$, we may apply (III.B.1.4), obtaining

$$\text{(B.2.5)} \qquad P(D)X = [P(D)X] + B,$$

† The reason for using the closed half-line here is to ensure the existence of $x(+0)$, $x'(+0)$, . . . , $x^{(n)}(+0)$, thereby making the integral in (B.2.1) a simple type of improper integral.

where $[P(D)X]$ is the g.f. defined by the $\mathscr{K}_+(R)$ function $P(d/dt)X(t)$, and where B is a boundary term equal to a linear combination of $\delta(t)$, $\delta'(t), \ldots,$ $\delta^{(n-1)}(t)$ with coefficients depending on the coefficients of $P(d/dt)$ and on the initial values

$$x(+0) = x_0, \quad x'(+0) = x_1, \quad \ldots, \quad x^{(n-1)}(+0) = x_{n-1}.$$

For any function $U(t) \in \mathscr{K}_+(R)$, we have by (III.A.2.11)

$$\int_0^t (t - \tau)^{l-1} e^{\gamma_m(t-\tau)}\, U(\tau)\, d\tau = (l-1)!\, (D + \gamma_m)^{-l} U,$$

so that, taking $P(d/dt)X(t) = [P(D)X(t)]$ for U, (B.2.4) becomes

$$\begin{aligned} X(t) &= F(t) + \sum_{l,m=1}^{L,M} (l-1)!\, c_{lm}(D + \gamma_m)^{-l}[P(D)X] \\ &= F(t) + \sum_{l,m=1}^{L,M} (l-1)!\, c_{lm}(D + \gamma_m)^{-l} P(D)X \\ &\quad - \sum_{l,m=1}^{L,M} (l-1)!\, c_{lm}(D + \gamma_m)^{-l} B, \end{aligned}$$

where (B.2.5) served to obtain the second equality.

Gathering terms, we rewrite this as

$$\text{(B.2.6)} \qquad \left\{1 - P(D) \sum_{l,m=1}^{L,M} (l-1)!\, c_{lm}(D + \gamma_m)^{-l}\right\} X = F - \sum_{l,m=1}^{L,M} (l-1)!\, c_{lm}(D + \gamma_m)^{-l} B$$

and call it, as is to be expected, the equation of evolution of the original problem.

The algebra of operators on $\mathscr{D}'_+$ is applicable: the rational operator $\{\ \ \}$ can be put in the form $A(D)B^{-1}(D)$ where A and B are derivative polynomials. As this has the unique inverse $A^{-1}(D)B(D)$, we may assert that (B.2.6) has a solution in $\mathscr{D}'_+$ and that for any given set $x_0, x_1, \ldots, x_{n-1}$ it is unique, being given by

$$\text{(B.2.7)} \qquad X = A^{-1}(D)\, B(D)F - A^{-1}(D)\, B(D) \sum_{l,m=1}^{L,M} (l-1)!\, c_{lm}(D + \gamma_m)^{-l} B.$$

If the original problem has a solution, it coincides with $X(t)$ on $(0, +\infty)$, and it is determinate only if $x_0, x_1, \ldots, x_{n-1}$ are known, or if these initial values can be determined from (B.2.1). The converse is not true: X may be a solution of the equation of evolution without determining a solution of (B.2.1), in which case the latter does not have a solution satisfying the stated continuity and differentiability conditions. Thus, once (B.2.7) has been computed, it is necessary to examine its ordinary continuity and differentiability properties and, if they suffice, to check, by substitution in (B.2.1), whether $x(t)$, the restriction of $X(t)$ to the domain $[0, +\infty)$, is a solution to the original problem.

Two examples illustrate the applicability of this routine.

Example 1.

(B.2.8) $$x(t) = \sin t + 2\int_0^t \cos(t - \tau)x(\tau)\,d\tau \qquad (t > 0).$$

There is no need here to determine a priori initial conditions $x_0, x_1, \ldots$ as the derivatives of x do not appear in the equation. Let X be the continuation by zero of $x(t)$ defined in (B.2.3). Referring to the table of the Appendix, or computing directly from $\cos t = \frac{1}{2}(e^{it} + e^{it})$ and the identities

$$\int_0^t e^{i(t-\tau)}X(\tau)\,d\tau = (D - i)^{-1}X,$$

$$\int_0^t e^{-i(t-\tau)}X(\tau)\,d\tau = (D + i)^{-1}X,$$

we find

$$\int_0^t \cos(t - \tau)X(\tau)\,d\tau = \frac{1}{2}[(D - i)^{-1} + (D + i)^{-1}]X = \frac{D}{D^2 + 1}X.$$

The g.f. equation corresponding to (B.2.8) thus is

$$X = H(t)\sin t + \frac{2D}{D^2 + 1}X,$$

from which results the equation of evolution $\left(\left(1 - \frac{2D}{D^2 + 1}\right) = \frac{D^2 - 2D + 1}{D^2 + 1}\right.$ as operators on $\left.\mathscr{D}_+\right)$:

$$\frac{D^2 - 2D + 1}{D^2 + 1}X = H(t)\sin t.$$

The solution to this is obtained from the straightforward computation

$$\begin{aligned} X &= (D - 1)^{-2}\{(D^2 + 1)\,H(t)\sin t\} \\ &= (D - 1)^{-2}\,\delta(t) \\ &= e^tD^{-2}[e^{-t}\,\delta(t)] = e^tD^{-2}\,\delta(t). \end{aligned}$$

Thus, finally,

(B.2.9) $$X(t) = te^t\,H(t).$$

This is continuous on $(0, +\infty)$. Substitution in (B.2.8) shows that $x(t) = te^t$ is a solution to the original problem. It is the only solution, since X is the only solution of the corresponding equation of evolution.

Example 2.

(B.2.10) $$x(t) = \cos t + 2\int_0^t \sin(t - \tau)x'(\tau)\,d\tau \qquad (t > 0).$$

We seek a solution with x continuous on $[0, +\infty)$ and with x' piecewise continuous on this same closed half-line.

In the discussion preceding Example 1, we saw that the equation of evolution of a problem like (B.2.10) includes a term depending on the initial value $x(+0)$. As this is not given to us directly, let us try to find it from (B.2.10): as $t \to +0$ the integral on the right tends to zero and $\cos t$ tends to 1. Thus, if there exists a solution with the assumed continuity and differentiability properties, it must take the initial value

$$x(+0) = 1. \tag{B.2.11}$$

Then X, the continuation by zero defined in (B.2.3), satisfies

$$DX = [DX] + \delta(t). \tag{B.2.12}$$

By direct computation, or from the table of the Appendix,† for $U \in \mathscr{K}_+(R)$

$$\int_0^t \sin(t - \tau)\, U(\tau)\, d\tau = (D^2 + 1)^{-1}\, U(t),$$

so that solving (B.2.12) for $[DX]$ (the g.f. defined by the ordinary derivative dX/dt) and substituting this for U gives

$$\int_0^t H(t - \tau) \sin(t - \tau) X'(\tau)\, d\tau = (D^2 + 1)^{-1}(DX - \delta(t)).$$

The equation of evolution consequently is obtained by gathering terms in

$$X = H(t)\cos t + \frac{2}{D^2 + 1}(DX - \delta),$$

and is

$$\left(1 - \frac{2D}{D^2 + 1}\right) X = H(t)\cos t - \frac{2}{D^2 + 1}\,\delta,$$

$$\frac{(D - 1)^2}{D^2 + 1}\, X = H(t)\cos t - \frac{2}{D^2 + 1}\,\delta.$$

From this, we find in succession

$$X = (D - 1)^{-2}\{(D^2 + 1)\, H(t)\cos t\} - 2(D - 1)^{-2}\,\delta(t),$$

$$X = (D - 1)^{-2}(D - 2)\,\delta(t). \tag{B.2.13}$$

But $(D - 1)^{-2}\delta = e^t D^{-2}\delta = te^t\, H(t)$, so (B.2.13) finally gives

$$X = (D - 2)te^t\, H(t)$$
$$= e^t\, H(t) + te^t\, H(t) - 2te^t\, H(t),$$

$$X = (1 - t)e^t\, H(t). \tag{B.2.14}$$

Both $X(t)$ and $dX(t)/dt$ are continuous on $(0, +\infty)$ so $x(t)$, the restriction of X to $[0, +\infty)$ (with $x(0) = X(+0)$) may be tried out in the original problem (B.2.10). An elementary computation shows that it effectively satisfies this equation.

---

† When Table I of the Appendix is used here, it is with the help of the convolution identity (III.C.2.15)

$$P^{-1}(D)\, U(t) = [P^{-1}(D)\,\delta(t)] * U(t).$$

Remark. It should be noted, though the matter will not be considered here, that a considerably wider range of integral equations of convolution type can be solved operationally when operators in D with noninteger exponents are employed [17].

3. The Algebra of Translation Operators on $\mathscr{D}'_+$

Throughout this section h denotes an arbitrary *positive* constant and T denotes the translation operator on $\mathscr{D}'_+$ which is defined by its action on every $F \in \mathscr{D}'_+$ by

(B.3.1) $$TF(t) = F(t - h).$$

The integer powers T^p of the operator T are defined by

(B.3.2) $$T^p F(t) = F(t - ph)$$

for every $F \in \mathscr{D}'_+$. This is obviously consistent with (B.3.1) and gives

(B.3.3) $$T^pT^q = T^qT^p = T^{p+q} \qquad (p, q \text{ integer}),$$

in particular, T^0 is the identity operator on $\mathscr{D}'_+$, and $TT^{-1} = T^{-1}T = T^0$, so T^{-1} is the unique inverse (left and right) of T.

The operator T has the property that any series of the form

(B.3.4) $$\Omega = \sum_{k=0}^{\infty} a_k T^k,$$

where the a_k are arbitrary complex numbers, defines an operator on $\mathscr{D}'_+$. This is because for any $F \in \mathscr{D}'_+$ we have, on applying the series term by term,

(B.3.5) $$F(t) = \sum_{k=0}^{\infty} a_k F(t - kh),$$

and this is a convergent series in $\mathscr{D}'_+$. Indeed, given any $\varphi \in \mathscr{D}_-$, there exists b_φ with $\varphi(t) = 0$ for $t \geqslant b_\varphi$ so

$$\langle \Omega F, \varphi \rangle = \left\langle \sum_{k=0}^{K} a_k F(t - kh), \varphi \right\rangle,$$

where K is the largest integer such that $a_F + Kh \leqslant b_\varphi$ ($[a_F, +\infty)$ is a half-line in which F is carried).

Series of this kind are manipulated like power series. Thus, if Ω_1, Ω_2 are the series

$$\Omega_1 = \sum_{k=0}^{\infty} a_k T^k, \qquad \Omega_2 = \sum_{k=0}^{\infty} b_k T^k,$$

the following operators on $\mathscr{D}'_+$ and their series representations are obtained:

(B.3.6) $$c_1\Omega_1 + c_2\Omega_2 = \sum_{k=0}^{\infty} [c_1 a_k + c_2 b_k] T^k \qquad (c_1, c_2 \in C),$$

(B.3.7) $$\Omega_1\Omega_2 = \Omega_2\Omega_1 = \sum_{k=0}^{\infty} c_k T^k,$$

where

(B.3.7′) $$c_k = \sum_{l=0}^{k} a_l b_{k-l} \qquad (k = 0, 1, 2, \ldots).$$

(B.3.6) is obvious. (B.3.7) is easily verified since, for any $F \in \mathscr{D}'_+$ and $\varphi \in \mathscr{D}_-$, $\langle \Omega_1\Omega_2 F, \varphi\rangle = \langle \Omega_2\Omega_1 F, \varphi\rangle$—a fact whose verification is trivial as only a finite number of terms in the sum $\sum_{k=0}^{\infty} \langle c_k T^k F, \varphi\rangle$ differ from zero. It is also obvious that for any finite sum

$$P(T) = \sum_{k=-M}^{N} a_k T^k \qquad (M, N \text{ integers} \geqslant 0)$$

and any series Ω like (B.3.6), $P\Omega = \Omega P$ as operators on $\mathscr{D}'_+$.

In other words, as far as linear combinations and multiplication are concerned, for the set of operators on $\mathscr{D}'_+$ consisting of series like (B.3.3) and of expressions like P above, the rules of everyday algebra apply. In particular, the polynomial

(B.3.8) $$P(T) = a_p T^p + a_{p-1} T^{p-1} + \cdots + aT + a_0$$

can be factored as follows:

(B.3.9) $$P(T) = a_p (T - r_1)^{p_1} (T - r_2)^{p_2} \cdots (T - r_l)^{p_l},$$

where $r_1, r_2, \ldots, r_l$ are the zeros of the algebraic polynomial $a_p x^p + \cdots + a_0$ with the multiplicities $p_1, p_2, \ldots, p_l$ respectively ($p_1 + p_2 + \cdots + p_l = p$).

Theorem B.3.1. *The operator $T - r$ has a unique inverse $(T - r)^{-1}$ on $\mathscr{D}'_+$ also denoted by $1/(T - r)$. For $r = 0$ it is T^{-1} defined by* (B.3.2) *with $p = -1$. For $r \neq 0$, it is given by*

(B.3.10) $$(T - r)^{-1} = -\sum_{k=0}^{\infty} \frac{T^k}{r^{k+1}}.$$

Proof. The $r = 0$ case has been disposed of, so we take $r \neq 0$. $T - r = -r(1 - T/r)$, so the problem reduces to finding the inverse of $(1 - T/r)$ on $\mathscr{D}'_+$. The algebraic identity

$$\frac{1}{1 - \dfrac{x}{r}} = \sum_{k=0}^{\infty} \left(\frac{x}{r}\right)^k, \qquad \text{valid for } \left|\frac{x}{r}\right| < 1,$$

suggests we try $\sum_{k=0}^{\infty} T^k/r^k$ which converges for all $r \neq 0$; this gives as a tentative inverse for $(T - r)$:

$$\Omega = -\sum_{k=0}^{\infty} \frac{T^k}{r^{k+1}}.$$

We have, on multiplying out,

$$(T - r)\Omega = -\frac{T}{r} - \frac{T^2}{r^2} - \cdots - \frac{T^n}{r^n} - \cdots$$

$$+ 1 + \frac{T}{r} + \frac{T^2}{r^2} + \cdots + \frac{T^n}{r^n} + \cdots$$

$$= 1,$$

which proves that Ω is a right-inverse of $(T - r)$. Since, as we saw earlier, multiplication of these operators is commutative $((T - r)\Omega = \Omega(T - r))$, it follows from the algebraic Theorem I.4.1 that Ω is the unique inverse of $T - r$. ∎

Corollary B.3.1. *The operator* $(T - r)^p$ *(integer* $p > 0$*) has a unique inverse. For* $r = 0$ *it is defined by* (B.3.2) *with* $-p$ *in place of* p. *For* $r \neq 0$ *it is*

(B.3.11)
$$(T - r)^{-p} = (T - r)^{-1} \cdots (T - r)^{-1}$$
$$= (-1)^p \sum_{l=0}^{\infty} \binom{l + p - 1}{l} \frac{T^l}{r^{l+p}}.$$

Proof. The $r = 0$ case was dealt with in (B.3.3). For $r \neq 0$ it follows easily from the preceding theorem and the commutativity of operator multiplication that

$$(T - r)^{-p} = (T - r)^{-1} \cdots (T - r)^{-1} \qquad (p \text{ factors}).$$

There remains but to prove the second equality in (B.3.11). One way to do this is to perform the multiplication. Another is to observe that if $|x| < 1$,

(B.3.12)
$$\frac{1}{(1 - x)^p} = \frac{1}{(p - 1)!} \frac{d^{p-1}}{dx^{p-1}} \left(\frac{1}{1 - x}\right)$$
$$= \frac{1}{(p - 1)!} \frac{d^{p-1}}{dx^{p-1}} \left(\sum_{k=0}^{\infty} x^k\right)$$
$$= \sum_{k=p-1}^{\infty} \frac{k(k - 1) \cdots (k - p + 2)}{(p - 1)!} x^{k-p+1},$$

and since $\dfrac{1}{(1 - x)^p} = \left(\sum_{k=0}^{\infty} x^k\right)^p$ it follows that the coefficient of x^l in this product of series is equal to the coefficient of x^l in (B.3.12):

$$\frac{(l + p - 1)(l + p - 2) \cdots (l + 1)}{(p - 1)!} = \binom{l + p - 1}{l}.$$

We saw earlier that power series in T are manipulated like ordinary algebraic power series, consequently the coefficient of T^l in the product

$$\left(-\sum_{k=0}^{\infty}\frac{T^k}{r^{k+1}}\right)^p = \frac{(-1)^p}{r^p}\left(\sum_{k=0}^{\infty}\frac{T^k}{r^k}\right)^p$$

is that given in (B.3.11). (B.3.10) is seen to be a particular case of this. ∎

Corollary B.3.2. *The translation polynomial $P(T)$ defined in* (B.3.8) (B.3.9) *has a unique inverse on $\mathscr{D}'_+$ given by*

$$\text{(B.3.13)} \qquad P^{-1}(T) = \frac{1}{a_p}(T - r_1)^{-p_1}(T - r_2)^{-p_2}\cdots(T - r_l)^{-p_l}.$$

The proof is simple. Also simple, because it follows the lines used for polynomials in the operator D on $\mathscr{D}_+$, is the proof of the fact that $P^{-1}(T)$ can be decomposed into a sum of partial fractions:

$$\text{(B.3.14)} \qquad P^{-1}(T) = \sum_{j=1}^{l}\left\{\frac{\alpha_{jp_j}}{(T - r_j)^{p_j}} + \frac{\alpha_{jp_j-1}}{(T - r_j)^{p_j-1}} + \cdots + \frac{\alpha_{j1}}{(T - r_j)}\right\}$$

whose numerators are determined in the way that applies when T is replaced by the indeterminate x of ordinary algebra (§ I.6). In fact any rational operator $A(T)\, B^{-1}(T)$ (A, B polynomials) is decomposable into partial fractions, as was the case with $A(D)\, B^{-1}(D)$.

The parallel between the algebra of rational operators in D on $\mathscr{D}'_+$ and that of rational operators in T on $\mathscr{D}'_+$ should be sufficiently obvious by now to obviate the need for any further elaboration of the theory of the latter. The development and proofs for the operators in T are easily adapted from those of part A of Chapter III. We shall consequently go directly to the consideration of a class of applications of the algebra of these operators to difference equations.

4. Operational Solution of the I.V. Problem for Linear Difference Equations with Constant Coefficients

We seek a function $x(t)$ which on the half-line $t \geqslant 0$ satisfies the *homogeneous linear difference equation of order n with constant coefficients*:

$$\text{(B.4.1)} \qquad a_p x(t - ph) + a_{p-1}x(t - (p - 1)h) + \cdots + a_0 x(t) = 0.$$

Stated thus, the problem is indeterminate. If, however, p of the terms on the left are known, the equation can be solved for the remaining term. We do this by providing *initial values*, i.e., by explicitly giving a function $b(t)$ defined on $[-ph, 0)$ with the stipulation that

$$\text{(B.4.2)} \qquad x(t) = b(t) \qquad \text{for } -ph \leqslant t < 0,$$

where we shall here always take $b(t)$ to be piecewise continuous for convenience.

Then for $0 \leqslant t < h$ the equation (B.4.1) can be solved explicitly:

$$\text{(B.4.1}')\qquad x(t) = -\frac{1}{a_0}(a_p b(t - ph) + a_{p-1}b(t - (p - 1)h) + \cdots + a_1 b(t - h)),$$

and one can obtain $x(t)$ in $[h, 2h), \ldots, [kh, (k + 1)h), \ldots$ by successive resubstitutions. It is obvious, then, that this I.V. problem has a solution for given $b(t)$ and that this solution is unique. What we wish to do now is to show how this solution can be found by using the algebra of operators in T derived in § 3.

Let us split $b(t)$ into the n functions:

$$\text{(B.4.3)}\quad \xi_j(t) = \begin{cases} 0 & \text{if } t < -jh \\ b(t) & \text{if } -jh \leqslant t < -(j-1)h \quad (j = 1, 2, \ldots, n). \\ 0 & \text{if } -(j-1)h \leqslant t. \end{cases}$$

We define the function

$$\text{(B.4.4)}\qquad X(t) = \begin{cases} 0 & \text{if } t < -ph \\ b(t) & \text{if } -ph \leqslant t < 0 \\ x(t) & \text{(the solution of (B.4.1)) if } 0 \leqslant t, \end{cases}$$

which is a $\mathscr{K}_+(R)$ function if $b(t)$ is piecewise continuous.

Let us examine the value of the function

$$P(T)X(t) = a_p X(t - ph) + a_{p-1}X(t - (p - 1)h) + \cdots + a_0 X(t)$$

for all $t \in R$.

For $0 < t$, it follows from (B.4.4) (third line) and (B.4.1.) that $P(T)\ X(t) = 0$. As $X(t)$ is carried in $[-ph, +\infty)$ we have $X(t - lh) = 0$ when $-jh \leqslant t < -(j-1)h$ and $l \geqslant p - j + 1$. As a consequence, we find that

$$P(T)\ X(t) = 0 \qquad \text{when } t < -ph,$$

$$P(T)\ X(t) = a_0 X(t) \qquad \text{when } -ph \leqslant t < -(p - 1)h,$$

$$P(T)\ X(t) = a_0 X(t) + a_1 X(t - h) \qquad \text{when } -(p - 1)h \leqslant t < -(p - 2)h,$$

. . . .

$$P(T)\ X(t) = a_0 X(t) + \cdots + a_{p-j}X(t - (p - j)h) \qquad \text{when } -jh \leqslant t < -(j-1)h,$$

. . . .

$$P(T)\ X(t) = a_0 X(t) + \cdots + a_{p-1}X(t - (p - 1)h) \qquad \text{when } -h \leqslant t < 0.$$

These may be rewritten in the light of (B.4.3) as

$$
\begin{aligned}
&P(T)\,X(t) = 0 && \text{when } t < -ph,\\
&P(T)\,X(t) = a_0\xi_p(t) && \text{when } -ph \leqslant t < -(p-1)h,\\
&P(T)\,X(t) = a_0\xi_{p-1}(t) + a_1T\xi_p(t) && \text{when } -(p-1)h \leqslant t < -(p-2)h,\\
&\cdots\cdots\cdots\cdots\cdots\cdots\cdots\cdots\cdots\cdots\cdots\cdots\cdots\cdots\cdots\cdots\\
&P(T)\,X(t) = a_0\xi_j(t) + a_1T\xi_{j+1}(t) + \cdots + a_{p-j}T^{p-j}\xi_p(t) &&\\
& && \text{when } -jh \leqslant t < -(j-1)h,\\
&\cdots\cdots\cdots\cdots\cdots\cdots\cdots\cdots\cdots\cdots\cdots\cdots\cdots\cdots\cdots\cdots\\
&P(T)\,X(t) = a_0\xi_1(t) + a_1T\xi_2(t) + \cdots + a_{p-1}T^{p-1}\xi_p(t) &&\\
& && \text{when } -h \leqslant t < 0,\\
&P(T)\,X(t) = 0 && \text{when } 0 < t.
\end{aligned}
$$

(B.4.5)

For $j = 1, 2, \ldots, p$, the function

$$a_0\xi_j + a_1T\xi_{j+1} + \cdots + a_{p-j}T^{p-j}\xi_p$$

vanishes outside the interval $-jh \leqslant t < -(j-1)h$. Therefore, no two of the functions forming the right-hand sides of the equalities (B.4.5) are carried in the same interval, and we may add all these equalities, obtaining

$$
\begin{aligned}
\text{(B.4.6)}\qquad P(T)X = a_0(\xi_p + \xi_{p-1} + \cdots + \xi_1) &+ a_1T(\xi_p + \xi_{p-1} + \cdots + \xi_2)\\
&+ \cdots + a_{p-j}T^{p-j}(\xi_p + \xi_{p-1} + \cdots + \xi_{p-j+1})\\
&+ \cdots + a_{p-1}T^{p-1}\xi_p,
\end{aligned}
$$

a relation valid for all $t \in R$ and called the *equation of evolution* of the I.V. problem (B.4.1, 2).

Denoting the right-hand side of the equation of evolution by B—we shall call it the boundary term—this equation takes the form

$$\text{(B.4.7)}\qquad P(T)X = B,$$

where, incidentally, B can also be written as

$$
\begin{aligned}
\text{(B.4.8)}\qquad B = a_0\xi_1 + (a_0 + a_1T)\xi_2 + \cdots&\\
+ (a_0 + a_1T + \cdots + a_{p-1}T^{p-1})\xi_p&.
\end{aligned}
$$

As with the ordinary I.V. problem for differential equations with constant coefficients, both the original difference equation and the p initial values (B.4.3) imposed on its solution are englobed into one expression, the equation of evolution. The latter, being a relation between $\mathscr{K}_+(R)$ functions on R and some of their translations, can be handled with the operator algebra of § 3. Specifically, we have the solution

$$\text{(B.4.9)}\qquad X(t) = P^{-1}(T)B,$$

where $P^{-1}(T)$ is best computed by expanding the right-hand side of (B.3.13) in the form of a sum of fractions (B.3.14). The restriction of $X(t)$ to the domain $t \geqslant 0$ is $x(t)$, the unique solution of (B.4.1, 2).

It is left to the reader to carry out the simple verification of the fact that the nonhomogeneous linear difference equation

(B.4.10) $$a_p x(t - ph) + a_{p-1}x(t - (p-1)h) + \cdots + a_0 x(t) = f(t) \qquad (t \geqslant 0),$$

where $f(t)$ is any given piecewise continuous function on $[0, +\infty)$, and where the initial values of $x(t)$ in $[-ph, 0)$ are as given in (B.4.2), leads to the equation of evolution

(B.4.11) $$P(T)X = F + B,$$

where B is the same as in (B.4.7) and where

(B.4.12) $$F(t) = \begin{cases} 0 & \text{if } t < 0 \\ f(t) & \text{if } 0 \leqslant t. \end{cases}$$

Manifestly, the initial-value problem for systems of difference equations can also be treated by these same operational procedures.

Example. Solve

$$\frac{1}{h}(x(t - h) - x(t)) = f(t) \qquad (0 \leqslant t)$$

given that $x(t) = c$ (constant) when $-h \leqslant t < 0$.

The equation of evolution is found to be

(B.4.13) $$\frac{1}{h}(T - 1)X = F - \frac{c(t)}{h},$$

where

$$c(t) = \begin{cases} 0 & \text{if } t \notin [-h, 0) \\ c & \text{if } -h \leqslant t < 0, \end{cases}$$

so

$$(T - 1)X = hF - c(t).$$

The solution is then, in view of (B.3.10) with $r = 1$,

$$\begin{aligned} X(t) &= -\sum_{k=0}^{\infty} T^k(hF - c(t)) \\ &= -h\sum_{k=0}^{\infty} F(t - kh) + \sum_{k=0}^{\infty} c(t - kh). \end{aligned}$$

As $\sum_{k=0}^{\infty} c(t - kh) = cH(t + h)$ and as $F(t - kh)$ is carried in $[kh, +\infty)$, this solution can be written

(B.4.14) $$X(t) = -h\sum_{k=0}^{[t/h]} F(t - kh) + cH(t + h),$$

where $[t/h]$ is the largest integer $\leqslant t/h$.

Write T_h for T, so (B.4.13) becomes

$$\text{(B.4.13')} \qquad \frac{1}{h}(T_h - 1)X_h = F - \frac{c(t)}{h}.$$

Since $\displaystyle\lim_{h\to 0} \frac{c(t)}{h} = c\,\delta(t)$ and, formally at least,

$$\lim_{h\to 0}\left[\frac{1}{h}(T_h - 1)X_h\right] = -DY, \qquad Y \in \mathscr{D}'_+.$$

we get, formally, in the limit, from (B.4.13')

$$-DY = F - c\,\delta(t)$$

whose solution is

$$Y = -\int_0^t F(\tau)\,d\tau + c\,H(t).$$

This is actually the limit of the right-hand side of (B.4.14) so $\lim_{h\to 0} X_h = -Y$.

Remark. Infinite series of operators of the form

$$\sum_{k,l=0}^{\infty} a_{kl} T^k D^{-l}$$

also represent operators on $\mathscr{D}'_+$. They will not be considered here. One area of application of such operators, mixed difference-differential equations, will be touched on in Chapter VII.

*5. The Operational Method of Mikusiński

The algebra of operators in D and T on the $\mathscr{D}'_+$ space of L. Schwartz that has been the subject of this and the preceding chapter is not the only path to the direct operational solution of the I.V. problem for linear differential or difference equations with constant coefficients. It has been introduced here, among other reasons, because of its simplicity, its physical significance, the usefulness of $\mathscr{D}'_+$ theory as a prototype for many other g.f. classes, and because it is a prototype for other operational calculi (§§ 4, 5, Chapter 0; and Volume II).

Contemporary with the Schwartz theory is the calculus of J. Mikusiński's operators (1949). These operators are also sometimes called generalized functions or convolution quotients. The reader will find a very lucid introduction to the Mikusiński theory and its application in a book by A. Erdélyi [17]. See also the appendix to [31]. A more complete treatment and some discussion of the relation between g.f.'s à la Schwartz (distributions) and Mikusiński operators is provided in the textbook of Mikusiński [39].

Here we simply note that while g.f.'s are obtained from fundamental sequences of functions, rather as irrational numbers are obtained from sequences of rationals (an idea also proposed, incidentally, by Mikusiński [37]), a Mikusiński operator is obtained from two functions somewhat as a rational number is obtained from two integers. Starting from the set C of functions continuous on $[0, +\infty)$ one shows (Titchmarsh) that

$$f, g \in C \text{ and } f * g \equiv 0 \Rightarrow \text{either } f \equiv 0 \text{ or } g \equiv 0.$$

(If f and g change signs only finitely often in every interval $[0, a]$ this is easy to prove.) Then C is, with respect to ordinary addition and the convolution product, a commutative ring without divisors of zero (as are the integers under addition and multiplication). One then shows that to every pair f, $g \in C$ corresponds an object called the convolution quotient f/g (e.g., f/f corresponds to our $\delta(t)$) just as to the ordinary integers m, n corresponds the rational number m/n. The algebra of these convolution quotients under addition and convolution then yields a direct operational calculus for differential and difference equations with constant coefficients, and for certain partial differential equations in two variables.

EXERCISES

Part A

[*Note:* Exercises 2–8 refer to ordinary I.V. problems in the sense and with the notation of § A.2, with $t_0 = 0$. In each case find the system of evolution, solve it operationally, and check whether a solution to the ordinary problem is thereby obtained. (Knowledge of parts A,·B of Chapter III and §§ IV.A.1, 2, 3, 4, 5 is sufficient for these exercises. However, the student who has read part C of Chapter III and §§ IV.A.6, 7, 8 is advised to employ the methods of the latter.)]

1. By introducing the functions

$$y_1(t) = x(t), \quad y_2(t) = \frac{dx}{dt}, \quad \ldots, \quad y_p(t) = \frac{d^{p-1}x}{dt^{p-1}}$$

the I.V. problem (III.B.1, 2) can be transformed into an equivalent I.V. problem for a system of p first-order differential equations in the unknowns $y_1, y_2, \ldots, y_p$. Perform this transformation, write out the corresponding system of evolution for the g.f.'s $Y_1, Y_2, \ldots, Y_p$ (the continuations by zero of $y_1, \ldots, y_p$). Solve this system by the operator method and verify that the original and transformed problems are indeed equivalent.

2.
$$\frac{dx_1}{dt} - 3x_1 + x_2 = f, \qquad \frac{dx_2}{dt} + x_2 - 4x_1 = 0;$$

(x_1^0, x_2^0 arbitrary) (normal).

3.
$$-\frac{dx_1}{dt} + 13x_1 - \frac{dx_2}{dt} + 28x_2 + 26x_3 = 0$$

$$16x_1 - \frac{dx_2}{dt} + 40x_2 + 38x_3 = 0,$$

$$2x_1 - \frac{dx_2}{dt} + 7x_2 - \frac{dx_3}{dt} + 7x_3 = 0$$

($x_1^0 = 1$, $x_2^0 = x_3^0 = 0$) (normal).

4.
$$\frac{d^2x_1}{dt^2} + 6x_1 + 7x_2 = f(t), \qquad 3x_1 + \frac{d^2x_2}{dt^2} + 2x_2 = 0$$

$(x_1^0 = x_2^0 = 0,\ x_1^1 = -x_2^1 = 1)$ (normal).

5.
$$\frac{d^2x_1}{dt^2} + 2\frac{d^2x_2}{dt^2} - \frac{d^2x_3}{dt^2} + x_3 = 0,$$
$$x_1 + \frac{d^2x_2}{dt^2} + x_3 = 1,$$
$$\frac{d^2x_1}{dt^2} - x_1 + \frac{d^2x_2}{dt^2} + 6x_2 + x_3 = 0$$

$(x_1^0 = 1,\ x_1^1 = x_2^0 = x_2^1 = x_3^0 = x_3^1 = 0)$. (normal).

6.
$$\frac{dx_1}{dt} + 2x_1 + \frac{dx_2}{dt} - x_2 = -e^{-it},$$
$$\frac{dx_1}{dt} + 2x_1 + \frac{dx_2}{dt} + x_2 = e^{it}$$

$(x_1^0,\ x_2^0$ arbitrary).

What relation between x_1^0, x_2^0 is necessary for this ordinary I.V. problem to have a solution?

7.
$$\frac{d^2x_1}{dt^2} + 6x_1 + \frac{d^2x_2}{dt^2} - x_2 = f_1,$$
$$\frac{d^2x_1}{dt^2} + \frac{d^2x_2}{dt^2} + 2x_2 = f_2$$

$(x_1^0,\ x_1',\ x_2^0,\ x_2'$ arbitrary).

What relations between the initial values of the unknowns and the driving functions and what continuity and ordinary differentiability conditions imposed on f_1, f_2 give this I.V. problem a solution in the ordinary sense?

8.
$$\frac{d^2x_1}{dt^2} + \frac{dx_1}{dt} + \frac{dx_2}{dt} + x_3 = f_1,$$
$$\frac{dx_1}{dt} - \frac{dx_2}{dt} - x_3 = f_2,$$
$$-x_1 - \frac{dx_2}{dt} - 2x_2 + 2x_3 = f_3$$

$(x_1^0,\ x_1',\ x_2^0,\ x_3'$ arbitrary).

Give relations between initial values as well as ordinary differentiability conditions on f_1, f_2, f_3 required for a solution in the ordinary sense.

9. Find $x_1(t)$, $x_2(t)$ continuous on $[0, +\infty)$ and satisfying for $t > 0$ the system

$$\int_0^t x_1(\tau)\,d\tau + 2\frac{dx_1}{dt} - \int_0^t x_2(\tau)\,d\tau = \cos t,$$
$$-\int_0^t x_1(\tau)\,d\tau + \int_0^t x_2(\tau)\,d\tau + 3x_2 = 0.$$

***10.** If, in Exercise 9, there is added to the equations (valid for $t > 0$), the condition $x_2(+0) = 1$, solutions x_1, x_2 that are both continuous on $[0, +\infty)$ do not exist. (Why?) In that case, taking for $j = 1, 2$

$$X_j(t) = \xi_j(t) + c_j\,\delta(t)$$

with $\xi_j \in \mathscr{K}_+(R)$ carried in $[0, +\infty)$, and replacing the integrals by $Q_j = D^{-1}X_j$, the original equations may be interpreted as g.f. equalities valid on the open half-line $(0, +\infty)$. From this interpretation, deduce the equations of evolution and solve operationally for Q_1, Q_2.

***11.** Given the ordinary I.V. problem (A.2.1, 2, 3) for first-order differential equations [i.e., $N = 1$ in (A.2.2, 3)], prove that when the determinant of the coefficients a_{ij}^0 does not vanish, the system is normal in the sense of (b), p. 148. (Refer to the arguments leading to Theorem III.B.1.1 for hints.)

***12.** Repeat Exercise 11 but with $N = 2$.

13. (For the student conversant with matrix algebra). Put the system of equations of evolution (A.2.7) in matrix form; express the term B of (A.2.8) by means of matrix versions of (III.B.1.6) and (III.B.1.7).

Part B

14. Find $x(t)$ such that

$$\frac{d^2x}{dt^2} - \gamma^2 x = f(t)$$

for $0 < t < a$ and such that $x(+0) = x(a - 0) = 0$. Transform this boundary-value problem into an I.V. problem for $t > 0$ with $x(+0) = 0$ and $x'(+0) = x_1$, then solve this problem operationally. In the solution assign to x_1 a value which makes $x(a - 0) = 0$, thus obtaining a solution to the given boundary-value problem. Restrictions on f?

15. Solve operationally the boundary-value problem

$$\frac{d^2x}{dt^2} + \gamma^2 x = 0 \ (0 < t < a)\ x(+0) = x(a - 0) = 0.$$

What relation between a and γ is required for a solution?

16. Find $x(t)$ such that

$$\frac{d^4x}{dt^4} - \gamma^4 x = 0 \qquad (0 < t < a)$$

and

$$x(+0) = x''(+0) = x(a - 0) = x''(a - 0) = 0.$$

Do this by the operational method and indicate the relation between γ and a required for the existence of solutions.

17. Solve operationally the boundary-value problem

$$\frac{d^4x}{dt^4} + \gamma^2 x = 0 \qquad (0 < t < a)$$

where

$$x(+0) = x''(+0) = x(a-0) = x'(a-0) = 0.$$

Indicate the relation required between γ and a for the existence of solutions.

18. Solve the equation

$$x(t) = at^n + \int_0^t \sin \omega(t - \tau)x(\tau)\, d\tau \qquad (t \geqslant 0, n \geqslant 0).$$

19. Solve the equation

$$x(t) = ae^{\omega it} + b\int_0^t e^{i\omega(t-\tau)}x(\tau)\, d\tau \qquad (t \geqslant 0).$$

20. Solve the equation

$$x(t) = ae^{\omega it} + b\int_0^t e^{i\omega(t-\tau)}x'(\tau)\, d\tau \qquad (t \geqslant 0).$$

****21.** Solve Abel's integral equation

$$t^n = \int_0^t (t - \tau)^{-1/2} x'(\tau)\, d\tau \qquad (t \geqslant 0, n \geqslant 0).$$

22. Solve the difference equation

$$x(t) - (r_1 + r_2)x(t - h) + r_1 r_2 x(t - 2h) = f(t) \qquad (t \geqslant 0),$$

where $x(t) = 0$, for $t < 0$ and $r_1 \neq r_2$.

23. Solve the system

$$x_1(t) - x_2(t - h) = e^t,$$
$$x_1(t - h) - x_2(t) = e^{-t} \qquad (t \geqslant 0),$$
$$x_1(t) = x_2(t) = 1,$$

for $-h \leqslant t < 0$.

24. The difference operator Δ^p was defined in Exercise I.5. Find the solution of

$$\Delta^2 x(t) + k^2 x(t) = 0 \qquad (t \geqslant 0)$$

where $x(t) = 1$ for $-h \leqslant t < 0$ and $\Delta x(t) = 0$ for $-h \leqslant t < 0$.

25. The Fibonacci numbers are the nonnegative integers f_n verifying the recurrence relation

$$f_n = f_{n-1} + f_{n-2} \quad (n = 0, 1, 2, \ldots) \quad \text{where } f_{-1} = 1, f_{-2} = 0.$$

Reduce the solution of this recurrence relation to an I.V. problem for a difference equation applied to the g.f.'s $f_n\ \delta(t - n)$ and show that

$$f_n = \frac{1}{\sqrt{5}}\left[\left(\frac{1 + \sqrt{5}}{2}\right)^n - \left(\frac{1 - \sqrt{5}}{2}\right)^n\right].$$

26. Verify summarily that the algebra of operators in T of § B.3 (where $h > 0$) can be developed directly for the operand space of all functions carried in forward half-lines, without using any test space $\left(\sum_{n=0}^{\infty} a_n T^n f(t) \text{ converges at every } t \in R\right)$. The point of the procedure of § B.3 is its applicability to generalized functions as exemplified by Exercise 25.

CHAPTER V

** THE STRUCTURE OF $\mathscr{D}'_+$. INDIVIDUAL G.F.'S

A. G.F.'S AS CONTINUOUS FUNCTIONALS

1. Preface

Except for occasional references to uniform continuity (of a function of t) or uniform convergence (of a sequence or parametric family of functions of t), our study of g.f.'s up to this point has required few concepts that do not belong to elementary, rather than advanced, calculus. Yet, without slurring over any points of mathematical rigor, even this modest panoply has been the means of covering a fair extent of territory of theoretical interest and practical value.

Two subjects, parametric families of g.f.'s and the convolution of g.f.'s, have so far been treated with a degree of generality which, though amply sufficient for the greater number of physical applications of $\mathscr{D}'_+$, can be appreciably widened if the structure of g.f.'s of class $\mathscr{D}'_+$ is examined more thoroughly. Several times in the discussion (Chapters II, III, and IV) of these topics it was seen that confining oneself to g.f.'s of finite K-order yielded stronger results. Now, it so happens that the injection of this hypothesis is only an apparent restriction; because, as we shall see, every $\mathscr{D}'_+$ g.f. is in fact of finite K-order, *locally*. It is with such questions, among others, that this chapter and the next are concerned.

In this chapter we shall verify that the g.f.'s defined in Chapter II by fundamental sequences are the same as the distributions of class $\mathscr{D}'_+$ of L. Schwartz and prove what may be called the *fundamental structure theorem* of $\mathscr{D}'_+$ theory; namely, that, locally, i.e., on every finite open interval, a $\mathscr{D}'_+$ g.f. coincides with a (generalized) derivative of finite order of a continuous function. This is followed by a brief description of the relation between various approaches to g.f. theory, and finally by the study of the convolution operation in $\mathscr{D}'_+$ without the restrictions of § III.C.5.

2. Positive G.F.'s of Class $\mathscr{D}'_+$

$F \in \mathscr{D}'_+$ carried in $[a, +\infty)$ is said to be positive if it has a defining fundamental sequence $\{f_n(t)\}$ carried in $[a, +\infty)$ such that, for every positive integer n, $f_n(t) \geqslant 0$, $t \in R$. For any $\varphi \in \mathscr{D}_-$ which assumes only nonnegative values it then follows that $\langle F, \varphi\rangle \geqslant 0$.

Let $F \in \mathscr{D}'_+$ be positive and be carried in $[a, +\infty)$. Take an arbitrary $b > a$ and, given any $\varepsilon > 0$, take

$$\text{(A.2.1)} \qquad \psi(t) = (-1)D^{-1}\rho_\varepsilon(t - b - \varepsilon) = -\int_{+\infty}^{t} \rho_\varepsilon(t - b - \varepsilon)\, dt$$

where $\rho_\varepsilon(t)$ is the test function already encountered in Chapter I, § 2, and Chapter II, § A.7, and whose definition is given by

$$\text{(A.2.2)} \qquad \rho_\varepsilon(t) = \begin{cases} 0 & \text{for } |t| \geqslant \varepsilon \\ \dfrac{k}{\varepsilon}\, e^{\varepsilon^2/(t^2-\varepsilon^2)} & \text{for } |t| < \varepsilon \end{cases}$$

$$\left(k = 1\Big/\int_{-1}^{1} e^{1/(t^2-1)}\, dt, \quad \text{so} \quad \int_{-\infty}^{\infty} \rho_\varepsilon(t)\, dt = 1\right).$$

The test function $\psi(t)$ is carried in $(-\infty, b + 2\varepsilon]$ and has the constant value 1 for $t \leqslant b$, so that if $t \leqslant b$,

$$\text{(A.2.3)} \quad \int_{-\infty}^{\infty} f_n(t)\, \psi(t)\, dt \geqslant \int_{-\infty}^{t} f_n(\tau)\, d\tau = \int_{-\infty}^{t} |f_n(\tau)|\, d\tau \quad (n = 1, 2, \ldots),$$

where $\{f_n\}$ is a defining fundamental sequence of F such that $f_n(t) \geqslant 0$ $(n = 1, 2, \ldots)$ and is carried in $[a, +\infty)$.

These inequalities and the existence of $\lim_{n\to\infty} \langle f_n, \psi\rangle$ entail the existence of a nonnegative constant K_b such that

$$\text{(A.2.4)} \qquad \int_{-\infty}^{t} |f_n(\tau)|\, d\tau \leqslant K_b \qquad (t \leqslant b).$$

But then for any $\varphi \in \mathscr{D}_-$ which is carried in $(-\infty, b]$

$$\text{(A.2.5)} \qquad |\langle f_n, \varphi\rangle| \leqslant K_b \max_{a \leqslant t \leqslant b} |\varphi(t)| \qquad (n = 1, 2, 3, \ldots),$$

whence

$$\text{(A.2.6)} \qquad |\langle F, \varphi\rangle| \leqslant K_b \max_{a \leqslant t \leqslant b} |\varphi(t)|.$$

Now, consider a sequence $\{\varphi_l\}$ of test functions all carried in $(-\infty, b]$ and for which there exists $\varphi_0 \in \mathscr{D}_-$ such that on every finite interval $[\alpha, b]$ $(\alpha < a)$, $\lim_{l\to\infty} \varphi_l(t) = \varphi_0(t)$ uniformly, i.e., such that for every $\alpha < a$

$$\text{(A.2.7)} \qquad \lim_{l\to\infty} \left(\max_{\alpha \leqslant t \leqslant b} |\varphi_l(t) - \varphi_0(t)|\right) = 0.$$

From (A.2.6) there results, then,

$$\lim_{l\to\infty} \langle F, \varphi_l - \varphi_0\rangle = 0,$$

(A.2.8) $$\lim_{l\to\infty} \langle F, \varphi_l\rangle = \langle F, \varphi_0\rangle.$$

Think of the φ_l as "points" in the set $\mathscr{D}_-$, and interpret (A.2.7) to mean that these points converge to the point φ_0. Then the functional F (which is a complex-valued function with a well-defined value at each point of $\mathscr{D}_-$), when viewed in this pseudo-geometric fashion, behaves in a manner analogous to that of an ordinary continuous function, g, of a real variable x, which, when the sequence $\{x_l\}$ of real numbers converges to $x_0 \in R$ as $l \to \infty$, satisfies $\lim_{l\to\infty} g(x_l) = g(x_0)$.

This analogy is behind the reason for calling F a continuous functional on $\mathscr{D}_-$. F also has the algebraic property of linearity defined in Chapter II (i.e., $\langle F, c_1\varphi_1 + c_2\varphi_2\rangle = c_1\langle F, \varphi_1\rangle + c_2\langle F, \varphi_2\rangle$) and so is more fully described as a *continuous linear functional* on $\mathscr{D}_-$ (briefly: c.l.f.).

Thus, what (A.2.6) tells us is this: every positive g.f. of class $\mathscr{D}'_+$ is a c.l.f. on $\mathscr{D}_-$.

Remark 1. The notion of positivity of a $\mathscr{D}'_+$ g.f. can be "localized." By this, we mean that a g.f. $F \in \mathscr{D}'_+$ can be viewed as being positive merely on some finite open interval (a, b) if at least one of its fundamental sequences $\{f_n(t)\}$ has $f_n(t) \geqslant 0$ $(n = 1, 2, \ldots)$ when $a < t < b$. The arguments given above can be adapted to show that for every interval (α, β), where $a < \alpha < \beta < b$, there exists $K_{\alpha\beta} < \infty$ such that

$$|\langle F, \varphi\rangle| \leqslant K_{\alpha\beta} \max_{\alpha\leqslant t\leqslant\beta} |\varphi(t)|$$

for every $\varphi \in \mathscr{D}_-$ carried in (α, β).

3. Boundedness Properties of Fundamental Sequences on $\mathscr{D}_-$

Given a finite interval I of R and a function f, whose domain A contains all but a finite number of points of I, and whose values on $I \cap A$ are bounded, we shall designate by $\|f\|_I$ (sometimes called the norm, or M-norm, of f on I) the quantity defined by

(A.3.1) $$\|f\|_I = \sup_{t\in A\cap I} |f(t)|.$$

When f is defined and continuous throughout I, and I is a closed finite interval, this is the same as

(A.3.1′) $$\|f\|_I = \max_{t\in I} |f(t)|.$$

If $f \in \mathscr{K}_+(R)$ is carried in $[a, +\infty)$ and $\varphi \in \mathscr{D}_-$ is carried in $(-\infty, b]$, where $b \geqslant a$, then, with this notation, we have, setting $I = [a, b]$,

(A.3.2) $$|\langle f, \varphi\rangle| = \left|\int_{-\infty}^{\infty} f(t)\,\varphi(t)\,dt\right| \leqslant (b - a)\,\|f\|_I\,\|\varphi\|_I.$$

In the preceding section we saw that if a fundamental sequence on $\mathscr{D}'_+$, $\{f_n(t)\}$, consists of nonnegative functions carried in $[a, +\infty)$ then for any $b \geqslant a$, there holds the relation (A.2.4), which in the norm notation with $I = [a, b]$ we write

$$\|D^{-1}f_n\|_I \leqslant K_b \qquad (n = 1, 2, \ldots). \tag{A.3.3}$$

When the positivity hypotheses on $\{f_n(t)\}$ are abandoned, these inequalities are no longer true in general. However, a very natural question then suggests itself: if we no longer suppose the $f_n(t)$ to be nonnegative, can we find an integer $p \geqslant 0$ such that (A.3.3) remains true when the left-hand side is relaxed to $\|D^{-p}f_n\|_I$ instead of $\|D^{-1}f_n\|_I$?

The grounds for such a conjecture are vague and intuitive; viz., $D^{-p}f_n(t)$, being the fruit of repeated integrations, is "smoother" (changes signs no more often) than $f_n(t)$, so that the sequence $\{D^{-p}f_n(t)\}_n$ is more likely to have some of the properties of a positive sequence. It is an important fact that this conjecture turns out to be entirely verified. This, and more, is the burden of the following

Lemma A.3.1. *Given an arbitrary sequence, $\{f_n(t)\}$, of $\mathscr{K}_+(R)$ functions all carried in the same forward half-line $[a, +\infty)$ and such that for every $\varphi \in \mathscr{D}_-$ the numerical sequence $\{\langle f_n, \varphi\rangle\}$ is bounded by a constant, $B(\varphi)$, depending on φ but not on n. Then to every real number b correspond a nonnegative integer p and a constant K such that* ($I = [a, b]$)

$$\|D^{-p}f_n\|_I \leqslant K \qquad (n = 1, 2, \ldots). \tag{A.3.4}$$

Proof. If all but a finite number of $f_n(t)$ are identical the Lemma is obvious. Therefore we suppose from here on that an infinity of the f_n are distinct. The proof given here assumes the $f_n(t)$ to be real-valued. The case of complex-valued $f_n(t)$ is left to the reader.

When $b \leqslant a$, $p = 0$ and $K = 0$ will obviously do. Therefore, we go on to the case $a < b$, setting

$$M_n^p = \|D^{-p}f_n\|_I \qquad (n = 1, 2, \ldots;\ p = 0, 1, 2, \ldots). \tag{A.3.5}$$

The proof is by contraposition: assuming the conclusion (A.3.4) to be false will enable us to construct a $\varphi \in \mathscr{D}_-$ for which the sequence $\{|\langle f_n, \varphi\rangle|\}$ is not bounded, contrary to the hypothesis. The component steps of this proof are labeled here below as (i) through (vii) in order to make them more apparent.

(i) If (A.3.4) does not hold for any integer $p \geqslant 0$ each of the sequences $\{M_n^0\}_n, \{M_n^1\}_n, \ldots, \{M_n^p\}_n, \ldots$ is unbounded and we can take one element from each one of them so as to obtain a sequence $\{M_{n_p}^p\}_p$ which is monotonic increasing and unbounded. To simplify the appearance of subsequent expressions, we relabel the elements of this sequence thus:

$$M_{n_p}^p = L_p \qquad (p = 0, 1, 2, \ldots), \tag{A.3.6}$$

so that its monotonicity and unboundedness are expressed by

$$\text{(A.3.7)} \qquad L_0 \leqslant L_1 \leqslant \cdots \leqslant L_p \leqslant L_{p+1} \cdots \lim_{p\to\infty} L_p = +\infty.$$

(ii) Let p_1 be an integer such that $L_{p_1} \geqslant 2$. Next select inductively a sequence $\{p_k\}_k$ of integers such that

$$\text{(A.3.8)} \qquad L_{p_k} \frac{(b-a)^{p_{k+1}-p_k}}{(p_{k+1}-p_k)!} < \frac{1}{2} \qquad (k = 1, 2, \ldots).$$

Recalling a property of multinomial coefficients,

$$\frac{(m+n+\cdots+s)!}{m!\,n!\cdots s!} \geqslant 1,$$

and using (A.3.7), we deduce that for any positive integers k, i,

$$L_{p_k} \frac{(b-a)^{p_{k+i}-p_k}}{(p_{k+i}-p_k)!} \leqslant L_{p_k} \frac{(b-a)^{p_{k+1}-p_k}}{(p_{k+1}-p_k)!} \cdots L_{p_{k+i-1}} \frac{(b-a)^{p_{k+i}-p_{k+i-1}}}{(p_{k+i}-p_{k+i-1})!}.$$

On applying (A.3.8) on the right-hand side, we find

$$\text{(A.3.9)} \qquad L_{p_k} \frac{(b-a)^{p_{k+i}-p_k}}{(p_{k+i}-p_k)!} < \frac{1}{2^i} \qquad (i, k = 1, 2, \ldots).$$

(iii) Each of the functions $D^{-p_k} f_{n_k'}(t)$ ($k = 1, 2, \ldots$ and $n_k' = n_{p_k}$) being piecewise continuous (continuous when $p_k > 0$), we can assert that there exists a nondegenerate closed subinterval $J_k = [c_k, d_k]$ of I throughout which

$$\text{(A.3.10)} \qquad |D^{-p_k} f_{n'_k}(t)| \geqslant \frac{L_{p_k}}{2}.$$

Let $\varphi_k \in \mathscr{D}_-$ designate a function with positive and zero values only [obtained by taking a $\rho_\varepsilon(t)$ of the type (A.2.2) with $\varepsilon \leqslant (d_k - c_k)/2$ and translating it] carried in J_k and normalized, i.e., such that

$$\text{(A.3.11)} \qquad \int_{-\infty}^{\infty} \varphi_k(t)\, dt = 1.$$

$D^{-p_k} f_{n_k'}(t)$, being real-valued, does not change its sign in J_k; this fact, coupled with (A.3.10) and (A.3.11) ensures that

$$\text{(A.3.12)} \qquad |\langle D^{-p_k} f_{n_k'}, \varphi_k \rangle| = \int_{c_k}^{d_k} |D^{-p_k} f_{n_k'}(t)|\, \varphi_k(t)\, dt$$

$$\geqslant \tfrac{1}{2} L_{p_k} \int_{c_k}^{d_k} \varphi_k(t)\, dt = \tfrac{1}{2} L_{p_k}.$$

(iv) The steadily increasing character of $\{L_{p_k}\}_k$ and this last inequality prove that we can define by induction a subsequence $k_1, k_2, \ldots, k_j, \ldots$ of the integers $\{k\}$ such that (for simplicity we denote by p_j' the integer p_{k_j} and n_{k_j}' by n_j'')

$$|\langle D^{-p_j'}f_{n_j''}, \varphi_{k_j}\rangle| > j + 1 + \left|\sum_{l=1}^{j-1}\langle f_{n_j''}, D^{-p_l'}\varphi_{k_l}\rangle\right|,^{\dagger}$$

which can also be written

$$|\langle f_{n_j''}, D^{-p_j'}\varphi_{k_j}\rangle| > j + 1 + \left|\sum_{l=1}^{j-1}\langle f_{n_j''}, D^{-p_l'}\varphi_{k_l}\rangle\right|. \tag{A.3.13}$$

(v) The series

$$\varphi(t) = \sum_{l=1}^{\infty} D^{-p_l'}\varphi_{k_l}(t) \tag{A.3.14}$$

converges for $t \in R$ and defines a test function carried in $(-\infty, b]$; furthermore this series converges uniformly in the interval I. For the sake of concentrating on the mainstream of our reasoning, let us momentarily accept these assertions without proof. (This omission will be amended very soon.)

The uniform convergence of this series for φ and the fact that it vanishes for $t \geqslant b$ (because each of its terms does) justifies our writing, n_j'' being an arbitrary element of $\{n_j''\}$,

$$\begin{aligned}\langle f_{n_j''}, \varphi\rangle &= \sum_{l=1}^{j-1}\langle f_{n_j''}, D^{-p_l'}\varphi_{k_l}\rangle + \langle f_{n_j''}, D^{-p_j'}\varphi_{k_j}\rangle \\ &\quad + \sum_{l=j+1}^{\infty}\langle f_{n_j''}, D^{-p_l}\varphi_{k_l}\rangle \\ &= \Sigma_1 + \langle f_{n_j''}, D^{-p_j'}\varphi_{k_j}\rangle + \Sigma_2,\end{aligned}$$

from which we deduce

$$|\langle f_{n_j''}, \varphi\rangle| \geqslant |\langle f_{n_j''}, D^{-p_j'}\varphi_{k_j}\rangle| - |\Sigma_1| - |\Sigma_2|,$$

and, with the aid of (A.3.13),

$$|\langle f_{n_j''}, \varphi\rangle| > j + 1 - |\Sigma_2|. \tag{A.3.15}$$

(vi) From (A.3.11) follows

$$\max_{t\in R} |D^{-1}\varphi_{k_l}(t)| = \|D^{-1}\varphi_{k_l}\|_I = 1, \tag{A.3.16}$$

which, for integer $r \geqslant 2$, entails

$$|D^{-r}\varphi_{k_l}(t)| = \left|\int_b^t \frac{(t-\tau)^{r-2}}{(r-2)!}D^{-1}\varphi_{k_l}(\tau)\,d\tau\right| \leqslant \|D^{-1}\varphi_{k_l}\|_I\frac{|t-b|^{r-1}}{(r-1)!},$$

so that

$$|D^{-r}\varphi_{k_l}(t)| \leqslant \frac{|t-b|^{r-1}}{(r-1)!}, \tag{A.3.17}$$

which also agrees with (A.3.16) when $r = 1$.

† Note that $D^{-p_1'}\varphi_{k_1} + D^{-p_2'}\varphi_{k_2} + \cdots + D^{-p_j'-1}\varphi_{k_{j-1}} = \psi_{j-1}$ is a test function resulting from the first $j - 1$ steps of the induction procedure and observe that $|\langle f_{n_j''}, \psi_{j-1}\rangle| \leqslant B(\psi_{j-1})$, a bound which is independent of the choice of $f_{n''_j}$.

This inequality, with (A.3.9), gives, whenever $l > j$, so that $p_l' > p_j'$,

(A.3.18)
$$\begin{aligned} |\langle f_{n_j''}, D^{-p_l'}\varphi_{k_l}\rangle| &= |\langle D^{-p_j'}f_{n_j''}, D^{-(p_l'-p_j')}\varphi_{k_l}\rangle| \\ &= \left|\int_a^b D^{-p_j'}f_{n_j''}(t)\, D^{p_j'-p_l'}\varphi_{k_l}(t)\, dt\right| \\ &\leqslant L_{p_j'} \int_a^b \frac{|t-b|^{p_l'-p_j'-1}}{(p_l'-p_j'-1)!}\, dt \\ &= L_{p_j'} \frac{(b-a)^{p_l'-p_j'}}{(p_l'-p_j')!} \leqslant \frac{1}{2^{k_l-k_j}}. \end{aligned}$$

This furnishes a bound for the absolute value of each individual term in Σ_2 in (A.3.15), ensuring that

$$|\Sigma_2| \leqslant \sum_{l=j+1}^{\infty} \frac{1}{2^{k_l-k_j}} \leqslant \sum_{\nu=1}^{\infty} \frac{1}{2^\nu} = 1,$$

and, finally,

(A.3.19)
$$|\langle f_{n_j''}, \varphi\rangle| > j.$$

Thus if the conclusion (A.3.4) were incorrect, we should have

$$\lim_{j\to\infty} |\langle f_{n_j''}, \varphi\rangle| = +\infty$$

for this particular $\varphi \in \mathscr{D}_-$.

(vii) The proof of this lemma is now complete except for the question about the series (A.3.14). That, however, is easily cleared up.

First of all, each term in (A.3.14) vanishes for $t \geqslant b$, so $\varphi(t)$ vanishes there also. Next, by (A.3.17), for any fixed $\alpha \in R$, the series $\sum_{l=1}^{\infty} D^{-p_l'}\varphi_{k_l}(t)$ is dominated term by term, for all $t \in [\alpha, b]$, by the series

$$\sum_{l=1}^{\infty} \frac{|\alpha - b|^{p_l'-1}}{(p_l'-1)!}$$

which converges. By the Weierstrass M-test (A.3.14) therefore converges uniformly in the interval $[\alpha, b]$—but the sum of a uniformly convergent series of continuous functions is continuous. Thus φ is continuous in every finite interval $[\alpha, b]$, i.e., at any $t \in R$. Exactly the same argument shows the series obtained by differentiating (A.3.14) r times termwise to be uniformly convergent also. It is a well-known theorem of advanced calculus [1] [6] [11] [19] [49] [55] that if a series $\sum_n u_n(t)$ of functions each having a continuous derivative on the interval $[\alpha, \beta]$ converges at a point of this interval and if the series of the derivatives $\sum_n u_n'(t)$ converges uniformly on $[\alpha, \beta]$, then $\sum_n u_n'(t) = \left(\sum_n u_n(t)\right)'$ throughout this interval. Consequently, $\varphi \in \mathscr{D}_-$. ∎

Remark. In connection with the first hypothesis of this lemma, it should be noted that if a sequence $\{f_n\}$ of $\mathscr{K}_+(R)$ functions is such that $\{|\langle f_n, \varphi\rangle|\}$ has for every $\varphi \in \mathscr{D}_-$ a finite bound $B(\varphi)$ independent of n then there automatically exists a half-line $[a, +\infty)$ in which all the $f_n(t)$ are carried. For proof, see Remark 4 of § II.A.7.

Lemma A.3.2 (The Fundamental Lemma for $\mathscr{D}'_+$). *If $\{f_n(t)\}$ is a fundamental sequence on $\mathscr{D}_-$ carried in $[a, +\infty)$ then to every $b \in R$ corresponds a smallest integer $p \geqslant 0$ for which there exists a finite number $K \geqslant 0$ such that*

$$\|D^{-p}f_n(t)\|_I \leqslant K \qquad (n = 1, 2, \ldots ; I = [a, b]). \tag{A.3.20}$$

Proof. Since $\{f_n\}$ is fundamental $\{|\langle f_n, \varphi\rangle|\}$ is bounded for every φ. This is then simply a particular case of the previous lemma. ∎

A consequence of this result is (recall Definition II.A.4.2)

Theorem A.3.1. *If $F \in \mathscr{D}'_+$ is carried in $[a, +\infty)$, there corresponds to every half-line $(-\infty, b]$ a smallest integer $r \geqslant 0$ for which there exists a finite number K such that for every $\varphi \in \mathscr{D}_-$ carried in $(-\infty, b]$*

$$|\langle F, \varphi\rangle| \leqslant K\,\|\varphi^{(r)}\|_I \qquad (I = [a, b]). \tag{A.3.21}$$

Proof. Let $\{f_n\} \in F$ be carried in $[a, +\infty)$ and let $\varphi \in \mathscr{D}_-$ be carried in $(-\infty, b]$. Then if p and K are the quantities whose existence is guaranteed by Lemma A.3.2, we have $(n = 1, 2, \ldots)$

$$|\langle f_n, \varphi\rangle| = |\langle D^{-p}f_n, \varphi^{(p)}\rangle| = \left|\int_a^b D^{-p}f_n(t)\, \varphi^{(p)}(t)\, dt\right|$$
$$\leqslant K\|\varphi^{(p)}\|_I.$$

The constants p, K may vary from one fundamental sequence carried in $[a, +\infty)$, $\{f_n\}$, to another, $\{g_n\}$, carried in the same half-line, even though $\{f_n\} \sim \{g_n\}$ (Exercise 2). The point is that there exists at least one p, K combination for which (A.3.20) holds, and so a smallest integer $p \geqslant 0$ can be found that satisfies the conclusions of the theorem. ∎

Remark. Let it be noted that this theorem does not prove that to the integer r whose existence it assures there corresponds a fundamental sequence $\{f_n\}$ of $\mathscr{K}_+$ functions such that $\|D^{-r}f_n\|_I$ is bounded. The example $\delta \in \mathscr{D}'_+$, for which $|\langle \delta, \varphi\rangle| = |\varphi(0)| \leqslant \|\varphi\|_I$ (whenever I contains the origin), shows that in fact the best we can hope for, in general, is that $\|D^{-r-1}f_n\|_I$ be bounded (Exercises 10, 19).

4. $\mathscr{D}'_+$ G.F.'s as Continuous Linear Functionals

Definition A.4.1 (Convergence in $\mathscr{D}_-$). *The sequence $\{\varphi_n\}$ of test functions converges to zero in $\mathscr{D}_-$ (we write $\lim_{n\to\infty} \varphi_n = 0$) as $n \to \infty$ if and only if:*

(a) *all its members are carried in the same half-line* $(-\infty, b]$,

(b) *on every bounded closed interval* $I \subset R$ *and for each integer* $p \geqslant 0$ *the functions* $\varphi_n^{(p)}(t)$ *converge uniformly to zero as* $n \to \infty$ *(i.e.,*

$$\lim_{n\to\infty} \|\varphi_n^{(p)}\|_I = 0 \qquad (p = 0, 1, 2, \ldots)).$$

The sequence $\{\varphi_n\}$ *is said to converge to* φ *in* $\mathscr{D}_-$ *as* $n \to \infty$ *when the sequence* $\varphi_n - \varphi$ *converges to zero in* $\mathscr{D}_-$. *This is written* $\lim_{n\to\infty} \varphi_n = \varphi$.

An example of this mode of convergence was seen in the series (A.3.14). Its partial sums converge to $\varphi(t)$ in the sense of the above definition.

For a parametric family $\varphi_\lambda \in \mathscr{D}_-$, where λ ranges over an interval of real numbers instead of a sequence, the definition of convergence in $\mathscr{D}_-$ as $\lambda \to \lambda_0$ is an obvious modification of the above definition. An instance of such families is provided by the following:

Example 1. Consider the parametric family $\psi_h \in \mathscr{D}_-$ (h ranges over the finite intervals $[-\eta, 0)$ and $(0, \eta]$ of the real axis) associated with a given $\varphi \in \mathscr{D}_-$ carried in $(-\infty, b]$ by means of

$$\psi_h(t) = \frac{\varphi(t + h) - \varphi(t)}{h}.$$

This has the property that, *in the sense of* $\mathscr{D}_-$ *convergence*, as well as in the ordinary pointwise sense,

$$\lim_{h\to 0} \psi_h(t) = \varphi'(t).$$

The proof is simple: (a) all the ψ_h are carried in the fixed half-line $(-\infty, b + \eta]$; (b) for every integer $p \geqslant 0$,

$$\frac{d^p}{dt^p}(\psi_h(t) - \varphi'(t)) = \frac{1}{h}\int_t^{t+h} (t + h - \tau)\varphi^{(p+2)}(\tau)\, d\tau$$

by Taylor's formula with integral remainder. For t in any closed finite interval $I = [c, d]$, $\varphi^{(p+2)}(\tau)$, being confined to $[c - \eta, d + \eta]$, has a finite maximum $M_p(I)$ there, so that

$$\left|\frac{1}{h}\int_t^{t+h} (t + h - \tau)\, \varphi^{(p+2)}(\tau)\, d\tau\right| \leqslant \frac{|h|}{2} M_p(I).$$

Consequently, for every finite interval I,

$$\lim_{h\to 0} \left\|\frac{d^p}{dt^p}(\psi_h - \varphi')\right\|_I = 0.$$

The proof is complete.

Example 2. Given $\varphi \in \mathscr{D}_-$, the mth divided difference

$$\psi_h(t) = \frac{\Delta_h^m \varphi(t)}{h^m} = \frac{1}{h^m}\sum_{l=0}^{m} (-1)^{m-l}\binom{m}{l}\varphi(t + lh)$$

is shown by reasoning in the spirit of Example 1 to converge to $\varphi^{(m)}(t)$ in the sense of $\mathscr{D}_-$ convergence (Exercise 4).

Definition A.4.2. *A functional F on $\mathscr{D}_-$ is a continuous linear functional if and only if:*

(a) *it is linear, i.e., for any scalars c_1, c_2 and any $\varphi_1, \varphi_2 \in \mathscr{D}_-$, it satisfies*

$$\langle F, c_1\varphi_1 + c_2\varphi_2\rangle = c_1\langle F, \varphi_1\rangle + c_2\langle F, \varphi_2\rangle; \tag{A.4.1}$$

(b) *it is continuous, i.e., whenever* $\lim_{n\to\infty} \varphi_n = 0$ *in* $\mathscr{D}_-$,

$$\lim_{n\to\infty} \langle F, \varphi_n\rangle = 0. \tag{A.4.2}$$

We now come to another characterization of g.f.'s which shows the relation between the constructive (via sequences) and the abstract approach to g.f.'s. (We note in passing that the proof of the second part of the theorem may be deferred by the reader until he studies Chapter VI, § 3, where this result is first applied.)

Theorem A.4.1. *$\mathscr{D}'_+$ is the set of continuous linear functionals on $\mathscr{D}_-$.*

Proof. The proof is in two parts:

(1) *$F \in \mathscr{D}'_+ \Rightarrow f$ is a c.l.f. on $\mathscr{D}_-$.*

That $F \in \mathscr{D}'_+$ is a linear functional, we already know. There remains only to show that it is continuous.

Let $\{\varphi_n\}$ be a sequence of test functions with $\lim_{n\to\infty} \varphi_n = 0$ in $\mathscr{D}_-$. By Definition A.4.1, there exists $(-\infty, b]$ in which every member of the sequence is carried. Following Theorem A.3.1, there exist an integer $r \geqslant 0$ and a constant $K \geqslant 0$ such that

$$|\langle F, \varphi_n\rangle| \leqslant K\|\varphi_n^{(r)}\|_I,$$

where $I = [a, b]$ and $[a, +\infty)$ is a half-line in which F is carried. Convergence of φ_n in $\mathscr{D}_-$ implies that

$$\lim_{n\to\infty} \|\varphi_n^{(r)}\|_I = 0.$$

Therefore $\lim_{n\to\infty} \langle F, \varphi_n\rangle = 0$.

(2) *F is a c.l.f. on $\mathscr{D}_- \Rightarrow F \in \mathscr{D}'_+$.*

We have to show that for any given c.l.f., F, on $\mathscr{D}_-$ there exists a fundamental sequence $\{f_n\}$ of $\mathscr{K}_+(R)$ functions that defines F.

First let us show that, *F being a c.l.f. on $\mathscr{D}_-$, there exists a half line $(-\infty, a)$ such that for every $\varphi \in \mathscr{D}_-$ carried in $(-\infty, a)$, $\langle F, \varphi\rangle = 0$.*

This can be done by assuming the contrary. In that case, there exists a test function carried in $(-\infty, 0)$ for which $\langle F, \varphi\rangle \neq 0$ and, if we take $\varphi_0 = \varphi/\langle F, \varphi\rangle$, the linearity of F gives $\langle F, \varphi_0\rangle = 1$. In the same way for every positive integer k there can be found $\varphi_k \in \mathscr{D}_-$ carried in $(-\infty, -k)$ for which $\langle F, \varphi_k\rangle = 1$. But the series $\sum_{k=0}^{\infty} \varphi_k(t)$ converges uniformly, and so do the series $\sum_{k=0}^{\infty} \varphi_k^{(l)}(t)$, on every finite closed interval, because in any such interval only a finite number of terms in these series do not vanish. This series, then, defines a function $\varphi(t) \in \mathscr{D}_-$ which is, in accordance with Definition A.4.1, the limit in $\mathscr{D}_-$ as $K \to \infty$ of $\sum_{k=0}^{K} \varphi_k$. By hypothesis F is linear and continuous so we would have

$$\langle F, \varphi\rangle = \lim_{K\to\infty} \left(\sum_{k=0}^{K} \langle F, \varphi_k\rangle\right) = 1 + \lim_{K\to\infty} K = +\infty,$$

a contradiction.

Now, $\rho_\varepsilon(t)$ being defined by (A.2.2), and t being an arbitrary fixed real number, denote by $\alpha_n(t-\tau)$ the function of τ,

$$\rho_{1/n}(t-\tau) = \rho_{1/n}(\tau - t),$$

and consider

$$f_n(t) = \langle F(\tau), \alpha_n(t-\tau)\rangle.† \tag{A.4.3}$$

This is a function of t which is carried in the forward half-line $[a - 1/n, +\infty)$ of the t axis—because, for any fixed $t < a - 1/n$, the function of τ, $\alpha_n(t-\tau)$, is carried in the half-line $(-\infty, a)$ of the axis and the value of F on every $\mathscr{D}_-$ function carried in this half-line is, by the previous argument, zero.

Furthermore, $f_n(t)$ is a continuous function of t on R (Exercise 6).

Thus $\{f_n(t)\}$ $(n = 1, 2, \ldots)$ is a sequence of $C(R)$ functions carried in the half-line $[a-1, +\infty)$ of the t-axis—ergo a sequence of $\mathscr{K}_+(R)$ functions of t carried in this half-line.

Let us now prove that it is a fundamental sequence on $\mathscr{D}_-$ and that it defines F. For this purpose, take an arbitrary $\varphi \in \mathscr{D}_-$ and let $(-\infty, b]$ be a half-line in which it is carried. Then

$$\int_{-\infty}^{\infty} f_n(t)\,\varphi(t)\,dt = \int_{a-1}^{b} f_n(t)\,\varphi(t)\,dt = \int_{a-1}^{b} \langle F(\tau), \alpha_n(t-\tau)\rangle\,\varphi(t)\,dt, \tag{A.4.4}$$

being an ordinary Riemann integral of a continuous function, is equal to

$$\lim_{K\to\infty} \sum_{k=1}^{K} f_n(a-1+k\Delta_K t)\,\varphi(a-1+k\Delta_K t)\,\Delta_K t \quad \text{where } \Delta_K t = \frac{b-a+1}{K}$$

$$= \lim_{K\to\infty} \sum_{k=1}^{K} \langle F(\tau), \alpha_n(-\tau + a - 1 + k\Delta_K t)\rangle\,\varphi(a-1+k\Delta_K t)\,\Delta_K t.$$

---

† The notation $\langle F(\tau), \alpha_n(t-\tau)\rangle$ means that we take F as a functional on the set $\mathscr{D}_-$ of functions of τ instead of functions of t.

The linearity of the functional $F(\tau)$ on the set $\mathscr{D}_-$ of functions of τ makes this equal to

$$\lim_{K\to\infty} \langle F(\tau), \sum_{k=1}^{K} \alpha_n(-\tau + a - 1 + k\Delta_K t)\, \varphi(a - 1 + k\Delta_K t)\, \Delta_K t\rangle.$$

Now, as $K \to \infty$, the $\mathscr{D}_-$ functions of τ,

$$\psi_K(\tau) = \sum_{k=1}^{K} \alpha_n(-\tau + a - 1 + k\Delta_K t)\, \varphi(a - 1 + k\Delta_K t)\, \Delta_K t$$

converge to the function

$$\int_{a-1}^{b} \alpha_n(t - \tau)\, \varphi(t)\, dt = \int_{-\infty}^{\infty} \alpha_n(t - \tau)\, \varphi(t)\, dt.$$

The latter belongs to $\mathscr{D}_-$ (the proof requires that one show it to be a $C^\infty(R)$ function; for that a trivial modification of the proof of Theorem III.C.2.1 suffices). Furthermore, $\psi_K(\tau)$ converges to $\int_{-\infty}^{\infty} \alpha_n(t - \tau)\, \varphi(t)\, dt$ in the sense of Definition A.4.1, a fact which the reader is asked to verify (Exercise 8).

The continuity of F as a functional on $\mathscr{D}_-$ then yields

$$\lim_{K\to\infty} \langle F(\tau), \psi_K(\tau)\rangle = \langle F(\tau), \lim_{K\to\infty} \psi_K(\tau)\rangle,$$

which, with (A.4.4), gives

$$\langle f_n, \varphi\rangle = \langle F(\tau), \langle \alpha_n(t - \tau), \varphi(t)\rangle\rangle. \tag{A.4.5}$$

From the solution of Exercise 5 of Chapter II it follows that

$$\lim_{n\to\infty} \langle \alpha_n(t - \tau), \varphi(\tau)\rangle = \varphi(t),$$

and that this convergence is in the sense of Definition A.4.1. Letting $n \to \infty$, the right-hand side of (A.4.5) then approaches the limit $\langle F, \varphi\rangle$ because of the continuity of the functional F. This proves that

$$\langle F, \varphi\rangle = \lim_{n\to\infty} \langle f_n, \varphi\rangle;$$

in other words $\{f_n\}$ is a fundamental sequence and therefore the functional $F \in \mathscr{D}'_+$. ∎

Remark on the Definition of G.F.'s. The preceding theorem shows that there is an approach to the theory of g.f.'s of class $\mathscr{D}'_+$ other than that of fundamental sequences; namely: first define convergence in $\mathscr{D}_-$ (Definition A.4.1), next define $\mathscr{D}'_+$ as the set of c.l.f.'s on $\mathscr{D}_-$ in the sense of Definition A.4.2, then develop the properties of g.f.'s as consequences of this definition. This is essentially the path followed by the inventor of this theory, L. Schwartz [43] [26], and later described, not for $\mathscr{D}'_+$ but for other g.f. classes, and extended by Gel'fand and Šilov [22] [23]. Introductory expositions of this approach were given by I. Halperin [26] and C. R. Saltzer [42] among others.

It is shown in § VI.4 of [43] that g.f.'s of various classes which are defined as continuous linear functionals can be expressed as limits of fundamental sequences [for $\mathscr{D}'_+$ the sequences $\{f_n\}$ defined in (A.4.3) above]. The idea of *starting* with equivalence classes of fundamental sequences and developing g.f. theory from there is due to J. Mikusiński [37]. G. Temple [50] [51] gave the first version of such a procedure for several g.f. classes; this was amplified and simplified for a particular class ($\mathscr{S}'$; especially adapted to the generalization of Fourier integrals) by Lighthill [34]. A feature of this approach—which we have followed here in a modified form (fundamental sequences of piecewise continuous functions instead of fundamental sequences of C^∞ functions)—is the fact that all the theory required for most applications to physical problems can be developed in mathematically quite elementary terms, as we have seen in Chapters I–IV.

J. Korevaar [32] also develops g.f.'s from fundamental sequences. These, however, are defined not in terms of their values on test functions but as sequences of integrable functions carried in $[0, +\infty)$ and such that to every finite interval $[0, b]$ there corresponds an integer $p \geqslant 0$ for which $D^{-p}f_n(t)$ converges uniformly on this interval. This approach has roots in a close ancestor of g.f. theory due to S. Bochner (see Chap. 6 of [4]); its equivalence to the other approaches mentioned derives from Theorem B.1.1 below.

5. The Limit Definition of G.F. Differentiation

Let $F(t) \in \mathscr{D}'_+$ and $h \in R$. The derivative $DF(t) \in \mathscr{D}'_+$ can be obtained in a fashion analogous to that which gives the ordinary derivative of a differentiable function of t:

(A.5.1) $$DF = \operatorname*{Lim}_{h\to 0} \frac{1}{h}(F(t+h) - F(t)).$$

To prove it, take $\varphi \in \mathscr{D}_-$, then

(A.5.2) $$\left\langle \frac{1}{h} F((t+h) - F(t)), \varphi \right\rangle = \left\langle F(t), \frac{\varphi(t-h) - \varphi(t)}{h} \right\rangle.$$

By the first part of Theorem A.4.1, F is a c.l.f. on $\mathscr{D}_-$. It then follows from Example 1, p. 192, that

(A.5.3) $$\lim_{h\to 0} \left\langle F(t), \frac{\varphi(t-h) - \varphi(t)}{h} \right\rangle = -\langle F(t), \varphi'(t)\rangle.$$

A simple modification of this argument proves that

(A.5.4) $$D^p F = \operatorname*{Lim}_{h\to 0} \left[\frac{1}{h^p} \sum_{l=0}^{p} (-1)^{p-l} \binom{p}{l} F(t+lh)\right].$$

Particular cases of these relations were considered in § II.B.5.

6. Characterization of Positive G.F.'s

Theorem A.6.1. *A necessary and sufficient condition for* F, *a functional on* $\mathscr{D}_-$, *to be a positive g.f. of class* $\mathscr{D}'_+$ *is that it be a linear functional and that for every* $\varphi \in \mathscr{D}_-$ *which takes only positive or zero values there hold the inequality*

$$\langle F, \varphi \rangle \geqslant 0. \tag{A.6.1}$$

Proof. Any $\mathscr{D}'_+$ g.f. is a linear functional and, as we saw in § 1, any positive g.f. of class $\mathscr{D}'_+$ satisfies (A.6.1). This proves the necessity of the condition.

To prove its sufficiency, note first that if F is a linear functional on $\mathscr{D}_-$ satisfying (A.6.1), there exists a half-line $(-\infty, a)$ such that for every $\varphi \in \mathscr{D}_-$ carried in this half-line, and taking only non-negative values,

$$\langle F, \varphi \rangle = 0. \tag{A.6.2}$$

Indeed, if this were not true, there would correspond to every half-line $(-\infty, -k)$ $(k = 0, 1, 2, \ldots)$ a function $\varphi_k \in \mathscr{D}_-$ carried in this half-line and whose values are everywhere zero or positive and such that

$$\langle F, \varphi_k \rangle = 1 \qquad (k = 0, 1, 2, \ldots). \tag{A.6.3}$$

The series $\sum_{k=0}^{\infty} \varphi_k$ converges in $\mathscr{D}_-$ to a nowhere negative function $\psi \in \mathscr{D}_-$ carried in $(-\infty, 0)$, and for every integer $K \geqslant 0$ the $\mathscr{D}_-$ function

$$\psi - \sum_{k=0}^{K} \varphi_k$$

takes only positive or zero values. But then, F being by hypothesis linear, it follows from (A.6.1) that

$$\left\langle F, \psi - \sum_{k=0}^{K} \varphi_k \right\rangle = \langle F, \psi \rangle - \sum_{k=0}^{K} \langle F, \varphi_k \rangle \geqslant 0 \qquad (K = 0, 1, 2, \ldots),$$

and, in view of (A.6.3),

$$\langle F, \psi \rangle \geqslant K + 1 \qquad (K = 0, 1, 2, \ldots).$$

As this contradicts the fact that $\langle F, \psi \rangle$ is well defined, we conclude that (A.6.2) must hold for all test functions carried in some half-line $(-\infty, a)$.

Next, we shall prove that the linearity of F and the hypothesis (A.6.1) suffice to ensure that F is a continuous functional on $\mathscr{D}_-$.

For this, take an arbitrary sequence $\{\varphi_n\}$ of test functions converging to zero in $\mathscr{D}_-$ and designate by $(-\infty, b)$ a half-line in which they are all carried. If

$$b \leqslant a \quad \text{then} \quad \langle F, \varphi_n \rangle = 0 \quad \text{and} \quad \lim_{n \to \infty} \langle F, \varphi_n \rangle = 0,$$

so we shall suppose $b > a$. Also let us set $I = [a - 1, b]$.

Convergence in $\mathscr{D}_-$ implies uniform convergence on every finite interval, and on I in particular, so that, setting

(A.6.4) $$\|\varphi_n\|_I = \varepsilon_n \qquad (n = 1, 2, \ldots),$$

we have

$$\lim_{n\to\infty} \varepsilon_n = 0.$$

To the complex-valued $\varphi_n(t)$ correspond the real-valued $u_n(t)$, $v_n(t)$ such that $\varphi_n = u_n + iv_n$. From (A.6.4) there results

$$\|u_n\|_I \leqslant \varepsilon_n, \qquad \|v_n\|_I \leqslant \varepsilon_n$$

and, so long as $a - 1 \leqslant t \leqslant b$,

(A.6.5) $$-\varepsilon_n \leqslant u_n(t) \leqslant \varepsilon_n, \qquad -\varepsilon_n \leqslant v_n(t) \leqslant \varepsilon_n.$$

The $\mathscr{D}_-$ function [obtained from $\rho_\varepsilon(t)$ of (A.2.2)]

$$\psi(t) = (-1)D^{-1}\rho_1(t - b - 1)$$

satisfies

(A.6.6) $$\psi(t) \begin{cases} = 0 & \text{if } t \geqslant b + 2 \\ \geqslant 0 & \text{if } b \leqslant t \leqslant b + 2 \\ = 1 & \text{if } t \leqslant b, \end{cases}$$

while the $\mathscr{D}_+$ function

$$\kappa(t) = \int_{-\infty}^{t} \rho_1(\tau - a + 2)\, d\tau$$

has the values

(A.6.7) $$\kappa(t) \begin{cases} = 0 & \text{if } t \leqslant a - 3 \\ \geqslant 0 & \text{if } a - 3 \leqslant t \leqslant a - 1 \\ = 1 & \text{if } a - 1 \leqslant t. \end{cases}$$

But then $\kappa(t)\, \varphi_n(t)$ coincides with $\varphi_n(t)$ for $t \geqslant a - 1$, while

(A.6.8) $$\langle F, \kappa\varphi_n\rangle = \langle F, \varphi_n\rangle$$

because

$$\langle F, \varphi_n\rangle = \langle F, \kappa\varphi_n\rangle + \langle F, \varphi_n - \kappa\varphi_n\rangle,$$

where the last term on the right is zero by (A.6.2) since $\varphi_n - \kappa\varphi_n$ is carried in $(-\infty, a)$. Also $\|\kappa\varphi_n\|_I = \|\varphi_n\|_I$.

From (A.6.5) and (A.6.6) we have

(A.6.9) $$\begin{aligned} -\varepsilon_n\psi(t) &\leqslant \kappa(t)\, u_n(t) \leqslant \varepsilon_n\psi(t), \\ -\varepsilon_n\psi(t) &\leqslant \kappa(t)\, v_n(t) \leqslant \varepsilon_n\psi(t), \end{aligned}$$

whence, because of the positivity of F as expressed in (A.6.1),

$$|\langle F, u_n\rangle| = |\langle F, \kappa u_n\rangle| \leqslant \varepsilon_n \, |\langle F, \psi\rangle|,$$

$$|\langle F, v_n\rangle| = |\langle F, \kappa v_n\rangle| \leqslant \varepsilon_n \, |\langle F, \psi\rangle|.$$

Letting $n \to \infty$, so $\varepsilon_n \to 0$, we conclude that

$$\lim_{n\to\infty} \langle F, \varphi_n\rangle = 0,$$

proving that F is indeed a continuous linear functional on $\mathscr{D}_-$.

A positive $\mathscr{D}'_+$ g.f. was defined (§ 1 above) to be a g.f. having a defining sequence $\{f_n\}$ of everywhere positive or vanishing $\mathscr{K}_+(R)$ functions. To obtain such a sequence for F, we have only to take f_n as defined in (A.4.3). It was shown, in the portion of the proof of Theorem A.4.1 following (A.4.3), that this $\{f_r\}$ is a fundamental sequence belonging to the equivalence class F. Since $f_n(t)$ is obviously nonnegative, because of (A.6.1), our proof is complete. ∎

B. $\mathscr{D}'_+$ G.F.'s AS DERIVATIVES OF FUNCTIONS

1. The Fundamental Structure Theorems

A $\mathscr{K}_+(R)$ function, whether it be differentiable in the ordinary sense or not, does have g.f. derivatives of every order. This result, one of the attractions of g.f. theory, was rather easily obtained in Chapter II. We are now in a position to complement it with a kind of converse: every $\mathscr{D}'_+$ g.f. is, locally, a g.f. derivative of finite order of a $\mathscr{K}_+(R)$ function.

The precise meaning of this statement is embodied in the fundamental structure Theorems B.1.2 and B.1.3 enunciated further below.

Here and in § VI.6 we shall make use of the concept of *equicontinuity of a sequence of functions:*

Definition B.1.1. *A sequence $\{f_n(t)\}$ of functions continuous on an interval I is called equicontinuous if and only if to every positive ε corresponds a positive δ_ε independent of n such that for any t_1 and t_2 in I*

(B.1.1) $$|t_1 - t_2| < \delta_\varepsilon \Rightarrow |f_n(t_1) - f_n(t_2)| < \varepsilon \qquad (n = 1, 2, \ldots).$$

An elementary property of equicontinuous sequences is given in

Lemma B.1.1. *If the sequence $\{f_n(t)\}$ is equicontinuous on the closed bounded interval $[a, b]$ and if it is pointwise convergent on this interval (i.e., for every $t \in [a, b]$ there exists the finite $\lim_{n\to\infty} f_n(t) = f(t)$) then $f(t) \in C[a, b]$ and the sequence converges to $f(t)$ uniformly on $[a, b]$.*

Proof. Given any $\varepsilon > 0$ and the $\delta_{\varepsilon/2}$ corresponding to $\varepsilon/2$ provided by Definition B.1.1, we have only to let $n \to \infty$ on the right in (B.1.1) to see that

$$|t_1 - t_2| < \delta_{\varepsilon/2} \Rightarrow |f(t_1) - f(t_2)| \leqslant \frac{\varepsilon}{2} < \varepsilon,$$

from which we conclude that $f \in C[a, b]$.

Again by Definition B.1.1 to a given $\varepsilon > 0$ corresponds $\delta_{\varepsilon/3}$ such that for any t_1 and t_2 in $[a, b]$

(B.1.2) $$|t_1 - t_2| < \delta_{\varepsilon/3} \Rightarrow |f_n(t_1) - f_n(t_2)| < \frac{\varepsilon}{3} \qquad (n = 1, 2, \ldots).$$

Take the points

$$\tau_j = a + j\delta_{\varepsilon/3} \qquad (j = 0, 1, \ldots, \nu)$$

where ν is the integer for which $\tau_\nu \leqslant b < \tau_{\nu+1}$. Because of the pointwise convergence of $\{f_n(t)\}$ there corresponds to each $j = 0, 1, \ldots, \nu$ an integer N_j such that

(B.1.3) $$n > N_j \Rightarrow |f_n(\tau_j) - f(\tau_j)| \leqslant \frac{\varepsilon}{3}.$$

For any $t \in [a, b]$ there is an integer j $(= 0, 1, 2, \ldots, \nu)$ with $t \in [\tau_j, \tau_{j+1})$ and

(B.1.4) $$|f(t) - f_n(t)| \leqslant |f(t) - f(\tau_j)| + |f(\tau_j) - f_n(\tau_j)| + |f_n(\tau_j) - f_n(t)|.$$

Here the third difference on the right is less than $\varepsilon/3$, because of (B.1.2), while the first difference on the right does not exceed $\varepsilon/3$, as we see by letting $n \to \infty$ in (B.1.2). Taking $N = \max_{1 \leqslant j \leqslant \nu} N_j$, it therefore follows from (B.1.3) and (B.1.4) that

$$n > N \Rightarrow |f(t) - f_n(t)| < \frac{\varepsilon}{3} + \frac{\varepsilon}{3} + \frac{\varepsilon}{3} = \varepsilon.$$

This, since N is independent of t, proves the convergence of $\{f_n(t)\}$ to $f(t)$ to be uniform on $[a, b]$. ∎

Preliminary to the fundamental structure theorem, we consider

Theorem B.1.1. *Let $\{f_n\}$ be a fundamental sequence belonging to $F \in \mathscr{D}'_+$. To every half-line $(-\infty, b]$ corresponds a smallest integer $q \geqslant 0$ and an associated function $g \in C(-\infty, b]$ such that $\{D^{-q}f_n\}_n$ converges to g uniformly on $(-\infty, b]$ and such that*

(B.1.5) $$\langle F, \varphi \rangle = \langle D^q g, \varphi \rangle$$

for every $\varphi \in \mathscr{D}_-$ carried in $(-\infty, b]$. q is called the C-order of $\{f_n\}$ on this half-line and is related to the integer p of Lemma A.3.2 *by the inequalities $p \leqslant q \leqslant p + 1$.*

Proof. Let $\{f_n\}$ be carried in $[a, +\infty)$, then if $b \leqslant a$, the choice $q = 0$, $g(t) = 0$ will do. Therefore suppose $b > a$ from now on. If all the f_n are identical on $(-\infty, b]$, and are continuous there, then $q = 0$ and $g = f_n$ is the answer. If the f_n are identical $\mathscr{K}_+(R)$ functions on $(-\infty, b]$ but with simple discontinuities then $q = 1$ and $g = D^{-1}f_n \in C(-\infty, b]$.

For the general case, we turn to Lemma A.3.2, according to which there exists a smallest integer $p \geqslant 0$ and a constant M such that

$$\|D^{-p}f_n\|_I \leqslant M \qquad (n = 1, 2, \ldots; I = [a, b]). \tag{B.1.6}$$

while, for all $t < a$, $f_n(t) = 0$.

It may be that the $D^{-p}f_n$ converge uniformly on $(-\infty, b]$ to a function of the type called for—in which case, the theorem is proved with $q = p$. If this situation, however, does not prevail, we may use (B.1.6) and the fact that $D^{-p}f_n(t) = 0$ for $t \leqslant a$ to conclude that, when t_1 and t_2 are in $[a, b]$ and $q = p + 1$,

$$\begin{aligned} |D^{-q}f_n(t_2) - D^{-q}f_n(t_1)| &= \int_{t_1}^{t_2} D^{-p}f_n(\tau)\, d\tau \\ &\leqslant M\,|t_2 - t_1| \qquad (n = 1, 2, \ldots). \end{aligned} \tag{B.1.7}$$

Comparison of these inequalities with (B.1.1), in which one takes $\delta_\varepsilon = \varepsilon/M$, reveals $\{D^{-q}f_n\}_n$ to be an equicontinuous sequence on $[a, b]$. In fact each $D^{-q}f_n$ is continuous on $(-\infty, b]$ and vanishes for $t \leqslant a$ so that

$$\lim_{n\to\infty} D^{-q}f_n(t) \doteq 0 \qquad \text{when } t \leqslant a. \tag{B.1.8}$$

Let us now show that for any $t_0 \in [a, b]$ $\lim\limits_{n\to\infty} D^{-q}f_n(t_0)$ exists. (From here on we assume the $f_n(t)$ to be real-valued; as usual, the complex-valued case is left to the reader.)

Since $D^{-q}f_n(a) = 0$, (B.1.7) with $t_1 = a$ and $t_2 = t_0$ gives $|D^{-q}f_n(t_0)| \leqslant M(b - a)$. Thus, for any fixed $t_0 \in [a, b]$, the numerical sequence $\{D^{-q}f_n(t_0)\}_n$ is bounded and so, by the Bolzano-Weierstrass theorem [19, p. 12], has one or more limit points. If there were several, there would exist two different subsequences $\{n_k\}_k$ and $\{n_j\}_j$ of the natural numbers and two real numbers $l_1 \neq l_2$, such that

$$\begin{aligned} &l_1 - l_2 = 5\eta, \\ &|D^{-q}f_{n_k}(t_0) - l_1| < \eta \qquad \text{for all } k > K, \\ &|D^{-q}f_{n_j}(t_0) - l_2| < \eta \qquad \text{for all } j > J. \end{aligned} \tag{B.1.9}$$

In this case, for all t in the interval $[t_0 - \eta/M, t_0 + \eta/M]$ and $k > K$ we will have, thanks to (B.1.7) and (B.1.9),

$$|D^{-q}f_{n_k}(t) - l_1| \leqslant |D^{-q}f_{n_k}(t) - D^{-q}f_{n_k}(t_0)| + |D^{-q}f_{n_k}(t_0) - l_1| < 2\eta,$$

and for all t in the same interval and all $j > J$:

$$|D^{-q}f_{n_j}(t) - l_2| < 2\eta;$$

so that, *with these choices of t, j, k,*

$$|D^{-q}f_{n_k}(t) - D^{-q}f_{n_j}(t)| > \eta.$$

It follows from this inequality that if now we take for $\varphi \in \mathscr{D}_-$ the function $\rho_\varepsilon(t - t_0)$ of (A.2.2) with $\varepsilon = \eta/M$, we obtain

$$\lim_{k\to\infty} \langle D^{-q}f_{n_k}, \varphi\rangle \neq \lim_{j\to\infty} \langle D^{-q}f_{n_j}, \varphi\rangle. \tag{B.1.10}$$

This contradiction to the hypothesis that $\{D^{-q}f_{n_k}\}_k$ and $\{D^{-q}f_{n_j}\}_j$ are subsequences of the same fundamental sequence† $\{D^{-q}f_n\}_n$ proves that the assumption $l_1 \neq l_2$ is untenable and we conclude that

$$\lim_{n\to\infty} D^{-q}f_n(t) = g(t) \tag{B.1.11}$$

exists for every $t \in [a, b]$.

From Lemma B.1.1 and the equicontinuity of $\{D^{-q}f_n\}$ we see that $g(t)$ is continuous on $[a, b]$ and that $\{D^{-q}f_n(t)\}$ converges to this function uniformly on $[a, b]$. In view of (B.1.8) these statements hold on the half-line $(-\infty, b]$ as well.

Finally, restricting the proof of Theorem II.B.6.1 to functions carried in $(-\infty, b]$ instantly shows that for every $\varphi \in \mathscr{D}_-$ carried in $(-\infty, b]$,

$$\lim_{n\to\infty} \langle D^{-q}f_n, \varphi\rangle = \langle g, \varphi\rangle, \tag{B.1.12}$$

and since $\operatorname{Lim}_{n\to\infty} D^{-q}f_n = D^{-q}F$, we have only to examine the proof of Theorem II.B.4.1, but with φ carried in $(-\infty, b]$ only, to see that the operator D^q can be applied to each of the g.f.'s in (B.1.12) with the result

$$\langle F, \varphi\rangle = \langle D^q g, \varphi\rangle \qquad (\varphi \in \mathscr{D}_- \text{ carried in } (-\infty, b]). \quad \blacksquare$$

Remark. The above theorem has a converse (Exercise 17). Consequently, a fundamental sequence on $\mathscr{D}_-$ can be characterized as one such that to every $b > a$ corresponds an integer $q \geqslant 0$ for which $D^{-q}f_n(t)$ converges uniformly on $[a, b]$. This property is taken as a *definition* of fundamental sequences in the theory of Korevaar [32] (cf. also Mikusiński and Sikorski [40]), and the properties of g.f.'s are developed therefrom without any appeal to test functions. Let it be noted that $\{f_n\} \sim \{h_n\}$ does not entail that these sequences are of the same order on every half-line. Thus, $f_n(t) \equiv 0$ ($n = 1, 2, \ldots$) gives a sequence of order zero on $(-\infty, b]$ whereas $h_n(t) = n \sin nt \cdot H(t)$ gives a sequence of order 2 on $(-\infty, b]$; yet $\{f_n\} \sim \{h_n\}$.

---

† Actually it is $\{f_n\}$ that is a fundamental sequence by hypothesis. But then so is $\{D^{-q}f_n\}$ as a result of Section III.A.2.

Corollary B.1.1. *If $\{f_n\}$ is a fundamental sequence on $\mathscr{D}_-$, then to every finite closed interval $I = [c, d]$ corresponds a smallest integer $q \geqslant 0$, such that the sequence $\{D^{-q}f_n(t)\}_n$ converges uniformly on I to a function $g_J(t)$ defined and continuous on this interval. (q is called the C-order of $\{f_n\}$ on I.)*

Proof. The preceding theorem applied to $(-\infty, d]$ guarantees that for some $p \geqslant 0$, $\{D^{-p}f_n\}_n$ converges uniformly on this half-line, and therefore on $[c, d]$. There may be smaller values of p which will do on $[c, d]$, however. For the integer q of the statement, we simply take the smallest one. ∎

Apropos the theorem below, we recall that local equality of g.f.'s was defined in Chapter II, § A.8

Theorem B.1.2. *Given $F \in \mathscr{D}'_+$ and the finite open interval $J = (c, d)$ there exist a smallest integer $q \geqslant 0$ and a $\mathscr{K}_+(R)$ function g_J carried in$[c, d]$ and continuous in (c, d) such that $F = D^q g_J$ on J. F is said to be of C-order q on J.*

Proof. Every fundamental sequence in the equivalence class F has, by Corollary B.1.1, finite C-order on the closed interval $[c, d]$; $\{f_n\}$ being such a fundamental sequence, of C-order p, the function $f_J(t)$ defined by

(B.1.13) $$f_J(t) = \lim_{n\to\infty} D^{-p}f_n(t) \qquad (c \leqslant t \leqslant d)$$

is continuous on $[c, d]$.

The function g_J defined by

(B.1.14) $$g_J(t) = \begin{cases} f_J(t) & \text{for } c < t < d \\ 0 & \text{for } t < c \text{ and for } t > d, \end{cases}$$

has the property

(B.1.15) $$D^p g_J = F \text{ on } J = (c, d).$$

The truth of the conclusion is now obvious.

Note that g_J is not unique. Adding to such a function

$$H(t - c)H(d - t)P_{q-1}(t),$$

where P_{q-1} is an arbitrary polynomial of degree $q - 1$, gives another g_J. ∎

Remark. The actual value of the C-order q of $F \in \mathscr{D}'_+$ on any given interval is rarely needed. The knowledge that it exists as a finite integer is all one usually requires.

Theorem B.1.3. *Given $F \in \mathscr{D}'_+$, carried in $[a, +\infty)$, to every open half-line $(-\infty, b)$ correspond a smallest integer q and a unique function $g_b(t)$ continuous in $(-\infty, b)$, and vanishing for $t < a$ and for $t > b$, such that $F = D^q g_b$ on $(-\infty, b)$. q is said to be the C-order of F on $(-\infty, b)$.*

Proof. For every half-line $[a, +\infty)$ in which F is carried, (recall Definition II.A.4.2) and given $b \in R$, there exists a smallest integer $r \geqslant 0$ and a function $g \in \mathscr{K}_+(R)$, continuous on $(-\infty, b)$ and vanishing for $t < a$ and $t > b$, with $F = D^r g$ on $(-\infty, b)$. This we get from Theorem B.1.1 quite as Theorem B.1.2 is derived from Corollary B.1.1. Let r, g be the combination thus associated with one half-line $[a, +\infty)$ and r', g' the pair corresponding to another half-line $[a', +\infty)$. We wish to show that $r = r'$ and $g = g'$, for then $q = r$ and $g_b = g$ satisfy the conclusions of the theorem.

Suppose $r' > r$. From $\langle D^r g, \varphi\rangle = \langle D^{r'} g', \varphi\rangle$ ($\varphi \in \mathscr{D}_-$ carried in $(-\infty, b)$) follows $g' = D^{r-r'} g$ on $(-\infty, b)$. Now, $D^{r-r'} g$ is given by $r' - r$ successive integrations of a continuous function on $(-\infty, b)$ so $g = \dfrac{d^{r'-r} g'}{dt^{r'-r}}$, an ordinary derivative, on that half-line. But then r' is not the smallest nonnegative integer with the stated properties. We conclude that $r' = r$. That $g' = g$ follows immediately. ∎

Example. *Order of a positive* $F \in \mathscr{D}'_+$. There exists at least one $\{f_n\} \in F$ all of whose elements f_n are real-valued and nowhere negative. In view of the inequality (A.2.4) and Theorem B.1.1, the continuous functions $D^{-2} f_n$ converge uniformly on every half-line $(-\infty, b]$. This and Theorem B.1.3 guarantee that the C-order of F on any open backward half-line $(-\infty, b)$ is two or less [e.g., $\delta(t)$ is of C-order two, while the function $F(t) = H(t)\sin^2 t$ is a g.f. of C-order zero; $F(t) = H(t)\cos^2 t$ on the other hand is of C-order one].

A positive g.f. of class $\mathscr{D}'_+$ is thus of finite C-order not just locally but on R: there exists a $C(R)$ function carried in a forward half-line $g(t) = \lim_{n\to\infty} D^{-2} f_n(t)$ such that $D^2 g = F$ without restriction to a particular half-line or interval.

Remark. The reader will note that the notion of C-order on R used here differs from that of K-order defined in § III.C.5. $\delta(t)$ is of C-order two on $R(\delta(t) = D^2 t_+)$ while it is of K-order one $(\delta(t) = DH(t))$. In the case of the g.f. t_+ defined in § II.C.2 the C-order on R and the K-order are both zero since t_+ is a $C(R)$ function carried in $[0, +\infty)$. Clearly, *if* $F \in \mathscr{D}'_+$ *is of finite K-order p, it is also of C-order* $q \leqslant p + 1$ *on R.* (The relation between q and the index r of Theorem A.3.1 is examined in Exercise 19.) Concerning the notion of finite local order see also McShane [1s].

2. Some Consequences

If $F \in \mathscr{D}'_+$ is of C-order q on $(-\infty, b)$, then $D^p F$ $(p > 0)$ is of C-order not exceeding $p + q$ on this open half line. Furthermore, we obtain

Theorem B.2.1. *Let* $F \in \mathscr{D}'_+$ *and let* $(-\infty, b)$ *be an open half-line. Then if for every integer* $p \geqslant 0$, *the C-order of* $D^p F$ *on* $(-\infty, b)$ *does not exceed some*

fixed integer $q \geqslant 0$, F *coincides on* $(-\infty, b)$ *with a function belonging to* $C^\infty(-\infty, b)$.

Proof. From the hypothesis, it follows that for every integer $p \geqslant 0$, $D^{p-q}F$ coincides with a function $g_p(t)$ continuous on $(-\infty, b)$. Since $g_{p-1}(t) = D^{-1}g_p(t) = D^{p-q-1}F$ for every such integer, $g_p(t)$ is the pth derivative, in the ordinary sense, of $g_0(t)$ on $(-\infty, b)$.

Thus $g_0(t) \in C^\infty(-\infty, b)$. As g_0 coincides with $D^{-q}F$ on $(-\infty, b)$, and as generalized and ordinary derivatives coincide on every open half-line where the latter exist, it follows that $F = g_q$ on $(-\infty, b)$ and the conclusion results. ∎

Naturally, we want to know whether this theorem can be extended to the case where the D^pF are of uniformly bounded C-order merely on some finite open interval (c, d). To show that it can, we make use of

Lemma B.2.1. *If* $F \in \mathscr{D}'_+$ *and* $DF = 0$ *on the open interval* (c, d) *then* F *coincides with a constant function on* (c, d).

Proof. Let φ_0 be a test function carried in (c, d), such that

(B.2.1) $$\int_{\infty}^{-\infty} \varphi_0(t)\, dt = \int_{d}^{c} \varphi_0(t)\, dt = 1.$$

Any $\varphi \in \mathscr{D}_-$ that is carried in (c, d) can be expressed in the form

(B.2.2) $$\varphi(t) = a\varphi_0(t) + D\psi(t)$$

where ψ is a test function carried in (c, d).

Indeed, whatever the value of the constant a, the function $\varphi - a\varphi_0$ is carried in (c, d), i.e., for some $\varepsilon > 0$ this function vanishes outside the closed interval $[c + \varepsilon, d - \varepsilon]$. But then, for $t \leqslant c + \varepsilon$, the functions $D^{-1}\varphi$ and $D^{-1}\varphi_0$ assume the constant values

$$\int_{d-\varepsilon}^{c+\varepsilon} \varphi(t)\, dt \qquad \text{and} \qquad \int_{d-\varepsilon}^{c+\varepsilon} \varphi_0(t)\, dt,$$

respectively. If we assign to a the value

(B.2.3) $$a = \int_{d-\varepsilon}^{c+\varepsilon} \varphi(t)\, dt$$

it follows that $\psi = D^{-1}(\varphi - a\varphi_0)$ is carried in (c, d).

We can now prove the lemma. Given any $\varphi \in \mathscr{D}_-$ carried in (c, d), with a satisfying (B.2.3), there results

$$\begin{aligned} \langle F, \varphi \rangle &= \langle F, a\varphi_0 \rangle + \langle F, D\psi \rangle \\ &= a\langle F, \varphi_0 \rangle - \langle DF, \psi \rangle. \end{aligned}$$

As DF vanishes on (c, d), $\langle DF, \psi\rangle = 0$, so that, denoting by k the value of $\langle F, \varphi_0\rangle$, this relation can be written

$$\langle F, \varphi\rangle = k \int_d^c \varphi(t)\, dt = k \int_{\infty}^{-\infty} \varphi(t)\, dt \tag{B.2.4}$$

which proves that F coincides on (c, d) with a function assuming the constant value k on that interval. ∎

Suppose now that $F \in \mathscr{D}'_+$ has all its derivatives D^pF $(p = 0, 1, 2, \ldots)$ of C-order $\leqslant q$ on the interval (c, d). The fundamental Theorem B.1.2 then ensures the existence of $\mathscr{K}_+(R)$ functions

$$g_p(t) = D^{p-q}F \quad \text{on } (c, d) \qquad (p = 0, 1, 2, \ldots). \tag{B.2.5}$$

From this it follows that the (generalized) derivative Dg_p coincides (as a g.f.) with g_{p+1} on (c, d). On the other hand, the continuous function $D^{-1}g_{p+1}$ has an (ordinary and therefore g.f.) derivative equal to g_{p+1} on (c, d) so that the g.f.

$$D(g_p - D^{-1}g_{p+1}) = 0 \qquad \text{on } (c, d)$$

and it follows from the lemma above that there exist constants k_p such that on (c, d)

$$g_p = D^{-1}g_{p+1} + k_p \qquad (p = 0, 1, 2, \ldots).$$

Consequently, g_p is differentiable in the ordinary sense on (c, d) and

$$\frac{dg_p}{dt} = g_{p+1} \quad \text{on } (c, d) \qquad (p = 0, 1, 2, \ldots).$$

We conclude that $g_p \in C^\infty(c, d)$ and deduce

Theorem B.2.2. *If, on the interval (c, d), the C-orders of all the derivatives D^pF of $F \in \mathscr{D}'_+$ are bounded by the same integer $q \geqslant 0$, then, on this interval, F coincides with a function $g \in C^\infty(c, d)$.*

Corollary B.2.1. *If $F \in \mathscr{D}'_+$ satisfies on an interval (c, d) a linear homogeneous differential equation of the form*

$$D^pF + a_1(t)D^{p-1}F + \cdots + a_p(t)F = 0$$

whose coefficients $a_j(t) \in C^\infty(c, d)$ $(j = 1, \ldots, p)$ then F coincides with a $C^\infty(c, d)$ function on this interval [i.e., on (c, d) F coincides with the ordinary solution of the equation].

Proof. Let g be the C-order of F on (c, d). Since, on (c, d),

$$D^pF = -a_1D^{p-1}F - \cdots - a_pF$$

the C-order of D^pF on this interval does not exceed $q + p - 1$.

Applying the operator D to both sides of this equation gives an expression for $D^{p+l}F$ in terms of the D^jF with $0 \leqslant j \leqslant p$, so $D^{p+1}F$ also has a C-order not exceeding $q + p - 1$. Successive applications of the operator D show that $D^{p+l}F$ is of C-order $\leqslant q + p - 1$ for any positive integer l. The result now follows from the preceding theorem. ∎

3. The Carrier of a G.F.

Though the carrier (support) of a function of a real variable was defined in Chapter I, we have made no direct use of this notion; it was always sufficient for our purposes to deal with intervals or half-lines outside which a function, or a $\mathscr{D}'_+$ g.f., vanishes, i.e., in which it is carried. Nevertheless, the idea of identifying a set of R, which is in some sense the set where a particular $F \in \mathscr{D}'_+$ "differs from zero," is one about which our intuition tends to nag us persistently. [Consider, for instance, $\delta(t - t_0)$ or $\delta''(t - t_0)$; even though these g.f.'s have no values as functions of t, one is inclined to think of them as being everywhere zero except at the point t_0 of the axis of reals.]

Given $F \in \mathscr{D}'_+$, consider any open interval (c, d) such that $\langle F, \varphi\rangle = 0$ for every $\varphi \in \mathscr{D}_-$ carried in (c, d). The union of all such intervals is an open set in R, which we denote by N and call the *nullity set of* $F \in \mathscr{D}'_+$ [26].

By definition, the *carrier* (*support, supporting set*) *of* $F \in \mathscr{D}'_+$ *is the complement of* N; that is, the *closed set* $R - N$ of the axis of reals.

With this definition, which is due to L. Schwartz, the carrier of $\delta(t - t_0)$, and that of $\delta''(t - t_0)$ too, is the point $t_0 \in R$. This agrees with the intuitive ideas we had for these two g.f.'s. If $F \in \mathscr{K}_+(R)$ then the carrier of the function and that of the g.f. F are the same, so our definition is a proper generalization. Also, we observe that if $F \in \mathscr{D}'_+$ is carried in a half-line $[a, +\infty)$ (Def. II.A.4.2) the carrier of F is necessarily contained in this half-line, a fact whose proof follows from an easy argument by contradiction. As a consequence of the relation $(DF,\varphi) = -(F, \varphi')$ we see that the carrier of DF is contained in that of F. Also, if $\alpha \in C^\infty(R)$, the carrier of αF is contained in the set of points belonging to the carriers of α and of F both. Numerous applications of the carrier concept are given in [43] [26]. Here we limit ourselves to this

Theorem B.3.1. *If the carrier of* $F \in \mathscr{D}'_+$ *is a single point* $t_0 \in R$, *then* F *is of the form*

(B.3.1)
$$F = \sum_{k=0}^{N} C_k\, \delta^{(k)}(t - t_0),$$

where N *is a finite integer and the* C_k *are constants.*

Proof. As $F \in \mathscr{D}'_+$ there exists some real number a such that F is carried in $[a, +\infty)$, i.e., at least one fundamental sequence $\{f_n(t)\} \in F$ consists of functions which all vanish for $t < a$. It follows from an observation made above that necessarily $a \leqslant t_0$. Take a function $\alpha \in \mathscr{D}_+$ carried in $(a - 1, +\infty)$ such that $\alpha(t) = 1$ for $t \geqslant a$. The equalities

$$\alpha(t)f_n(t) = f_n(t) \qquad (n = 1, 2, \ldots)$$

show that the $\mathscr{D}'_+$ g.f.'s αF and F are identical. But then, for any $\varphi \in \mathscr{D}_-$ which is carried in the open half-line $(-\infty, t_0)$,

$$\langle F, \varphi \rangle = \langle \alpha F, \varphi \rangle = \langle F, \alpha\varphi \rangle.$$

As $\alpha\varphi$ is carried in the finite interval $(a - 1, t_0)$, which, by the hypotheses of the theorem, belongs to the nullity set of F, we have $\langle F, \varphi \rangle = 0$ for every such φ.

Take a half-line $(-\infty, b)$ with $b > t_0$. Theorem B.1.1 provides an integer $q \geqslant 0$ and a function $g(t)$ continuous on $(-\infty, b)$ such that on this half-line $F = D^q g$. The function g is the uniform limit on $(-\infty, b)$ of a fundamental sequence $\{D^{-q} f_n\}$ and we may, without loss of generality, suppose $\{f_n\}$ to be the sequence referred to above so that a and $\alpha(t)$ preserve the same meaning. Consequently, $g(t)$ has these properties

(B.3.2) $$g(t) = 0 \qquad \text{for } t \leqslant a,$$

(B.3.3) $$D^q g = F = 0 \in \mathscr{D}'_+ \quad \text{on the interval } (a - 1, t_0).$$

Drawing on the result of Exercise 23 we conclude that $g(t)$ equals a polynomial of degree $q - 1$ on $(a - 1, t_0)$. This polynomial vanishes on the interval $(a - 1, a)$ by (B.3.2) and must therefore be identically zero. We have proved that

(B.3.4) $$g(t) = 0 \qquad \text{for } t < t_0,$$

and since g is continuous, we can also assert that $g(t_0) = 0$.

On the other hand, whenever $\varphi \in \mathscr{D}_-$ is carried in the interval (t_0, b), which is contained in the nullity set of F, we have

$$\langle F, \varphi \rangle = \langle D^q g, \varphi \rangle$$

so that (again by Exercise 23) on (t_0, b)

$$g(t) = P_{q-1}(t), \ .$$

where P_{q-1} is a polynomial of degree $q - 1$ in t.

Consider now the $C(R)$ function $G(t)$, which coincides with g on $(-\infty, b)$ and is defined by

(B.3.5) $$G(t) = \begin{cases} 0 & \text{for } t \leqslant t_0 \\ P_{q-1}(t) & \text{for } t_0 \leqslant t. \end{cases}$$

Actually $F = D^qG$, not merely on $(-\infty, b)$, but on the entire axis of reals. To verify this, take a function $\beta(t) \in \mathscr{D}_-$ carried in $(-\infty, b)$ and for which

$$\beta(t) = 1 \qquad \text{when } t \leqslant t_0 + \frac{b - t_0}{2}.$$

Any $\varphi \in \mathscr{D}_-$ can be decomposed into $\varphi = \beta\varphi + (1 - \beta)\varphi$ where $\beta\varphi$ is carried in $(-\infty, b)$ and $(1 - \beta)\varphi$ is carried in a finite open interval of the form $((t_0 + b)/2, d)$ and thereby contained in the nullity set of F. We then have

(B.3.6)
$$\begin{aligned}\langle F, \varphi\rangle &= \langle F, \beta\varphi\rangle + \langle F, (1 - \beta)\varphi\rangle \\ &= (D^qG, \beta\varphi\rangle + 0,\end{aligned}$$

and since G coincides with the polynomial P_{q-1} in $((t_0 + b)/2, +\infty)$, the zero on the right in (B.3.6) may just as well be written $\langle D^qG, (1 - \beta)\varphi\rangle$, proving that $\langle F, \varphi\rangle = \langle D^qG, \varphi\rangle$ for every $\varphi \in \mathscr{D}_-$, i.e. proving that

(B.3.7)
$$F = D^qG.$$

The function $G(t)$ has continuous ordinary derivatives of every order in $(-\infty, t_0)$ and $(t_0, +\infty)$. The equality (B.3.1) therefore finally results from (B.3.5), (B.3.7) and Corollary II.B.1.1. ∎

4. Convolution in $\mathscr{D}'_+$

The convolution of g.f.'s was defined in a rather indirect manner in Chapter III for g.f.'s of finite K-order. While this was quite sufficient for the consideration of problems of physical origin, it lacked the generality desirable in a more complete mathematical theory. It is fitting, therefore, that we now attend to this topic. A certain brevity of treatment is achieved here at the reader's expense: by unloading most of the proofs required into the exercise hopper. He should find these proofs entirely straightforward. This fact, and the absence in this text of applications of the convolution of g.f.'s not of finite order, are offered in defense of this cavalier approach.

Definition B.4.1. *The convolution $F * G$ of $F \in \mathscr{D}'_+$ and $G \in \mathscr{D}'_+$ is the $\mathscr{D}'_+$ g.f. defined by the fundamental sequences $\{f_n * g_n\}$ where $\{f_n\} \in F$, $\{g_n\} \in G$.*

The consistency of this definition has to be established. This means that $\{f_n * g_n\}$ must be shown to be a fundamental sequence, and also that $\{f_n * g_n\} \sim \{f'_n * g'_n\}$ when $\{f_n\} \sim \{f'_n\}$ and $\{g_n\} \sim \{g'_n\}$. (The primes, in f'_n and g'_n, do not indicate differentiation.)

Take $\varphi \in \mathscr{D}_-$; this function is carried in a half-line $I = (-\infty, b_\varphi]$. According to Theorem B.1.1, there exist integers $p, q \geqslant 0$ such that $\{D^{-p}f_n\}_n$

and $\{D^{-q}g_n\}_n$ are uniformly convergent on $(-\infty, b_\varphi]$. Therefore, there exists a constant M such that

(B.4.1) $\quad \|D^{-p}f_n\|_I \leqslant M \quad \text{and} \quad \|D^{-q}g_n\|_I \leqslant M \quad (n = 1, 2, \ldots).$

Also to every $\varepsilon > 0$ corresponds an integer $N(\varepsilon)$ such that

(B.4.2) $$m, n > N(\varepsilon) \Rightarrow \|D^{-p}f_m - D^{-p}f_n\|_I < \frac{\varepsilon}{2M} \quad \text{and}$$
$$\|D^{-q}g_m - D^{-q}g_n\|_I < \frac{\varepsilon}{2M}.$$

By Theorem III.C.2.3

$$D^{-p-q}(f_n * g_n) = D^{-p}f_n * D^{-q}g_n$$

and

$$D^{-p-q}(f_n * g_n - f_m * g_m)$$
$$= D^{-p}f_n * (D^{-q}g_n - D^{-q}g_m) + D^{-q}g_m * (D^{-p}f_n - D^{-p}f_m).$$

Using (B.4.1) and (B.4.2) on the right-hand side, we obtain

(B.4.3) $$m, n > N(\varepsilon) \Rightarrow \|D^{-p-q}(f_n * g_n) - D^{-p-q}(f_m * g_m)\|_I < \varepsilon,$$

and therefore $m > N(\varepsilon)$ and $n > N(\varepsilon)$ ensures that

(B.4.4) $$|\langle f_n * g_n, \varphi\rangle - \langle f_m * g_m, \varphi\rangle|$$
$$= |(-1)^{p+q}\langle D^{-p-q}(f_n * g_n) - D^{-p-q}(f_m * g_m), \varphi^{(p+q)}\rangle| \leqslant \varepsilon \|\varphi^{(p+q)}\|_I.$$

(If $\{f_n, g_n\}$ are carried in $[a_f, +\infty)$ and $[a_g, +\infty)$,

$$\langle f_n * g_n, \varphi\rangle = 0 \qquad \text{when } b_\varphi \leqslant a_f + a_g.$$

Therefore the argument above is necessary only for those $\varphi \in \mathscr{D}_-$ with $b_\varphi > a_f + a_g$.)

In view of the Cauchy convergence principle for complex numbers, this proves that $\{\langle f_n * g_n, \varphi\rangle\}$ is a convergent sequence of complex numbers; $\{f_n * g_n\}$ is, therefore, a fundamental sequence. Adding to this result the solution of Exercise 25 completes the justification of Definition B.4.1.

A simple change of variables shows that for $f_n, g_n \in \mathscr{K}_+(R)$, $\varphi \in \mathscr{D}_-$,

$$\int_{-\infty}^{\infty}\int_{-\infty}^{\infty} f_n(t - \tau)\, g_n(\tau)\, \varphi(t)\, d\tau\, dt = \int_{-\infty}^{\infty}\int_{-\infty}^{\infty} f_n(t)\, g_n(\tau)\, \varphi(t + \tau)\, d\tau\, dt,$$

which we write as follows:

(B.4.5) $$\langle f_n * g_n, \varphi\rangle = \langle f_n(t), \langle g_n(\tau), \varphi(t + \tau)\rangle\rangle.$$

From this and Definition B.4.1, we conclude that the value of the g.f. $F * G$ as a functional on the $\mathscr{D}_-$ functions of t is equal to

(B.4.6)
$$\langle (F * G)(t), \varphi(t)\rangle = \langle F(t), \langle G(\tau), \varphi(t + \tau)\rangle\rangle = \langle G(t), \langle F(\tau), \varphi(t + \tau)\rangle\rangle,$$

where it must be understood that, in the inner brackets on the right, t is a parameter and $\varphi(t + \tau) \in \mathscr{D}_-$ is a function of τ for fixed t.

The following are direct consequences of the analogous properties of $\mathscr{K}_+(R)$ functions under convolution ($E, F, G \in \mathscr{D}'_+$):

(B.4.7)
$$\begin{cases} F * G = G * F, \\ (E * F) * G = E * (F * G), \\ E * (F + G) = E * F + E * G. \end{cases}$$

If F is carried in $[a_F, +\infty)$ and G in $[a_G, +\infty)$, then $F * G$ is carried in $[a_F + a_G, +\infty)$.

These other relations are left for the reader to prove [with the aid of (B.4.6) or of Definition B.4.1 and the results of § III.C.2]:

(B.4.8) $$D^p(F * G) = (D^pF) * G = F * (D^pG) \qquad (p \text{ arbitrary integer}).$$

(B.4.9) $$D^pF = \delta^{(p)} * F \qquad (\text{integer } p \geqslant 0).$$

(B.4.10) $$\delta(t - h) * F(t) = F(t - h).$$

Using the definition of D^p with noninteger p given in Chapter III, the restriction to integer p in the above relations can be lifted.

The theorem on the continuity of rational operators in D of the form $A(D)\, B^{-1}(D)$ can now be shown to have this generalization:

Theorem B.4.1. *If the sequence* $\{F_n\}$ *of* $\mathscr{D}'_+$ *g.f.'s converges to* $F \in \mathscr{D}'_+$ *then for any* $G \in \mathscr{D}'_+$

(B.4.11) $$\operatorname*{Lim}_{n\to\infty} (G * F_n) = G * F = G * (\operatorname*{Lim}_{n\to\infty} F_n).$$

Proof. By (B.4.6), for any $\varphi(t) \in \mathscr{D}_-$,

$$\langle (G * F_n)(t), \varphi(t)\rangle = \langle F_n(t), \langle G(\tau), \varphi(t + \tau)\rangle\rangle.$$

But $\langle G(\tau), \varphi(t + \tau)\rangle = \psi(t) \in \mathscr{D}_-$, as a result of Exercise 30, and therefore

$$\lim_{n\to\infty} \langle F_n(t), \psi(t)\rangle = \langle F(t), \psi(t)\rangle.$$

The conclusion follows. ∎

EXERCISES

[*Note:* All the exercises proposed here are in the (**) class insofar as this is a (**) level chapter. Those marked with a (*) are supplementary.]

Part A

1. Give several examples of fundamental sequences of $\mathscr{K}_+$ functions, $\{f_n(t)\}$, for which the $f_n(t)$ are not everywhere nonnegative and which do not verify (A.3.3).

2. Give an example of a fundamental sequence $\{f_n\} \in 0(\in \mathscr{D}'_+)$ that satisfies (A.3.20) for $p = 1$ but not for $p = 0$. Generalize this to show that given any integer $p \geqslant 0$, no matter how large, there exist in the equivalence class of $0 \in \mathscr{D}'_+$ fundamental sequences which satisfy (A.3.20) for that value of p and no smaller one. Review the proof of Theorem A.3.1 in the light of this result.

3. Let $\varphi_n \in \mathscr{D}_-$ $(n = 1, 2, \ldots)$ be carried in the half-line $(-\infty, b]$. Prove that if $\lim_{n\to\infty} \|\varphi_n^{(p)}\|_I$ exists for every integer $p \geqslant 0$ and every closed finite interval $I = [a, b] (a < b)$ there exists $\varphi \in \mathscr{D}_-$ such that $\lim_{n\to\infty} \varphi_n = \varphi$ in the sense of Definition A.4.1.

4. Prove the statement of Example 2, p. 192.
(See Exercise I.5.)

5. $\varphi_n \in \mathscr{D}_-$ $(n = 1, 2, \ldots)$, $\varphi \in \mathscr{D}_-$, and $\alpha \in C^\infty(R)$. Show that $\lim_{n\to\infty} \varphi_n = \varphi$ in the sense of Definition A.4.1 entails $\lim_{n\to\infty} \alpha\varphi_n = \alpha\varphi$ in the same sense. (See Exercise I.2.)

6. Given F, a c.l.f. on $\mathscr{D}_-$ in the sense of Definition A.4.2, prove that the function $f_n(t)$ defined in (A.4.3) belongs to $C(R)$.

7. Given F, a c.l.f. on $\mathscr{D}_-$ in the sense of Definition A.4.2, prove that the function $f_n(t)$ defined in (A.4.3) belongs to $\mathscr{D}_+$ and that

$$\frac{d^p f_n(t)}{dt^p} = \langle F(\tau), \alpha_n^{(p)}(t - \tau)\rangle.$$

8. Prove that

$$\lim_{K\to\infty} \psi_K(\tau) = \int_{-\infty}^{\infty} \alpha_n(t - \tau)\varphi(t)\, dt$$

in the sense of Definition A.4.1. [$\psi_K(t)$ is the function defined on p. 195.]

9. Following the reasoning of part 2 of the proof of Theorem A.4.1, show that the function $f_n(t)$ defined in (A.4.3) verifies for every integer $k \geqslant 0$ the relation

$$D^{-k} f_n(t) = \langle F(\tau), D^{-k}\alpha_n(t - \tau)\rangle.$$

***10.** Given $F \in \mathscr{D}'_+$ carried in $[a, +\infty)$ and such that

$$|\langle F, \varphi\rangle| \leqslant K\|\varphi^{(r)}\|_I$$

for all $\varphi \in \mathscr{D}_-$ carried in $(-\infty, b+1]$ where $I = [a-1, b+1]$ and K, r (integer $\geqslant 0$) are constants. Apply the result of Exercise 9 to show that $\|D^{-r-1}f_n(t)\|_J \leqslant K (n = 1, 2, \ldots)$ where $J = (-\infty, b]$.

***11.** Let $\{v_k\}$ be an arbitrary sequence of complex numbers. Construct

$$f \in C^\infty(-\infty, 0]$$

such that

$$f^{(k)}(0) = v_k \qquad (k = 0, 1, 2, \ldots).$$

[First, note that, if convergent for all t, the series

$$\sum_{k=0}^{\infty} v_k \frac{t^k}{k!}$$

is a solution. If the series does not converge take a function $\alpha(t) \in \mathscr{D}_-$ such that $\alpha(t) = 0$ for $|t| \geqslant 1$ and $\alpha(t) = 1$ for $|t| \leqslant \frac{1}{2}$ and also define $b_k = \max\limits_{0 \leqslant l \leqslant k} |v_l|$. Verify that

$$\sum_{k=0}^{\infty} v_k \frac{t^k}{k!} \alpha(b_k t) \in C^\infty(-\infty, 0]$$

and is a solution.] (Compare H. Mirkil [2s].)

***12.** (Application of Exercise 11) Let $c < 0$ and $a(t) \in C^\infty[0, +\infty)$ be given. Show that there exists $b(t) \in \mathscr{D}_+$ carried in $[c, +\infty)$ such that $b(t) \equiv a(t)$ for $t \geqslant 0$. Apply this to prove that if in the initial-value problem (B.2.1, 2) of Chapter II, § B.2, the hypothesis

$$a_j(t) \in C^\infty(R) \qquad (j = 0, 1, \ldots, p)$$

is relaxed to $a_j(t) \in C^\infty[0, +\infty)$, it is still possible to enlarge the ordinary I.V. problem to a $\mathscr{D}'_+$ problem.

13. (O.C.) In Exercise II.6 fundamental (on $\mathscr{D}$) sequences of $\mathscr{K}(R)$ functions and the class $\mathscr{D}'$ of g.f.'s were defined. Given a bounded interval $I = [c, d]$ let $\alpha(t) \in \mathscr{D}_+$ be such that $\alpha(t) \equiv 1$ for $t \geqslant c$. To the fundamental (on $\mathscr{D}$) sequence, associate the sequence of $\mathscr{K}_+(R)$ functions $\alpha(t)f_n(t)$. Prove that $\{\alpha f_n\}$ is fundamental on $\mathscr{D}_-$. Given $F \in \mathscr{D}'$, and recalling Lemma A.3.1 and Theorem A.3.1, prove that there exist a smallest integer $r \geqslant 0$ and a constant $K < \infty$ such that

$$|\langle F, \varphi \rangle| \leqslant K \|\varphi^{(r)}\|_I$$

for all $\varphi \in \mathscr{D}$ carried in I. [*Note:* In [43] it is this index r that is defined to be the order of F on (c, d).]

***14.** (O.C.) Let $\varphi_n \in \mathscr{D}$ $(n = 1, 2, \ldots)$. These functions are said to converge to zero in $\mathscr{D}$ if and only if they are all carried in some bounded interval

$$I = [a, b] \quad \text{and} \quad \lim_{n \to \infty} \|\varphi_n^{(p)}\|_I = 0 \quad (p = 0, 1, 2, \ldots).$$

(Compare Definition A.4.1.) A functional F on $\mathscr{D}$, whose values are denoted by $\langle F, \varphi \rangle$, is said to be a continuous linear functional (c.l.f.) if and only if

$$\langle F, c_1\varphi_1 + c_2\varphi_2 \rangle = c_1\langle F, \varphi_1 \rangle + c_2\langle F, \varphi_2 \rangle \qquad (c_1, c_2 \in C;\ \varphi_1, \varphi_2 \in \mathscr{D})$$

and

$$\lim_{n\to\infty} \langle F, \varphi_n \rangle = 0$$

whenever $\lim_{n\to\infty} \varphi_n = 0$ in the sense of $\mathscr{D}$ convergence (compare Definition A.4.2). Prove that $\mathscr{D}'$ is the set of c.l.f.'s on $\mathscr{D}$ (use Exercise 13 and the pattern of proof of Theorem A.4.1). [*Note:* $\mathscr{D}'$ is often *defined* as the set of c.l.f.'s on $\mathscr{D}$ [23] [26] [43] [46].]

15. (O.C.) The class $\mathscr{E}'$ of g.f.'s and fundamental (on $\mathscr{E}$) sequences were defined in Exercise II.7. Show that to every $F \in \mathscr{E}'$ carried in the finite interval I correspond a smallest integer $r \geqslant 0$ and a constant $K < \infty$ such that $|\langle F, \varphi \rangle| \leqslant K \|\varphi^{(r)}\|_I$. ($F$ is carried in I if some $\{f_n\} \in F$ is carried in I.)

***16.** (O.C.) The $\varphi_n \in \mathscr{E}$ $(n = 1, 2, \ldots)$ are said to converge to zero in $\mathscr{E}$ if for every finite interval $I \subset R$

$$\lim_{n\to\infty} \|\varphi_n^{(p)}\|_I = 0 \qquad (p = 0, 1, 2, \ldots).$$

Show that the class $\mathscr{E}'$ of g.f.'s is identical to the set of continuous linear functionals on $\mathscr{E}$. (F is c.l.f. on $\mathscr{E}$ if

$$\langle F, c_1\varphi_1 + c_2\varphi_2 \rangle = c_1\langle F, \varphi_1 \rangle + c_2\langle F, \varphi_2 \rangle$$

and $\lim_{n\to\infty} \langle F, \varphi_n \rangle = 0$ when $\lim_{n\to\infty} \varphi_n = 0$ in the sense of convergence in $\mathscr{E}$.)

Part B

17. All the members of a sequence $\{f_n\}$ of $\mathscr{K}_+(R)$ functions are carried in the same half-line $[a, +\infty)$; also to every $b > a$ corresponds an integer $r_b \geqslant 0$ such that the sequence $\{D^{-r_b} f_n\}_n$ is uniformly convergent on $[a, b]$. Show that $\{f_n\}$ is a fundamental sequence on $\mathscr{D}_-$ (see the Remark following Theorem B.1.1).

18. $F \in \mathscr{D}'_+$ is of C-order q on $(-\infty, b)$. The sequence $\{f_n\} \in F$ is of C-order p on $(-\infty, b]$ so

$$\lim_{n\to\infty} D^{-p} f_n(t) = h(t)$$

uniformly on $(-\infty, b]$. Show that $h(t) \in C^{p-q}(-\infty, b)$ and that $\dfrac{d^{p-q}h(t)}{dt^{p-q}} = g_b(t)$ for $t < b$ (g_b defined in Theorem B.1.3).

***19.** $F \in \mathscr{D}'_+$, $(-\infty, b]$ given, r as defined in Theorem A.3.1. Prove that the fundamental sequence of the functions $f_n(t)$ defined in (A.4.3) has the property that $D^{-r-2} f_n$ converges uniformly on every half-line $(-\infty, b']$ where $b' < b$. Deduce that q [the C-order of F on $(-\infty, b)$] is related to r by $r \leqslant q \leqslant r + 2$. [*Hint:* Do Exercise 10 first and use the pattern of proof of Theorem B.1.1.]

20. (O.C.) $F \in \mathscr{D}'$, $I = (c, d)$ a finite open interval. Show that there exist a smallest integer $q \geqslant 0$ and a function $g_I(t) \in \mathscr{K}$, continuous on (c, d) and vanishing elsewhere such that $F = D^r g_I$ on (c, d). [*Hint:* Do Exercise 13 first.]

***21.** $F \in \mathscr{D}'_+$, (c, d) a finite open interval. (a, b) an arbitrary finite open interval such that $(a, b) \supset [c, d]$. Show that, as a (practically immediate) consequence of

Theorem B.1.2, there exists a function $G(t) \in C(R)$ that is carried in (a, b) and which has the property that $F = D^r G$ on the interval (c, d) (r the same as in Exercise 12).

***22.** Verify that Exercise 13 immediately makes it possible to extend the result of Exercise 21 to the case where $F \in \mathscr{D}'$.†

23. Prove that if $F \in \mathscr{D}'_+$, or $F \in \mathscr{D}'$, has $D^p F = 0$ on the finite interval (c, d), F coincides with a polynomial of degree $p - 1$ on this interval. (Consider Lemma B.2.1.)

24. Give an example showing that the carrier of a g.f. is not necessarily the intersection of the carriers of the functions that make up one of its fundamental sequences. Show that if $F \in \mathscr{D}'_+$ is carried in $[a, +\infty)$ (Definition II.A.4.2) the carrier of F is contained in this half-line.

25. Show that

$$\{f'_n\} \sim \{f_n\} \text{ and } \{g'_n\} \sim \{g_n\} \Rightarrow \{f_n * g_n\} \sim \{f'_n * g'_n\}$$

(notation of Definition B.4.1).

26. Prove the relation (B.4.5).

27. Prove (B.4.8).

28. Prove (B.4.9).

29. Prove (B.4.10).

30. Show that if $F \in \mathscr{D}'_+$ and $\varphi \in \mathscr{D}_-$, the function

$$\langle F(\tau), \varphi(t + \tau) \rangle = \psi(t) \in \mathscr{D}_-$$

(compare Exercise 7).

---

† This also holds true if, instead of (c, d), one takes a bounded open set $\Omega_0 \subset R$, and, if, instead of (a, b), one takes a bounded open set $\Omega_1 \subset R$ such that $\Omega_1 \supset \bar{\Omega}_0$ (the closure of Ω_0). This more general proposition constitutes L. Schwartz's fundamental structure theorem for $\mathscr{D}'$ (Theorem XXI, Chap. II, Vol. I of [43]). Proofs, by methods of classical analysis, employing Lebesgue integration, of this, as well as the $\mathscr{D}'_+$ and $\mathscr{E}'$ versions of Schwartz's theorem, have been given by Ravetz [41].

CHAPTER VI

STRUCTURE OF $\mathscr{D}'_+$. COMPLETENESS

In this chapter, the structural investigation of $\mathscr{D}'_+$ is pursued—this time for certain families of g.f.'s, instead of for individual elements of $\mathscr{D}'_+$ as in the preceding chapter. We shall see that the parallelism between g.f. theory and Cantor's theory of real numbers goes much further than was indicated in § II.A.10, in that there exist $\mathscr{D}'_+$ analogs of the Cauchy convergence principle and the Bolzano-Weierstrass Theorem for real numbers.

A sequence of *rational* numbers satisfying (II.A.10.1) is called [25] *fundamental* and defines a real number just as a fundamental sequence of $\mathscr{K}_+(R)$ functions defines a $\mathscr{D}'_+$ g.f. A sequence $\{\alpha_n\}$ of *real* numbers such that for every $\varepsilon > 0$ there exists an integer N_ε and

(1) $$m, n > N_\varepsilon \Rightarrow |\alpha_n - \alpha_m| < \varepsilon,$$

is called a *Cauchy sequence* (thus, a fundamental sequence in Cantor's theory is simply a Cauchy sequence, all of whose elements are rational). An essential property of the set of real numbers is the fact that repeating with real numbers the procedure applied to the rationals gives nothing new: every Cauchy sequence of real numbers converges to a real number (Cauchy convergence principle for the reals). This property, called the *completeness* of the set of real numbers, is also true of the set of complex numbers: every Cauchy sequence of complex numbers (definition by direct transcription of (1), converges to a complex number. (We have, of course, used this familiar theorem on numerous occasions in the preceding pages.)

A sequence $\{F_n\}$ of $\mathscr{D}'_+$ g.f.'s is called a (weak) Cauchy sequence if and only if for every $\varphi \in \mathscr{D}_-$ the sequence $\{\langle F_n, \varphi\rangle\}_n$ of complex numbers is a Cauchy sequence. In view of the Cauchy convergence principle just recalled, this means that $\lim_{n\to\infty} \langle F_n, \varphi\rangle$ exists and so defines a functional F on $\mathscr{D}_-$ such that

(2) $$\lim_{n\to\infty} \langle F_n, \varphi\rangle = \langle F, \varphi\rangle.$$

Because F itself turns out automatically to be an element of $\mathscr{D}'_+$, this set is, by analogy with the real- and complex-numbers cases, said to have the property of *completeness* (also: "weak completeness"). This is substantiated in § 3 below and applied in the two subsequent sections.

Any infinite bounded set of $\mathscr{D}'_+$ g.f.'s contains a convergent subsequence; this property, the $\mathscr{D}'_+$ analog of the familiar Bolzano-Weierstrass theorem for real numbers, is proved in § 5.

These properties are obtained as consequences of the generalization of Theorem V.A.3.1 to sequences of g.f.'s.

1. The Lebesgue Method of Resonance

Most of the results of Chapter V were, in our development, derived from Lemma V.A.3.1. In the present chapter, Theorem 2.1 below is made to play an equally crucial role. To prove this theorem we shall employ the so-called Lebesgue method of resonance.

This method which also serves for Theorem VIII.11.1 and Exercise VI.11 and VI.12, is such a valuable tool in diverse branches of mathematical analysis [21] that it is well worth a separate examination designed to bring out basic features. It is to this that the present section is devoted, using as a vehicle for an unencumbered presentation of Lebesgue's idea the solution[†] of the following:

Problem (P). *Given a sequence $\{\vec{V}_n\}$ of three-dimensional vectors such that for every three-dimensional vector $\vec{\Phi}$ there exists a finite nonnegative real number $B(\vec{\Phi})$ which is a uniform bound for the scalar products $\vec{V}_n \cdot \vec{\Phi}$, i.e., for which there hold the inequalities*

$$|\vec{V}_n \cdot \vec{\Phi}| \leqslant B(\vec{\Phi}) \; (n = 1, 2, \ldots). \tag{1.1}$$

Prove that the absolute values $|\vec{V}_n| = \sqrt{\vec{V}_n \cdot \vec{V}_n}$ are uniformly bounded, i.e., that there exists a finite constant M such that

$$|\vec{V}_n| \leqslant M \qquad (n = 1, 2, \ldots). \tag{1.2}$$

Solution. The proof is by contradiction. If (1.2) were not true, there would exist a subsequence $\{\vec{V}_{n_i}\}_i$ of $\{\vec{V}_n\}$ such that the numerical sequence $\{|\vec{V}_{n_i}|\}_i$ is monotone increasing and unbounded. It will then simplify the notation, without diminishing the generality of our argument, to assume that $\{\vec{V}_n\}$ itself has this property; in fact to assume that

$$1 < |\vec{V}_1| < |\vec{V}_2| < \cdots < |\vec{V}_n| < |\vec{V}_{n+1}| < \cdots \tag{1.3}$$

---

† An easy solution of this same problem without the Lebesgue method is given in Exercise 1. However, it does not extend to the g.f. applications because it hinges on the finite dimensionality of the vectors. The resonance procedure does not.

and

(1.4) $$\lim_{n\to\infty} |\vec{V}_n| = +\infty.$$

We shall show that under these circumstances there would have to exist a vector $\vec{C}$ and a subsequence $\{\vec{V}_{n_j}\}_j$ of $\{\vec{V}_n\}$ for which

(1.5) $$\lim_{j\to\infty} |\vec{V}_{n_j} \cdot \vec{C}| = +\infty,$$

in violation of the hypothesis (1.1).

$\vec{C}$ is obtained as the sum of a convergent series $\sum_{j=1}^{\infty} \vec{\Phi}_j$, whose terms are determined in a step-by-step process in which the jth step consists in choosing $\vec{\Phi}_j$ and $\vec{V}_{n_j}$ simultaneously on the basis of the outcome of the previous $(j-1)$ selections.

Before exhibiting the details of this procedure, let us note these properties:

(a) Any series $\sum_{j=1}^{\infty} \vec{\Phi}_j$ for which $|\vec{\Phi}_j| \leqslant 1/2^j$ is absolutely convergent, and therefore convergent.

(b) Given an arbitrary real number $M > 0$, no matter how large, and an arbitrary $\varepsilon > 0$, no matter how small, there exist a vector Φ_ε of length $\leqslant \varepsilon$ and a member $\vec{V}_{n_\varepsilon}$ of the sequence $\{\vec{V}_n\}$ such that $|\vec{V}_{n_\varepsilon} \cdot \vec{\Phi}_\varepsilon| > M$. [For example, for every integer $n > 0$ take

$$\vec{u}_n = \frac{\varepsilon}{|\vec{V}_n|} \vec{V}_n$$

so $\vec{u}_n \cdot \vec{V}_n = \varepsilon\, |\vec{V}_n|$, in which case, by (1.4), there exists an integer, which we call n_ε, such that $\vec{u}_{n_\varepsilon} \cdot \vec{V}_{n_\varepsilon} > M$; this $\vec{u}_{n_\varepsilon}$ could serve as the $\vec{\Phi}_\varepsilon$ in question.]

(c) For any member $\vec{V}_n$ of the given sequence, no matter how large $|\vec{V}_n|$ may be, we have $|\vec{V}_n \cdot \vec{\Phi}| \leqslant 1/2^k$ for all vectors $\vec{\Phi}$ whose length is small enough [$\leqslant 1/(2^k\, |\vec{V}_n|)$ in fact].

These facts we now exploit as follows:

(i) Using property (b) with $\varepsilon = \frac{1}{2}$ and $M = 2$ find a vector $\vec{\Phi}_1$ with $|\vec{\Phi}_1| < \frac{1}{2}$ and a positive integer n_1 such that

$$|\vec{V}_{n_1} \cdot \vec{\Phi}_1| > 2.$$

(ii) Since, by the hypothesis (1.1), $|\vec{V}_n \cdot \vec{\Phi}| < B(\vec{\Phi})$ for all natural numbers n, we can use property (b) with $\varepsilon = 1/(2^2\, |\vec{V}_{n_1}|)$ to find a vector $\vec{\Phi}_2$ and a positive integer $n_2 > n_1$ such that

(1.6) $$|\vec{\Phi}_2| \leqslant \frac{1}{2^2\, |\vec{V}_{n_1}|} < \frac{1}{2^2},$$

while at the same time

$$|\vec{V}_{n_2} \cdot \vec{\Phi}_2| > 3 + B(\vec{\Phi}_1). \tag{1.7}$$

(iii) The above are the first two steps of an inductive procedure. We preface the description of the jth step with the observation that, by (1.1),

$$|\vec{V}_n \cdot (\vec{\Phi}_1 + \vec{\Phi}_2 + \cdots + \vec{\Phi}_{j-1})| \leqslant B(\vec{\Phi}_1 + \vec{\Phi}_2 + \cdots + \vec{\Phi}_{j-1})$$

for all natural numbers n and any $\vec{\Phi}_1, \vec{\Phi}_2, \ldots, \vec{\Phi}_{j-1}$ resulting from the previous $j - 1$ steps.

But then by property (b), with $\varepsilon = 1/(2^j\,|\vec{V}_{n_{j-1}}|)$, we can find a vector $\vec{\Phi}_j$ and a positive integer $n_j > n_{j-1}$ such that

$$|\vec{\Phi}_j| \leqslant \frac{1}{2^j\,|\vec{V}_{n_{j-1}}|} < \frac{1}{2^j}, \tag{1.8}$$

while at the same time

$$|\vec{V}_{n_j} \cdot \vec{\Phi}_j| > j + 1 + B(\vec{\Phi}_1 + \vec{\Phi}_2 + \cdots + \vec{\Phi}_{j-1}). \tag{1.9}$$

This procedure yields a particular sequence of vectors $\{\vec{\Phi}_j\}$ and a subsequence $\{\vec{V}_{n_j}\}_j$ of $\{\vec{V}_n\}$ such that

(α) $\sum_{j=1}^{\infty} \vec{\Phi}_j$ converges [by (1.8) and property (a)]; denote its sum by $\vec{C}$.

(β)

$$\left|\sum_{l=j+1}^{\infty} \vec{\Phi}_l\right| \leqslant \sum_{l=j+1}^{\infty} |\vec{\Phi}_l| \leqslant \frac{1}{|\vec{V}_{n_j}|} \sum_{l=j+1}^{\infty} \frac{1}{2^l} \leqslant \frac{1}{|\vec{V}_{n_j}|}$$

[use (1.3) and (1.8)].

(γ)

$$\left|\vec{V}_{n_j} \cdot \left(\sum_{l=j+1}^{\infty} \vec{\Phi}_l\right)\right| \leqslant 1$$

[by (β) and property (c)].

We also have, for every integer $j \geqslant 1$,

$$\begin{aligned}|\vec{V}_{n_j} \cdot \vec{C}| &= \left|\vec{V}_{n_j} \cdot \left(\sum_{l=1}^{j-1} \vec{\Phi}_l\right) + \vec{V}_{n_j} \cdot \vec{\Phi}_j + \vec{V}_{n_j} \cdot \left(\sum_{l=j+1}^{\infty} \vec{\Phi}_l\right)\right| \\ &\geqslant |\vec{V}_{n_j} \cdot \vec{\Phi}_j| - \left|\vec{V}_{n_j} \cdot \left(\sum_{l=1}^{j-1} \vec{\Phi}\right)\right| - \left|\vec{V}_{n_j} \cdot \left(\sum_{l=j+1}^{\infty} \vec{\Phi}_l\right)\right|,\end{aligned} \tag{1.10}$$

so that applying (1.9) and (γ) we conclude that

$$|\vec{V}_{n_j} \cdot \vec{C}| \geqslant j. \tag{1.11}$$

This proves that (1.5) holds and, therefore, that the assumption (1.3) is incompatible with (1.1). The proof of (1.2) is complete. ∎

Note that by (1.10), (1.9), and (γ), the principal contribution to $|\vec{V}_{n_j} \cdot \vec{C}|$ comes from the term $\vec{V}_{n_j} \cdot \vec{\Phi}_j$; the name "resonance method" is related to this property [21].

2. Bounded Sequences in $\mathscr{D}'_+$

Definition 2.1. *A sequence $\{F_n\}$ of $\mathscr{D}'_+$ g.f.'s is bounded (weakly bounded) if to every $\varphi \in \mathscr{D}_-$ corresponds a finite number $B(\varphi)$ such that*

$$|\langle F_n, \varphi\rangle| \leqslant B(\varphi) \qquad (n = 1, 2, \ldots). \tag{2.1}$$

Every $F_n \in \mathscr{D}'_+$ is an algebraically linear functional on $\mathscr{D}_-$ and is carried in a forward half-line $[a, +\infty)$ in the sense of Definition II.A.4.2. With these properties an adaptation (Exercises 2, 3) of the argument of Remark 4 p. 53, yields the proof of

Lemma 2.1. *To a bounded sequence $\{F_n\}$ in $\mathscr{D}'_+$ corresponds a half-line $[a, +\infty)$ in which every element of the sequence is carried. (We shall say that the sequence $\{F_n\}$ is carried in $[a, +\infty)$.)*

A particular type of bounded sequence of g.f.'s, to wit, those composed of $\mathscr{K}_+(R)$ functions, was considered in detail in the preceding chapter. A most important property of such sequences was provided by Theorem V.A.3.1, and it is one which, in essence, holds also when the restriction to $\mathscr{K}_+(R)$ is lifted. This is expressed in

Theorem 2.1. *Let $\{F_n\}$ be a bounded sequence in $\mathscr{D}'_+$ that is carried in $[a, +\infty)$. To every backward half-line $(-\infty, b]$ corresponds an integer $r \geqslant 0$ and a finite constant K such that for every $\varphi \in \mathscr{D}_-$ carried in $(-\infty, b]$ there hold the inequalities*

$$|\langle F_n, \varphi\rangle| \leqslant K \,\|\varphi^{(r)}\| \qquad (n = 1, 2, \ldots), \tag{2.2}$$

where $\|\varphi\| = \sup\limits_{t \in R} |\varphi(t)|$.

Preliminaries to the proof. For $b \leqslant a$ the theorem is obvious: take $K = 0$ and $r = 0$. Therefore, we consider a fixed $b > a$. Let us define for each integer $p \geqslant 0$ the quantities (nonnegative finite, or $+\infty$†)

$$|F_n|_p = \sup \frac{|\langle F_n, \varphi\rangle|}{\|\varphi^{(p)}\|} \qquad (n = 1, 2, \ldots), \tag{2.3}$$

† Of course the symbol $+\infty$ does not denote a real number. To write $|F_n|_p = +\infty$ is simply a convenient way of indicating that for any $A > 0$ there exists a $\varphi_A \in \mathscr{D}_-$ carried in $(-\infty, b]$ such that $(|< F_n, \varphi_A >|/\|\varphi_A^{(p)}\|) > A$. Thus the term "quantity" is being loosely used in reference to $|F_n|_p$.

where the *supremum* (*least upper bound*) *is taken over the set of all those* $\varphi \in \mathscr{D}_-$ *which are carried in* $(-\infty, b]$ *and which have* $\|\varphi^{(p)}\| \neq 0$ *and* $\|\varphi^{(p)}\| < \infty$.

The conclusion (2.2) of the theorem then states that there exist an integer $r \geqslant 0$ and a finite constant, K, such that

$$|F_n|_r \leqslant K \qquad (n = 1, 2, \ldots). \tag{2.4}$$

Of course, it is by contradiction that we shall achieve the desired proof: we assume (2.4) to be false—which means that we *assume each of the sequences*

$$\{|F_n|_0\}_n, \quad \{|F_n|_1\}_n, \quad \ldots, \quad \{|F_n|_p\}_n, \quad \ldots \tag{2.5}$$

to be *unbounded*. This will enable us to construct a function $\varphi \in \mathscr{D}_-$ carried in $(-\infty, b]$ and a subsequence $\{F_{n_j}\}_j$ of $\{F_n\}$ such that $|\langle F_{n_j}, \varphi\rangle| > j$, in contradiction to the boundedness hypothesis on $\{F_n\}$.

If p is a nonnegative integer and $\varphi \in \mathscr{D}_-$ then $\varphi = D^{-p}\psi$ $(\psi \in \mathscr{D}_-)$ so that the defining relation (2.3) can be recast as

$$|F_n|_p = \sup \frac{|\langle F_n, D^{-p}\psi\rangle|}{\|\psi\|}, \tag{2.3$'$}$$

where the supremum is taken over all $\psi \in \mathscr{D}_-$ carried in $(-\infty, b]$ and having finite $\|\psi\| \neq 0$.

Setting $I = [a, b]$, there exists (Theorem V.A.3.1) a smallest integer $r_n \geqslant 0$ such that there exists a finite K_n satisfying

$$|\langle F_n, \varphi\rangle| \leqslant K_n \|\varphi^{(r_n)}\|_I \tag{2.6}$$

for all $\varphi \in \mathscr{D}_-$ carried in $(-\infty, b]$.† We may suppose that

$$K_1 \leqslant K_2 \leqslant \cdots \leqslant K_n \leqslant K_{n+1} \leqslant \cdots, \tag{2.7}$$

as this monotonicity can always be arrived at either by rearranging the indices of the F_n or by replacing some of the K_n by larger finite quantities.

Proof of the theorem. The construction mentioned above of the particular $\varphi \in \mathscr{D}_-$ and the selection of the subsequence $\{F_{n_j}\}_j$ such that $\lim_{j\to\infty} |\langle F_{n_j}, \varphi\rangle| = +\infty$ follow the lines of the construction of $\vec{C}$ and the selection of $\{\vec{V}_{n_j}\}_j$ in the treatment of Problem (P) in § 1.

† In passing, remark that $\|\varphi^{(r_n)}\|_I \leqslant \|\varphi^{(r_n)}\|$, so that it follows that there exists a smallest nonnegative integer $\rho_n \leqslant r_n$ such that $|\langle F_n, \varphi\rangle| \leqslant L_n\|\varphi^{(\rho_n)}\|$ with finite L_n and for all $\varphi \in \mathscr{D}_-$ carried in $(-\infty, b]$.

What makes this possible is the fact that a three-dimensional vector $\vec{V}$ and a g.f. $F \in \mathscr{D}'_+$ have in common the property of being continuous linear functionals:

(A) *$\vec{V}$ is a c.l.f. on the linear space E_3* of three-dimensional vectors. The value of this functional at every $\vec{\Phi} \in E_3$ is given by the scalar product $\vec{V} \cdot \vec{\Phi}$. It is linear because

$$\vec{V} \cdot (c_1\vec{\Phi}_1 + c_2\vec{\Phi}_2) = c_1\vec{V} \cdot \vec{\Phi}_1 + c_2\vec{V} \cdot \vec{\Phi}_2.$$

It is continuous because $\lim_{n\to\infty} \vec{\Phi}_n = \vec{0}$ (in the usual sense of E_3) entails $\lim_{n\to\infty} \vec{V} \cdot \vec{\Phi}_n = 0$.

(B) *F is a c.l.f. on the linear space $\mathscr{D}_-$*, as was seen in part (a) of Theorem V.A.4.1 (continuity in the sense that $\lim_{n\to\infty} \varphi_n = 0$ in the mode of Definition V.A.4.1 entails $\lim_{n\to\infty} \langle F, \varphi_n\rangle = 0$).

With this in mind, let us re-examine the solution of Problem (P) and replace each stage thereof with an appropriate $\mathscr{D}'_+$ counterpart. In this fashion, the proof of the present theorem will unfold as a definite parallel to the easier vector algebra situation.

Corresponding to the properties (a), (b), (c) of p. 218 we put:

(a′) Any series $\sum_{j=1}^{\infty} D^{-n_j}\psi_j$, where $\{n_j\}_j$ is a monotonic sequence of distinct natural numbers, where the $\psi_j \in \mathscr{D}_-$, are all carried in $(-\infty, b]$, and have $\|\psi_j\| \leqslant 1$, converges in $\mathscr{D}_-$ to a function $\varphi \in \mathscr{D}_-$ carried in $(-\infty, b]$.

The truth of this statement follows from the inequalities

$$|D^{-n_j}\Psi_j(t)| \leqslant \frac{|b-t|^{n_j}}{n_j!} \|\Psi_j\|,$$

as the reader may easily confirm.

(b′) Given an arbitrary positive M, no matter how large, and given an arbitrary integer $\nu \geqslant 0$ and an $\varepsilon > 0$, no matter how small, there exists $\psi \in \mathscr{D}_-$ carried in $(-\infty, b]$ with $\|\psi\| \leqslant \varepsilon$ and there exists a member F_{n_ν} of $\{F_n\}$ such that

$$|\langle F_{n_\nu}, D^{-\nu}\psi\rangle| > M.$$

This is an immediate consequence of (2.3′) with $p = \nu$ and of the assumption that $\{|F_n|_\nu\}_n$ is unbounded.

(c′) For any member F_n of the given sequence, no matter how large the r_n and K_n associated with it by (2.6) may be, we have

$$|\langle F_n, D^{-p}\psi\rangle| \leqslant \frac{1}{2^k}$$

for all integer $p \geqslant r_n$ and all $\psi \in \mathscr{D}_-$ carried in $(-\infty, b]$, providing

$$\|\psi\|_I \leqslant \frac{e^{a-b}}{K_n 2^k}.$$

(This follows from (2.6) and the inequality

$$\| D^{r_n - p}\psi\|_I \leqslant \frac{(b-a)^{p-r_n}}{(p-r)_n!}\|\psi\|_I \leqslant e^{b-a}\|\psi\|_I$$

which is valid when ψ is carried in $(-\infty, b]$.)

Parallel to the inductive selection procedure described in items (i), (ii), (iii) of Problem (P), pp. 218–219, we now have:

(i′) Taking $M = 2$, $\varepsilon = \frac{1}{2}$, and $\nu = 0$ in (b′) above, we can assert the existence of $\psi_1 \in \mathscr{D}_-$ carried in $(-\infty, b]$, with $\|\psi_1\| = \frac{1}{2}$, and the existence of $F_{n_1} \in \{F_n\}$ such that

$$|\langle F_{n_1}, \psi_1\rangle| > 2.$$

(ii′) Let r_{n_1} and K_{n_1} be the constants associated with F_{n_1} via (2.6) and let $p_2 = \max(r_{n_1}, 2)$. As $\{F_n\}$ is by hypothesis bounded, (2.1) holds, giving

$$|\langle F_{n_1}, \psi_1\rangle| \leqslant B(\psi_1).$$

Then, by property (b′), there exist a g.f. $F_{n_2} \in \{F_n\}$ and a $\mathscr{D}_-$ function ψ_2 carried in $(-\infty, b]$ with

$$\|\psi_2\| = \frac{e^{a-b}}{2^2 K_{n_1}}$$

such that

$$|\langle F_{n_2}, D^{-p_2}\psi_2\rangle| > 3 + B(\psi_1).$$

(ii″) The integer r_{n_2} corresponding to F_{n_2} via (2.6) may or may not be larger that p_2. Set

$$p_3 = \max(r_{n_2}, p_2 + 1).$$

Then, by (b′), there exist a natural number n_3 and $\psi_3 \in \mathscr{D}_-$, carried in $(-\infty, b]$ and having

$$\|\psi_3\| = \frac{e^{a-b}}{2^3 K_{n_2}},$$

such that

$$|\langle F_{n_3}, D^{-p_3}\psi_3\rangle| > 4 + B(\psi_1 + D^{-p_2}\psi_2).$$

(iii′) We have just described the first three steps of a step-by-step procedure the jth of which employs the results of the first $(j-1)$ steps and property (b′) to assert the existence of a natural number n_j and of $\psi_j \in \mathscr{D}_-$, carried in $(-\infty, b]$ with

$$\|\psi_j\| = \frac{e^{a-b}}{2^j K_{n_{j-1}}} \tag{2.8}$$

and such that

(2.9) $|\langle F_{n_j}, D^{-p_j}\psi_j\rangle| > j + 1 + B(D^{-p_1}\psi_1 + D^{-p_2}\psi_2 + \cdots + D^{-p_{j-1}}\psi_{j-1})$

where

(2.10) $\qquad p_j = \max\,(r_{n_{j-1}}, p_{j-1} + 1) \qquad (p_1 = 0$ by convention).

The sequence $\{D^{-p_j}\psi_j\}$, and the subsequence $\{F_{n_j}\}_j$ whose existence is thus arrived at, have these properties:

(α') $\sum_{j=1}^{\infty} D^{-p_j}\psi_j$ converges *in* $\mathcal{D}_-$ to a function $\varphi \in \mathcal{D}_-$ and is carried in $(-\infty, b]$.

This follows from (α') above, because the p_j are distinct by (2.1).

The same is true for the series $\sum_{l=j+1}^{\infty} D^{-p_l}\,\psi_l$.

(γ')

$$\left|\left\langle F_{n_j}, \sum_{l=j+1}^{\infty} D^{-p_l}\psi_l\right\rangle\right| \leqslant 1.^{\dagger}$$

Now, whatever the natural number j, we have

$$\begin{aligned}|\langle F_{n_j}, \varphi\rangle| &= \left|\left\langle F_{n_j}, \sum_{l=1}^{j-1} D^{-p_l}\psi_l\right\rangle + \langle F_{n_j}, D^{-p_j}\psi_j\rangle\right.\\ &\qquad \left. + \left\langle F_{n_j}, \sum_{l=j+1}^{\infty} D^{-p_l}\psi_l\right\rangle\right|\\ &\geqslant -\left|\left\langle F_{n_j}, \sum_{l=1}^{j-1} D^{-p_l}\psi_l\right\rangle\right| + |\langle F_{n_j}, D^{-p_j}\psi_j\rangle|\\ &\qquad -\left|\left\langle F_{n_j}, \sum_{l=j+1}^{\infty} D^{-p_l}\psi_l\right\rangle\right|,\end{aligned}$$

so that

(2.11) $$|\langle F_{n_j}, \varphi\rangle| \geqslant -B\left(\sum_{l=1}^{j-1} D^{-p_l}\psi_l\right) + |\langle F_{n_j}, D^{-p_j}\psi_j\rangle| - 1,$$

† To get this estimate we make use of the fact that $\sum_{l=j+1}^{\infty} D^{-p_l}\psi_l$ (j fixed) being convergent in the $\mathcal{D}_-$ sense we have

$$\langle F_{n_j}, \sum_{l=j+1}^{\infty} D^{-p_l}\psi_l\rangle = \sum_{l=j+1}^{\infty} \langle F_{n_j}, D^{-p_l}\psi_l\rangle.$$

Then, bearing in mind that inequality (2.8) also holds with l in place of j, we can apply property (c') and the inequality $\|\psi\|_{\mathrm{I}} \leqslant \|\psi\|$ to each term on the right hand side, since, by (2.10), $p_l \geqslant r_{n_j}$ for $l = j + 1, j + 2, \ldots$.

as a result of (γ') and the inequality

$$\left|\left\langle F_n, \sum_{l=1}^{j-1} D^{-p_l}\psi_l \right\rangle\right| \leqslant B\left(\sum_{l=1}^{j-1} D^{-p_l}\psi_l\right)$$

valid for all natural numbers n in view of (2.1).

Finally (2.9) and (2.11) leave the result

$$|\langle F_{n_j}, \varphi\rangle| > j,$$

proving that the assumption that (2.2) is false is incompatible with the hypothesis that $\{F_n\}$ is bounded. ∎

Remark. In this section, we have considered only bounded sequences of g.f.'s. The definition of boundedness carries over in obvious fashion to arbitrary sets of g.f.'s, e.g., to parametric families where the parameter ranges over an interval instead of over the natural numbers. The lemma and theorem also carry over. The proof results from the observation that an unbounded set contains an unbounded sequence.

3. Completeness of $\mathscr{D}_+$

Theorem 3.1. *$\mathscr{D}'_+$ is complete. That is, if a sequence $\{F_n\}$ of $\mathscr{D}'_+$ g.f.'s is such that for every $\varphi \in \mathscr{D}_-$*

$$\lim_{n\to\infty} \langle F_n, \varphi\rangle$$

exists, then there exists a unique $F \in \mathscr{D}'_+$ to which $\{F_n\}$ converges:

$$F = \operatorname*{Lim}_{n\to\infty} F_n. \tag{3.1}$$

Proof. $\lim_{n\to\infty} \langle F_n, \varphi\rangle$ is a complex number. Denote it by $F(\varphi)$ to indicate that there is one such number for each $\varphi \in \mathscr{D}_-$ and that it is the value of a functional on $\mathscr{D}_-$ which we may call F.

We need to show that $F \in \mathscr{D}'_+$; or, referring to Theorem V.A.4.1, that F is a continuous linear functional on $\mathscr{D}_-$ in the sense of Definition V.A.4.2. That it is linear we see immediately: c_1, c_2 being complex numbers and $\varphi_1, \varphi_2 \in \mathscr{D}_-$, there holds

$$F(c_1\varphi_1 + c_2\varphi_2) = c_1F(\varphi_1) + c_2F(\varphi_2) \tag{3.2}$$

as a consequence of the elementary properties of limits.

Now $\{|\langle F_n, \varphi\rangle|\}_n$ is bounded for every $\varphi \in \mathscr{D}_-$; for, this sequence being convergent, there exists a natural number N_φ such that $n > N_\varphi$ entails $|\langle F_n, \varphi\rangle - F(\varphi)| < 1$ and therefore

$$n > N_\varphi \Rightarrow |\langle F_n, \varphi\rangle| < 1 + |F(\varphi)|,$$

so that for all n

$$|\langle F_n, \varphi\rangle| \leqslant B(\varphi)$$

with

$$B(\varphi) = \max\,(|\langle F_1, \varphi\rangle|, |\langle F_2, \varphi\rangle|, \ldots, |\langle F_N, \varphi\rangle|, 1 + |F(\varphi)|).$$

From the lemma of the preceding section, we know that all the F_n are carried in some common half-line $[a, +\infty)$. The functional F then also has $F(\varphi) = 0$ for all $\varphi \in \mathscr{D}_-$ carried in $(-\infty, a)$. Theorem 2.1 provides, given $b \in R$, for the existence of an integer $r_b \geqslant 0$ and a finite constant K_b, such that

$$|\langle F_n, \varphi\rangle| \leqslant K_b\,\|\varphi^{(r_b)}\|$$

whenever $\varphi \in \mathscr{D}_-$ is carried in $(-\infty, b]$. It follows that

$$|F(\varphi)| = \lim_{n\to\infty} |\langle F_n, \varphi\rangle| \leqslant K_b\,\|\varphi^{(r_b)}\| \tag{3.3}$$

for these same functions φ.

Let $\{\varphi_j\}$ be any sequence of test functions converging to zero in $\mathscr{D}_-$. They are all carried in some half-line $(-\infty, b]$ (Definition V.A.4.1) and they and their derivatives of any order k converge uniformly on every finite closed interval; on the interval $[a - 1, b]$ among others.

If $\alpha \in \mathscr{D}_+$ is a function carried in $[a - 1, +\infty)$ and $\alpha(t) = 1$ throughout $[a - \frac{1}{2}, b]$, the functions $\varphi_j - \alpha\varphi_j$ are carried in $(-\infty, a)$ so that

$$F(\varphi_j - \alpha\varphi_j) = 0 \qquad (j = 1, 2, \ldots).$$

Therefore, in view of (3.2),

$$F(\varphi_j) = F(\alpha\varphi_j) \qquad (j = 1, 2, \ldots),$$

which, thanks to (3.3), gives

$$|F(\varphi_j)| \leqslant K_b\,\|(\alpha\varphi_j)^{(r_b)}\| = K_b\,\|(\alpha\varphi_j)^{(r_b)}\|_J \tag{3.4}$$

where $J = [a - 1, b]$. It follows, from the very simple Exercise V.5, that

$$\lim_{j\to\infty} \|(\alpha\varphi_j)^{(r_b)}\|_J = 0.$$

Thus (3.4) proves the continuity of the functional F. Combined with the linearity expressed in (3.2), this makes F a c.l.f. on $\mathscr{D}_-$, i.e., $F \in \mathscr{D}'_+$ and its value may then be written as $\langle F, \varphi\rangle$. ∎

4. Parametric Derivatives and Integrals

An important consequence of the completeness of $\mathscr{D}'_+$ is

Theorem 4.1. *Given a parametric g.f. $F_\lambda \in \mathscr{D}'_+$ with Λ an interval of the real line. Then if, for every $\varphi \in \mathscr{D}_-$,*

(a) $\dfrac{d\langle F_\lambda, \varphi\rangle}{d\lambda}$ *exists, F_λ has a parametric derivative*

$$\frac{\partial F_\lambda}{\partial \lambda} \quad \text{and} \quad \left\langle \frac{\partial F}{\partial \lambda}, \varphi \right\rangle = \frac{d\langle F_\lambda, \varphi\rangle}{d\lambda}\ ;$$

(b) $\int_\alpha^\beta \langle F_\lambda, \varphi\rangle\, d\lambda$ *exists, F_λ has a parametric integral*

$$\int_\alpha^\beta F_\lambda\, d\lambda \quad \text{and} \quad \left\langle \int_\alpha^\beta F_\lambda\, d\lambda, \varphi \right\rangle = \int_\alpha^\beta \langle F_\lambda, \varphi\rangle\, d\lambda.$$

The proofs of these statements are straightforward applications of Theorem 3.1 and constitute Exercises 5 and 6.

Many other useful properties of parametric g.f.'s derive from the completeness of $\mathscr{D}'_+$. For these, the student is referred to [23].

5. The Problem of Division

$G \in \mathscr{D}'_+$ being given, as well as a function $\alpha \in C^\infty$ which is nowhere zero, the problem of finding a solution $F \in \mathscr{D}'_+$ of the equation

$$\alpha F = G \tag{5.1}$$

is trivial: $F = (1/\alpha)G$.

Such is no longer the case when α has zeros. We shall examine in detail only one particular case of this problem, namely:

Given $G \in \mathscr{D}'_+$, find the solution(s) $F \in \mathscr{D}'_+$, if it (they) exists, of the equation

$$tF = G. \tag{5.2}$$

For those $\varphi \in \mathscr{D}_-$ which are carried either in $(-\infty, 0)$ or in $(0, +\infty)$ the values of $\langle F, \varphi\rangle$ are immediately found to equal $\langle (1/t)G, \varphi\rangle$ so

$$F = \frac{1}{t}G \quad \text{in } (-\infty, 0) \quad \text{and in } (0, +\infty). \tag{5.3}$$

Any $\varphi \in \mathscr{D}_-$ for which $\varphi(0) = 0$ is, in view of Taylor's formula (Exercise I.6), of the form $\varphi(t) = t\psi(t)$ with $\psi \in \mathscr{D}_-$, so that any $\mathscr{D}'_+$ solution of (5.2) will satisfy

$$\langle tF, \psi\rangle = \langle F, \varphi\rangle = \langle G, \psi\rangle \tag{5.4}$$

with this type of test function.

Let $\varphi_0 \in \mathscr{D}_-$ have $\varphi_0(0) = 1$ and let φ be an arbitrary test function. The function $\lambda(t) = \varphi(t) - \varphi(0)\,\varphi_0(t)$ belongs to $\mathscr{D}_-$ and $\lambda(0) = 0$ so

$$\lambda(t) = t\psi(t) \qquad (\psi \in \mathscr{D}_-)$$

and we can decompose every $\varphi \in \mathscr{D}_-$ into the form

$$\varphi(t) = \varphi(0)\,\varphi_0(t) + t\psi(t). \tag{5.5}$$

If the solution $F \in \mathscr{D}'_+$ of our problem exists, it therefore verifies

$$\langle G, \psi\rangle = \langle tF, \psi\rangle = \langle F, t\psi\rangle = \langle F, \varphi - \varphi(0)\varphi_0\rangle,$$

whence

$$\langle F, \varphi\rangle = \varphi(0)\langle F, \varphi_0\rangle + \langle G, \psi\rangle, \tag{5.6}$$

a convenient formula for computing the value of F at any $\varphi \in \mathscr{D}_-$ providing the value of F at the particular function $\varphi_0 \in \mathscr{D}_-$ is known.

If both $F_1 \in \mathscr{D}'_+$ and $F_2 \in \mathscr{D}'_+$ are solutions of (5.2), we see from (5.6) that

$$\langle F_1 - F_2, \varphi\rangle = \langle F_1 - F_2, \varphi_0\rangle\,\varphi(0).$$

In other terms, there then exists a scalar c such that

$$F_1 - F_2 = c\delta(t), \tag{5.7}$$

and we have proved that if the problem has a solution it is not unique: all solutions are obtainable from any one of them by the addition of $c\delta(t)$ with arbitrary constant c (cf. also Exercise 18). This is comparable to the integration problem of Lemma V.B.2.1.

It yet remains for us to show that a solution exists in $\mathscr{D}'_+$. Let us do so by constructing one explicitly.

Starting from an arbitrary fundamental sequence $\{g_n\} \in G$, the relation (5.3) suggests using $\{(1/t)g_n(t)\}$ to define F. In general, however, $(1/t)g_n$ is not in $\mathscr{K}_+(R)$ so this new sequence won't do. The obvious remedy to try is surgery: excise the singularities at the origin and retain the $\mathscr{K}_+$ functions

$$k_n(t) = \begin{cases} 0 & \text{if } |t| < \varepsilon_n < 1 \\ \dfrac{1}{t}\, g_n(t) & \text{if } |t| > \varepsilon_n, \end{cases} \tag{5.8}$$

where the ε_n are chosen so that

$$\int_{-\varepsilon}^{\varepsilon} |g_n(t)|\, dt \leqslant \frac{1}{n} \qquad (n = 1, 2, \ldots).$$

For any $\varphi \in \mathscr{D}_-$ with $\varphi(0) = 0$ we can then, thanks to (5.4), write

$$\langle F, \varphi\rangle = \lim_{n\to\infty} \int_{-\infty}^{\infty} g_n(t)\,\psi(t)\,dt = \lim_{n\to\infty} \int_{-\infty}^{\infty} k_n(t)\,\varphi(t)\,dt \tag{5.9}$$

$$\left(\left|\int_{-\varepsilon_n}^{\varepsilon_n} g_n(t)\,\psi(t)\,dt\right| \leqslant \frac{1}{n} \max_{-1\leqslant t\leqslant 1} |\psi(t)|\right).$$

The sequence $\{k_n\}$, though it provides a solution of (5.2) for the subset of $\mathscr{D}_-$ consisting of test functions that vanish at the origin, is not necessarily a fundamental sequence† and must therefore be modified.

For this purpose, let us settle on some $\varphi_0 \in \mathscr{D}_-$ having $\varphi_0(0) = 1$ and express every $\varphi \in \mathscr{D}_-$ in terms of its decomposition (5.5). We now seek to construct a solution $F_0 \in \mathscr{D}'_+$ such that $\langle F_0, \varphi_0\rangle = 0$. To guide us, we have the observation that in view of (5.6) this particular solution satisfies

$$\langle F_0, \varphi\rangle = \langle G, \psi\rangle.$$

Solving (5.5) for ψ we arrive at

$$(5.10) \qquad \langle F_0, \varphi\rangle = \left\langle G, \frac{\varphi - \varphi(0)\varphi_0}{t}\right\rangle = \left\langle \frac{1}{t}\, G, \varphi - \varphi(0)\varphi_0\right\rangle.$$

This suggests that we look for a convergent sequence $\{l_n\}$ of $\mathscr{D}'_+$ g.f.'s such that

$$(5.11) \qquad \lim_{n\to\infty} \langle l_n, \varphi\rangle = \left\langle \frac{1}{t}\, G, \varphi - \varphi(0)\varphi_0\right\rangle.$$

Such a sequence is provided by

$$l_n(t) = k_n(t) - \langle k_n, \varphi_0\rangle\, \delta(t) \quad (n = 1, 2, \ldots)$$

whose values at any $\varphi \in \mathscr{D}_-$ are

$$\langle l_n, \varphi\rangle = \langle k_n, \varphi\rangle - \langle k_n, \varphi_0\rangle\, \varphi(0) = \langle k_n, \varphi - \varphi(0)\varphi_0\rangle.$$

The function $\varphi - \varphi(0)\varphi_0$ vanishes at the origin; it can therefore be substituted for φ in (5.9) with the result (5.11), regardless of whether $\langle k_n, \varphi\rangle$ and $\langle k_n, \varphi_0\rangle$ converge individually or not.

Thus, $\{l_n\}$ is a convergent sequence of $\mathscr{D}'_+$ g.f.'s; by the completeness Theorem 3.1 $\operatorname{Lim}_{n\to\infty} l_n \in \mathscr{D}'_+$ and we can assert, in view of (5.11) and (5.10) that

$$(5.12) \qquad F_0 = \operatorname{Lim}_{n\to\infty} l_n.$$

This concludes the proof of

Theorem 5.1. *Given $G \in \mathscr{D}'_+$, the equation $tF = G$ has an infinity of solutions F belonging to $\mathscr{D}'_+$; any two of them differ by $c\delta(t)$, where c is an arbitrary scalar. A particular solution can be constructed explicitly from any fundamental sequence of G.*

† For example, if $g_n(t) = p_n(t - 1/n)$ [p_n = the "pulse" of (II.A.2.1)], then

$$k_n(t) \geqslant \frac{n^2}{2} \qquad \text{for } \frac{1}{n} \leqslant t \leqslant \frac{2}{n},$$

while $k_n(t) = 0$ everywhere else. Functions $\varphi(t) \in \mathscr{D}_-$ are then easily found for which $\langle k_n, \varphi\rangle$ diverges as $n \to \infty$.

6. Relative Compactness of $\mathscr{D}'_+$

Equicontinuous sequences of functions, which were introduced in § V.B.1, have a very fundamental property, which both suggests and serves to prove Theorem 6.2 below. This property is expressed in the classical

Theorem 6.1 (Theorem of Ascoli-Arzelà). *A uniformly bounded and equicontinuous sequence $\{g_n\}$ of functions defined on a finite closed interval $[a, b]$ contains a subsequence that converges uniformly to a function $g(t) \in C[a, b]$.*

Proof. The rational numbers in $[a, b]$ can be arranged in a sequence $\{r_k\}_k$, and they form a set that is dense in $[a, b]$ (i.e., every $t \in [a, b]$ is the limit point of a subset of $\{r_k\}$).

The sequence of complex numbers $\{g_n(r_1)\}_n$, being bounded, satisfies the Bolzano-Weierstrass Theorem for complex numbers, and so contains at least one convergent subsequence, which we denote by $\{g_{n1}(r_1)\}_n$. $\{g_{n1}\}$, being a subsequence of $\{g_n\}$, is also uniformly bounded on $[a, b]$ so the numerical sequence $\{g_{n1}(r_2)\}_n$ is bounded and contains at least one subsequence, call it $\{g_{n2}(r_2)\}_n$, that converges. Continuing in this fashion, we obtain the sequences of functions $\{g_{n1}\}_n, \{g_{n2}\}_n, \ldots, \{g_{nk}\}_n, \ldots$, each of which is a subsequence of all the preceding ones and is such that $\{g_{nk}(r_k)\}_n$ converges. Taking the first member of the first of these function sequences, the second of the second, and so on, we obtain the "diagonal" sequence $\{g_{nn}\}$ of functions which for any given natural number k has the property that the complex numbers $g_{nn}(r_k)$ with $n > k$ form a subsequence of the numerical sequence $\{g_{nk}(r_k)\}_n$, and consequently converge. Therefore, for every given natural number k, there exists a complex number, call it $g(r_k)$, such that

$$g(r_k) = \lim_{n\to\infty} g_{nn}(r_k). \tag{6.1}$$

We shall show next that $g(t) = \lim\limits_{n\to\infty} g_{nn}(t)$ exists not only at rational but at all $t \in [a, b]$ and that this convergence is uniform on $[a, b]$, a fact which automatically ensures that $g \in C[a, b]$.

Given $\varepsilon > 0$, there exists, in consequence of the equicontinuity of $\{g_{nn}\}_n$, $\delta > 0$, such that

$$|t_1 - t_2| < \delta \Rightarrow |g_{nn}(t_1) - g_{nn}(t_2)| < \frac{\varepsilon}{3} \qquad (n = 1, 2, \ldots). \tag{6.2}$$

Let $\rho_1, \rho_2, \ldots, \rho_\nu$ be given rationals in $[a, b]$ such that

$$a + j\delta \leqslant \rho_j < a + (j+1)\delta \qquad (j = 0, 1, 2, \ldots, \nu),$$

where $\nu\delta \leqslant b < (\nu + 1)\delta$.

Then, given any $t \in [a, b]$, there exists a ρ_j with $|\rho_j - t| < \delta$ and, for any integers $0 < n$, $0 < m$,

$$(6.3) \qquad \begin{aligned} |g_{nn}(t) - g_{mm}(t)| &\leqslant |g_{nn}(t) - g_{nn}(\rho_j)| + |g_{nn}(\rho_j) \\ &\quad - g_{mm}(\rho_j)| + |g_{mm}(\rho_j) - g_{mm}(t)| \\ &< \frac{\varepsilon}{3} + |g_{nn}(\rho_j) - g_{mm}(\rho_j)| + \frac{\varepsilon}{3}, \end{aligned}$$

where we have used (6.2) to get the $\varepsilon/3$ terms.

By (6.1) there are associated with $\rho_0, \rho_1, \ldots, \rho_\nu$, respectively, positive integers $N_0, N_1, \ldots, N_\nu$ such that

$$m, n > N_j \Rightarrow |g_{nn}(\rho_j) - g_{mm}(\rho_j)| < \frac{\varepsilon}{3} \qquad (j = 0, 1, \ldots, \nu).$$

If then we denote by N the largest of these N_j, it follows from (6.3) that

$$(6.4) \qquad n, m > N \Rightarrow |g_{nn}(t) - g_{mm}(t)| < \frac{\varepsilon}{3} + \frac{\varepsilon}{3} + \frac{\varepsilon}{3} = \varepsilon.$$

N depends on ε but is independent of t in $[a, b]$ so (6.4) expresses a well-known sufficient condition for the uniform convergence of $\{g_{nn}\}$ on $[a, b]$. ∎

Remark. Our discussion of equicontinuity has been limited to *sequences* of functions because that is all we need in the context of Chapters V and VI. Definition V.B.1.1, however, can be extended to arbitrary families of functions in the most obvious way. Also (since an infinite family of functions contains subsequences) in the statement of the Ascoli-Arzelà theorem, the sequence $\{g_n\}$ can be replaced by an infinite equicontinuous family g_λ. These questions and many fruitful uses of the A-A theorem are covered in such texts as [12] [19].

Consider next a bounded sequence $\{F_n\}$ of $\mathscr{D}'_+$ g.f.'s. All its members are carried in the same forward half-line $[a, +\infty)$. Also, given any integer $j > 0$, there exist, by Theorem 2.1, a constant K_j and an integer $r_j \geqslant 0$ such that $|\langle F_n, \varphi\rangle| \leqslant K_j \|\varphi^{(r_j)}\|$ holds, independent of n, for all $\varphi \in \mathscr{D}_-$ carried in $(-\infty, a + \frac{1}{2} + j]$.

This, combined with the result of Exercise V.10, makes it possible to deduce the following facts: for a given integer j, and setting $q_j = r_j + 2$, the g.f. $D^{-q_j}F_n$ coincides on $(-\infty, a + j)$ with a function $g_n \in C(-\infty, a + j]$; $g_n(t) = 0$ for $t \leqslant a$, the function sequence $\{g_n\}_n$ is equicontinuous on the bounded closed interval $[a, a + j]$. (The straightforward derivation of these facts is left to the student.)

From the Ascoli-Arzelà theorem, it then follows that $\{g_n\}_n$ contains a subsequence $\{g_{n_j}\}$ which converges uniformly on $[a, a + j]$, and therefore on $(-\infty, a + j]$, to a function $G_j \in C(-\infty, a + j]$ with $G_j(t) = 0$ for $t \leqslant a$. Recalling the proof of Theorem II.B.6.1, we see that for every $\varphi \in \mathscr{D}_-$ carried in $(-\infty, a + j]$, j being fixed,

$$\lim_{n_j \to \infty} \langle D^{-q_j} F_{n_j}, \varphi \rangle = \langle G_j, \varphi \rangle,$$

from which we get for these same $\varphi \in \mathscr{D}_-$

$$\lim_{n_j \to \infty} \langle F_{n_j}, \varphi \rangle = (-1)^{q_j} \langle G_j, \varphi^{(q_j)} \rangle.$$

The conclusion which we draw from these observations is this: *if $\{F_n\}$ is a bounded sequence in $\mathscr{D}'_+$ carried in $[a, +\infty)$ then to each half-line $(-\infty, a + j]$ corresponds at least one subsequence $\{F_{n_j}\}_j$ such that there exists*

$$\lim_{n_j \to \infty} \langle F_{n_j}, \varphi \rangle \tag{6.5}$$

when $\varphi \in \mathscr{D}_-$ is carried in $(-\infty, a + j]$.

This suggests that we apply to $\{F_n\}$ a "diagonalization" process somewhat analogous to that used in the proof of Theorem 6.1. Let $\{F_{n1}\}$ be a subsequence of $\{F_{n1}\}$ which satisfies (6.5) in $(-\infty, a + 1]$, let $\{F_{n2}\}$ be a subsequence of $\{F_{n1}\}$ which satisfies (6.5) in $(-\infty, a + 2]$, and so on. The resulting subsequences then satisfy

$$\{F_{n1}\} \supset \{F_{n2}\} \supset \cdots \supset \{F_{nj}\} \supset \{F_{nj+1}\} \supset \cdots$$

and we take the nth element in the nth sequence ($n = 1, 2, \ldots$) obtaining the subsequence $\{F_{nn}\}_n$ of $\{F_n\}$. $\{F_{nn}\}$ has the property that for any $\varphi \in \mathscr{D}_-$ there exists

$$\lim_{n \to \infty} \langle F_{nn}, \varphi \rangle. \tag{6.6}$$

Indeed, this φ is carried in some half-line $(-\infty, a + j]$ and all, except possibly the first $j - 1$, elements of $\{F_{nn}\}$ belong to $\{F_{nj}\}$ so that (6.6) is a consequence of (6.5).

But $\mathscr{D}'_+$ is complete (Theorem 3.1) so (6.6) entails the convergence of $\{F_{nn}\}$ to a $\mathscr{D}'_+$ g.f., which we may call F. This proves

Theorem 6.2. *Every bounded sequence $\{F_n\}$ of $\mathscr{D}'_+$ g.f.'s contains at least one subsequence that converges to an element of $\mathscr{D}'_+$.*

Since any infinite family of $\mathscr{D}'_+$ g.f.'s contains a sequence we may enunciate the more general

Theorem 6.3 (Relative Compactness of $\mathscr{D}'_+$). *Every bounded infinite family of $\mathscr{D}'_+$ g.f.'s contains at least one subsequence that converges to an element of $\mathscr{D}'_+$.*

EXERCISES

[*Note*: All the exercises proposed here are in the (**) class insofar as this is a (**) level chapter. These marked with a (*) are supplementary.]

1. Solve problem (P), p. 217, by elementary vector algebra (consider the sequences $\{\vec{i}\cdot\vec{\Phi}_n\}$, $\{\vec{j}\cdot\vec{\Phi}_n\}$, $\{\vec{k}\cdot\vec{\Phi}_n\}$, where $\vec{i}, \vec{j}, \vec{k}$ are the usual orthogonal unit vectors).

2. Let $F \in \mathscr{D}'_+$ be carried in $[a, +\infty)$ not in $[0, +\infty)$ (Definition II.A.4.2). By Theorem V.B.1.3 there exist an integer $q \geqslant 0$ and a function $g(t) \in C(-\infty, 1) \cap \mathscr{K}_+(R)$ such that $F = D^q g$ on $(-\infty, 1)$. Let $[c, +\infty)$ be the half-line with largest c containing the carrier of the function $g(t)$. Then $a \leqslant c < 0$ and there exists $\varphi \in \mathscr{D}_-$ carried in $(c, c+1)$ such that $\langle g, \varphi\rangle \neq 0$. Take $\alpha(t) \in \mathscr{D}_+$ carried in $(c-1, +\infty)$ with $\alpha(t) \equiv 1$ for $t \geqslant c$ and verify that $\psi(t) = \alpha(t)D^{-q}\varphi(t)$ is a $\mathscr{D}$-function carried in $(c-1, c+1)$ such that $|\langle F, \psi\rangle| = |\langle g, \varphi\rangle|$.

3. Bearing in mind Exercise 2 apply the general idea of Remark 4, p. 53, to prove Lemma 2.1.

4. $F_\lambda \in \mathscr{D}'_+$ is a parametric g.f. with $\Lambda \subset C$ and $c \in R$. Also, for every $\varphi \in \mathscr{D}_-$, there exists the finite $\lim\limits_{\lambda\to c} \langle F_\lambda, \varphi\rangle$. Prove that there exist in the complex plane, C, circles Γ of nonvanishing radius centered at c such that the F_λ with $\lambda \in \Gamma \cap \Lambda$ form a bounded set of $\mathscr{D}'_+$ g.f.'s. Give examples showing that the radii of such Γ cannot be preassigned at will. (This is in contrast with convergent *sequences* of g.f.'s: every such *sequence* forms a bounded set of g.f.'s but not every convergent family F_λ is bounded.)

5. Prove part (a) of Theorem 4.1.

6. Prove part (b) of Theorem 4.1. (Use the convergence of sequences Riemann sums.)

7. $F \in \mathscr{D}'_+$ is continuous with respect to λ on $[\alpha, \beta]$. Prove that the parametric integral $\int_\alpha^\beta F_\lambda \, d\lambda$ exists.

8. The parameter domain of $F_\lambda \in \mathscr{D}'_+$ is $\Lambda = [0, +\infty)$;

$$\int_0^\beta \langle F_\lambda, \varphi\rangle \, d\lambda \quad \text{and} \quad \lim_{\beta\to\infty} \int_0^\beta \langle F_\lambda, \varphi\rangle \, d\lambda$$

exist for every $\varphi \in \mathscr{D}_-$. Prove that the parametric integral

$$G = \int_0^\infty F_\lambda \, d\lambda$$

exists ($G \in \mathscr{D}'_+$).

***9.** (O.C.) If the sequence $\{F_n\}$ of $\mathscr{D}'_+$ g.f.'s is bounded and (c, d) is a bounded interval, there exist an integer $r \geqslant 0$ and a constant K such that $|\langle F_n, \varphi\rangle| \leqslant K\|\varphi^{(r)}\|$ for all $\varphi \in \mathscr{D}_-$ carried in (c, d). From this, deduce the same property for a bounded sequence of $\mathscr{D}'$ g.f.'s (boundedness in $\mathscr{D}'$ is defined as in $\mathscr{D}'_+$ but with $\varphi \in \mathscr{D}$ instead of $\varphi \in \mathscr{D}_-$).

***10.** (O.C.) State and prove a $\mathscr{D}'$ version of Theorem 3.1. (Use the result of Exercise 9.)

***11.** (A.R.) Use the Lebesgue resonance method to prove Lemma V.A.3.1 following the general lines of the proof of Theorem 2.1. (Compare your proof with that given in Chapter V and observe that the latter is a variant of the Lebesgue method.)

***12.** (A.R.) Given $\{F_n\}$, a sequence of continuous linear functionals on $\mathscr{D}_-$ in the sense of Definition V.A.4.2. It is possible to prove directly, without using Theorem 2.1, that if $\{\langle F_n, \varphi\rangle\}_n$ converges for every $\varphi \in \mathscr{D}_-$, the functional F whose values are given by

$$\langle F, \varphi\rangle = \lim_{n\to\infty} \langle F_n, \varphi\rangle$$

is also a c.l.f. on $\mathscr{D}_-$. To carry out this proof of Theorem 3.1, proceed as follows:

(a) observe that if F were not a c.l.f., there would exist a sequence $\{\varphi_k\}$ of $\mathscr{D}_-$ functions converging to zero in the sense of Definition V.A.4.1 while there would exist $c > 0$ such that $|\langle F, \varphi_k\rangle| \geqslant c$ $(k = 1, 2, \ldots)$;

(b) let $(-\infty, b]$ be a half-line carrying $\{\varphi_k\}$, then we may assume that for $k = 1, 2, \ldots$

$$\|\varphi_k^{(j)}\|_{I_k} \leqslant \frac{1}{4^k} \qquad \text{for } j = 0, 1, \ldots, k \text{ and } I_k = [b-k, b]$$

(if need be, take a subsequence and relabel);

(c) observe that the $\psi_k = 2^k\varphi_k$ form a sequence converging to zero in $\mathscr{D}_-$, that $\sum_{k=0}^{\infty} \psi_k$ converges to a $\mathscr{D}_-$ function, and that $\lim_{k\to\infty} |\langle F, \psi_k\rangle| = +\infty$;

(d) subsequences $\{F_{n_p}\}$ and $\{\psi_{k_p}\}$ can be obtained by a step-by-step procedure in which ψ_{k_1} is chosen so that $|\langle F, \psi_{k_1}\rangle| > 1$ and the pth step consists in choosing $\psi_{k_p}(F_{n_1}, \ldots, F_{n_{p-1}}, k_1, \ldots, k_{p-1}$ having been obtained in the first $p-1$ steps) so that

$$|\langle F_{n_j}, \psi_{k_p}\rangle| < 2^{j-p} \qquad (j = 1, 2, \ldots, p-1)$$

while

$$|\langle F, \psi_{k_p}\rangle| > \sum_{j=1}^{p-1} |\langle F, \psi_{k_j}\rangle| + p + 1;$$

(e) next, in the pth step, F_{k_p} is chosen so that

$$|\langle F_{k_p}, \psi_{k_p}\rangle| > \sum_{j=1}^{p-1} |\langle F_{k_p}, \psi_{k_j}\rangle| + p + 1$$

[this is possible because $\lim_{n\to\infty} \langle F_n, \varphi\rangle = \langle F, \varphi\rangle$ and because of (d)];

(f) verify that $|\langle F_{k_p}, \sum_{j=1}^{\infty} \psi_{k_j}\rangle| > p$ and deduce that F is a c.l.f. on $\mathscr{D}'_+$.

This method, which is used in [23] to show the completeness of $\mathscr{D}'$, also serves for other g.f. classes such as $\mathscr{E}'$. Since every $\mathscr{K}_+$ function is obviously a c.l.f. on $\mathscr{D}_-$, it provides a means of going directly from the Definition II.A.3.1 to Theorem V.A.4.1 and then from the latter to Theorem VI.3.1.

***13.** (A.R.). Given that F is a c.l.f. on $\mathscr{D}_-$ in the sense of Definition V.A.4.2, prove that to the half-line $(-\infty, b]$ corresponds an integer $r \geqslant 0$ such that for every sequence $\{\varphi_n\}$ of $\mathscr{D}_-$ functions carried in $(-\infty, b]$, it suffices that

$$(1)\quad \lim_{n\to\infty} \|\varphi_n^{(r)}\|_{I_r} = 0 \qquad (I_r = [b - r, b])$$

to ensure that

$$(2)\quad \lim_{n\to\infty} \langle F, \varphi_n\rangle = 0.$$

[Outline of solution: if (1) did not entail (2) for any integer $r \geqslant 0$, there would exist for each such integer r a sequence $\{\varphi_{rk}\}_k$ carried in $(-\infty, b]$ satisfying (1) for the corresponding r but with $|\langle F, \varphi_{rk}\rangle| \geqslant 1$ $(k = 1, 2, \ldots)$. Show that by appropriately selecting one member from each of these sequences, it is possible to obtain a sequence $\{\psi_n\}_n$ of $\mathscr{D}_-$ functions carried in $(-\infty, b]$ and such that

$$\|\psi_n^{(r)}\|_{I_n} < 2^{-n} \qquad \text{for all } r \leqslant n$$

while $|\langle F, \psi_n\rangle| \geqslant 1$. Since $\lim_{n\to\infty} \psi_n = 0$ in the sense of Definition V.A.4.1, this contradicts the hypothesis that F is a c.l.f. on $\mathscr{D}_-$.] For the $\mathscr{D}'$ case, see [26].

***14.** (A.R.) From the result of Exercise 13, deduce that if F is a c.l.f. on $\mathscr{D}_-$ and $I = (-\infty, b]$ a given half-line, there exist integer $r \geqslant 0$ and constant K such that, for every $\varphi \in \mathscr{D}_-$ carried in $(-\infty, b]$,

$$(3)\quad |\langle F, \varphi\rangle| \leqslant K\,\|\varphi^{(r)}\|_{I_r}.$$

[A proof analogous to the one given in [26] for $\mathscr{D}'$ and bounded interval I, φ carried in I, is this:

(a) take r as given by Exercise 13;

(b) if (3) did not hold, a sequence $\{\varphi_n\}$ of $\mathscr{D}_-$ functions carried in $(-\infty, b]$ could be found such that

$$|\{F, \varphi_n\rangle| \geqslant n\|\varphi_n^{(r)}\|_{I_r} \qquad (n = 1, 2, \ldots);$$

(c) Let

$$\psi_n(t) = (n\|\varphi_n^{(r)}\|_{I_r})^{-1}\varphi_n(t)$$

so $\lim_{n\to\infty} \psi_n = 0$ in the sense of Definition V.A.4.1, while

$$|\langle F, \psi_n\rangle| \geqslant 1 \qquad (n = 1, 2, \ldots),$$

contradicting the continuity of F.]

***15.** (A.R.) Deduce Theorem V.A.3.1 from Exercise 14.

16. Find $\dfrac{1}{t}\,\delta(t)$.

17. Find

$$\frac{1}{\sin t}\sum_{n=0}^{\infty} \delta(t - n\pi).$$

$$\left[\text{Note: } \frac{1}{\sin t} = \frac{1}{t}\left(\frac{t}{\sin t}\right).\right]$$

18. $F \in \mathscr{D}'_+$ and $tF = 0$. Show that the carrier of F (defined in § V.B.3) consists of the point $0 \in R$ alone, and apply Theorem V.B.3.1 to show that $F = c\delta(t)$.

19. $F \in \mathscr{D}'_+$ and $t^p F = 0$ (p integer $\geqslant 0$). Show that

$$F = \sum_{k=0}^{p-1} c_k \delta^{(k)}(t).$$

[One solution consists in using the idea of Exercise 18. Another consists in extending the decomposition formula (5.5).]

***20.** (A.R.) The function of t, $\rho_\varepsilon(t - \tau)$, is defined in (I.2.11). Letting ε range over the positive rationals, τ over the rationals, yields a denumerable collection, Q, of $\mathscr{D}_-$ (actually $\mathscr{D}$) functions. Since every $\varphi \in \mathscr{D}_-$ equals $\lim_{\varepsilon \to 0} (\rho_\varepsilon * \varphi)$, where convergence is in the sense of Definition II.A.4.1 (recall Exercise V.8), it is easy to prove that φ is also the limit, in the same sense, of a sequence of finite linear combinations with rational coefficients of members of Q (i.e., expressions of the form

$$\sum_{k=0}^{n} a_k \rho_{r_k}(t - \tau_k), \qquad a_k = \alpha_k + i\beta_k, \ \alpha_k, \beta_k, r_k, \tau_k \text{ rational}).$$

Carry out such a proof and observe that the set, $\mathscr{R}$, of all such finite linear combinations with rational coefficients is denumerable.

***21.** (A.R.) The members of the set $\mathscr{R}$ defined in Exercise 20 can be disposed sequentially as $\psi_1, \psi_2, \ldots, \psi_j, \ldots$. This makes it possible to give a proof of Theorem 6.2 different from that in the text, simply by following closely the pattern of the proof of the Ascoli-Arzelà theorem, but with the ψ_j in place of the rationals, and other appropriate adaptations, taking into account the definition of convergence and equicontinuity in $\mathscr{D}'_+$. Carry out the details of such a proof.

CHAPTER VII

*THE LAPLACE TRANSFORM

The reader can take up this chapter directly after Chapter IV.

The Laplace transform is much in favor among engineers as a tool for the solution of initial-value problems connected with ordinary and partial differential equations. Here we shall give a brief introduction to the theory and applications of the Laplace transform (L.T.) both for the usual functions discussed in most introductory textbooks on the subject and for certain g.f.'s of class $\mathscr{D}'_+$. The purpose of this account is to give the reader some ideas: on a definition of the L.T. that is not exclusively formalistic, on the close relation between what are here called the direct and the indirect operational methods, and on the applicability of the L.T. to the solution of initial-value problems for partial differential equations. Here we can afford to drastically limit the number of illustrative applications. There is no shortage of textbooks and articles on this subject, containing numerous worked-out examples at all levels. For a deeper insight into the theory in its non-g.f. aspects, the reader is referred to the scholarly treatises of Doetsch [14], Van der Pol and Bremmer [52] and Widder [54]. For worked-out examples and exercises see [3] [7] [8].

1. The Laplace Transform of a Function

Many $\mathscr{D}'_+$ g.f.'s are functionals not just on $\mathscr{D}_-$ but on larger sets of test functions. Thus, $H(t)$ and $\delta(t)$ take, on every function of the form e^{-st} with $s > 0$, the values

$$\langle H(t), e^{-st}\rangle = \int_0^\infty e^{-st}\,dt = \lim_{A\to\infty}\int_0^A e^{-st}\,dt = \frac{1}{s},$$

$$\langle \delta(t), e^{-st}\rangle = (e^{-st})_{t=0} = 1.$$

The Laplace transform of a g.f. $F \in \mathscr{D}'_+$ is simply the function of s defined by $\langle F, e^{-st}\rangle$, and the properties of this transform are simply adaptations with $\varphi = e^{-st}$ of some of the familiar properties of $\langle F, \varphi\rangle$ studied so far for the case $\varphi \in \mathscr{D}_-$.

Actually, what we shall deal with here are the Laplace transforms of functions and g.f.'s that are carried in the forward half-line $[0, +\infty)$. *The symbol $\mathscr{K}_{++}(R)$ stands for the subset of $\mathscr{K}_{+}(R)$ consisting of all $\mathscr{K}_{+}(R)$ functions that vanish for $t < 0$.* More often than not, $\mathscr{K}_{++}(R)$ will be abbreviated to $\mathscr{K}_{++}$ in what follows.

Definition 1.1. *The Laplace transform of $F(t) \in \mathscr{K}_{++}(R)$ is the function $f(s)$ defined by*

$$f(s) = \langle F(t), e^{-st} \rangle = \int_0^\infty e^{-st} F(t)\, dt \tag{1.1}$$

when the integral converges. $f(s)$ is also designated by $\mathscr{L}\{F\}$ or $\mathscr{L}\{F, s\}$. [$F(t)$ is called the object function, $f(s)$ the image function.]

(The definition is given here for $\mathscr{K}_{++}$ functions only, because that is all we need for the extension to g.f.'s.)

Not every $\mathscr{K}_{++}$ function has a Laplace transform. The function $F(t)$ which vanishes for $t < 0$ and is equal to e^{t^2} for $t > 0$, does not have an L.T. since the integral $\int_0^\infty e^{-st} e^{t^2}\, dt$ is divergent for any value of s. A $\mathscr{K}_{++}$ function $F(t)$, for which there exist real constants C and M such that, for all t,

$$|F(t)| \leqslant M e^{ct} \tag{1.2}$$

is said to be of *exponential order c*.

Such a function has a L.T. for all values of $s > c$. Indeed, the integral on the right in the inequality

$$\left| \int_0^\infty F(t)\, e^{-st}\, dt \right| \leqslant M \int_0^\infty e^{-(s-c)t}\, dt$$

is finite for all $s > c$, so that $f(s)$ is defined for all s on the half-line $(c, +\infty)$.

There exist functions that are not of exponential order but still have a Laplace transform (Exercise 1) defined on a forward half-line of the real s axis. In fact, we have

Theorem 1.1. *Let $F \in \mathscr{K}_{++}$ and let $f(s) = \mathscr{L}\{F\}$ be convergent for the real value s_0 of s. Then $f(s)$ is defined on the half-line $(s_0, +\infty)$.*

Proof. By definition

$$\int_0^\infty e^{-st} F(t)\, dt = \lim_{A \to \infty} \int_0^A e^{-st} F(t)\, dt,$$

where the integral $\int_0^A$ is the usual simple type of improper integral associated with a piecewise-continuous integrand. Recalling that

$$D^{-1}(e^{-s_0 t} F(t)) = \int_0^t e^{-s_0 \tau} F(\tau)\, d\tau$$

vanishes for $t = 0$, we integrate by parts ($D^{-1}[e^{-s_0 t}F(t)]$ is continuous) in

$$\text{(1.3)} \qquad \int_0^A e^{-st}F(t)\,dt = \int_0^A e^{-(s-s_0)t}e^{-s_0 t}F(t)\,dt$$

$$= e^{-(s-s_0)A}\int_0^A e^{-s_0 t}F(t)\,dt$$

$$+ (s - s_0)\int_0^A e^{-(s-s_0)t}D^{-1}(e^{-s_0 t}F(t))\,dt.$$

By hypothesis $\int_0^\infty e^{-s_0 t}F(t)\,dt$ is finite and $D^{-1}(e^{-s_0 t}F(t))$ is continuous. There exists therefore a finite M such that $|D^{-1}(e^{-s_0 t}F(t))| \leqslant M$ for all real t. It follows that when $s > s_0$ both terms on the right in (1.3) and, consequently, the one on the left, tend to a finite limit as $A \to +\infty$ so that

$$\text{(1.4)} \qquad \int_0^\infty e^{-st}F(t)\,dt = (s - s_0)\int_0^\infty e^{-(s-s_0)t}D^{-1}(e^{-s_0 t}F(t))\,dt \quad \blacksquare$$

While $F \in \mathscr{K}_{++}$ does not have to be of exponential order to have a Laplace transform, $D^{-1}F$ does. This is a consequence of

Lemma 1.1. *If $\mathscr{L}\{F\}$ converges for the positive value s_0 of s and $F \in \mathscr{K}_{++}(R)$ then $D^{-1}F$ is a function of exponential order s_0 satisfying*

$$\text{(1.5)} \qquad |D^{-1}F(t)| \leqslant Me^{s_0 t}$$

for some finite M.

Proof. Integrating by parts (observe that $D^{-1}F$ is continuous) gives

$$\text{(1.6)} \qquad \int_0^t e^{-s_0\tau}F(\tau)\,d\tau = e^{-s_0\tau}(D^{-1}F(\tau))\Big|_{\tau=0}^{\tau=t} + s_0\int_0^t e^{-s_0\tau}(D^{-1}F(\tau))\,d\tau$$

which, since $D^{-1}F(\tau)$ vanishes for $\tau = 0$, takes the form

$$\text{(1.7)} \qquad s_0\Phi(t) + \Phi'(t) = \int_0^t e^{-s_0\tau}F(\tau)\,d\tau$$

when we put

$$\text{(1.8)} \qquad \Phi(t) = \int_0^t e^{-s_0\tau}(D^{-1}F(\tau))\,d\tau.$$

The integral on the right in (1.7) represents a continuous function of t, which has the finite limit $\mathscr{L}\{F, s_0\}$ as $t \to +\infty$. Its absolute value is therefore bounded above by some finite constant B, and we may write

$$|s_0\Phi(t) + \Phi'(t)| \leqslant B.$$

Applying the familiar shift relation, we find, in succession,

$$|e^{-s_0 t}D[e^{s_0 t}\Phi(t)]| \leqslant B,$$

$$|e^{s_0 t}\Phi(t)| \leqslant B\int_0^t e^{s_0\tau}\,d\tau = \frac{B}{s_0}(e^{s_0 t}-1)$$

$$|\Phi(t)| \leqslant \frac{B}{s_0}(1-e^{-s_0 t}) \leqslant \frac{B}{s_0}.$$

The conclusion now follows from (1.6) that

$$|e^{-s_0 t}D^{-1}F(t)| \leqslant B\left(1+\frac{1}{s_0}\right).$$

so M in (1.5) equals $B(1 + 1/s_0)$. ∎

Remark. The condition $s_0 > 0$ is necessary (Exercise 2). Since the existence of $\mathscr{L}\{F\}$ for any real $s = c$ entails its convergence for all s on the half-line $(c, +\infty)$ there is always an $s_0 > 0$ satisfactory for the above lemma providing $\mathscr{L}\{F\}$ converges for some real s.

Theorem 1.2. *If $F \in \mathscr{K}_{++}$ and $\mathscr{L}\{F\}$ converges for some positive value s_0 of s then $\mathscr{L}\{D^{-1}F\}$ converges and satisfies*

$$\mathscr{L}\{D^{-1}F\} = \frac{1}{s}\mathscr{L}\{F\} \tag{1.9}$$

whenever $s > s_0$.

Proof. From the usual integration by parts ($D^{-1}F(t)$ is continuous) and the fact that $D^{-1}F(t)$ vanishes for $t \leqslant 0$,

$$\int_0^A e^{-st}F(t)\,dt = e^{-sA}D^{-1}F(A) + s\int_0^A e^{-st}D^{-1}F(t)\,dt. \tag{1.10}$$

In view of (1.5)

$$|e^{-sA}D^{-1}F(A)| \leqslant Me^{-(s-s_0)A}$$

and this tends to zero as $A \to +\infty$, providing $s > s_0$. We have then only to let $A \to +\infty$ in (1.10) to get (1.9). ∎

Remark. The inequality $s > s_0$ in this theorem can be broadened to $s \geqslant s_0$. Such a refinement is not necessary for us here, and we leave it to the interested reader to look up the proof in [14].

Corollary 1.1. *If $F \in \mathscr{K}_{++}$ and $\mathscr{L}\{F\}$ converges for some positive value s_0 of s, then $\mathscr{L}\{D^{-p}F\}$ (integer $p > 0$) converges and satisfies*

$$\mathscr{L}\{D^{-p}F\} = \frac{1}{s^p}\mathscr{L}\{F\} \tag{1.11}$$

whenever $s > s_0$.

For the relation between the Laplace transform of a $\mathscr{K}_{++}$ function and its ordinary derivative dF/dt, we find a result that has connections with Theorem II.B.1.1:

Theorem 1.3. *Let $F \in \mathscr{K}_{++}(R)$ be continuous on $(0, +\infty)$ and let it be of exponential order s_0 (real). If the ordinary derivative dF/dt exists and is a $\mathscr{K}_{++}(R)$ function, then $\mathscr{L}\{dF/dt\}$ converges for $s > s_0$ and satisfies the relation*

$$\mathscr{L}\left\{\frac{dF}{dt}\right\} = s\mathscr{L}\{F\} - F(+0) \qquad (s > s_0). \tag{1.12}$$

Proof. Since $F(t)$ is continuous on $(0, +\infty)$, we may integrate by parts,

$$\int_0^A e^{-st}\frac{dF}{dt}\,dt = e^{-st}F(t)\Big|_0^A + s\int_0^A e^{-st}F(t)\,dt.$$

When $A \to +\infty$ the right-hand side converges to

$$-F(+0) + s\mathscr{L}\{F\} \qquad \text{when } s > s_0$$

$[\lim_{A\to\infty} e^{-sA}F(A) = \lim_{A\to+\infty} Me^{-(s-s_0)A}]$. Therefore the left-hand integral is also convergent. ∎

Corollary 1.2. *If $F \in \mathscr{K}_{++}(R)$ is continuous on $(0, +\infty)$ and has ordinary derivatives*

$$\frac{dF}{dt}, \ldots, \frac{d^{p-1}F}{dt^{p-1}}$$

all belonging to $\mathscr{K}_{++}(R)$ and continuous on $(0, +\infty)$, if $F, \dfrac{dF}{dt}, \ldots, \dfrac{d^{p-1}F}{dt^{p-1}}$ are all of the same exponential order s_0 (real), and if there exists the ordinary derivative

$$\frac{d^pF}{dt^p} \in \mathscr{K}_{++}(R)$$

then $\mathscr{L}\left\{\dfrac{d^pF}{dt^p}\right\}$ exists for $s > s_0$ and satisfies for such s the relation

$$\mathscr{L}\left\{\frac{d^pF}{dt^p}\right\} = s^p\mathscr{L}\{F\} - s^{p-1}F(+0) - s^{p-2}\frac{dF(+0)}{dt}\cdots - \frac{d^{p-1}F(+0)}{dt^{p-1}}. \tag{1.13}$$

2. Principle of Application to Differential Equations with Constant Coefficients

The relations (1.12) and (1.13) are cornerstones of the popular Laplace transform method for solving certain initial-value problems of technological importance. To make clear the principles of this method, let us consider the ordinary I.V. problem: given the $\mathscr{K}_{++}(R)$ function $F(t)$, find a $\mathscr{K}_{++}$ function $x(t)$ continuous on $(0, +\infty)$ and having $dx/dt \in \mathscr{K}_{++}$ which satisfies (except at the isolated points of discontinuity of f) the equation with constant coefficients

(2.1) $$a_0 \frac{dx}{dt} + a_1 x = F(t),$$

and which assumes a given initial value

(2.2) $$x(+0) = x_0.$$

The method requires that $F(t)$ have a Laplace transform on some half-line $(c, +\infty)$, i.e., $D^{-1}F(t)$ must, in view of Lemma 1.1, be of exponential order s_0 where $s_0 > 0$ and $s_0 > c$. One then seeks a $\mathscr{K}_{++}$ function $x(t)$ continuous on $(0, +\infty)$ and which with dx/dt has a Laplace transform. This is done by taking the Laplace transform of both sides of (2.1), obtaining, with the help of (1.12) and (2.2), the relation

(2.3) $$(a_0 s + a_1)\mathscr{L}\{x\} = \mathscr{L}\{F\} + a_0 x_0,$$

from which the L.T. of the unknown function is obtained by purely algebraic means:

(2.4) $$\mathscr{L}\{x\} = \frac{1}{a_0 s + a_1}(\mathscr{L}\{F\} + a_0 x_0).$$

The final stages of this method now consist in finding the inverse Laplace transform of the function of s on the right-hand side of (2.4). For this we require these facts:

(i)

$$\frac{1}{a_0 s + a_1} = \frac{1}{a_0} \frac{1}{s + a_1/a_0} = \frac{1}{a_0} \int_0^\infty e^{-st} e^{-(a_1/a_0)t}\, dt$$

when $s > a_1/a_0$ (so

$$\frac{a_0 x_0}{a_0 s + a_1} = \mathscr{L}\{x_0 e^{-(a_1/a_0)t} H(t)\}$$

and

$$\frac{1}{a_0 s + a_1} = \frac{1}{a_0} \mathscr{L}\{e^{-(a_1/a_0)t} H(t)\});$$

(ii) if F and G are $\mathscr{K}_{++}$ functions having L.T.'s $f(s)$ and $g(s)$ then $f(s)\, g(s)$ is the L.T. of the convolution $F * G$ (§ 4 below);

(iii) two $\mathscr{K}_{++}$ functions that have L.T.'s are equal if and only if their L.T.'s are equal.

From (i) and (ii), we deduce

$$(2.5)\qquad \frac{1}{a_0 s + a_1}(\mathscr{L}\{F\} + a_0 x_0)$$
$$= \mathscr{L}\left\{\frac{1}{a_0}\, e^{-(a_1/a_0)t}H(t) * F(t) + x_0 e^{-(a_1/a_0)t}H(t)\right\}.$$

From (iii) we conclude that the function

$$(2.6)\qquad x(t) = \frac{1}{a_0}\, e^{-(a_1/a_0)t}H(t) * F(t) + x_0 e^{-(a_1/a_0)t}\, H(t)$$

is the *unique* solution of the given I.V. problem *that has a Laplace transform.*

Following Doetsch, we may describe the general lines of this procedure diagrammatically as in Figure 13.

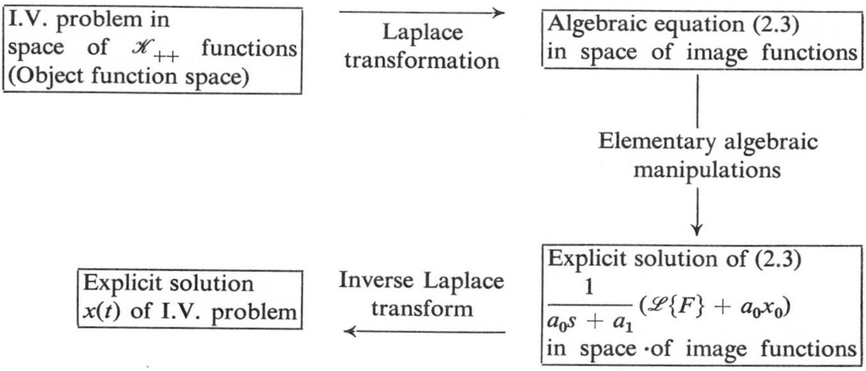

FIGURE 13

This method is an *indirect operational method* insofar as it consists in first transforming the original problem into an "image" problem whose attraction is that it can be solved by ordinary algebra. Since the method used in Chapters III and IV—here called a *direct operational method*—gave us a practical solution procedure, as well as existence and uniqueness theorems, under less restrictive conditions, we shall not insist further on this particular class of applications of the Laplace transform.

3. Uniqueness of the Inverse Laplace Transform

If $F \in \mathscr{K}_+$ the set of $\langle F, \varphi\rangle$ when φ ranges over $\mathscr{D}_-$ completely determines F according to Theorem II.A.7.1.

If $F \in \mathscr{K}_{++}$ and if $\mathscr{L}\{F\} = \langle F(t), e^{-st}\rangle$ exists for some real $s = s_0$ the set of values $\langle F(t), e^{-st}\rangle$, where s ranges over the half-line $[s_0, +\infty)$, completely determines F according to the somewhat analogous

Theorem 3.1. *Let $F, G \in \mathscr{K}_{++}$ have Laplace transforms $f(s)$, $g(s)$. Then $F(t)$ and $G(t)$ are equal if and only if $f(s) = g(s)$ on some closed forward half-line $[s_0, +\infty)$.*

Proof. That $F = G \Rightarrow f(s) = g(s)$ is obvious. Conversely, suppose

$$f(s) - g(s) = a(s) = 0 \qquad \text{when } s \geqslant s_0. \tag{3.1}$$

Here, putting $A(t) = F(t) - G(t)$,

$$a(s) = \int_0^\infty e^{-st} A(t)\, dt. \tag{3.1$'$}$$

From the relation (1.4), with $A(t)$ in place of $F(t)$, we get

$$a(s) = (s - s_0) \int_0^\infty e^{-(s-s_0)t} B(t)\, dt, \tag{3.2}$$

where

$$B(t) = D^{-1}(e^{-s_0 t}A(t)) = \int_0^t e^{-s_0 u} A(u)\, du$$

is continuous on $[0, +\infty)$ and has

$$\lim_{t\to\infty} B(t) = a(s_0) = 0. \tag{3.3}$$

From (3.1) and (3.2), it follows that

$$a(s_0 + n) = n \int_0^\infty e^{-nt} B(t) = 0 \qquad (n = 1, 2, \ldots). \tag{3.4}$$

The change of variables $e^{-t} = x$ transforms this into

$$\begin{aligned} a(s_0 + n) &= n\int_0^1 x^{n-1}B(-\log x)\, dx = \int_0^1 x^{n-1}\, C(x)\, dx \\ &= 0 \qquad (n = 1, 2, \ldots), \end{aligned} \tag{3.4$'$}$$

where $C(x) = B(-\log x)$ is a continuous function of x on the closed interval $[0, 1]$ if we define $C(0) = 0$, as suggested by (3.3).

It is a consequence of (3.4′), via Theorem 3.2 below, that $C(x) \equiv 0$ on $[0, 1]$. But then $B(t) \equiv 0$, and since $e^{-s_0 t}A(t) = dB/dt$ at every point of continuity of $A(t)$, we have $A(t) = 0$ at every point of continuity. The conclusion that the $\mathscr{K}_{++}$ functions F and G are equal follows. The proof will therefore be complete once we have proved:

Theorem 3.2. *If $C(x) \in C[0, 1]$ and if*

$$\int_0^1 x^m\, C(x)\, dx = 0 \qquad (m = 0, 1, 2, \ldots), \tag{3.5}$$

then $C(x) \equiv 0$.

Proof. We give the proof for real-valued $C(x)$. The complex-valued case then follows immediately. Assume the conclusion to be false, i.e., $C(x) \not\equiv 0$. In this case there exists a point ξ in [0, 1] such that $C(\xi) = 2c \neq 0$. We may as well assume $c > 0$ [otherwise consider the function $-C(x)$]. Because $C(x)$ is continuous there then exists an interval $[\xi - \delta, \xi + \delta]$ (if $\xi \in (0, 1)$)—or an interval $[0, \delta]$ or $[1 - \delta, 1]$ (if $\xi = 0$ or $\xi = 1$)—throughout which $C(x) \geqslant c$. Let us suppose it is the first case that arises—the others are treated in so similar a fashion that we need not consider them in any further detail. Then

$$C(x) \geqslant c \qquad \text{when } \xi - \delta \leqslant x \leqslant \xi + \delta. \tag{3.6}$$

The rest of the proof consists in showing the existence of a polynomial $P_N(x)$ such that

$$\int_0^1 P_N(x)\, C(x)\, dx \neq 0.$$

Since this contradicts (3.5), we conclude that the assumption that $C(x)$ does not vanish identically on [0, 1] is untenable. The principle behind the construction of $P_N(x)$ is to make $\int_{\xi-\delta}^{\xi+\delta} P_N C\, dx$ the predominant part of $\int_{-1}^{1} P_N C\, dx$.

A succession of simple facts, suggested by elementary graphical considerations (Figure 14) and easily checked by computation, will lead us to the explicit construction of such a polynomial $P_N(x)$:

(i) The graph of $u(x) = x(1 - x)$ is a parabola symmetric about the line $x = \frac{1}{2}$ where it reaches its maximum $u(\frac{1}{2}) = \frac{1}{4}$. The minimum of $u(x)$ in the interval $[-\frac{1}{2}, \frac{3}{2}]$ is $u(-\frac{1}{2}) = u(\frac{3}{2}) = -\frac{3}{4}$.

(ii) Given $\xi \in [0, 1]$ the function $y(x) = u(x + \frac{1}{2} - \xi)$ has the same graph

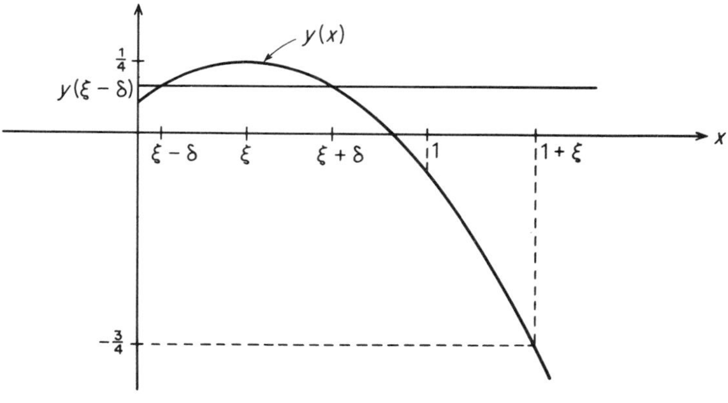

FIGURE 14

as $u(x)$ but translated horizontally so as to have its maximum at $x = \xi$. Consequently, when $x \in [0, 1]$,

$$x + \xi - \tfrac{1}{2} \in [-\tfrac{1}{2}, \tfrac{3}{2}].$$

Therefore $-\frac{3}{4} \leqslant y(x) \leqslant \frac{1}{4}$ when $x \in [0, 1]$.

(iii) From (ii) follows

$$y(x) - y(\xi - \delta)\begin{cases} \geqslant 0 & \text{when } x \in [\xi - \delta, \xi + \delta] \\ \geqslant y\left(\xi - \dfrac{\delta}{2}\right) - y(\xi - \delta) = \dfrac{3}{4}\,\delta^2 & \text{when } x \in \left[\xi - \dfrac{\delta}{2}, \xi + \dfrac{\delta}{2}\right] \end{cases}$$

and also

$$-1 < y(x) - y(\xi - \delta) \leqslant 0 \qquad \text{when } x \in [0, \xi - \delta] \quad \text{or} \quad x \in [\xi + \delta, 1].$$

If N is a positive integer, the polynomial

$$P_N(x) = (1 + y(x))^N$$

is seen, as a consequence of (iii), to satisfy

$$\text{(3.7)} \qquad P_N(x) \geqslant 1 \qquad \text{when } x \in [\xi - \delta, \xi + \delta],$$

$$\text{(3.8)} \qquad P_N(x) \geqslant \left(1 + \frac{3}{4}\,\delta^2\right)^N > 1 + \frac{3N}{4}\,\delta^2 \qquad \text{when } x \in \left[\xi - \frac{\delta}{2}, \xi + \frac{\delta}{2}\right],$$

$$\text{(3.9)} \qquad |P_N(x)| \leqslant 1 \qquad \text{when } x \in [0, \xi - \delta] \text{ and when } x \in [\xi + \delta, 1].$$

From

$$\int_0^1 P_N(x)\,C(x)\,dx = \int_0^{\xi-\delta} P_N C\,dx + \int_{\xi+\delta}^1 P_N C\,dx + \int_{\xi-\delta}^{\xi+\delta} P_N C\,dx$$

we get

$$\text{(3.10)} \qquad \left|\int_0^1 P_N C\,dx\right| \geqslant \left|\int_{\xi-\delta}^{\xi+\delta} P_N C\,dx\right| - \left|\int_0^{\xi-\delta} P_N C\,dx + \int_{\xi+\delta}^1 P_N C\,dx\right|$$

$$= |I_1| - |I_2|.$$

Let M be an upper bound of $C(x)$ on $[0, 1]$; taking note of (3.9) then yields the estimate

$$\text{(3.11)} \qquad |I_2| \leqslant M,$$

whereas (3.6), (3.7), (3.8) lead to

$$\text{(3.12)} \quad |I_1| = I_1 = \int_{\xi-\delta}^{\xi+\delta} P_N C\,dx > \int_{\xi-\delta/2}^{\xi+\delta/2} P_N C\,dx \geqslant \left(1 + \frac{3N}{4}\,\delta^2\right) c \int_{\xi-\delta/2}^{\xi+\delta/2} dx$$

$$= c\delta\left(1 + \frac{3\delta^2}{4}\,N\right).$$

Using (3.11) and (3.12) in (3.10), we see that assigning to N a sufficiently large integer value gives

$$\int_0^1 P_N C\,dx > 0.$$

This is the contradiction to (3.5) we have sought.

Remark. On examining the use to which this last theorem was put in the proof of Theorem 3.1, we observe that not all the hypotheses of the latter were actually used. Instead of $f(s) = g(s)$ for all $s \geqslant s_0$, it suffices to require $f(s_0 + n) = g(s_0 + n)$ $(n = 0, 1, 2, \ldots)$. This is a particular case of a more general theorem due to Lerch [14] [54] (Exercise 5).

4. The Inverse Laplace Transform

There exist explicit formulae for computing $F(t)$ when $f(s) = \mathscr{L}\{F\}$ is known. We shall not discuss any of them in this volume, but shall adhere instead to the practice of many elementary texts on this subject, contenting ourselves with a more pedestrian approach. This consists in pointing out that if one builds up a table of $\mathscr{L}\{F\}$ for various functions F, the table can be read backwards from the $\mathscr{L}\{F\}$ column to the F column. Because of the uniqueness property of § 3, this introduces no ambiguity. Furthermore, even a simple table makes possible the determination of inverse Laplace transforms of more complicated functions of s thanks to

Theorem 4.1. *If F, $G \in \mathscr{K}_{++}$ are of exponential order s_0,*

$$\mathscr{L}\{F * G\} = \mathscr{L}\{F\} \cdot \mathscr{L}\{G\} \tag{4.1}$$

when $s > s_0$.

[The reader who has gone through Chapter V will recognize that (4.1) is an extension of the relation (V.B.4.5) with $\varphi(t)$ replaced by e^{-st}.]

Proof. As both F and G vanish for $t < 0$,

$$F * G = \int_0^t F(t-\tau)\,G(\tau)\,d\tau = \int_0^t F(\tau)\,G(t-\tau)\,d\tau$$

is also in $\mathscr{K}_{++}$. By hypothesis there exists $M < \infty$ such that

$$|F(t)| \leqslant Me^{s_0 t} \quad \text{and} \quad |G(t)| \leqslant Me^{s_0 t}; \tag{4.2}$$

as a consequence $|(F * G)(t)| \leqslant Be^{s_0 t}$ with an appropriate $B < \infty$ and we can assert that $F * G$ has a Laplace transform that converges for all $s > s_0$. It is obtained by letting $A \to \infty$ in

$$I_A(s) = \int_0^A e^{-st} \int_0^t F(t-\tau)\,G(\tau)\,d\tau\,dt. \tag{4.3}$$

This iterated integral constitutes one way of computing the double integral

$$\iint_T e^{-st} F(t - \tau) G(\tau) \, dS, \tag{4.4}$$

where T is the triangle shown in Figure 15.

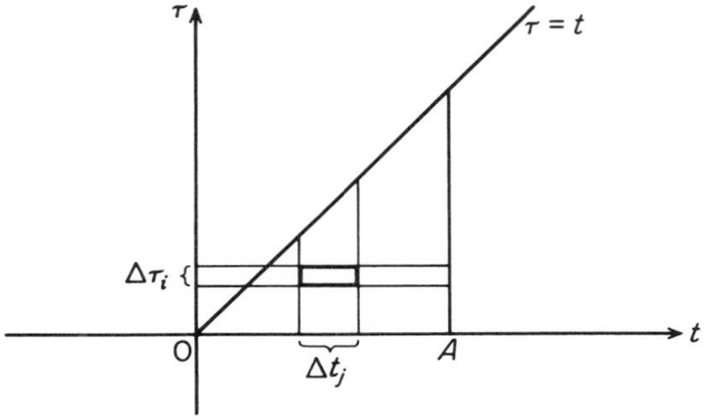

FIGURE 15

Specifically, $I_A(s)$ is the limit of double Riemann sums in which the elementary areas are rectangles of the kind indicated in Figure 15. Instead of these, one can also use Riemann sums in which the elementary areas are parallelograms obtained with a grid consisting of a set of lines $\tau = \tau_0$, $\tau = \tau_1, \ldots, \tau = \tau_i, \ldots, \tau = \tau_n$ perpendicular to the τ axis and of a set of lines parallel to the hypotenuse of T and which correspond to a succession $u_0, u_1, u_j, \ldots, u_m$ of fixed values of the variable $u = t - \tau$ lying in the interval $0 \leqslant u \leqslant A$. Such a grid is shown in Figure 16.

When this grid is refined so that the diameters of these parallelograms tend to zero, the corresponding Riemann sums, when summed over the index i first and over j next, converge to

$$I_A(s) = \int_0^A e^{-su} F(u) \int_0^{A-u} e^{-s\tau} G(\tau) \, d\tau \, du. \tag{4.5}$$

From (4.2), we get for $s > s_0$

$$\left| \int_{A-u}^{\infty} e^{-s\tau} G(\tau) \, d\tau \right| \leqslant \frac{M}{s - s_0} e^{-(s-s_0)A} e^{(s-s_0)u},$$

whence

$$\left| \int_0^A e^{-su} F(u) \int_{A-u}^{\infty} e^{-s\tau} G(\tau) \, d\tau \, du \right| \leqslant \frac{M^2}{s - s_0} e^{-(s-s_0)A} A$$

so that

$$\left| I_A(s) - \int_0^A e^{-su} F(u) \, du \int_0^{\infty} e^{-s\tau} G(\tau) \, d\tau \right| \leqslant \frac{M^2}{s - s_0} A e^{-(s-s_0)A}.$$

When $s > s_0$ the term on the right tends to zero as $A \to +\infty$ and we conclude that

$$\lim_{A\to+\infty} I_A(s) = \int_0^\infty e^{-su} F(u)\, du \int_0^\infty e^{-s\tau} G(\tau)\, d\tau.$$

An instance of the application of this theorem was the passage from relation (2.4) to (2.5).

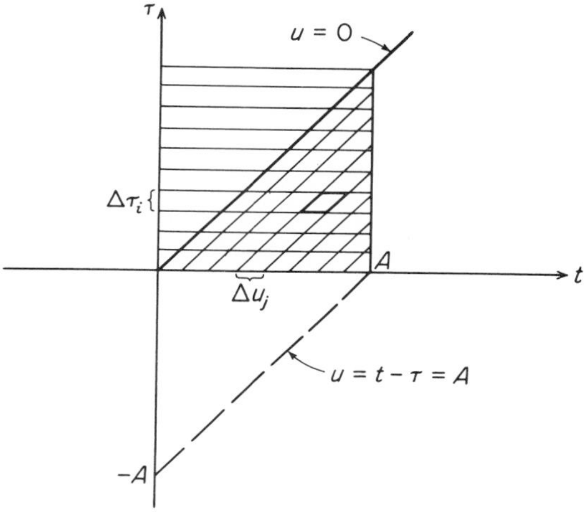

FIGURE 16

Another *example* is the determination of the inverse Laplace transform of $\dfrac{a}{a^2 + s^2} f(s)$ where $f(s) = \mathscr{L}\{F\}$, $F \in \mathscr{K}_{++}$ being of exponential order. (This occurs in the indirect operational solution of the I.V. problem for a second-order differential equation with constant coefficients.) Because, as computation easily shows,

$$\mathscr{L}\{\sin at\} = \frac{a}{a^2 + s^2},$$

Theorem 4.1 gives

$$\frac{a}{a^2 + s^2} f(s) = \mathscr{L}\left\{\int_0^t \sin a(t - \tau)\, F(\tau)\, dt\right\}. \tag{4.6}$$

Other relations that are valuable for extracting from a table of Laplace transforms more information than it shows superficially are

$$f(s - a) = \mathscr{L}\{e^{at}F(t)\}, \qquad s > a + s_0, \tag{4.7}$$

$$f^{(n)}(s) = \mathscr{L}\{(-t)^n F(t)\}, \quad s > s_0 \qquad (n = 1, 2, \ldots). \tag{4.8}$$

In these $f(s) = \mathscr{L}\{F\}$ and $F \in \mathscr{K}_{++}$ is assumed to be of exponential order s_0 [so $t^n F(t)$ is of exponential order $s_0 + \varepsilon$ for any $\varepsilon > 0$]. The proofs are perfectly simple with this hypothesis (Exercises 3, 6).

5. Laplace Transforms of $\mathscr{D}'_{++}$ G.F.'s of Exponential Type

Let $F \in \mathscr{K}_{++}$ be of exponential order s_0 and take $s > s_0$. Then

$$f(s) \leqslant M \int_0^\infty e^{-(s-s_0)t}\, dt = \frac{M}{s - s_0}$$

and, therefore,

$$\lim_{s \to +\infty} f(s) = 0.$$

This property added to (4.8) indicates that a function $f(s)$ cannot be the Laplace transform of an exponential order $F \in \mathscr{K}_{++}$ if it does not belong to $C^\infty(s_0, +\infty)$ for some s_0 and vanish as $s \to +\infty$ (Exercise 3). Thus, even such simple functions as $f(s) \equiv 1$ $(s > s_0)$ and

$$f(s) = a_0 s^n + a_1 s^{n-1} + \cdots + a_n \qquad (s > s_0)$$

cannot be the Laplace transforms of functions F of the kind described. In fact, the only mathematical objects that have Laplace transforms that do not vanish as $s \to +\infty$ are certain generalized functions that are not functions of t. Important among these are those members of $\mathscr{D}'_+$ which are finite-order g.f. derivatives $D^p G$ of functions $G \in \mathscr{K}_{++}$ for which $\mathscr{L}\{G\}$, as defined in § 1 above, is convergent for some real s_0.

Designating by $\mathscr{D}'_{++}$ the set of $\mathscr{D}'_+$ g.f.'s that are carried in $[0, +\infty)$ we write

Definition 5.1. *$F \in \mathscr{D}'_{++}$ is of exponential type if and only if for some finite integer $p \geqslant 0$*

(5.1) $$F = D^p G,$$

where $G \in \mathscr{K}_{++}(R)$ is of exponential order. [More precisely we call F of exponential type (p_0, s_0) if G is of exponential order s_0 and p_0 is the smallest non-negative integer for which a relation like (5.1) with $G \in \mathscr{K}_{++}$ holds.]

A general theory of Laplace transforms of $\mathscr{D}'_+$ g.f.'s was first given by L. Schwartz [45]. The theory, in terms of fundamental sequences of functions, for g.f.'s of exponential type, is covered by J. Korevaar [32]. An extensive table of Laplace transforms of $\mathscr{D}'_+$ g.f.'s and examples of applications to some partial differential equations, are given in J. Lavoine [33]. Definition 5.1 differs from that of [32] in that we take $G \in \mathscr{K}_{++}$ instead of G integrable; this simply has the effect that for certain G the values of p_0 in the two definitions differ by one.

Let $F \in \mathscr{D}'_{++}$ be of exponential type (p_0, s_0). The following are then easily seen to hold:

(5.2) $$D^q F \in \mathscr{D}'_{++} \quad \text{expo. type } (p_0 + q, s_0) \quad (q \text{ integer}),$$

(5.3) $$F(t - h) \in \mathscr{D}'_{++} \quad (\text{if } h \geqslant 0) \quad \text{expo. type } (p_0, s_0).$$

In part B of Chapter II (Example 2, p. 73, and Exercise II.37), we saw that the g.f. derivative D^pG can be obtained as a g.f. limit of divided differences:

$$D^p G(t) = \operatorname*{Lim}_{h\to 0} \frac{1}{h^p} \sum_{l=0}^{p} (-1)^{p-l} \binom{p}{l} G(t + lh).$$

If $G(t) \in \mathscr{K}_{++}(R)$ is of exponential order s_0 and we let h run through the sequence $-1, -\frac{1}{2}, \ldots, -1/n, \ldots$ this gives for F, defined by (5.1),

(5.4) $$F(t) = \operatorname*{Lim}_{n\to\infty} F_n(t),$$

where

(5.5) $$F_n(t) = (-n)^p \sum_{l=0}^{p} (-1)^{p-l} \binom{p}{l} G\left(t - \frac{l}{n}\right)$$

is for each natural number n obviously a $\mathscr{K}_{++}(R)$ function. It is also of exponential order s_0 since

(5.6) $$|G(t)| \leqslant Me^{s_0 t}$$

brings about

$$|F_n(t)| \leqslant n^p \sum_{l=0}^{p} \binom{p}{l} \left|G\left(t - \frac{l}{n}\right)\right| \leqslant Me^{s_0 t} \sum_{l=0}^{p} \binom{p}{l} e^{-s_0 l/n} n^p$$
$$= n^p M(1 + e^{-s_0/n})^p e^{s_0 t}.$$

When $s_0 \geqslant 0$, $e^{-s_0/n} \leqslant 1$ $(n = 1, 2, \ldots)$; whereas, when $s_0 < 0$,

$$e^{-s_0/n} \leqslant e^{-s_0} \qquad (n = 1, 2, \ldots).$$

Thus, with each given value of s_0, there is associated a constant, B, such that

(5.7) $$|F_n(t)| \leqslant n^p B e^{s_0 t} \qquad (n = 1, 2, \ldots).$$

The sequence $\{F_n\}$ is thus seen to be a fundamental sequence of F, which has the particular property that all its members are of the same exponential order s_0 as G, so that for each positive integer n the quantity

$$\langle F_n(t), e^{-st}\rangle = \mathscr{L}\{F_n\}$$

is well defined for $s > s_0$.

With the aid of this particular fundamental sequence for F, we can demonstrate

Theorem 5.1. *If $F \in \mathscr{D}'_{++}$ is of exponential type, with $F = D^pG$, where $G \in \mathscr{K}_{++}(R)$ is of exponential order s_0, then for all $s > s_0$ the quantity $\langle F(t), e^{-st}\rangle$ is well defined and*

$$\langle F(t), e^{-st}\rangle = (-1)^p\langle G(t), D^p e^{-st}\rangle. \tag{5.8}$$

Proof. Consider the sequence $\{F_n\}$ defined by (5.5). What we wish to show is that, besides being fundamental on $\mathscr{D}_-$, it is also fundamental on the set of all functions e^{-st} where $s > s_0$.

From (5.5) and a simple change of variables in the integral, we have

$$\langle F_n(t), e^{-st}\rangle = \left\langle G(t), (-1)^p n^p \sum_{l=0}^{p} (-1)^{p-l}\binom{p}{l} e^{-s(t+l/n)}\right\rangle \tag{5.9}$$

where (Exercise I.5) for some θ_1, depending on t and $1/n$ with $0 < \theta_1 < 1$,

$$\begin{aligned} n^p \sum_{l=0}^{p} (-1)^{p-l}\binom{p}{l} e^{-s(t+l/n)} &= \left(\frac{d^p e^{-s\tau}}{d\tau^p}\right)_{\tau=t+\theta_1 p/n} \\ &= (-s)^p e^{-s(t+\theta_1 p/n)} \end{aligned} \tag{5.10}$$

For given n, p, and s the left-hand side of this relation is a $C^\infty(R)$ function of t; the same, therefore, applies to the right-hand side (where θ_1 is a function of t). By a similar argument involving the Theorem of the Mean, we have for some $0 < \theta_2 < 1$

$$\begin{aligned} \left(\frac{d^p e^{-s\tau}}{d\tau^p}\right)_{\tau=t+\theta_1 p/n} - \left(\frac{d^p e^{-s\tau}}{d\tau^p}\right)_{\tau=t} &= \theta_1(t)\,\frac{p}{n}\left(\frac{d^{p+1}e^{-s\tau}}{d\tau^{p+1}}\right)_{\tau=t+\theta_2\theta_1 p/n} \\ &= \frac{p}{n}(-s)^{p+1}e^{-st}e^{-s\theta_3 p/n}\theta_1(t), \end{aligned} \tag{5.11}$$

where $\theta_3 = \theta_1\theta_2$ is in (0, 1) and the last function on the right is $C^\infty(R)$ in t because the left-hand side is.

From (5.7), (5.8), (5.9), we then obtain

$$\begin{aligned} &\left|\langle F_n, e^{-st}\rangle - \left\langle G, (-1)^p\left(\frac{d^p e^{-s\tau}}{d\tau^p}\right)_{\tau=t}\right\rangle\right| \\ &\qquad = \left|(-1)^p \frac{p}{n}\int_0^\infty G(t)\,(-s)^{p+1}e^{-st}e^{-s\theta_3 p/n}\theta_1(t)\,dt\right|. \end{aligned} \tag{5.12}$$

For any fixed s, there exists a constant B, independent of $0 < \theta_3 < 1$ and of the positive integer n, such that $e^{-s\theta_3 p/n} \leqslant B$, also $|\theta_1| \leqslant 1$. Therefore, taking $s > s_0$, the right-hand side of (5.12) is majorized, in view of (5.6), by

$$BM\,|s|^{p+1}\frac{p}{n}\int_0^\infty e^{-(s-s_0)t}\,dt.$$

This tends to zero as $n \to \infty$. The conclusions of the theorem follow.

When $s > 0$ we define, by analogy with $D^{-m}\varphi$ $(\varphi \in \mathscr{D}_-)$, for integer $m > 0$,

$$D^{-m}e^{-st} = \int_{+\infty}^{t}\int_{+\infty}^{t_{m-1}}\cdots\int_{+\infty}^{t_2} e^{-st_1}\,dt_1\,dt_2\cdots dt_{m-1} = (-1)^m s^{-m}e^{-st}. \tag{5.13}$$

From this, the identity $D^pD^qe^{-st} = D^{p+q}e^{-st}$ is seen to hold for all integer p and q when $s > 0$.

Corollary 5.1. *If $F \in \mathscr{D}'_{++}$ is of exponential type then there exists an open forward half-line $(s_0, +\infty)$ with $s_0 > 0$ such that for all (negative, zero, or positive) integer q*

$$\langle D^qF(t), e^{st}\rangle = (-1^q)\langle F(t), D^qe^{-st}\rangle = s^q\langle F(t), e^{-st}\rangle. \tag{5.14}$$

The proof, which consists in an examination of cases and the observation that when $G(t)$ is of exponential order the same is true for $D^{-m}G$ (integer $m > 0$), is left as Exercise 7. The restriction $s_0 > 0$ is required for negative integer q so that the definition (5.13) and Theorem 1.2 may be used.

Corollary 5.2. *If $F = D^pG$ (integer $p \geqslant 0$), where $G \in \mathscr{K}_{++}(R)$ has a Laplace transform for $s = s_0 > 0$, then $\langle F, e^{-st}\rangle$ is well defined for all $s > s_0$.*

Proof. By Lemma 1.1, $D^{-1}G(t)$ is of exponential order s_0. Therefore, Theorem 5.1 applies to $F = D^{p+1}(D^{-1}G)$.

The definition of the Laplace transform of $\mathscr{D}'_{++}$ g.f.'s of exponential type can now be given as a natural extension of that for $\mathscr{K}_{++}(R)$ functions:

Definition 5.2. *If $F \in \mathscr{D}'_{++}$ is of exponential type, the Laplace transform $\mathscr{L}\{F\}$ of F is the function*

$$\mathscr{L}\{F\} = f(s) = \langle F(t), e^{-st}\rangle \tag{5.15}$$

which is defined on some forward half-line $(s_0, +\infty)$. (F is called the object g.f., $f(s)$ its image function.)

Some remarks concerning this definition are in order:

(a) In view of Corollary 5.2, any g.f. of the form $F = D^pG$, where $G \in \mathscr{K}_{++}$ is not of exponential order but is merely Laplace transformable (i.e., is such that $\mathscr{L}\{G\}$ exists for some real s), is actually of exponential type because $F = D^{p+1}(D^{-1}G)$ where $D^{-1}G$ is a continuous function of exponential order.

(b) In the actual computation of $\mathscr{L}\{F\}$ by means of the relation (5.8), all that is needed is *some* $G \in \mathscr{K}_{++}(R)$ of exponential order [or even just Laplace transformable in view of (a)] and *some* integer $p \geqslant 0$ with $F = D^pG$. Indeed from Corollary 5.1 it follows that the definition is consistent inasmuch as $F = D^{p_1}G_1 = D^{p_2}G_2$ entails $G_2 = D^{p_1-p_2}G_1$—so that $\mathscr{L}\{F\}$ as computed from G_1 coincides, at least on some half-line carried in $(0, +\infty)$, with $\mathscr{L}\{F\}$ as computed from G_2. From (5.14) and Theorem 3.1, it also follows that *the Laplace transforms of two exponential type g.f.'s F, G are equal on some half-line* $(s_0, +\infty)$ *if and only if* $F = G$.

Since this implies that an exponential type g.f. is uniquely determined by the knowledge of its Laplace transform on *some* half-line $(s_0, +\infty)$ we shall not bother usually, to find the smallest s_0 (which may be $-\infty$, as in Example 1 below) determining the largest half-line of validity of the Laplace transform of any given g.f.

(c) Even though a given $F \in \mathscr{D}'_{++}$ may be of exponential type, $\langle F, e^{-st}\rangle$ cannot be computed as $\lim_{n\to\infty} \langle F_n, e^{-st}\rangle$ with just any fundamental (on $\mathscr{D}_-$) sequence belonging to the equivalence class of F (Exercise 8). The sequence (5.5), however, does always give

$$\lim_{n\to\infty} \langle F_n, e^{-st}\rangle = \mathscr{L}\{F\}.$$

(d) We note, incidentally, that, while we do not study them in this book, there exist $\mathscr{D}'_{++}$ g.f.'s which are not of exponential type but which have a Laplace transform—one example is

$$F = \sum_{n=0}^{\infty} \frac{1}{n!}\, \delta^{(n)}(t - n),$$

for which $\langle F, e^{-st}\rangle = e^{se^{-s}}$. Also there are non-$\mathscr{D}'_{++}$ g. f.'s which have transforms, e.g.,

$$F = \sum_{n=0}^{\infty} \frac{1}{n!}\, \delta^{(n)}(t) \notin \mathscr{D}'_{+} \quad \text{but} \quad \langle F, e^{-st}\rangle = e^{s}.$$

Example 1

$$\delta^{(q)}(t - h) \qquad (h \geqslant 0).$$

If $h \geqslant 0$,

$$\delta^{(q)}(t - h) \in \mathscr{D}'_{++} \quad \text{and} \quad \delta^{(q)}(t - h) = D^{q+1}H(t - h)$$

whence, by (5.14), and taking $s > 0$,

$$\mathscr{L}\{\delta^{(q)}(t - h)\} = \langle D^{q+1}H(t - h), e^{-st}\rangle = s^{q+1}\langle H(t - h), e^{-st}\rangle$$
$$= s^{q+1}\int_h^{\infty} e^{-st}\, dt.$$

There results the important identity

$$\mathscr{L}\{\delta^{(q)}(t - h)\} = s^q e^{-sh} \qquad (s > 0;\, h \geqslant 0). \tag{5.16}$$

The sequence (5.5) corresponding to $\delta(t)$ consists of the familiar functions

$$p_n(t) = -n\left(H\left(t - \frac{1}{n}\right) - H(t)\right)$$

and gives, in agreement with (5.16),

$$\langle \delta(t), e^{-st} \rangle = \lim_{n\to\infty} n \int_0^{1/n} e^{-st}\, dt = 1.$$

Observe that $\lim_{n\to\infty} \langle p_n(t), e^{-st} \rangle = \langle \delta(t), e^{-st} \rangle$ exists for *any* real number s, whereas $\langle \delta(t), e^{-st} \rangle$ can be computed as $\langle DH(t), e^{-st} \rangle$ only for $s > 0$. This example shows that a $\mathscr{D}'_{++}$ g.f. of exponential type (p_0, s_0) may very well have a Laplace transform for $s < s_0$. For our purposes, however, (see (b) above) we shall find it sufficient always to confine our consideration of this transform to the half-line $(s_0, +\infty)$.

Example 2

$$t_+^\lambda \qquad (\lambda \neq -1, -2, \ldots).$$

For $\lambda \geqslant 0$ t_+^λ is a $\mathscr{K}_{++}(R)$ function of exponential order and its Laplace transform is (take $u = st$ and $s > 0$)

$$\text{(5.17)} \qquad \mathscr{L}\{t_+^\lambda\} = \int_0^\infty e^{-st} t^\lambda\, dt = \frac{1}{s^{\lambda+1}} \int_0^\infty e^{-u} u^\lambda\, du$$

$$= \frac{\Gamma(\lambda + 1)}{s^{\lambda+1}} \qquad (s > 0).$$

The g.f. t_+^λ is defined for real $\lambda < 0$ $(\lambda \neq -1, -2, \ldots)$ in § II.C.2. Setting, for instance, $k = [-\lambda] + 1$ where $[-\lambda]$ is the largest integer $\leqslant -\lambda$ we have, from Definition II.C.2.1 and Definition 5.2 above,

$$\text{(5.18)} \qquad \mathscr{L}\{t_+^\lambda\} = \left\langle \frac{1}{(\lambda + 1)(\lambda + 2)\cdots(\lambda + k)} D^k t_+^{\lambda+k}, e^{-st} \right\rangle.$$

This is defined for all $s > 0$ and negative $\lambda \neq -1, -2, \ldots$ because $t_+^{\lambda+k} \in \mathscr{K}_{++}(R)$ and is of exponential order. Applying (5.14), we find

$$\mathscr{L}t\{_+^\lambda\} = \frac{s^k}{(\lambda + 1)\cdots(\lambda + k)} \langle t_+^{\lambda+k}, e^{-st} \rangle,$$

which, by (5.17), becomes

$$\mathscr{L}\{t_+^\lambda\} = \frac{s^k}{(\lambda + 1)\cdots(\lambda + k)} \cdot \frac{\Gamma(\lambda + k + 1)}{s^{\lambda+k+1}},$$

so that, finally, we have *for all real* $\lambda \neq -1, -2, \ldots$ *and* $s > 0$

$$\text{(5.19)} \qquad \mathscr{L}\{t_+^\lambda\} = \frac{\Gamma(\lambda + 1)}{s^{\lambda+1}}.$$

A particular case is this $[H(t) = t_+^0]$:

$$\text{(5.20)} \qquad \mathscr{L}\{H\} = \frac{1}{s}.$$

Example 3

$$\frac{t_+^{\lambda-1}}{\Gamma(\lambda)} \qquad (\lambda \text{ real}).$$

The g.f. $t_+^{\lambda-1}/\Gamma(\lambda)$ was defined in § II.C.3 for all real λ. For $\lambda \neq 0, -1, -2, \ldots$ we get from (5.19)

$$\frac{t_+^{\lambda-1}}{\Gamma(\lambda)} = \frac{1}{s^\lambda} \qquad (s > 0). \tag{5.21}$$

In Example 1 above, we showed that $\mathscr{L}\{\delta^{(k)}\} = s^k$. We now see that defining, as we did in § II.C.3,

$$\frac{t_+^{\lambda-1}}{\Gamma(\lambda)} = \delta^{(-\lambda)} \qquad \text{for } \lambda = 0, -1, -2, \ldots,$$

makes the relation (5.21) *valid for all real* λ.

6. Laplace Transform Images of Operations on $\mathscr{D}'_{++}$

As was indicated in § 2, it is because analytic operations in the object space, like D^p, are reflected in the image space by algebraic operations that the Laplace transform provides a foundation for indirect operational methods. When the object space is enlarged from the set of exponential order $\mathscr{K}_{++}(R)$ functions to the set of exponential type $\mathscr{D}'_{++}$ g.f.'s the image space is also enlarged so that it contains such functions as polynomials in s. Furthermore, *the rules of correspondence between object and image spaces are rendered more simple than in the ordinary function case.*

An illustration of this point is the relation (1.12) which gives as an image $\mathscr{L}\{dF/dt\}$ of the result of the operation d/dt the combination $s\mathscr{L}\{F\} - F(+0)$ of a product and a sum. If we use the Laplace transform on $\mathscr{D}'_{++}$ instead, we find by (5.14) that

$$\mathscr{L}\{DF\} = s\mathscr{L}\{F\},$$

i.e., *generalized differentiation* in the *object* space corresponds to *simple multiplication* by s in the *image space*. When $F \in \mathscr{K}_{++}$ satisfies the conditions for the validity of (1.12), we have ($[DF]$ is the g.f. defined by the $\mathscr{K}_{++}$ function dF/dt)

$$DF = [DF] + F(+0)\,\delta(t),$$

whence

$$\langle DF, e^{-st}\rangle = \left\langle \frac{dF}{dt}, e^{-st}\right\rangle + F(+0)\,\langle \delta(t), e^{-st}\rangle,$$

or, in view of (5.14) and (5.16),

$$s\mathscr{L}\{F\} = \mathscr{L}\{DF\} = \mathscr{L}\{[DF]\} + F(+0) \qquad (s > s_0),$$

and this is (1.12) again—but obtained in a *conceptually* more direct fashion since each individual term in this identity now represents the Laplace transform of an individual term belonging to $\mathscr{D}'_{++}$.

If $F \in \mathscr{K}_{++}$ is of exponential order s_0, with jumps at the isolated points t_i $(i = 1, 2, \ldots, n)$, and $dF/dt \in \mathscr{K}_{++}$, we have, by Theorem II.B.1.1 and (5.16),

$$(6.1)\quad \mathscr{L}\{DF\} = \mathscr{L}\{[DF]\} + \sum_{i=0}^{n} (F(t_i + 0) - F(t_i - 0))e^{-st_i} \qquad (s > s_0).$$

A number of identities indicate what operations on Laplace transforms correspond to basic operations on the object g.f.'s. These identities are obtained very simply by examining known relations of the type

$$\langle \Omega F, \varphi \rangle = \langle F, \tilde{\Omega}\varphi \rangle$$

between the operator Ω on $\mathscr{D}'_+$ and its transpose $\tilde{\Omega}$ on $\mathscr{D}_-$ (Chapter III, part A). When Ω carries $F \in \mathscr{D}'_{++}$ into $\Omega F \in \mathscr{D}'_{++}$, and when the relation remains valid with e^{-st} in place of φ, and on some half-line $(s_0, +\infty)$, we have an identity of the kind sought. Specifically, we find

Theorem 6.1. *If F, $G \in \mathscr{D}'_{++}$ are of exponential type (exponent s_0) there hold the identities*

$$(6.2)\qquad \mathscr{L}\{c_1 F + c_2 G\} = c_1 \mathscr{L}\{F\} + c_2 \mathscr{L}\{G\}$$

(c_1, c_2 *complex constants*) $(s > s_0)$;

$$(6.3)\qquad \mathscr{L}\{D^q F\} = s^q \mathscr{L}\{F\}$$

(*q integer*, $s > \max(0, s_0)$);

$$(6.4)\qquad \mathscr{L}\{F(t - h)\} = e^{-sh}\mathscr{L}\{F(t)\}$$

$(h \geqslant 0, s > s_0)$;

$$(6.5)\qquad f(s - a) = \mathscr{L}\{e^{at}F(t)\}$$

$(s > s_0 + a)$ *if* $f(s) = \mathscr{L}\{F(t)\}$ $(s > s_0)$;

$$(6.6)\qquad \mathscr{L}\{(D - r)^q F(t)\} = (s - r)^q \mathscr{L}\{F(t)\}$$

$(s > \max(0, s_0 + |r|)$;

$$(6.7)\qquad \mathscr{L}\{F * G\} = \mathscr{L}\{F\} \cdot \mathscr{L}\{G\}$$

$(s > s_0)$;

$$(6.8)\qquad \mathscr{L}\{(-t)^n F(t)\} = \frac{d^n}{ds^n}\mathscr{L}\{F(t)\}$$

$(s > s_0)$ $(n = 0, 1, 2, \ldots)$.

Proof. (6.3) has been proved (Corollary 5.1). (6.2), (6.4), (6.5) are first proved in obvious fashion for $\mathscr{K}_{++}(R)$ functions of exponential order and then extended to exponential type g.f.'s with the aid of Definition 5.2 and Corollary 5.1. (6.6) follows from the shift relation

$$(D - r)^q F = e^{rt} D^q (e^{-rt} F(t))$$

with the aid of (6.3) and (6.5). (6.7) is derived from Theorem 4.1, Definition 5.2, and Corollary 5.1. We leave (6.8) as an exercise.

Notice that from (6.7) and the definition of convolution in $\mathscr{D}'_+$, we get a connection with (6.3) and (6.4), viz.,

(6.9) $$D^q F = \delta^{(q)} * F \Rightarrow \mathscr{L}\{D^q F\} = \mathscr{L}\{\delta^{(q)}\}\mathscr{L}\{F\} = s^q \mathscr{L}\{F\},$$

(6.10) $$F(t - h) = \delta(t - h) * F(t) \Rightarrow \mathscr{L}\{F(t - h)\} = \mathscr{L}\{\delta(t - h)\} \cdot \mathscr{L}\{F(t)\} = e^{-sh}\mathscr{L}\{F(t)\}.$$

7. Correspondence between Laplace Transforms and Green's Functions

Another point worth noting is the simple correspondence between a table of Laplace transforms and a table of Green's functions for the types of I.V. problem treated in Chapters III, IV. This results from the relation (6.6) and the fact that $\mathscr{L}\{\delta(t)\} = 1$, which gives

(7.1) $$\mathscr{L}\{(D - r)^q\, \delta(t)\} = (s - r)^q \qquad (q \text{ integer}, s > r).^\dagger$$

It is this equality that explains the resemblance between the two tables given in the Appendix. [The restriction q integer can be relaxed to q real if $(D - r)^q$ on $\mathscr{D}'_+$ is interpreted as in § III.A.7.]

8. Applications to Mixed Difference-differential Equations

Equations of the form

(8.1) $$P_0(D)x(t) + P_1(D)x_1(t - h) + \cdots + P_N(D)x(t - Nh) = F(t),$$

where the $P_1(D)$ are derivative polynomials and h is a constant, are called linear mixed differential-difference equations. Initial-value problems for such equations, with $t > 0$ and $h > 0$, furnish a mathematical description for many phenomena in engineering, biology, and economics, where it takes

† For positive integer q this also holds with $s < r$. However, as indicated under (b) on p. 254 above, the knowledge of the L.T. on some half-line $(s_0, +\infty)$ suffices to determine the object g.f. Taking $s_0 = r$ in the present case has the advantage that there is no need to consider separately the negative q.

a finite length of time (multiple of the constant h) for the effect of some disturbance to be felt.

Explicitly computing the solutions of such initial-value problems is usually more laborious than for differential equations with constant coefficients, because it is necessary to resort to infinite series expansions in situations where a more compact decomposition into partial fractions was sufficient for a straight D.E.

Merely as an indication both of the physical genesis of such problems and of the manner of their solution with the Laplace transform, we may consider this

Example. A computing service begins operating at time $t = 0$ when it begins to receive routine work from the outside at a time rate $F(t) \in \mathscr{K}_{++}(R)$ of exponential order s_0. At every point of continuity of $F(t)$, the volume, $X(t)$, of work in process at time t then satisfies (in this simplistic model) the equation

$$\frac{dX(t)}{dt} = \beta X(t - h) + F(t) \tag{8.2}$$

in which $\beta X(t - h)$ represents the rate at which self-generated work is contributed. (Customers examining the results of computations decide, after an interval h, to have some complementary calculations done; also a percentage of completed computations is discovered after a delay h to have been erroneous.†)

With these hypotheses $X(t) = 0$ for $t < 0$ and at every point of continuity of F in $(-\infty, h)$, $dX/dt = F(t)$.

This has a solution $X(t)$ continuous in $(-\infty, h)$, and proceeding with this to the equation (8.2), it is easy to see that $dX/dt \in \mathscr{K}_{++}$ and that $X(t)$ can be extended to be continuous on $(-\infty, 2h)$, $(-\infty, 3h)$, etc. (Existence and uniqueness of the solution can be demonstrated with this step-by-step procedure.)

Because of this continuity, we have $X(+0) = 0$ and the g.f. derivative DX equals the g.f. $[DX]$. As a consequence, the g.f. equation of evolution for (8.1) is

$$DX(t) - \beta X(t - h) = F(t). \tag{8.3}$$

F being of exponential order s_0, it is plausible that X is so too. If this is so, we can take Laplace transforms on both sides, obtaining for all $s > s_0$, in view of (6.3) and (6.4),

$$(s - \beta e^{-sh})\mathscr{L}\{X\} = \mathscr{L}\{F\}$$

$$\mathscr{L}\{X\} = \frac{1}{s - \beta e^{-hs}} \mathscr{L}\{F\}. \tag{8.4}$$

† We are considering, of course, a purely hypothetical situation.

Let us now verify that the right-hand side has an inverse Laplace transform that is in $\mathscr{K}_{++}(R)$ and of exponential order. For this we examine the series expansion

$$\frac{1}{s - \beta e^{-hs}} = \frac{1}{s}\,\frac{1}{1 - (\beta/s)e^{-hs}} = \sum_{l=0}^{\infty} \frac{\beta^l}{s^{l+1}}\, e^{-lhs}$$

which converges for $s > \beta$ [and therefore for $s > \max(\beta, s_0)$].

From (5.19), with $q = l + 1$, we have

$$\frac{1}{s^{l+1}} = \{\mathscr{L} t_+^l / l!\} \qquad (l = 0, 1, 2, \ldots)$$

so that, applying (6.4),

(8.5) $$\frac{e^{-lhs}}{s^{l+1}} = \mathscr{L}\{(t - lh)_+^l / l!\}\,.$$

The series

(8.6) $$S(t) = \sum_{l=0}^{\infty} \frac{\beta^l (t - lh)_+^l}{l!}\,,$$

all but the first l terms of which vanish for $t \leqslant lh$, defines a continuous function $S(t)$ carried in $[0, +\infty)$ and whose first derivative, in the ordinary sense, is a $\mathscr{K}_{++}(R)$ function. Taking partial sums $\sum_{l=0}^{N}$ and letting $N \to \infty$ shows that

$$\mathscr{L}\{S\} = \frac{1}{s - \beta e^{-hs}}\,.$$

We have then only to refer to (6.7) to conclude that

(8.7) $$\frac{1}{s - \beta e^{-hs}} \mathscr{L}\{F\} = \mathscr{L}\{S * F\} \qquad (s > \max(\beta, s_0))$$

which, in view of the uniqueness of Laplace transforms, leaves us with the solution of (7.2) (and also of (7.1), since $DX = [DX]$):

(8.8) $$X(t) = S(t) * F(t).$$

More explicitly, $X(t) = 0$ for $t < 0$ and

(8.9) $$X(t) = \sum_{l=0}^{N} \frac{\beta^l}{l!} \int_0^{t-lh} (t - lh - \tau)^l\, F(\tau)\, d\tau$$

when $Nh \leqslant t < (N + 1)h$.

Remark 1. We observe that instead of taking F in $\mathscr{K}_{++}$, we could just as well treat the equation (8.3) with $F \in \mathscr{D}'_{++}$ of exponential type and would then get a solution $X \in \mathscr{D}'_{++}$ of exponential type. This remains true for the equation of evolution corresponding to the initial-value problem for the more general equation (8.1).

**9. Application to Differential Equations with Polynomial Coefficients

The Laplace transform image of a linear differential equation with constant coefficients is an algebraic equation. The Laplace transform image of a linear differential equation with polynomial coefficients is another linear differential equation with polynomial coefficients. The image equation is sometimes simpler; of lower order, for example. Therein lies the advantage of this transformation for some initial-value problems.

The principle of the method may be seen in the examination of the equation [14]

$$t\frac{d^2x}{dt^2} - (2\nu - 1)\frac{dx}{dt} + tx = 0. \tag{9.1}$$

Assuming this to have an ordinary function solution $x(t)$ for $t > 0$, we set as usual

$$X(t) = \begin{cases} 0 & \text{for } t < 0 \\ x(t) & \text{for } t > 0, \end{cases}$$

so that substituting

$$DX = [DX] + x(+0)\,\delta(t),$$

$$D^2X = [D^2X] + x(+0)\,\delta'(t) + x'(+0)\,\delta(t)$$

in (9.1) gives the g.f. equation of evolution

$$tD^2X - (2\nu - 1)DX + tX$$

$$= x(+0)t\,\delta'(t) + x'(+0)t\,\delta(t) - (2\nu - 1)x(+0)\,\delta(t).$$

This, recalling that $t\,\delta(t) = 0$ and $t\,\delta'(t) = -\delta(t)$, becomes

$$tD^2X - (2\nu - 1)DX + tX = -2\nu x(+0)\,\delta(t). \tag{9.2}$$

[The fact that, though the original differential equation is of order 2, its equation of evolution is independent of the initial condition $x'(+0)$, is due to the presence of the factor t in the first term of (9.1). Such an equation is said to be singular.] (9.2) takes its simplest form if $\nu x(+0) = 0$, i.e., if either ν or $x(+0)$ vanishes. This is the case that we now consider.

Let us assume that (9.2), with vanishing right-hand side, possesses a solution $X \in \mathscr{D}'_{++}$ of exponential type. We then take the Laplace transform image of the equation. From (6.8) and (6.3) we get, on setting $\bar{x}(s) = \mathscr{L}\{X\}$,

$$\mathscr{L}\{tD^2X\} = -\frac{d}{ds}\mathscr{L}\{D^2X\} = -\frac{d}{ds}(s^2\mathscr{L}\{X\})$$

$$= -2s\bar{x} - s^2\frac{d\bar{x}}{ds},$$

$$\mathscr{L}\{tX\} = -\frac{d\bar{x}}{ds}, \qquad \mathscr{L}\{DX\} = s\bar{x}.$$

The image equation is thus

$$(s^2 + 1)\frac{d\bar{x}}{ds} + (2\nu + 1)s\bar{x} = 0. \tag{9.3}$$

While the equation in object space is of the second order, the image equation is a first-order differential equation—one which can be integrated by quadrature since it gives

$$\frac{d\bar{x}}{\bar{x}} = -(2\nu + 1)\frac{s\,ds}{s^2 + 1},$$

whence (C is an arbitrary constant)

$$\log|\bar{x}| = -(\nu + \tfrac{1}{2})\log(s^2 + 1) + \log C$$

and

$$\bar{x}(s) = C(s^2 + 1)^{-\nu - 1/2}. \tag{9.4}$$

At this point, let us review the situation: on the assumption that (9.2) with $\nu x(+0) = 0$ has a solution that is both in $\mathscr{D}'_{++}$ and of exponential type, we got a Laplace transform image equation which we have solved. We can now conclude [from the uniqueness property of the Laplace transform stated in Remark (b), p. 254, and the rules of correspondence between operations in object and image space] that if the function $C(s^2 + 1)^{-\nu-1/2}$ has an inverse Laplace transform $\mathscr{L}^{-1}\{C(s^2 + 1)^{-\nu-1/2}\} \in \mathscr{D}'_{++}$ and of exponential type this g.f. must be a solution of (9.2). Thus all that remains is to determine the inverse transform of the right-hand side of (9.4). Three separate cases arise:

(i) *ν is of the form* $\nu = -k + \frac{1}{2}$ $(k = 1, 2, \ldots)$. Then $\bar{x}(s)$ is a polynomial in s^2, and, since $\mathscr{L}\{\delta^{(p)}(t)\} = s^p$, (9.2) has a solution X which is equal to a derivative polynomial applied to $\delta(t)$. For instance, if $\nu = -\frac{3}{2}$, $\bar{x}(s) = C(s^2 + 1)$, then

$$X(t) = C\,\delta''(t) + C\,\delta(t).$$

Substitution in (9.2) easily confirms this to be a solution [recall (II.B.3.10)]

$$t\delta^{(iv)}(t) + t\delta''(t) + 4\delta'''(t) + 4\delta'(t) + t\delta''(t) + t\delta(t)$$
$$= -4\delta''' - 2\delta' + 4\delta''' + 4\delta' - 2\delta' = 0.$$

In this case (9.1) has the trivial solution $x(t) = 0$ whereas (9.2) has non-trivial g.f. solutions.

(ii) $\nu < \frac{1}{2}$ *not of the form* (i). Rather than discuss this case in general, let us illustrate its approach with a treatment for the particular choice $\nu = -1$, so $\bar{x} = C\sqrt{1 + s^2}$. We observe that by (9.4)

$$\frac{d\bar{x}}{ds} = C\frac{s}{\sqrt{s^2 + 1}} = \mathscr{L}\{-tX\},$$

and that

$$\frac{s}{\sqrt{s^2+1}} = s\bar{y}(s),$$

where

$$\bar{y} = \frac{C}{\sqrt{s^2+1}} = \mathscr{L}\{Y\}$$

and Y is the solution of (9.2) with $\nu = 0$. Consequently, using (6.3), we get

$$-tX = DY, \tag{9.5}$$

and the solution for $\nu = -1$, if it exists, can thus be deduced from that for $\nu = 0$. Following the discussion of (iii) we shall see that X, verifying (9.5), does indeed exist in $\mathscr{D}'_{++}$.

(iii) $\nu > -\frac{1}{2}$. For such ν we have $\lim_{s\to+\infty} \bar{x}(s) = 0$. There is, therefore, an "a priori" chance that $X(t)$ will turn out to be a $\mathscr{K}_{++}(R)$ function. We shall consider this case only for $\nu = 0, 1, 2, \ldots$.

To find $\mathscr{L}^{-1}\{(s^2+1)^{-\nu-1/2}\}$ we expand $(s^2+1)^{-\nu-1/2}$ by means of the binomial formula

$$\frac{C}{(1+s^2)^{\nu+1/2}} = \frac{C}{s^{2\nu+1}}\left(1+\frac{1}{s^2}\right)^{-\nu-1/2} \tag{9.6}$$

$$= \frac{C}{s^{2\nu+1}}\sum_{l=0}^{\infty}\binom{-\nu-\frac{1}{2}}{l}\left(\frac{1}{s^2}\right)^l,$$

where the series converges for $s > 1$.

Here we have

$$\binom{-\nu-\frac{1}{2}}{l} = \frac{(-\nu-\frac{1}{2})(-\nu-\frac{1}{2}-1)\cdots(-\nu-\frac{1}{2}-l+1)}{l!}$$

$$= \frac{(-1)^l}{l!}\,\frac{(2\nu+1)(2\nu+3)\cdots(2\nu+2l-1)}{2^l}$$

$$= \frac{(-1)^l}{l!}\,\frac{(2\nu+2l-1)(2\nu+2l-3)\cdots(2\nu+1)}{2^l}$$

$$\cdot\frac{2(\nu+l)\cdot 2(\nu+l-1)\cdots 2(\nu+1)\cdot(2\nu)!}{2^l[(\nu+l)(\nu+l-1)\cdots(\nu+1)](2\nu)!}$$

and, more compactly,

$$\binom{-\nu-\frac{1}{2}}{l} = \frac{(-1)^l}{l!}\,\frac{(2\nu+2l)!\,\nu!}{2^{2l}(\nu+l)!\,(2\nu)!}. \tag{9.7}$$

At the same time, by (5.21),

$$\frac{1}{s^{2\nu+1+2l}} = \mathscr{L}\left\{\frac{t_+^{2\nu+2l}}{(2\nu + 2l)!}\right\}.$$

Formally, then, (9.6) yields ($t_+^\lambda = t^\lambda H(t)$)

$$(9.8) \quad \frac{C}{(1 + s^2)^{\nu+1/2}} = \mathscr{L}\left\{H(t)\frac{\nu!}{(2\nu)!}\, 2^{2\nu}C\sum_{l=0}^{\infty}(-1)^l\left(\frac{t}{2}\right)^{2\nu+2l}\frac{1}{l!\,(\nu + l)!}\right\},$$

which we write

$$\frac{C}{(1 + s^2)^{\nu+1/2}} = \mathscr{L}\{C\,S(t)H(t)\}.$$

From the inequality $\dfrac{(\nu + 2l)!}{l!\,(\nu + l)!} \leqslant 2^{\nu+2l}$ we get, since $\nu \geqslant 0$,

$$\left(\frac{t}{2}\right)^{2l}\frac{1}{l!\,(\nu + l)!} \leqslant 2^\nu\frac{t^{2l}}{(\nu + 2l)!} \leqslant 2^\nu\frac{t^{2l}}{(2l)!}.$$

This shows that the series on the right in (9.8) is dominated term by term by the series

$$2^\nu\sum_{l=0}^{\infty}\frac{t^{2l}}{(2l)!},$$

which consists merely of the terms with even exponent in the series for $2^\nu e^t$.

All this shows that

$$S(t) = 2^{2\nu}C\sum_{l=0}^{\infty}\frac{(-1)^l}{l!\,(\nu + l)!}\left(\frac{t}{2}\right)^{2\nu+2l} \leqslant C\cdot 2^{3\nu}e^t.$$

From this one deduces two essential facts:

(a) the power series $S(t)$ converges uniformly on every finite interval of $(0, +\infty)$ [as a consequence $S(t) \in C^\infty(R)$];

(b) for every $s > 1$

$$\int_0^\infty e^{-st}S(t)\,dt = \sum_{l=0}^{\infty}\int_0^\infty e^{-st}a_l(t)\,dt,$$

where

$$S(t) = \sum_{l=0}^{\infty} a_l(t)$$

[this proves that (9.8) is not just a formal but a fully valid relation when $s > 1$].

We have thus obtained a solution of equation (9.2) in the form of the infinite series $X(t) = CS(t)H(t)$. As $S(t) \in C^\infty(R)$, the generalized and the ordinary derivatives coincide on $(0, +\infty)$ and $S(t)$ is also a solution of (9.1) for $t > 0$. Note that, for $\nu \geqslant 1$,

$$S(+0) = S(0) = 0$$

so $X(+0) = 0$ as required by the condition $\nu x(+0) = 0$. For $\nu = 0$, $X(+0) = C$.

[The term t can be factored out of the series dS/dt regardless of the value of the integer $\nu \geqslant 0$. Momentarily denoting the solution for $\nu = 0$ by Y, we see that the solution X of (9.5) is immediately obtained by canceling out t on both sides of the equation.]

Remark 1. The restriction $\nu = 0, 1, 2, \ldots$ in the computation of case (iii) was made for convenience only. Actually, any $\nu \geqslant 0$ will do as well, providing the factorials are replaced by appropriate gamma functions $[\lambda! = \Gamma(\lambda + 1)]$.

Remark 2. *Bessel functions.* If in case (iii) above we take

$$\frac{C \cdot 2^\nu \nu!}{(2\nu)!} = 1, \tag{9.9}$$

the solution of (9.1) can be written as

$$X(t) = t^\nu J_\nu(t) H(t), \tag{9.10}$$

where

$$J_\nu(t) = \sum_{l=0}^{\infty} \frac{(-1)^l}{l!\,(\nu + l)!} \left(\frac{t}{2}\right)^{\nu+2l} \tag{9.11}$$

is called the Bessel function of the first kind of order ν ($\geqslant 0$).

This function satisfies Bessel's equation

$$t^2 \frac{d^2 \tau}{dt^2} + t \frac{dz}{dt} + (t^2 - \nu^2)z = 0, \tag{9.12}$$

from which (9.1) is obtained on setting

$$x(t) = t^\nu z(t) H(t). \tag{9.13}$$

10. A Partial Differential Equation Problem

To the applied mathematician, the physicist, and the engineer, the primary interest of the Laplace transform, as far as partial differential equations (p.d.e.) are concerned, is its fruitfulness as a source of procedures for solving such equations. These procedures, when imposed on sufficiently restricted types of functions and g.f.'s, are entirely rigorous, yielding solution formulae that are fully justified. Often these same solution formulae remain correct even when applied to other, broader, classes of g.f.'s to which the Laplace transform is in no way applicable. Thus, besides actually producing restricted classes of solutions, the L.T. has heuristic value insofar as it *suggests* the form taken by larger classes of solutions (it neither proves them to be, nor gives any hint as to whether there are any others). This already happens with ordinary differential equations with constant coefficients, and we saw that for them the broader class of solutions is obtained through the operational calculus in $\mathscr{D}'_+$. For p.d.e.'s also the broader class of solutions can be obtained rigorously by direct operational methods, but on g.f. spaces that depend on the equation and which will not be taken up before Volume II.

The rest of this chapter is meant as an introduction to the Laplace transform method for some p.d.e. problems. Two examples, both standard, are treated with the g.f. version of the Laplace transform. With these in mind, the reader should have absolutely no difficulty in extending to g.f.'s, by himself, the multitudinous applications to p.d.e.'s of the classical (non-g.f.) Laplace transform that are covered in detail in many available textbooks.

The first of these examples is presented at some length (§§ 10, 11, 12) so as to indicate the heuristic role of the L.T. method, the conditions under which the L.T. method is rigorously justified, and to illustrate the relationship between the ordinary and the g.f. versions of a p.d.e. problem. The second example is given in slightly more abbreviated style.

The starting point for the first example is

Problem A. *Find $y(x, t)$ such that*

$$\frac{\partial^2 y}{\partial x^2} = \frac{1}{c^2}\frac{\partial^2 y}{\partial t^2} \qquad (t > 0,\ x > 0), \tag{10.1}$$

$$y(x, +0) = \frac{\partial y}{\partial t}(x, +0) = 0 \qquad (x > 0), \tag{10.2}$$

$$y(+0, t) = f(t) \qquad (t > 0), \tag{10.3}$$

$$\lim_{x\to+\infty} y(x, t) = 0 \qquad (t > 0). \tag{10.4}$$

Here $y(x, t)$ represents the deflection from the x axis of the points of a very long homogeneous flexible string with one extremity tied down on the x axis [this is the meaning of (10.4)] and the other in motion along the y axis, as described in (10.3). Equation (10.1) is called the wave equation in one (spatial) dimension, or the equation of the vibrating string. The conditions (10.2) indicate that the string starts from a rest position coinciding with the positive x axis, and with zero initial velocity.

Parametric equation of evolution. We start with the assumption that the problem has a solution $y(x, t)$ which with $(\partial y/\partial t)(x, t)$ is a continuous function of t on the half-line $0 < t$ and for every fixed $x > 0$. Then the function

$$Y(x, t) = \begin{cases} y(x, t) & \text{if } t > 0, x > 0 \\ y(x, +0) = 0 & \text{if } t = 0, x > 0 \\ 0 & \text{if } t < 0, x > 0 \end{cases} \tag{10.5}$$

is continuous in t for all real t. The same holds for $\partial Y/\partial t$.

As $Y = 0$ for $t < 0$, we see that the relation

$$\frac{\partial^2 Y}{\partial x^2} = \frac{1}{c^2} \frac{\partial^2 Y}{\partial t^2} \tag{10.6}$$

is satisfied for $t < 0$, $x > 0$ as well as for $t > 0$, $x > 0$.

If both terms in (10.6) are piecewise continuous, we can multiply both sides by any $\varphi(t) \in \mathscr{D}_-$ and integrate over the t axis. This means that we are taking $Y(x, t)$ to be a $\mathscr{D}'_+$ g.f. in the variable t and depending on the parameter x. Denote by D g.f. differentiation with respect to t. Then by Corollary II.B.1.1 and (10.2)

$$\begin{aligned} DY &= \left[\frac{\partial Y}{\partial t}\right] + y(x, +0)\, \delta(t) = \left[\frac{\partial Y}{\partial t}\right], \\ D^2 Y &= \left[\frac{\partial^2 Y}{\partial t^2}\right] + y(x, +0)\, \delta'(t) + \frac{\partial y}{\partial t}(x, +0)\, \delta(t) = \left[\frac{\partial^2 Y}{\partial t^2}\right], \end{aligned} \tag{10.7}$$

where $[\partial Y/\partial t]$ and $[\partial^2 Y/\partial t^2]$ are the g.f.'s defined by the ordinary derivatives. Substituting in (10.6) and taking values on $\varphi(t) \in \mathscr{D}_-$ gives

$$\left\langle \frac{\partial^2 Y}{\partial x^2}, \varphi \right\rangle = \frac{1}{c^2} \langle D^2 Y, \varphi \rangle. \tag{10.8}$$

If

$$\frac{\partial^2}{\partial x^2} \langle Y, \varphi \rangle = \left\langle \frac{\partial^2 Y}{\partial x^2}, \varphi \right\rangle, \tag{10.9}$$

the ordinary derivative $\partial^2 Y/\partial x^2$ coincides with the parametric derivative (in the sense of § II.B.7) $\partial^2 Y/\partial x^2$ of the g.f. Y. In that case equation (10.8) with the conditions (10.2) is equivalent to the g.f. equation

$$\frac{\partial^2 Y}{\partial x^2} = \frac{1}{c^2} D^2 Y \quad [x \text{ parameter} > 0,\ Y(x, t) \in \mathscr{D}'_{++} \text{ in } t]. \tag{10.10}$$

We may call this the *parametric equation of evolution* for Problem A, and we accompany it by these *boundary conditions* suggested by (10.3) and (10.4):

(10.11) $$\lim_{x \to +0} Y(x, t) = F(t) = \begin{cases} f(t) & \text{if } t > 0 \\ 0 & \text{if } t < 0, \end{cases}$$

(10.12) $$\lim_{x \to +\infty} Y(x, t) = 0.$$

Finding the solution of (10.10) subject to conditions (10.11) (10.12), we call **Problem B.**

Concerning the relationship between Problems A and B, we can a priori say this: all solutions $y(x, t)$ of Problem A of a broad, though not unrestricted, type [including those for which the ordinary and parametric derivatives $\partial^2/\partial x^2$ coincide and for which (10.3) (10.4) entail (10.11) (10.12)] are necessarily among the solutions of Problem B. On the other hand, solutions to the latter, even when they are not solutions in the usual sense of Problem A, turn out to be physically meaningful. Thus, the equation of evolution is a fruitful mathematical model of a physical phenomenon. (A more serious discussion of g.f. equations of evolution for certain partial differential equation problems requires the study of g.f.'s in several dimensions and is, therefore, not entered into here.)

11. Application of the Laplace Transform

The terms appearing in (10.10) (10.11) (10.12) are $\mathscr{D}'_+$ g.f.'s, i.e., they are functionals taking values on the function $\varphi \in \mathscr{D}_-$. If we wish to use the Laplace transform, it is necessary that all these terms be functionals taking values on all functions of the form e^{-st} with sufficiently large s. A way of ensuring this is to narrow Problem B down to

Problem B′. *Find the g.f. (in t) $Y(x,t) \in \mathscr{D}'_{++}$, which is of exponential type for every positive value of the parameter x and which satisfies the relations*

(11.1) $$\frac{\partial^2 Y}{\partial x^2} = \frac{1}{c^2} D^2 Y \qquad (x > 0),$$

(11.2) $$\lim_{x \to +0} Y(x, t) = F(t) \in \mathscr{D}'_{++} \qquad \text{(of exponential type)},$$

(11.3) $$\lim_{x \to +\infty} Y(x, t) = 0.$$

It must be stressed here that, while Y and F are required to be functionals on the function e^{-st} with sufficiently large s, the parametric limits in (11.2), (11.3) are taken in $\mathscr{D}'_+$ (i.e., in the sense of pointwise convergence on $\mathscr{D}_-$). Also, the derivative $\partial^2 Y/\partial x^2$, being a $\mathscr{D}'_+$ parametric derivative, must satisfy (10.9) for every $\varphi \in \mathscr{D}_-$.

If, in these two parametric limits and in the parametric derivative, the usual identities, which are valid for every $\varphi \in \mathscr{D}_-$, remained true when φ is replaced by e^{-st} with large enough s the relations (10.9) (11.2) (11.3) would assume the form

$$\left\langle \frac{\partial^2 Y}{\partial x^2}, e^{-st} \right\rangle = \frac{\partial^2}{\partial x^2} \langle Y, e^{-st} \rangle, \tag{11.4}$$

$$\lim_{x\to+0} \langle Y, e^{-st} \rangle = \langle F, e^{-st} \rangle, \tag{11.5}$$

$$\lim_{x\to+\infty} \langle Y, e^{-st} \rangle = 0. \tag{11.6}$$

Taking values of both sides of (11.1) at the functions e^{-st} and substituting from (11.4) gives

$$\frac{\partial^2}{\partial x^2} \langle Y, e^{-st} \rangle = \frac{1}{c^2} \langle D^2 Y, e^{-st} \rangle = \frac{s^2}{c^2} \langle Y, e^{-st} \rangle. \tag{11.7}$$

Thus, if there exists a solution of Problem B' for which (11.4) (11.5) (11.6) (11.7) hold, it is a solution of

Problem C. *Find* $Y(x, t) \in \mathscr{D}'_{++}$ *of exponential type and depending on the parameter* x *with* $x > 0$ *such that for all* s *exceeding some* $s_0 \in R$, *these relations hold:*

$$\frac{\partial^2}{\partial x^2} \langle Y(x, t), e^{-st} \rangle = \frac{s^2}{c^2} \langle Y, e^{-st} \rangle, \tag{11.7'}$$

$$\lim_{x\to+0} \langle Y, e^{-st} \rangle = \langle F, e^{-st} \rangle, \tag{11.5}$$

$$\lim_{x\to+\infty} \langle Y, e^{-st} \rangle = 0. \tag{11.6}$$

These relations can, by setting

$$u(x, s) = \langle Y(x, t), e^{-st} \rangle, \tag{11.8}$$

be rewritten as

$$\frac{d^2 u(x, s)}{dx^2} = \frac{s^2}{c^2} u(x, s), \tag{11.7''}$$

$$u(+0, s) = \mathscr{L}\{F\}, \tag{11.5'}$$

$$\lim_{x\to+\infty} u(x, s) = 0, \tag{11.6'}$$

where, in (11.7″), we do not use a partial derivative symbol because s may be considered as a parameter and x as the independent variable.

Equations (11.7″) (11.5′) (11.6′) have the agreeable property of being easy to solve since they constitute a boundary-value problem for a differential equation (11.7″) with constant coefficients (i.e., independent of x, dependent only on the *parameter* s). Such a problem can be solved, for instance, by the direct operational method, with the result (cf. § IV.B.1)

$$u(x, s) = e^{-(x/c)s}\mathscr{L}\{F\} \qquad (c > 0). \tag{11.8}$$

Appealing to (6.4) and the uniqueness property of the Laplace transform we arrive at the conclusion that Problem C has the solution

$$Y(x, t) = F\left(t - \frac{x}{c}\right). \tag{11.9}$$

The transition from Problem B′ to Problem C was given above under a number of restrictive hypotheses, and we could now, by applying the definition of g.f.'s of exponential type, verify that in the present instance these hypotheses, in particular the first equality (11.7), are actually satisfied by $Y(x, t)$ as defined in (11.9). We shall not go through with this here; instead, we shall adopt an attitude prevalent in many expositions of this subject and which, though it is not very analytic, has some pragmatic justification: we simply try out $F(t - x/c)$ in Problem B′.

This is easily done. F, being of exponential type, is of finite K-order, $F = D^pG$, where $G(t) \in \mathscr{K}_{++}(R)$ so Exercise 20 gives

$$\frac{\partial^2 F\left(t - \frac{x}{c}\right)}{\partial x^2} = \frac{1}{c^2}\, D^2F\left(t - \frac{x}{c}\right), \tag{11.10}$$

proving that (11.9) furnishes a solution to (11.1). That (11.9) satisfies (11.2) (11.3) is obvious even when $F \in \mathscr{D}'_{++}$ is not of exponential type. Thus, we do indeed have a solution to Problem B′. It has been found here, not directly, but by using the solution of Problem C (which is easy to obtain, thanks to the Laplace transform) to suggest a plausible form of $Y(x, t)$, which was subsequently checked by substitution in (11.1) (11.2) (11.3).

Remark. In order to apply the L.T., it is necessary to impose restrictions on the growth of $F(t)$ as $t \to +\infty$, since otherwise $\langle F(t), e^{-st}\rangle = \mathscr{L}\{F\}$ may not exist. This was done here by requiring F to be of exponential type. We are then faced with the question whether Problem B may not have other solutions besides those of Problem B′.

The answer, in the particular case at hand, is affirmative. Any $F(t) \in \mathscr{D}'_{++}$ satisfies (11.10) [proof: use the fact that F is of finite order locally (Chapter V), or follow the lines of Theorem II.A.6.1] so $Y(x, t) = F(t - x/c)$ is a solution of Problem B whenever $F \in \mathscr{D}_{++}$.

The mathematician is then confronted with the task of delineating existence and uniqueness theorems for Problem B under various hypotheses on $F(t)$. Such matters are postponed to Volume II; it is the heuristic uses of the L.T. that concern us now.

As far as the vibrating string is concerned, the notion of a non-exponential type and very rapidly increasing (as $t \to +\infty$)$F(t)$, equal to $H(t)e^{t^4} \in \mathscr{K}_{++}$ say, is obviously of meager interest to the engineer or physicist—though there are different physical problems where dismissing uniqueness and existence questions would be frivolous, even from the physical point of view.

12. Relation to Problem A

We are now in the familiar position reached time and again in Chapters III and IV: a g.f. equation of evolution (plus side conditions—Problem B′) suggested by the ordinary function formulation (Problem A) of a physical phenomenon has been solved.

Questions: (I) does this also solve the original problem? (II) if not, is the g.f. result relevant to the physical situation?

In the case of the I.V. problem for an ordinary linear differential equation with constant coefficients, the answer to (I) was given in complete generality by Theorem III.B.1.1. For systems of such equations (Chapter IV), we did not develop any such general theorem enabling one to predict a priori whether a solution of the g.f. problem is also a solution of the original ordinary function problem. Instead, each particular case was treated separately, following a simple and practical routine that consisted in solving the g.f. equations of evolution first and then looking at these solutions to see whether they also fitted the original problem. As rationalizations for this attitude, we offer these: the proof of a general theorem of the kind mentioned requires a good deal of labor, and, since the answer to question (II) is, "Yes, the g.f. solution is at least equally relevant to the physical situation under study," we spare ourselves that labor.

This outlook we shall also adopt with partial differential equations, both here and in Volume II; and for the same reasons, but amplified by the fact that broad "a priori" theorems on the relation between g.f. and ordinary solutions are very much more difficult to establish for p.d.e.'s (important segments of present-day mathematical research on p.d.e.'s lie in this area).

These observations of a general nature having been injected, let us concentrate on the particular case at hand, the connection between Problems A and B′. It depends entirely on the form of $F(t)$, as is brought out by some specific examples.

Example 1. $F(t) \in C^2(R)$.
Take the function

$$F_1(t) = \begin{cases} 0 & \text{if } t < 0 \\ \sin^3 t & \text{if } 0 \leqslant t \leqslant \pi \\ 0 & \text{if } t > \pi, \end{cases} \tag{12.1}$$

whose graph is shown in Figure 17.

It is obviously C^2 for $t \neq 0$, and is of exponential order because $|F_1(t)| \leqslant 1$. At $t = 0$, the left-hand derivatives of orders 1 and 2 are zero. The right-hand derivatives of orders 1 and 2 contain the factor $\sin t$ and, therefore, also vanish at $t = 0$. It follows that dF_1/dt, d^2F_1/dt^2 exist and are continuous at $t = 0$. The same holds at $t = \pi$ and we conclude that $F_1 \in C^2(R)$. Note, by the way, that F_1 is the $\mathscr{K}_+(R)$ function corresponding to the piecewise continuous function $H(t)\,H(\pi - t)\sin^3 t$ in the sense that "filling the gaps" at $t = 0$ and $t = \pi$ in the latter yields $F_1(t)$.

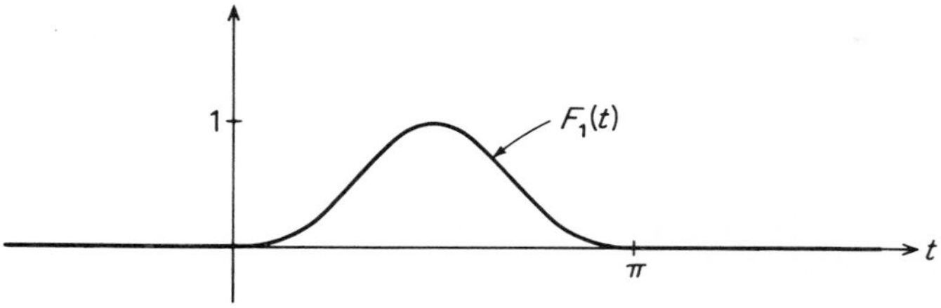

FIGURE 17

Referring to (11.9), we find that the solution of Problem B′ corresponding to this $F(t)$ is its translation to the right by the amount x/c:

$$Y_1(x, t) = F_1\left(t - \frac{x}{c}\right). \tag{12.2}$$

That this is also a solution of Problem A is a trivial matter to verify:

$$\frac{\partial^2 F_1\left(t - \frac{x}{c}\right)}{\partial x^2} \quad \text{and} \quad \frac{\partial^2 F_1\left(t - \frac{x}{c}\right)}{\partial t^2}$$

exist in the ordinary sense and are continuous, so substitution of F_1 in (10.1)–(10.4) is feasible and gives an immediate check.

$F_1(t - x/c)$ vanishes for $t - x/c \notin (0, \pi)$, and we see that at any given instant $t > 0$ the entire string coincides with the positive x axis except that portion for which $\max(0, c(t - \pi)) < x < ct$. There the string rises above the x axis in the shape of one half-cycle of the $\sin^3$ curve (if $t \geqslant \pi$), or of a portion thereof (if $t < \pi$). Thus, what we have physically is a bulge of width $c\pi$ traveling down the string in the positive x direction at the constant velocity c. Three successive photographs of the string are depicted in Figure 18. The projections onto the (t, x) plane of the peaks follow a straight line of slope c, indicating that the velocity of propagation is c.

Example 2. $F(t) \in C^1(R) \cap \mathscr{K}_+^2(R)$.
This time we take

$$F_2(t) = \begin{cases} 0 & \text{if } t < \pi \\ \sin^2 t & \text{if } 0 \leqslant t \leqslant \pi \\ 0 & \text{if } \pi < t, \end{cases} \tag{12.3}$$

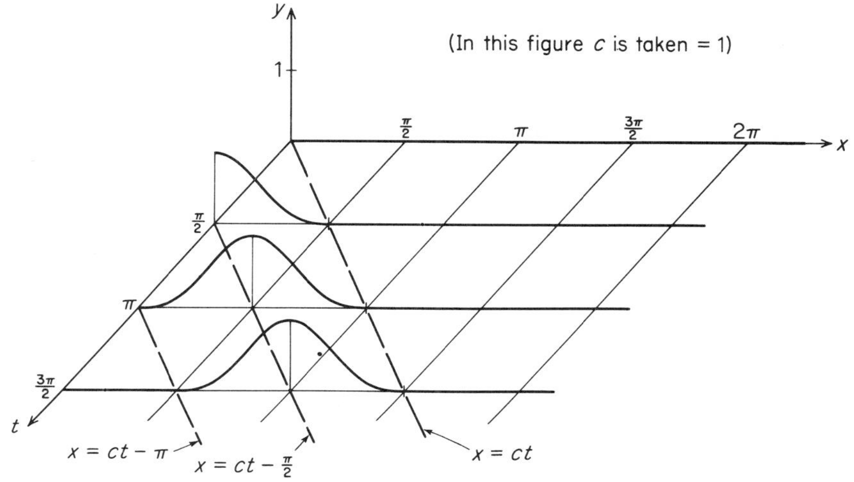

FIGURE 18

a $C^1(R)$ function of exponential order ($|F_2(t)| \leqslant 1$) having the ordinary derivative

$$\frac{d^2F_2(t)}{dt^2} = \begin{cases} 0 & \text{if } t < 0 \\ 2\cos 2t & \text{if } 0 \leqslant t \leqslant \pi \\ 0 & \text{if } \pi < t, \end{cases} \tag{12.4}$$

which is a $\mathscr{K}_{++}(R)$ function with jump discontinuities at $t = 0$ and $t = \pi$.

With the input $F_2(t)$, problem B′ has the solution

$$Y_2(x, t) = F_2\left(t - \frac{x}{c}\right). \tag{12.5}$$

At all points of the (t, x) plane *that do not lie on the lines $x = ct$ and $x = ct - \pi$* the ordinary second derivatives of $F_2(t - x/c)$ exist, are continuous, and are seen to satisfy Equation (10.1) of Problem A. That $F_2(t - x/c)$ satisfies the rest of the conditions of Problem A is easily verified.

Thus, as far as Problem A is concerned, we have here a solution for it, *providing we demand satisfaction of the wave equation* (10.1) *only outside two straight lines in the* (t, x) *plane.* To cavil at these exceptions would be foolish on our part, for it is plain to see that the description, given in the previous example, of the physical propagation of a disturbance along the string, holds just as well when $F_1(t)$ is replaced by $F_2(t)$. We conclude that Problem B′ is a very suitable mathematical idealization of the physical conditions in this case.

The progression of possible examples from here on is now self-evident: at the ith step, consider an input function $F_i(t)$ or g.f. whose "smoothness" specifications are one notch lower than those for $F_{i-1}(t)$. In each case, one then observes that the corresponding solution

$$Y_i(x, t) = F_i\left(t - \frac{x}{c}\right)$$

of Problem B′ satisfactorily lends itself to a physical interpretation as the propagation downstring of a disturbance. This reveals that too narrow an interpretation of Problem A constitutes a neglect of solutions of basic physical importance, and that taking the g.f. Problem B′ as the mathematical model for the physical situation greatly diminishes the risk of losing solutions. Theoretically, Problem B is even better, but we are confining ourselves to exponential-order g.f.'s because we used the Laplace transform. [From the practical point of view, this is not much of a restriction anyway (cf. the last sentence in the Remark § 11).]

Here, we wish to consider only two more particular cases:

Example 3. $F(t) \in C(R) \cap \mathscr{K}_+^2(R)$.

(12.6)
$$F_3(t) = \begin{cases} 0 & \text{if } t < 0 \\ \sin t & \text{if } 0 \leqslant t \leqslant \pi \\ 0 & \text{if } \pi < t. \end{cases}$$

$dF_3(t)/dt$ has jumps of unit magnitude at $t = 0$, $t = \pi$, so, with the usual notation for $[DF]$ as the g.f. defined by dF/dt,

(12.7)
$$D^2F_3(t) = [D^2F_3(t)] + \delta(t) + \delta(t - \pi).$$

If we denote by $\left[\dfrac{\partial^2 F_3}{\partial x^2}\left(t - \dfrac{x}{c}\right)\right]$ the ordinary partial derivative in the usual, non-g.f., sense [which is a $\mathscr{K}_{++}(R)$ function], and by $\dfrac{\partial^2 F_3}{\partial x^2}\left(t - \dfrac{x}{c}\right)$ the parametric derivative in the sense of § II.B.7, it can be verified, by taking values on $\varphi \in \mathscr{D}_-$, that, all terms being considered as $\mathscr{D}'_{++}$ g.f.'s in the variable t with x as parameter, there holds the relation

(12.8)
$$\frac{\partial^2 F_3\left(t - \dfrac{x}{c}\right)}{\partial x^2} = \left[\frac{\partial^2 F_3\left(t - \dfrac{x}{c}\right)}{\partial x^2}\right] + \frac{1}{c^2}\,\delta\left(t - \frac{x}{c}\right) + \frac{1}{c^2}\,\delta\left(t - \frac{x}{c} - \pi\right).$$

We know that $F_3(t - x/c)$ is a solution of Problem B′, i.e., that

(12.9)
$$\frac{\partial^2 F_3\left(t - \dfrac{x}{c}\right)}{\partial x^2} = \frac{1}{c^2}\,D^2F_3\left(t - \frac{x}{c}\right),$$

in which, on substituting from (12.7) and (12.8), we find that the δ terms cancel, leaving

$$\left[\frac{\partial^2 F_3\left(t-\dfrac{x}{c}\right)}{\partial x^2}\right] = \frac{1}{c^2}\left[D_t^2 F_3\left(t-\frac{x}{c}\right)\right]. \tag{12.10}$$

This equality can also be obtained directly by comparing the ordinary second derivatives with respect to x and t at all points of the (t, x) plane not on the lines $x = ct$ and $x = ct - \pi$. Thus, here, as in Example 2, the solution of Problem B′ is seen to verify Problem A outside these lines. The physical interpretation again is analogous.

[*Note.* The reader conversant with classical (non-g.f.) Laplace transform theory is referred to Churchill [7, § 38] for its application to this example. Churchill points out that it yields the correct answer "regardless of the validity of formal steps" and explains how this happens. This same explanation the reader in question can now couch in terms of g.f.'s by comparing the Laplace transforms of both sides of (12.7) and (12.8) and noticing how the Laplace transforms of the equations (12.9) and (12.10) are thereby made equal because of the cancellation of the transforms of the delta terms (cf. also [3]).]

Example 4. *The Green's "function" of Problems A and B*

$$F_4(t) = \delta(t). \tag{12.11}$$

No actual physical means of producing this motion at the free end of the string exists, of course. $\delta(t)$ can be considered as a mathematical idealization of a rapid up and down jerk, and the solution

$$Y_4(x, t) = \delta\left(t - \frac{x}{c}\right) \tag{12.12}$$

then shows that this impulse moves down the string at velocity c, passing any fixed point x (> 0) of the string without after-effect. Even though such an input and such a solution are strictly abstractions, they are helpful guides to our intuition of physical events. Just as in the case of ordinary differential equations (Chapter III.C) they are, so to speak, a unit input and a unit solution respectively. $Y_4(x, t)$ plays for this problem the same role as does the Green's function of the I.V. problem for ordinary differential equations. Indeed, for any $F(t) \in \mathscr{D}'_+$ which is of finite order (exponential type implies this), the input can be written in the form

$$F(t) * \delta(t) = F(t), \tag{12.13}$$

whose interpretation as a "sum" of unit impulses was given in § III.C.1. The solution $F(t - x/c)$ is then obtained from the Green's "function" $\delta(t - x/c)$:

$$F\left(t - \frac{x}{c}\right) = F(t) * \delta\left(t - \frac{x}{c}\right) \tag{12.14}$$

which is a "sum" of unit solutions.

13. A Practical L.T. Routine for P.D.E. Problems

So many text and reference books (e.g., [3] [7] [10] [14] [48] [55]) are rife with interesting and physically important illustrations of p.d.e. problems solved by means of the classical, non-g.f., Laplace transform, that it seems reasonable to dispense here with the detailed treatment of numerous examples. The reader can easily transcribe for himself into the g.f. form of the L.T. the examples and problems that he will find in these books. All he has to do for that is to interject analogs to Problems B, C, and B′ and reinterpret the L.T.'s. What is gained by such an exercise is an *improvement in mathematical consistency and the possibility of handling inputs that are not functions*; e.g., $\delta(t)$, which gives the fundamental (unit) solution from which the others are obtained by a convolution product.

As a guide, it may be helpful to consider one more illustrative problem, in brief—after the lengthy discourse that attended the vibrating-string case, a treatment that is more summary should suffice, and be welcome.

Problem. *A homogeneous semi-infinite solid coinciding with the portion of Euclidean space defined by $x > 0$ conducts heat in such fashion that the temperature at any point (x, y, z) with $x > 0$ is given by a function $u(x, t)$ that satisfies the equation*

$$\frac{\partial u}{\partial t} = k\frac{\partial^2 u}{\partial x^2} \qquad (t > 0, x > 0, k > 0). \tag{13.1}$$

A uniform temperature distribution $F(t)$ (piecewise continuous) is applied to the face $x = 0$ of the solid during the period $t > 0$, a fact which we express mathematically by the condition

$$u(+0, t) = F(t) \qquad (t > 0). \tag{13.2}$$

Given the added conditions

$$\lim_{x\to+\infty} u(x, t) = 0 \qquad (t > 0), \tag{13.3}$$

$$u(x, +0) = 0 \qquad (x > 0), \tag{13.4}$$

find $u(x, t)$.

Solution. (i) Consider x as a parameter in the $\mathscr{D}'_{++}$ g.f. $U(x, t)$ defined by

$$U(x, t) = \begin{cases} 0 & \text{if } t < 0 \\ u(x, t) & \text{if } t > 0. \end{cases} \tag{13.5}$$

Writing D for the g.f. differentiation operator in t, we are led to the g.f. equation of evolution

$$DU(x, t) = k \frac{\partial^2 U(x, t)}{\partial x^2} \qquad (x > 0) \tag{13.6}$$

in which $\partial^2 U/\partial x^2$ is now taken to be a parametric derivative in the sense of § II.B.7. This equation we accompany with the conditions

$$\operatorname*{Lim}_{x \to +0} U(x, t) = F(t) = \begin{cases} f(t) & \text{if } t > 0 \\ 0 & \text{if } t < 0, \end{cases} \tag{13.7}$$

$$\operatorname*{Lim}_{x \to +\infty} U(x, t) = 0. \tag{13.8}$$

This is the problem corresponding to Problem B in the vibrating-string example; when one adds the hypotheses: U, F of exponential type, one has the correspondent to Problem B′. The analog of Problem C is that of finding an exponential type $U(x, t)$ satisfying

$$\frac{\partial^2 \langle U(x, t), e^{-st} \rangle}{\partial x^2} = \frac{1}{k} \langle DU(x, t), e^{-st} \rangle, \tag{13.9}$$

$$\lim_{x \to +0} \langle U(x, t), e^{-st} \rangle = \langle F(t), e^{-st} \rangle, \tag{13.10}$$

$$\lim_{x \to +\infty} \langle U(x, t), e^{-st} \rangle = 0, \tag{13.11}$$

where we allow $F(t)$ to be a $\mathscr{D}'_{++}$ g.f. of exponential type.

(ii) Writing $v(x, s) = \mathscr{L}\{U(x, t)\} = \langle U(x, t), e^{-st} \rangle$, the problem (13.9) (13.10) (13.11) becomes, with the aid of (6.3),

$$\frac{\partial^2 v}{\partial x^2}(x, s) = \frac{1}{k} sv(x, s),$$

$$v(+0, s) = \mathscr{L}\{F\},$$

$$\lim_{x \to +\infty} v(x, s) = 0.$$

The solution is (§ IV.B.1)

$$v(x, s) = e^{-x\sqrt{s/k}} \mathscr{L}\{F\}. \tag{13.12}$$

It can be shown [8] that

$$e^{-x\sqrt{s/k}} = \mathscr{L}\left\{ \frac{xH(t)}{2\sqrt{k\pi t^3}} e^{-x^2/4kt} \right\}.$$

Therefore, by the convolution relation (6.7) and by the uniqueness of the Laplace transform, (13.12) gives

$$U(x, t) = \frac{H(t)x}{2\sqrt{k\pi t^3}} e^{-x^2/4kt} * F(t). \tag{13.13}$$

This is the solution to Problem C [(13.9)–(13.11)] and it suggests a form of solution to Problem B′ [(13.6)–(13.8)]. By substitution, it can be shown that it is in fact also a solution of the latter. We shall not carry out this verification for arbitrary $F(t) \in \mathscr{D}'_{++}$ of exponential type because it is a little laborious. Let us, however, do it for the important particular case ($\tau \geqslant 0$)

$$F(t) = \delta(t - \tau), \tag{13.14}$$

which, by (13.13) gives

$$U(x, t) = \frac{H(t-\tau)x}{2\sqrt{k\pi(t-\tau)^3}} e^{-x^2/4k(t-\tau)}. \tag{13.15}$$

For every $x > 0$, this is a $C^\infty(R)$ function carried in the half-line $[\tau, +\infty)$ [we fill the gap of $H(t - \tau)$ at $t = \tau$ by assigning to $U(x, \tau)$ the value $U(x, \tau + 0) = 0$]. Therefore, DU and $\partial U/\partial t$ coincide and we have only to compute the ordinary derivatives $\partial^2 U/\partial x^2$, $\partial U/\partial t$ to see that

$$k\frac{\partial^2 U}{\partial x^2} = \frac{\partial U}{\partial t}.$$

It is a simple exercise to derive from this the proof that (13.5) also holds (take values on $\varphi \in \mathscr{D}_-$). We also leave it to the reader to prove the veracity of (13.8).

To prove (13.7), take $\varphi \in \mathscr{D}_-$ and consider

$$\begin{aligned}\lim_{x\to+0} \langle U, \varphi\rangle &= \lim_{x\to+0}\left\langle \frac{H(t-\tau)x}{2\sqrt{k\pi(t-\tau)^3}} e^{-x^2/4k(t-\tau)}, \varphi(t)\right\rangle \\ &= \lim_{x\to+0} \frac{H(t)}{2\sqrt{k\pi}} \int_\tau^{+\infty} \frac{x}{(t-\tau)^{3/2}} e^{-x^2/4k(t-\tau)} \varphi(t)\, dt.\end{aligned}$$

If $\varphi(t) = 0$ for $t \geqslant \tau$, the integral vanishes and we have $\lim \langle U, \varphi\rangle = \varphi(\tau) = 0$, proving (13.7) for all such φ. For those $\varphi \in \mathscr{D}_-$ which are carried in $(-\infty, b]$ with $b > \tau$, further argument is necessary to show that

$$\lim_{x\to+0} \langle U, \varphi\rangle = \varphi(\tau).$$

To begin with, change variables to

$$u = \frac{x}{2\sqrt{k(t-\tau)}},$$

obtaining

$$\lim_{x\to+0}\langle U,\varphi\rangle=\lim_{x\to+0}\frac{2}{\sqrt{\pi}}\int_0^\infty e^{-u^2}\,\varphi\left(\tau+\frac{x^2}{4ku^2}\right)du. \tag{13.16}$$

Calling on the identity

$$\frac{2}{\sqrt{\pi}}\int_0^{+\infty}e^{-u^2}\,du=1, \tag{13.17}$$

we can write

$$\lim_{x\to+0}(\langle U,\varphi\rangle-\varphi(\tau))=\lim_{x\to+0}\frac{2}{\sqrt{\pi}}\int_0^\infty e^{-u^2}\left(\varphi\left(\tau+\frac{x^2}{4ku^2}\right)-\varphi(\tau)\right)du.$$

If we can prove that this limit is zero, we shall have proved (13.17) for the g.f. defined by (13.15). To do this, we begin by noting that $\varphi(t)$ vanishes for $t \geqslant b$ for some $b > \tau$ so that

$$\int_0^\infty e^{-u^2}\,\varphi\left(\tau+\frac{x^2}{4ku^2}\right)du=\int_{\frac{x}{2}\sqrt{\frac{b-\tau}{k}}}^\infty e^{-u^2}\,\varphi\left(\tau+\frac{x^2}{4ku^2}\right)du$$

Making use of the continuity of $\varphi(t)$, we find that to every $\varepsilon > 0$ corresponds $\eta > 0$ such that

$$u>\frac{x}{2\sqrt{k\eta}}\Rightarrow\frac{x}{4ku^2}<\eta\Rightarrow\left|\varphi\left(\tau+\frac{x}{4ku^2}\right)-\varphi(\tau)\right|<\frac{\varepsilon}{2}. \tag{13.18}$$

Therefore, so long as η is chosen to satisfy the above inequality, we have

$$\begin{aligned}
&\frac{2}{\sqrt{\pi}}\int_0^\infty e^{-u^2}\left|\varphi\left(\tau+\frac{x^2}{4ku^2}\right)-\varphi(\tau)\right|du \\
&=\frac{2}{\sqrt{2\pi}}\left(\int_0^{\frac{x}{2\sqrt{k\eta}}}+\int_{\frac{x}{2\sqrt{k\eta}}}^\infty\right)e^{-u^2}\left|\varphi\left(\tau+\frac{x^2}{4ku^2}\right)-\varphi(\tau)\right|du \\
&\leqslant\frac{2}{\sqrt{\pi}}\int_{\frac{x}{2}\sqrt{\frac{b-\tau}{k}}}^{\frac{x}{2\sqrt{k\eta}}}e^{-u^2}\left|\varphi\left(\tau+\frac{x^2}{4ku^2}\right)\right|du \\
&\qquad+\frac{2}{\sqrt{\pi}}\int_0^{\frac{x}{2\sqrt{k\eta}}}e^{-u^2}\,|\varphi(\tau)|\,du+\frac{\varepsilon}{\sqrt{\pi}}\int_{\frac{x}{2\sqrt{k\eta}}}^\infty e^{-u^2}\,du \\
&=A+B+C.
\end{aligned} \tag{13.19}$$

Only the values of $\varphi(t)$ in the interval $[\tau, b]$ arise in the integrands and, $\varphi(t)$ being continuous, there exists

$$M = \max_{\tau \leqslant t \leqslant b} |\varphi(t)|.$$

In A and B, replacement of the integrand by Me^{-u^2} can only increase the values of the integrals. At the same time, replacing the lower limit of C by 0 can only increase that term. These observations and use of (13.17) yield

$$(13.20) \quad |\langle U, \varphi\rangle - \varphi(\tau)| \leqslant A + B + C \leqslant 2M \int_0^{\frac{x}{2\sqrt{k\eta}}} e^{-u^2}\, du + \frac{\varepsilon}{2}$$

$$\leqslant M \frac{x}{\sqrt{k\eta}} + \frac{\varepsilon}{2}.$$

With this, it is now clear that, given any $\varepsilon > 0$, we have but to choose first η in accordance with (13.18) and then x such that $x < \varepsilon\sqrt{k\eta}/2M$ to get

$$(13.21) \qquad |\langle U, \varphi\rangle - \varphi(\tau)| < \frac{\varepsilon}{2} + \frac{\varepsilon}{2} = \varepsilon.$$

This proves that $\lim_{x \to +0} \langle U, \varphi\rangle = \varphi(\tau)$; (13.7) with $\delta(t)$ in place of $F(t)$ is satisfied by U as defined in (13.15).

Concerning the original problem (13.1)–(13.4), it can be shown, for instance, that for any continuous $F \in \mathscr{K}_{++}$

$$(13.22) \qquad U(x, t) = \frac{H(t-\tau)x}{2\sqrt{k\pi}} \int_0^t (t-\tau)^{-3/2} e^{-\frac{x^2}{4k(t-\tau)}} F(\tau)\, d\tau$$

is a solution. We shall not prove it here. Suffice it to point out that most of the argument leading to (13.21) is applicable when $\varphi \in \mathscr{D}_-$ is replaced by a $C(R)$ function of exponential order and that (13.22) defines a $C^\infty(R)$ function of x and of t.

EXERCISES

1. Show that the function $H(t)te^{t^2} \sin e^{t^2}$, which is not of exponential order, has a Laplace transform for $s > 0$.

2. The Laplace transform of $F(t) = e^{-t}H(t)$ converges for $s > -1$. Observe that $\mathscr{L}\{D^{-1}F(t)\}$ converges for $s > 0$ only. (This shows that the hypothesis $s_0 > 0$ in Lemma 1.1 cannot be relaxed except in particular cases.)

3. $F(t) \in \mathscr{K}_{++}(R)$ is of exponential order s_0. Show that $\mathscr{L}\{F\} = f(s) \in C^\infty(s_0, +\infty)$ and that for $n = 1, 2, \ldots$

$$f^{(n)}(s) = \mathscr{L}\{(-t)^n F(t)\} \qquad \text{for } s > s_0.$$

Verify that $\lim_{s \to +\infty} f^{(n)}(s) = 0 \qquad$ for $n = 0, 1, 2, \ldots$.

4. $F(t) \in \mathscr{K}_{++}$ has a Laplace transform $f(s)$ defined for $s > s_0$. Show that $\lim_{s \to +\infty} f(s) = 0$. [Write

$$\mathscr{L}\{F\} = \left(\int_0^a + \int_a^b + \int_b^{+\infty}\right) e^{-st} F(t)\, dt = I_1 + I_2 + I_3,$$

choose a small enough and b large enough to make $|I_1| < \varepsilon/3$, $|I_3| < \varepsilon/3$, then verify that $s \to +\infty \Rightarrow I_2 \to 0$.]

5. Carry out the details of the proof of Lerch's theorem (see Remark, p. 247).

6. $F \in \mathscr{K}_{++}(R)$ is of exponential order $s_0 \in R$. Show that $\mathscr{L}\{e^{at}F(t)\} = f(s - a)$ for $s > a + s_0$. For $h > 0$, show that $\mathscr{L}\{F(t - h)\} = e^{-sh}\mathscr{L}\{F\}$.

7. Carry out the proof of Corollary 5.1.

8. The sequence $\{F_n(t)\} = \{p_n(t) + e^{n^2} p_n(t - n)\}_n$ is fundamental on $\mathscr{D}_-$ and defines $\delta(t) \in \mathscr{D}'_+$. Can it be used directly for the computation of $\mathscr{L}\{\delta\}$?

9. Express $\mathscr{L}\left\{\delta(t) + 2\sum_{n=1}^{\infty} \delta(t - 2nh)\right\}$ as a hyperbolic function ($h > 0$).

10. Express $\mathscr{L}\left\{\delta(t) + 2\sum_{n=1}^{\infty} (-1)^n \delta(t - 2nh)\right\}$ as a hyperbolic function ($h > 0$).

11. Verify that $\dfrac{\partial}{\partial\lambda} \mathscr{L}\{t_+^\lambda\} = \mathscr{L}\left\{\dfrac{\partial t_+^\lambda}{\partial\lambda}\right\}$ for real $\lambda \neq -1, -2, \ldots$ and use this to find $\mathscr{L}\{t_+ \log t\}$.

12. $\log t_+$ is defined in § II.C.1 as the g.f. derivative of a $\mathscr{K}_+$ function. Use Exercise 11 to show that

$$\mathscr{L}\{\log t_+\} = \frac{1}{s}(\Gamma'(1) - \log s).$$

13. The g.f.'s t_+^{-k} ($k = 1, 2, \ldots$) are defined in Exercise II.50. Use Exercise 12 to show that

$$\mathscr{L}\{t_+^{-k-1}\} = -(-1)^k \frac{s^k}{k!}\left(\log s - \Gamma'(1) - \sum_{j=1}^{k} \frac{1}{j}\right).$$

14. $F \in \mathscr{K}_{++}$ is forward periodic [there exists $T > 0$ such that $F(t) = F(t + nT)$ for $t > 0$ and $n = 1, 2, \ldots$] Show that $\mathscr{L}\{F\}$ exists for $s > 0$ and express it in terms of

$\int_0^T e^{-st} F(t)\, dt$.

15. Use the result of Exercise 14 to obtain the answers to Exercises 9 and 10 with the help of relation (6.3).

16. Prove the relation (6.8) (recall Exercise 3).

17. Solve the difference-differential equation I.V. problem

$$\frac{d^2x(t)}{dt^2} + k^2x(t - h) = f(t) \qquad (t > 0)$$

where $h > 0$, $f \in \mathscr{K}_{++}$, and given the initial-value function $\xi(t) = x(t - h)$ for $0 \leqslant t \leqslant h$.

18. Solve the non-linear integral equation

$$x(t) = 2t \cos t + 2 \int_0^t x(t - \tau)\, x(\tau)\, d\tau \qquad (t \geqslant 0).$$

19. Find $X \in \mathscr{D}'_{++}$ of exponential type such that $2t\, D^2X + DX = \delta(t)$.

20. $F(t) \in \mathscr{D}'_+$ is of finite K-order; λ in $F(t + a\lambda)$ is a real parameter, and $a \in R$ is a constant. Show that the parametric derivative $\dfrac{\partial^2 F(t + a\lambda)}{\partial \lambda^2}$ exists and satisfies

$$D^2F(t + a\lambda) = \frac{1}{a^2} \frac{\partial^2 F(t + a\lambda)}{\partial \lambda^2}$$

[*Hint:* For sufficiently large $p \geqslant 0$, $D^{-p}F(t) \in C^2(R)$; also, recall Theorem II.B.7.1.]
(For exercises on the application of the Laplace transform to partial differential equations, see [7] [10] among others.)

CHAPTER VIII

PERIODIC G.F.'S; INTRODUCTION TO FOURIER SERIES

The g.f.'s to be considered here are carried, not in half-lines like those of $\mathscr{D}'_+$, but on the entire axis of reals, R. They are a generalization of ordinary periodic functions and have the attractive property that each one is representable as the sum of its own uniquely associated Fourier series, $\sum_{n=-\infty}^{\infty} c_n e^{in\omega x}$, whose coefficients are explicitly computable.

The resulting theory of generalized Fourier series is due to L. Schwartz [43] [46]. The guidelines for a simpler version were established by G. Temple [51] and further simplified and developed by M. J. Lighthill [34]. This theory is particularly well adapted to the needs of mathematical physics and engineering, and is immeasurably more simple than the modern classical theory of trigonometric series, whose subtleties make it a prime area of hard analysis. The price paid for this simplification is the loss of the concept of the value of a function $f(x)$ at a point $x \in R$—just as in $\mathscr{D}'_+$ only the value $\langle f, \varphi\rangle$ of a functional at a "point" $\varphi(t)$ of a test space of $C^\infty(R)$ functions will be computed. If we agree that physically $\langle f, \varphi\rangle$ is all that nature lets us measure anyway, the price in question does not represent much of a sacrifice —that is, so long as we narrow our interest to the more widely exploitable aspects of mathematics.

All that is intended here is an introductory account of the theory of generalized Fourier series and some hints on its applications. Both in the pattern of unwinding ideas and in the details of the demonstrations, the development is rather close to that of parts A and B of Chapter II. This is taken as justifying some informality in the presentation: here and there a loose description will take the place of a formal definition, or a reference to an analogous argument in Chapter II that of a proof.

1. Preliminaries

A function f on R is said to be *periodic, with period* $2L$, if and only if

(1.1) $$f(x) = f(x + 2L)$$

for all $x \in R$. Clearly then $f(x) = f(x + 2nL)$ for any integer n, whence it follows that there is no loss of generality in always taking $L > 0$.

Outstanding among the functions having period $2L$ are

(1.2) $$\sin n\omega x, \quad \cos n\omega x, \quad e^{in\omega x} \qquad (n \text{ integer}),$$

where, by definition,

(1.3) $$\omega = \frac{2\pi}{2L} = \frac{\pi}{L}.$$

Any piecewise continuous function with period $2L$ is integrable and satisfies for any $a, b \in R$ the easily verified (graphically, or change variable of integration) identities

(1.4) $$\int_a^b f(x)\,dx = \int_{a+2L}^{b+2L} f(x)\,dx, \quad \int_{-L}^{L} f(x)\,dx = \int_{-L+a}^{L+a} f(x)\,dx.$$

Direct integration yields these identities (m, n integers):

$$\frac{1}{L}\int_{-L}^{L} \cos m\omega x \sin n\omega x\,dx = 0,$$

$$\frac{1}{L}\int_{-L}^{L} \cos m\omega x \cos n\omega x\,dx = \begin{cases} 0 & \text{if } m \neq n \\ 2 & \text{if } m = n = 0 \\ 1 & \text{if } m = n \neq 0, \end{cases}$$

$$\frac{1}{L}\int_{-L}^{L} \sin m\omega x \sin n\omega x\,dx = \begin{cases} 0 & \text{if } m \neq n \\ 1 & \text{if } m = n. \end{cases}$$

From these and the Euler identity

(1.6) $$e^{i\theta} = \cos\theta + i\sin\theta$$

one derives (Exercise I.23)

(1.7) $$\frac{1}{2L}\int_{-L}^{L} e^{-im\omega x} e^{in\omega x}\,dx = \begin{cases} 0 & \text{if } m \neq \text{n} \\ 1 & \text{if } m = n. \end{cases}$$

We have need of a basic proposition:

Lemma 1.1. *Let $\varphi(x) \in C^p(R)$ have period $2L$. Then for $q = 1, 2, \ldots, p$ there hold the identities*

(1.8)

$$\frac{1}{2L}\int_{-L}^{L} e^{-in\omega x}\,\varphi(x)\,dx = \frac{1}{(in\omega)^q \cdot 2L}\int_{-L}^{L} e^{-in\omega x}\,\varphi^{(q)}(x)\,dx \quad (\text{integer } n \neq 0)$$

and the inequalities

(1.9) $$\left|\frac{1}{2L}\int_{-L}^{L} e^{-in\omega x}\,\varphi(x)\,dx\right| \leqslant B_q(\varphi)\frac{1}{|n|^q} \quad \text{(integer } n \neq 0\text{)},$$

(1.10) $$\left|\frac{1}{L}\int_{-L}^{L} \begin{Bmatrix}\cos n\omega x\\ \sin n\omega x\end{Bmatrix} \varphi(x)\,dx\right| \leqslant 2B_q(\varphi)\frac{1}{|n|^q} \quad \text{(integer } n \neq 0\text{)},$$

where

(1.11) $$B_q(\varphi) = \frac{1}{\omega^q}\max_{-L\leqslant x\leqslant L} |\varphi^{(q)}(x)|.$$

Proof. Integrate by parts

$$\int_{-L}^{L} e^{-in\omega x}\,\varphi(x)\,dx = \frac{1}{-in\omega}\,e^{-in\omega x}\,\varphi(x)\Big|_{-L}^{L} + \frac{1}{in\omega}\int_{-L}^{L} e^{-in\omega x}\,\varphi'(x)\,dx.$$

since $\varphi(L) = \varphi(-L)$, the integrated term on the right vanishes and we have (1.8) for $q = 1$. Repeated integration by parts gives (1.8) [note that $\varphi^{(j)}(-L) = \varphi^{(j)}(L)$ for $j = 0, 1, 2, \ldots, p$].

From (1.6) follows $|e^{i\theta}| = 1$, so (1.9) derives from (1.8) via the inequality (α.9) of the Appendix to Chapter I. (1.10) is easily obtained from (1.9).

We shall encounter infinite series of the form

(1.11) $$\sum_{n=-\infty}^{\infty} c_n e^{in\omega x};$$

these will be said to be convergent (to $f(x)$) if the partial sums

(1.12) $$S_N(x) = \sum_{n=-N}^{N} c_n e^{in\omega x}$$

converge $\left(\lim\limits_{N\to\infty} S_N(x) = f(x)\right)$. In view of the Cauchy convergence principle for complex numbers, a necessary and sufficient condition for (1.11) to be convergent is that to every $\varepsilon > 0$ correspond an integer N_ε such that

(1.13) $$N, M > N_\varepsilon \Rightarrow |S_N(x) - S_M(x)| < \varepsilon.$$

Remark. In many cases we shall meet with here, it turns out that

$$\sum_{n=1}^{\infty} c_n e^{in\omega x} \quad \text{and} \quad \sum_{n=0}^{-\infty} c_n e^{in\omega x}$$

are each absolutely convergent series. When this happens, the series $\sum_{n=-\infty}^{\infty} c_n e^{in\omega x}$ is *unconditionally convergent*, i.e., however arbitrarily the terms are rearranged or grouped, the resulting series still converges to the same sum. An instance of this convenient situation occurs in

Lemma 1.2. *If for some constant B and an integer* $k \geqslant 2$

$$|c_n| \leqslant B \frac{1}{|n|^k} \qquad (\text{integer } n \neq 0) \tag{1.14}$$

then the series $\sum_{n=-\infty}^{\infty} c_n e^{in\omega x}$ *converges absolutely and uniformly on R. Furthermore, it represents a function* $f(x) \in C^{k-2}(R)$ *with period 2L and there hold the equalities*

$$f^{(q)}(x) = \sum_{n=-\infty}^{\infty} c_n \frac{d^q(e^{in\omega x})}{dx^q} = \sum_{n=-\infty}^{\infty} c_n (in\omega)^q e^{in\omega x} \tag{1.15}$$

with $q = 0, 1, \ldots, k-2$.

Proof. From (1.14) and the fact that $|e^{in\omega x}| = 1$ we get for any integer $n \neq 0$

$$|c_n(in\omega)^q e^{in\omega x}| \leqslant \frac{B\omega^q}{|n|^{k-q}} \leqslant \frac{B\omega^q}{n^2} \qquad \text{if } q \leqslant k-2.$$

Setting

$$A_N^q(x) = \sum_{n=-N}^{N} |c_n(in\omega)^q e^{inx}|$$

it follows that $(M, N \neq 0)$

$$|A_M^q(x) - A_N^q(x)| \leqslant 2B\omega^q \sum_{n=M}^{N} \frac{1}{n^2}.$$

The series $\sum_{n=0}^{\infty} \frac{1}{n^2}$ being convergent, there corresponds to every $\eta > 0$ an integer N_η such that $\sum_{M}^{N} \frac{1}{n^2} < \eta$ whenever $M, N > N_\eta$. Given an arbitrary $\varepsilon > 0$, it then suffices to take $\eta = \varepsilon/2B\omega^q$ to secure

$$M, N > N_\eta \Rightarrow |A_N^q(x) - A_M^q(x)| < \varepsilon. \tag{1.15}$$

Thus the series $\sum_{-\infty}^{\infty} c_n(in\omega)^q e^{inx}$ is absolutely convergent. It is also uniformly convergent since N_η in (1.15) does not depend on the value of x. (All this, of course, is just a repetition of the proof of the Weierstrass M test [1] [6] [11] [19] [49] [55].)

The sum of a uniformly convergent series of continuous functions is continuous, so we may assert that

$$f_q(x) = \sum_{n=-\infty}^{\infty} c_n(in\omega)^q e^{inx} \qquad (0 \leqslant q \leqslant k-2) \tag{1.17}$$

represents a continuous function. That it has period $2L$ is obvious. It follows from a theorem of advanced calculus† that $f_q(x) = \frac{d}{dx} f_{q-1}(x)$, whence (1.15).

2. The Class $\mathscr{P}'_{2L}$ of G.F.'s with Period $2L$

Let $f(x)$ have period $2L$. It then suffices to describe the values of this function in the interval $[-L, L)$ to know it at all $x \in R$. If $f(x)$ is defined at all except possibly a finite number of points $-L \leqslant x_1 < x_2 < \cdots < x_l \leqslant L$, if $f(x)$ is continuous in each of the subintervals remaining in $[-L, L)$ when the $x_j (j = 1, \ldots, l)$ are removed, and if further $f(x_j + 0)$, $f(x_j - 0)$ exist and $f(x_j + 0) \neq f(x_j - 0)$, *the function $f(x)$ will be said to be of class $\mathscr{K}_{2L}(R)$.*

Let $g(x)$ have period $2L$ and be piecewise continuous (i.e., only a finite number of points of discontinuity in $[-L, L)$ and $g(\xi + 0)$, $g(\xi - 0)$ exist at each point ξ of discontinuity). It may have two kinds of points of discontinuity:

(a) points ξ where $g(\xi + 0) \neq g(\xi - 0)$,
(b) points ζ where $g(\zeta + 0) = g(\zeta - 0)$.
With $g(x)$ we then associate the $\mathscr{K}_{2L}(R)$ function

$$f(x) = \begin{cases} g(x) \text{ at every point of continuity of } g \\ \text{undefined at every } \xi \text{ point of } g \\ g(\zeta + 0) \text{ at every } \zeta \text{ point of } g, \end{cases} \tag{2.1}$$

which differs from g at a finite number of points in $[-L, L)$ only. The relationship between g and f is analogous to that considered in Chapter II between a piecewise continuous function carried in a forward half-line $[a, +\infty)$ and its associated $\mathscr{K}_+(R)$ function. As then, so now, we *define the sum* $f_1(x) + f_2(t)$ of two $\mathscr{K}_{2L}$ functions as the $\mathscr{K}_{2L}$ function associated with the (certainly piecewise continuous but possibly not $\mathscr{K}_{2L}$) function $f_1(x) + f_2(x)$. Two $\mathscr{K}_{2L}$ functions are equal if and only if they have the same points of discontinuity and coincide at every point of continuity.

The symbols $\mathscr{P}_{2L}(R)$, or $\mathscr{P}_{2L}$, designate the collection of functions $\varphi \in C^\infty(R)$ that have period $2L$. This is the collection of what we shall call *test functions* because their role in the present situation is like that of the $\mathscr{D}_-$ functions in $\mathscr{D}'_+$ theory.

---

† Let $\lim_{N\to\infty} f'_N(x)$ converge uniformly on $[a, b]$, where the $f'_N(x) = df_N(x)/dx$ are continuous. Let $\lim_{N\to\infty} f_N(x)$ exist for some $x_0 \in [a, b]$. Then on $[a, b]$

$$\frac{d}{dx}\left(\lim_{N\to\infty} f_N(x)\right) = \lim_{N\to\infty} f'_N(x).$$

Examples of $\mathscr{P}_{2L}$ functions are those listed in (1.2) above. Another—very useful—member of this class is

(2.2) $$\mathring{\rho}_\varepsilon(x) = \sum_{n=-\infty}^{\infty} \rho_\varepsilon(x - 2nL),$$

where $\varepsilon < L$ and $\rho_\varepsilon(x)$ is the function of x corresponding to that defined in (I.2.11). The series in (2.2) converges at every $x \in R$ since the carriers of the functions on the right do not overlap.

The graph of $\mathring{\rho}_\varepsilon(x)$ is shown in Figure 19.

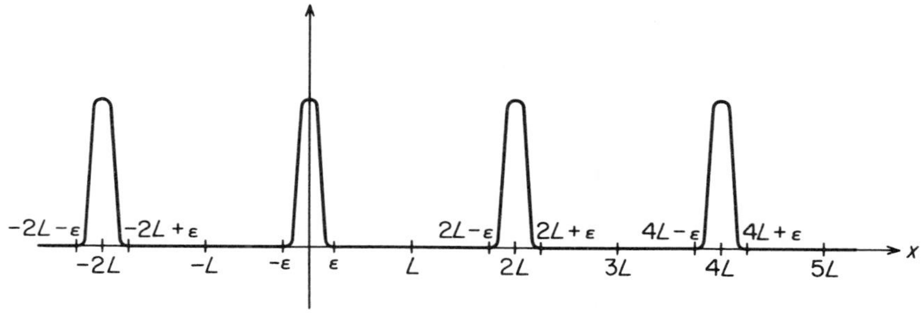

FIGURE 19

Every $\mathscr{K}_{2L}$ function determines an algebraically linear functional on $\mathscr{P}_{2L}$ whose value is

(2.3) $$\langle f, \varphi \rangle = \int_{-L}^{L} f(x)\, \varphi(x)\, dx.$$

[Note that, in view of the right-hand relation in (1.4), the integration in (2.3) does not have to be taken over the interval $[-L, L]$, any other interval of length $2L$ will do as well since $f(x)\,\varphi(x)$ has period $2L$.]

All the elements for a close duplication of the procedure of Chapter II are at hand. *A sequence* $\{f_n(x)\}$ of $\mathscr{K}_{2L}$ functions will be called *fundamental* (*on* $\mathscr{P}_{2L}$)† if and only if $\lim_{n\to\infty} \langle f_n, \varphi \rangle$ exists for every $\varphi \in \mathscr{P}_{2L}$. The functional F on $\mathscr{P}_{2L}$ whose values are computed as

(2.4) $$\langle F(x), \varphi(x) \rangle = \lim_{n\to\infty} \langle f_n(x), \varphi(x) \rangle$$

will be called a g.f. of period $2L$, and the set of these functionals we shall call $\mathscr{P}'_{2L}$. Since

$$f_n(x) = f_n(x + 2L) \qquad (n = 1, 2, \ldots)$$

† Throughout this chapter fundamental sequences are fundamental in this sense. We shall therefore, not always state explicitly the qualifier "on $\mathscr{P}_{2L}$" in the following pages.

we get

$$\langle f_n(x), \varphi(x)\rangle = \langle f_n(x + 2L), \varphi(x)\rangle \qquad (n = 1, 2, \ldots),$$

and with (2.4) this gives, for every $F \in \mathscr{P}_{2L}$,

$$\langle F(x), \varphi(x)\rangle = \langle F(x + 2L), \varphi(x)\rangle. \tag{2.5}$$

Consequently, the functional $F(x) \in \mathscr{P}'_{2L}$ has the property

$$F(x) = F(x + 2L), \tag{2.6}$$

which justifies calling it a g.f. with period $2L$. Two fundamental sequences are equivalent (on $\mathscr{P}_{2L}$) (write $\{f_n\} \sim \{g_n\}$) if and only if

$$\lim_{n\to\infty} \langle f_n, \varphi\rangle = \lim_{n\to\infty} \langle g_n, \varphi\rangle$$

for every $\varphi \in \mathscr{P}_{2L}$, and every $F \in \mathscr{P}'_{2L}$ *is characterized by an equivalence (in the* $\mathscr{P}'_{2L}$ *sense) class* of fundamental sequences; this class we designate by the same symbol, F.

A $\mathscr{K}_{2L}$ function $F(x)$ can be identified with the g.f. F that it defines via (2.4), and we usually do so. It is in this sense (of a one-to-one correspondence between $\mathscr{K}_{2L}$ and a subset of $\mathscr{P}'_{2L}$) that $\mathscr{K}_{2L}$ is often called a subset of $\mathscr{P}'_{2L}$. The justification for this identification of functions and functionals is:

Theorem 2.1. *Two* $\mathscr{K}_{2L}$ *functions* $F(x)$, $G(x)$ *are equal if and only if, for every* $\varphi \in \mathscr{P}_{2L}$,

$$\langle F, \varphi\rangle = \langle G, \varphi\rangle. \tag{2.7}$$

This is a close analog of Theorem II.A.7.1 and is proved in quite the same way [by using a translation $\mathring{\rho}_\varepsilon(x - \xi)$ of the function defined in (2.2) to discriminate between the functions F and G when they differ at a point of continuity]. The reader is advised to carry out the details.

It should be realized that all this theorem does is to guarantee that one $\mathscr{K}_{2L}$ function F can be distinguished from another by means of its functional values $\langle F, \varphi\rangle$ on the test functions. It does not enable us to compute function values $F(x)$ at the points of R (for that, it is necessary to use certain expressions of the form $\lim_{n\to\infty} \langle F, \varphi_n\rangle$), nor does it enable us to tell from the set of values $\langle F, \varphi\rangle$ whether or not F belongs to the subset $\mathscr{K}_{2L}$ of $\mathscr{P}'_{2L}$.

Example. *The g.f.* $\delta_{2L}(x) \in \mathscr{P}'_{2L}$.

An important g.f. of period $2L$ is obtained from the periodic extension

$$\mathring{p}_n(x) = \sum_{k=-\infty}^{\infty} p_n(x - 2kL) \tag{2.8}$$

of the rectangular pulse functions defined in (II.A.2.1). The graph of this function for an integer $n > 1/L$ is shown in Figure 20.

We have no trouble seeing that

$$\lim_{n\to\infty} \langle \mathring{p}_n(x), \varphi(x)\rangle = \varphi(0),$$

so $\{\mathring{p}_n\}$ is a fundamental sequence. It defines a periodic g.f. that will henceforth be designated as $\delta_{2L}(x)$.†

One is tempted to write

$$\delta_{2L}(x) = \sum_{k=-\infty}^{\infty} \delta(x - kL), \tag{2.9}$$

and can do so, providing both sides of the relation are understood to be functionals

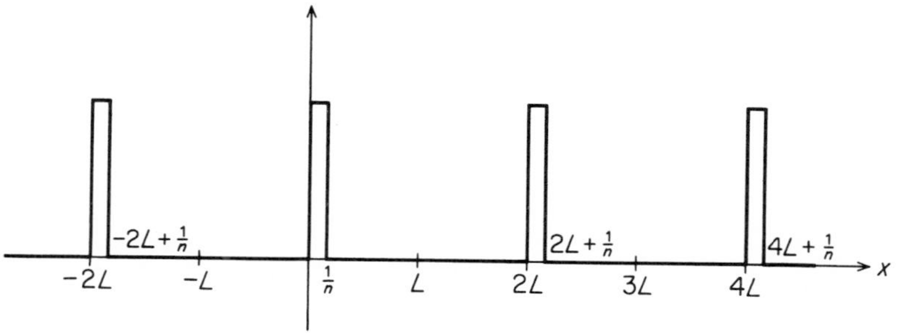

FIGURE 20

on $\mathscr{D}$ [the set of $C^\infty(R)$ functions carried in finite intervals (Exercises I.8 and II.6), not $\mathscr{D}_-$, $\mathscr{P}_{2L}$, nor $\mathscr{D}_+$]. In that case,

$$\langle \delta_{2L}(x), \varphi(x)\rangle = \sum_{k=-\infty}^{\infty} \varphi(kL),$$

which is finite because $\varphi(x)$ vanishes outside some finite interval $[a, b]$. Thus (2.9) is an equality between g.f's of class $\mathscr{D}'$, not one between g.f.'s of class $\mathscr{P}'_{2L}$.

3. The Basic Operations in $\mathscr{P}'_{2L}$.

Let $F(x) \in \mathscr{K}_{2L}$, $\varphi(x) \in \mathscr{P}_{2L}$, $L > 0$. Then (changing variables from x to $u = x - h$)

$$\langle F(x - h), \varphi(x)\rangle = \int_{-L}^{L} F(x - h)\, \varphi(x)\, dx = \int_{-L-h}^{L-h} F(u)\, \varphi(u + h)\, dh.$$

† The g.f. $\delta(x)$, determined by the sequence $\{p_n(x)\}$ defined in (II.A.2.1) is not a functional on $\mathscr{P}_{2L}$ since the members of a fundamental (on $\mathscr{P}_{2L}$) sequence have to be *periodic* with period $2L$.

Applying (1.4) and replacing u by x:

$$\int_{-L-h}^{-L-h} F(u)\,\varphi(u+h)\,du = \int_{-L}^{L} F(u)\,\varphi(u+h)\,du = \int_{-L}^{L} F(x)\,\varphi(x+h)\,dx.$$

In conclusion then

$$\langle F(x-h), \varphi(x)\rangle = \langle F(x), \varphi(x+h)\rangle \qquad (F \in \mathscr{K}_{2L}). \tag{3.1}$$

Definition 3.1. *Let $F_1(x)$, $F_2(x) \in \mathscr{P}'_{2L}$ with $\{f_n\} \in F$, $\{g_n\} \in G$. Let $h \in R$; $c_1, c_2 \in C$; $\alpha(x) \in \mathscr{P}_{2L}$. Then*

(a) *$(c_1F_1 + c_2F_2) \in \mathscr{P}'_{2L}$ is the g.f. defined by $\{c_1 f_n + c_2 g_n\}$,*
(b) *$F(x-h) \in \mathscr{P}'_{2L}$ is the g.f. defined by $\{f_n(x-h)\}$,*
(c) *$(\alpha(x)F(x)) \in \mathscr{P}'_{2L}$ is the g.f. defined by $\{\alpha(x)f_n(x)\}$.*

Theorem 3.1. *For every $\varphi(x) \in \mathscr{P}_{2L}$ and $F_1, F_2 \in \mathscr{P}'_{2L}$; $h \in R$; $c_1, c_2 \in C$; $\alpha(x) \in \mathscr{P}_{2L}$, there hold the identities*

$$\langle c_1F_1 + c_2F_2, \varphi\rangle = c_1\langle F_1, \varphi\rangle + c_2\langle F_2, \varphi\rangle, \tag{3.2}$$

$$\langle F(x-h), \varphi(x)\rangle = \langle F(x), \varphi(x+h)\rangle, \tag{3.3}$$

$$\langle \alpha(x)F(x), \varphi(x)\rangle = \langle F(x), \alpha(x)\varphi(x)\rangle. \tag{3.4}$$

To prove the consistency of the definition and the theorem, follow the ideas of § II.A.5.

Definition 3.2. *The g.f. derivative DF of $F \in \mathscr{P}'_{2L}$ is the functional DF on $\mathscr{P}_{2L}$ whose values are given by*

$$\langle DF, \varphi\rangle = (-1)\langle F, \varphi'\rangle. \tag{3.5}$$

Theorem 3.2. *For every $F \in \mathscr{P}'_{2L}$, $DF \in \mathscr{P}'_{2L}$.*

Proof. Left as an exercise. It follows the lines of the proof of Theorem II.A.6.1.

Corollary. *Every $F \in \mathscr{P}'_{2L}$ has derivatives of every nonnegative integer order p and they are all $\mathscr{P}'_{2L}$ g.f.'s satisfying*

$$\langle D^pF, \varphi\rangle = (-1)^p\langle F, \varphi^{(p)}\rangle. \tag{3.6}$$

Examples.

(1) $\langle D^p\delta_{2L}, \varphi\rangle = (-1)^p\langle \delta_{2L}, \varphi^{(p)}\rangle = (-1)^p\varphi^{(p)}(0)$.

(2) If $F(x)$ of period $2L$ is differentiable in the ordinary sense, DF and $dF(x)/dx$ are identical if $dF(x)/dx \in \mathscr{K}_{2L}$. For instance, the function $1[F(x) = 1, x \in R]$ has both ordinary and g.f. derivative $D1 = 0$.

4. Relation between Ordinary and G.F. Derivatives in $\mathscr{K}_{2L}(R)$

The formal definition of the class $\mathscr{K}^p_{2L}$ of functions with period $2L$ and with ordinary derivatives of orders up to p, all of them $\mathscr{K}_{2L}$ functions, resembles Definition II.B.1.1 (with periodicity added) enough to avoid the need for setting it out here.

With it, we get the $\mathscr{P}'_{2L}$ correspondent to Theorem II.B.1.1:

Theorem 4.1. *Let $f(x) \in \mathscr{K}^1_{2L}$ and let $[Df]$ be the $\mathscr{P}'_{2L}$ g.f. defined by the $\mathscr{K}_{2L}$ function $f'(x) = df(x)/dx$. Let the points of discontinuity of $f(x)$ in the open interval $(-L, L)$ be*

$$-L < x_1 < x_2 < \cdots < x_l < L.$$

Then the g.f. derivative Df, $[Df]$, and the jumps of $f(x)$ are related by

$$Df = [Df] + [f(-L+0) - f(L-0)]\delta_{2L}(x+L) + \sum_{j=1}^{l}(f(x_j+0) - f(x_j-0))\delta_{2L}(x-x_j). \tag{4.1}$$

Proof. It suffices to consider the particular case $l = 1$ to make the general one apparent. Then for any test function

$$\langle Df(x), \varphi(x)\rangle = (-1)\langle f(x), \varphi'(x)\rangle = (-1)\left\{\int_{-L}^{x_1} f(x)\,\varphi'(x)\,dx + \int_{x_1}^{L} f(x)\,\varphi'(x)\,dx\right\}.$$

Computing each of the integrals on the right by parts:

$$\begin{aligned}\langle Df, \varphi\rangle &= (-1)\Big\{f(x_1-0)\varphi(x_1) - f(-L+0)\varphi(-L) - \int_{-L}^{x_1} f'(x)\,\varphi(x)\,dx \\ &\qquad + f(L-0)\varphi(L) - f(x_1+0)\varphi(x_1) - \int_{x_1}^{L} f'(x)\,\varphi(x)\,dx\Big\} \\ &= (-1)\Big\{(f(L-0)\varphi(L) - f(-L+0)\varphi(-L)) \\ &\qquad + (f(x_1-0) - f(x_1+0))\varphi(x_1) - \int_{-L}^{L} f'(x)\,\varphi(x)\,dx\Big\}.\end{aligned}$$

As this holds true for all $\varphi \in \mathscr{P}_{2L}$, it is the expression of the g.f. equality

$$Df = [Df] + f(-L+0)\,\delta_{2L}(x+L) - f(L-0)\,\delta_{2L}(x-L) + (f(x_1+0) - f(x_1-0))\,\delta_{2L}(x-x_1). \tag{4.2}$$

From this, on observing that $\delta_{2L}(x - L) = \delta_{2L}(x + L)$, there follows (4.1). The proof for $l = 1$ is complete.

Note that because of periodicity $f(L - 0) = f(-L - 0)$ so that the coefficient of $\delta_{2L}(x + L)$ in (4.1) represents the jump of the function $f(x)$ at the point $x = -L$.

Example 1

$$f(x) = \begin{cases} -1 & \text{if } -L < x < 0 \\ +1 & \text{if } 0 < x < L \end{cases}, \qquad f(x) = f(x + 2L).$$

The graph is shown in Figure 21.

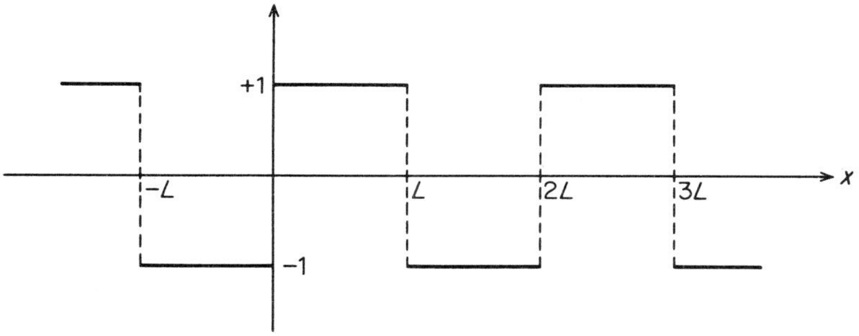

FIGURE 21

$f'(x)$ exists for $x \neq kL$ (k integer) and $f'(x) = 0$ there. Applying (4.1) then gives

$$Df = -2\delta_{2L}(x + L) + 2\delta_{2L}(x). \tag{4.3}$$

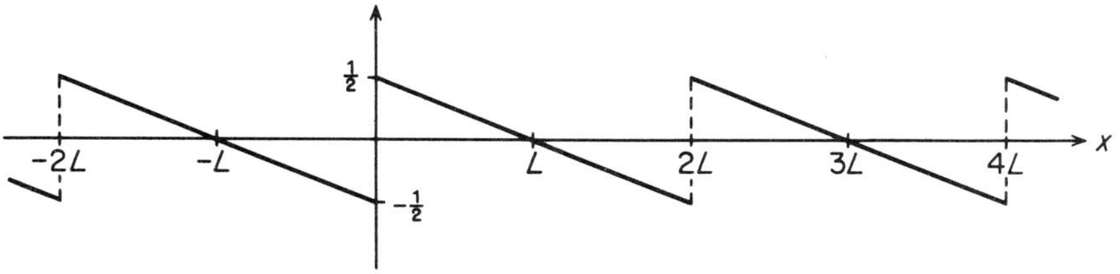

FIGURE 22

Example 2. Let $f(x)$ be the periodic sawtooth function depicted in Figure 22:

$$f(x) = \begin{cases} -\dfrac{1}{2} - \dfrac{x}{2L} & \text{if } -L < x < 0 \\[2ex] \dfrac{1}{2} - \dfrac{x}{2L} & \text{if } 0 < x < L. \end{cases}$$

This has $f'(x) = -1/2L$ except at $x = 2kL$ (k integer) where $f(x)$ has the jump $+1$. Consequently

$$Df = -\frac{1}{2L} + \delta_{2L}(x). \tag{4.4}$$

There is a $\mathscr{P}'_{2L}$ analog to Corollary II.B.1.1. Its form is obvious enough at this point so that we need not bother formally consigning it on paper.

5. Convergence in $\mathscr{P}'_{2L}$. Parametric Derivatives and Integrals

If $F \in \mathscr{P}'_{2L}$ and every member of the sequence $\{F_n\}$ is a $\mathscr{P}'_{2L}$ g.f., we shall say that $\{F_n\}$ converges to F in $\mathscr{P}'_{2L}$ and write

$$\operatorname*{Lim}_{n\to\infty} F_n = F \tag{5.1}$$

if and only if, for every $\varphi \in \mathscr{P}_{2L}$,

$$\lim_{n\to\infty} \langle F_n, \varphi\rangle = \langle F, \varphi\rangle. \tag{5.2}$$

Just as in $\mathscr{D}'_+$, (5.1) automatically entails

$$\operatorname*{Lim}_{n\to\infty} D^p F_n = D^p F \qquad (\text{integer } p > 0). \tag{5.3}$$

Convergence of infinite series, parametric derivatives, and integrals of parametric g.f.'s in $\mathscr{P}'_{2L}$ are defined as one would expect from the discussion of the $\mathscr{D}'_+$ case given in Chapter II. There is, therefore, no point in taking up the space to belabor the matter any further here.

6. The Fourier Series for $\delta_{2L}(x - \xi)$

The g.f. associated with the function

$$S_N(x - \xi) = \frac{1}{2L} \sum_{n=-N}^{N} e^{in\omega(x-\xi)} \tag{6.1}$$

has on $\psi(\xi) \in \mathscr{P}_{2L}$ the value

$$\langle S_N(x - \xi), \psi(\xi)\rangle = \sum_{n=N}^{N} c_n e^{in\omega x}, \tag{6.2}$$

where

$$c_n = \frac{1}{2L} \int_{-L}^{L} e^{-in\omega\xi} \psi(\xi)\, d\xi, \tag{6.3}$$

$$|c_n| \leqslant B_2(\psi) \frac{1}{n^2} \qquad (n \neq 0); \tag{6.4}$$

this last by Lemma 1.1. Calling on Lemma 1.2 (with $k \geqslant 2$), we find that $\lim_{N\to\infty} \langle S_N(x-\xi), \psi(\xi)\rangle$ exists and so determines a g.f. of class $\mathscr{P}'_{2L}$, which we denote by $S(x-\xi)$, and whose values are

$$\langle S(x-\xi), \psi(\xi)\rangle = \lim_{N\to\infty} \langle S_N(x-\xi), \psi(\xi)\rangle. \tag{6.5}$$

In other words, the sequence $\{S_N(x-\xi)\}_N$ of functions of ξ is a fundamental sequence.

Let us now seek a means of evaluating $\langle S(x-\xi), \varphi(\xi)\rangle$ for any $\varphi(\xi) \in \mathscr{P}_{2L}(R)$, directly, without going through a term-by-term evaluation and summation, as would be required by the expression in the right in (6.5). A truly delightful way of solving this problem was given by L. Schwartz [46], and is followed here.

First, observe that

$$e^{i\omega(x-\xi)}S(x-\xi) = S(x-\xi),^{\dagger} \tag{6.6}$$

whence

$$(e^{i\omega(x-\xi)} - 1)S(x-\xi) = 0.$$

That is, for every $\psi(\xi) \in \mathscr{P}_{2L}$

$$\langle (e^{i\omega(x-\xi)} - 1)S(x-\xi), \psi(\xi)\rangle = \langle S(x-\xi), (e^{i\omega(x-\xi)} - 1)\psi(\xi)\rangle = 0. \tag{6.6$'$}$$

The function

$$\alpha(\xi) = e^{i\omega(x-\xi)} - 1$$

is a $\mathscr{P}_{2L}$ function of ξ whose only zero in $[-L, L)$ is x and that is a simple zero $[\alpha'(x) \neq 0]$. At this point, we stop for the following

Lemma 6.1. *Let $\alpha(\xi) \in \mathscr{P}_{2L}$ have only one zero, x, in $[-L, L]$ and that a simple zero. Then every $\gamma(\xi) \in \mathscr{P}_{2L}$ for which $\gamma(x) = 0$ may be written in the form*

$$\gamma(\xi) = \alpha(\xi)\,\psi(\xi) \tag{6.7}$$

with $\psi(\xi) \in \mathscr{P}_{2L}$.

---

† $$|\langle e^{i\omega(x-\xi)}S_N(x-\xi), \psi(\xi)\rangle - \langle S_N(x-\xi), \psi(\xi)\rangle|$$
$$= \frac{1}{2L}\left|\int_{-L}^{L} (e^{-i\omega N(x-\xi)} + e^{i\omega(N+1)(x-\xi)})\,\psi(\xi)\,d\xi\right|$$
$$\leqslant B_2(\psi)\,\frac{2}{N^2}$$

by Lemma 1.1. It follows that the fundamental sequences $\{e^{i\omega(x-\xi)}S_N(x-\xi)\}$ and $S_N(x-\xi)\}$ are equivalent, i.e., the g.f. equality (6.6) holds.

Exercise I.6 easily yields these facts:

$$\alpha(\xi) = (\xi - x)\alpha_1(\xi), \qquad \alpha_1(\xi) \in \mathscr{P}_{2L}, \tag{6.8}$$

$$\gamma(\xi) = (\xi - x)\gamma_1(\xi), \qquad \gamma_1(\xi) \in \mathscr{P}_{2L}. \tag{6.9}$$

Consider the function $\gamma(\xi)/\alpha(\xi)$. It is C^∞ for $\xi \neq x$. Also, substituting from (6.8) and (6.9), the factors $(\xi - x)$ cancel out when $x \neq \xi$ so

$$\frac{\gamma(\xi)}{\alpha(\xi)} = \frac{\gamma_1(\xi)}{\alpha_1(\xi)} \qquad \text{for } x \neq \xi.$$

When $\xi \to x$, $\alpha_1(\xi) \to \alpha'(x)$ in view of (6.8). Since $\alpha'(x) \neq 0$ (because x is by hypothesis a simple zero) we see that $\gamma_1(\xi)/\alpha_1(\xi)$ is continuous at $x = \xi$. In fact, $\gamma_1(\xi)/\alpha_1(\xi)$ is a C^∞ function at x because γ_1 and α_1 are.

The function $\psi(\xi)$ defined by

$$\psi(\xi) = \begin{cases} \dfrac{\gamma(\xi)}{\alpha(\xi)} & \text{if } \xi \neq x \\[2ex] \dfrac{\gamma_1(x)}{\alpha_1(x)} & \text{if } \xi = x \end{cases} \tag{6.10}$$

which clearly has period $2L$ is therefore $\mathscr{P}_{2L}$.

We may now write

$$\gamma(\xi) = \alpha(\xi)\,\psi(\xi)$$

because this is a trivial identity for $x \neq \xi$, and because $\gamma(x) = \alpha(x) = 0$.

Returning to the g.f. $S(x - \xi)$, we observe that any $\varphi(\xi) \in \mathscr{P}_{2L}$ can be written in the form

$$\varphi(\xi) = \varphi(x) + (\varphi(\xi) - \varphi(x)).$$

Applying the previous lemma with $\alpha(\xi) = 1 - e^{i\omega(x-\xi)}$ to the function $\gamma(\xi) = \varphi(\xi) - \varphi(x)$, we see that there exists a $\mathscr{P}_{2L}$ function $\psi(\xi)$, such that

$$\varphi(\xi) = \varphi(x) + (e^{i\omega(x-\xi)} - 1)\,\psi(\xi). \tag{6.11}$$

Referring to the right-hand equality in (6.6), we obtain for the value of $S(x - \xi)$ at any $\varphi(\xi) \in \mathscr{P}_{2L}$

$$\langle S(x - \xi), \varphi(\xi)\rangle = \varphi(x)\langle S(x - \xi), 1\rangle. \tag{6.12}$$

[We have used here the fact that the function with constant value $\varphi(x)$ equals $\varphi(x) \cdot 1$ where 1 is the function of ξ with constant value 1.]

This proves that

$$S(x - \xi) = k\delta_{2L}(x - \xi) \tag{6.13}$$

where

$$k = \langle S(x - \xi), 1\rangle$$

From (6.2) (6.5) and applying (1.7)

$$k = \lim_{N\to\infty} \sum_{n=-N}^{N} \frac{1}{2L}\int_{-L}^{L} e^{in\omega(x-\xi)}\, d\xi = 1.$$

This remarkable result is part of

Theorem 6.1. *$\delta_{2L}(x - \xi)$ is represented by a complex Fourier series,*

$$\delta_{2L}(x - \xi) = \frac{1}{2L}\sum_{n=-\infty}^{\infty} e^{in\omega(x-\xi)}, \tag{6.14}$$

as well as by a real Fourier series,

$$\delta_{2L}(x - \xi) = \frac{1}{2L} + \frac{1}{L}\sum_{n=1}^{\infty} \cos n\omega(x - \xi). \tag{6.15}$$

These series converge unconditionally in $\mathscr{P}'_{2L}$.

Proof. (6.14) has just been proved. In the course of its proof, in connection with inequality (6.4) and the relation (6.5), we employed Lemma 1.2. This ensures the absolute convergence of the series

$$\frac{1}{2L}\sum_{-\infty}^{\infty} \langle e^{in\omega(x-\xi)}, \varphi(\xi)\rangle \qquad \text{when } \varphi \in \mathscr{P}_{2L}.$$

In an absolutely convergent series of complex numbers, the terms may be rearranged and grouped at will without altering the sum, a property which is called *unconditional convergence.* Since this holds for every $\varphi \in \mathscr{P}_{2L}$ we can assert that the g.f. series $\frac{1}{2L}\sum_{-\infty}^{\infty} e^{in\omega(x-\xi)}$ is unconditionally convergent (in the $\mathscr{P}'_{2L}$ g.f. convergence sense).

That being so, we may group the terms on the right in (6.14) by pairs [the nth with the $(-n)$th] without changing the sum; this gives (6.15).

Rephrased in terms of g.f. values on $\varphi \in \mathscr{P}_{2L}$, these conclusions take the following form:

Theorem 6.2. *$\varphi(x) \in \mathscr{P}_{2L}$ is represented by its complex Fourier series,*

$$\varphi(x) = \sum_{n=-\infty}^{\infty} c_n e^{in\omega x}, \tag{6.16}$$

with the Fourier coefficients

$$c_n = \frac{1}{2L}\langle \varphi(\xi), e^{-in\omega\xi}\rangle \qquad (\textit{all integer } n). \tag{6.17}$$

This same function is also represented by its real† *Fourier series,*

(6.18) $$\varphi(x) = \frac{a_0}{2} + \sum_{n=1}^{\infty} (a_n \cos n\omega x + b_n \sin n\omega x),$$

with the Fourier sine and cosine coefficients

(6.19) $$a_n = \frac{1}{L} \langle \varphi(\xi), \cos n\omega\xi \rangle, \; b_n = \frac{1}{L} \langle \varphi(\xi), \sin n\omega\xi \rangle$$

for $n = 0, 1, 2, \ldots.$
To every integer k corresponds $B_k(\varphi) < \infty$ *such that*

(6.20) $$|c_n| \leqslant \frac{B_k(\varphi)}{|n|^k} \qquad (\text{integer } n \neq 0),$$

(6.21) $$|a_n| \leqslant \frac{2B_k(\varphi)}{n^k}, \quad |b_n| \leqslant \frac{2B_k(\varphi)}{n^k} \qquad (n = 1, 2, \ldots),$$

and termwise differentiation of arbitrary order p ($= 0, 1, 2, \ldots$) *produces the Fourier series of* $\varphi^{(p)}(x)$ *which converges uniformly to* $\varphi^{(p)}(x)$.

Proof. Some elementary manipulations combined with Lemmas 1.1 and 1.2 [$\varphi \in C^\infty(R)$, remember] yield the proof without any difficulty.

7. Fourier Series of $\mathscr{P}'_{2L}$ G.F.'s

The representations (6.16) (6.18) with coefficients (6.17) and (6.19), respectively, are valid under considerably broader conditions, namely when φ is simply a g.f. of class $\mathscr{P}'_{2L}$. Of course, convergence is then g.f. ($\mathscr{P}'_{2L}$) convergence; but still unconditional, as in Theorem 6.1, insofar as terms in the series may be rearranged and grouped at will.

Theorem 7.1. *Any series* $\sum_{n=-\infty}^{\infty} c_n e^{in\omega x}$ *for which there exists a finite constant M and a positive integer r such that*

(7.1) $$|c_n| \leqslant M\,|n|^r \qquad (\textit{all integer } n \neq 0)$$

converges unconditionally in $\mathscr{P}'_{2L}$ *and defines a* $\mathscr{P}'_{2L}$ *g.f.*

Proof. Let $\varphi \in \mathscr{P}_{2L}$. Since $\varphi \in C^\infty(R)$, we can apply Lemma 1.1 with any positive integer p. Taking $q = p = r + 2$ gives

$$|\langle e^{in\omega x}, \varphi(x)\rangle| \leqslant LB_{r+2}(\varphi)\frac{1}{|n|^{r+2}}$$

† When φ is real-valued, every individual term of the series (6.18) is real-valued.

and so

$$\sum_{n=-\infty}^{\infty} |\langle c_n e^{in\omega x}, \varphi(x)\rangle| \leqslant |c_0| + 2LB_{r+2}(\varphi) \sum_{n=1}^{\infty} \frac{1}{n^2}.$$

Thus $\sum_{-\infty}^{\infty} \langle c_n e^{in\omega x}, \varphi(x)\rangle$ is absolutely convergent and its terms may be rearranged and grouped at will without changing the sum. Since

$$\sum_{n=-N}^{N} c_n e^{inx} = f_N(x) \in \mathscr{K}_{2L}$$

the sequence $\{f_N(x)\}$ is fundamental on $\mathscr{P}_{2L}$ and so defines an element of $\mathscr{P}'_{2L}$.

If condition (7.1) is not realized the series does not converge in $\mathscr{P}'_{2L}$: one can construct a $\varphi \in \mathscr{P}_{2L}$ such that

$$\lim_{N\to\infty} \sum_{n=-N}^{N} \langle c_n e^{in\omega x}, \varphi(x)\rangle = \infty$$

(Exercise 6.) This indicates that only those $F \in \mathscr{P}'_{2L}$ for which the Fourier coefficients

$$c_n = \frac{1}{2L} \langle F(x), e^{-in\omega x}\rangle$$

satisfy (7.1) can we hope to represent by their Fourier series.

The next result is both easy to prove and of fundamental importance:

Theorem 7.2. *Every $F \in \mathscr{P}'_{2L}$ which is of the form*

$$F = D^{p_1}G_1 + D^{p_2}G_2 + \cdots + D^{p_k}G_k, \tag{7.2}$$

where $G_1, G_2, \ldots, G_k \in \mathscr{K}_{2L}(R)$ and $p_1, p_2, \ldots, p_k$ are nonnegative integers, is represented by its complex Fourier series,

$$F(x) = \sum_{n=-\infty}^{\infty} c_n e^{in\omega x}, \tag{7.3}$$

where

$$c_n = \frac{1}{2L} \langle F(\xi), e^{-in\omega\xi}\rangle \qquad (\textit{integer } n). \tag{7.4}$$

The convergence in (7.3) *is unconditional in $\mathscr{P}'_{2L}$ and the coefficients satisfy* (7.1) *with* $r = \max(p_1, p_2, \ldots, p_k)$.

Proof. It suffices to prove the theorem for

$$F = D^pG \qquad (\text{integer } p \geqslant 0,\ G \in \mathscr{K}_{2L}). \tag{7.5}$$

Simple addition then gives the result when $k > 1$ in (7.2).

Let $\varphi \in \mathscr{P}_{2L}$. By Theorem 6.2

$$\varphi^{(p)}(x) = \sum_{n=-\infty}^{\infty} (in\omega)^p d_n e^{in\omega x} = \frac{1}{2L} \sum_{-\infty}^{\infty} \langle \varphi(\xi), e^{-in\omega\xi} \rangle (in\omega)^p e^{in\omega x} \tag{7.6}$$

where, thanks to (6.20) with $k = p + 2$,

$$|d_n(in\omega)^p| \leqslant \frac{B_{p+2}(\varphi)}{n^2}\omega^p \quad \text{(integer } n \neq 0). \tag{7.7}$$

From (7.5), we obtain

$$\begin{aligned} \langle F, \varphi \rangle = (-1)^p \langle G, \varphi^{(p)} \rangle &= (-1)^p \left\langle G, \sum_{n=-N}^{N} (in\omega)^p \, d_n e^{in\omega x} \right\rangle \\ &+ (-1)^p \left\langle G, \left(\sum_{n=N}^{+\infty} + \sum_{-\infty}^{n=-N} \right) d_n (in\omega)^p e^{in\omega x} \right\rangle \\ &= (-1)^p \langle G, S_N^{(p)} \rangle + (-1)^p \langle G, R_N^{(p)} \rangle. \end{aligned} \tag{7.8}$$

The modulus of the $\mathscr{K}_{2L}$ function G is bounded by some $M < \infty$ on $[-L, L)$ so (7.6) gives

$$|\langle G, R_N^{(p)} \rangle| \leqslant 2MB_{p+2}(\varphi)\omega^p \sum_{n=N+1}^{\infty} \frac{1}{n^2},$$

which, with (7.8), shows that

$$\langle F, \varphi \rangle = (-1)^p \lim_{N \to \infty} \langle G, S_N^{(p)} \rangle;$$

whence the relation

$$\langle F, \varphi \rangle = \lim_{N \to \infty} \langle F, S_N \rangle,$$

or, more explicitly,

$$\langle F, \varphi \rangle = \lim_{N \to \infty} \frac{1}{2L} \sum_{n=-N}^{N} \langle \varphi(\xi), e^{-in\omega\xi} \rangle \langle F(x), e^{in\omega x} \rangle.$$

This can also be written as

$$\langle F, \varphi \rangle = \lim_{N \to \infty} \left\langle \left(\frac{1}{2L} \sum_{n=-N}^{N} \langle F(x), e^{in\omega x} \rangle e^{-in\omega\xi} \right), \varphi(\xi) \right\rangle,$$

or, on noting that $\langle F(x), e^{in\omega x} \rangle = \langle F(\xi), e^{in\omega\xi} \rangle$ and that $\langle e^{-in\omega\xi}, \varphi(\xi) \rangle = \langle e^{-in\omega x}, \varphi(x) \rangle$,

$$\langle F, \varphi \rangle = \lim_{N \to \infty} \left\langle \left(\frac{1}{2L} \sum_{n=+N}^{-N} \langle F(\xi), e^{-in\omega\xi} \rangle e^{in\omega x} \right), \varphi(x) \right\rangle.$$

This proves that

$$F(x) = \operatorname*{Lim}_{N \to \infty} \sum_{n=-N}^{N} c_n e^{in\omega x} \tag{7.9}$$

with c_n defined in (7.4). Now, (7.5) and (7.4) give ($|G| \leqslant M$)

$$|c_n| \leqslant M\,|n|^p\omega^p \qquad (n \neq 0),$$

so that we may assert, thanks to Theorem 7.1, that $\sum_{-\infty}^{\infty} c_n e^{in\omega x}$ is unconditionally convergent in $\mathscr{P}'_{2L}$.

Grouping the nth with the $(-n)$th term in the complex Fourier series and noting that the resulting series is also unconditionally convergent, we have the proof of

Theorem 7.3. *Every $F \in \mathscr{P}'_{2L}$ which is of the form* (7.2) *is represented by its real Fourier series*

$$F(x) = \frac{a_0}{2} + \sum_{n=1}^{\infty} (a_n \cos n\omega x + b_n \sin n\omega x), \tag{7.11}$$

which converges unconditionally in $\mathscr{P}'_{2L}$. Its coefficients,

$$\begin{aligned} a_n &= \frac{1}{L}\langle F(\xi), \cos n\omega\xi\rangle \qquad (n = 0, 1, 2, \ldots); \\ b_n &= \frac{1}{L}\langle F(\xi), \sin n\omega\xi\rangle \qquad (n = 1, 2, \ldots), \end{aligned} \tag{7.12}$$

satisfy inequalities

$$|a_n| \leqslant Mn^r\omega^r, \quad |b_n| \leqslant Mn^r\omega^r \qquad (n = 1, 2, \ldots)$$

with $M < \infty$ and $r =$ $\max(p_1, p_2, \ldots, p_k)$.

Remark 1. The expansions (6.14) and (6.15) are readily verified to be particular cases of (7.3) and (7.11) respectively.

Remark 2. It will be shown in § 11 that *all $\mathscr{P}'_{2L}$ g.f.'s verify the hypotheses of these two theorems,* and so can be expanded in Fourier series convergent in $\mathscr{P}'_{2L}$. To the reader who is oriented to physical applications this may be of secondary interest; he can omit § 11 and simply accept this statement on faith.

Remark 3. A major attraction of these theorems from the point of view of applied mathematics is the fact that, because of the relation (5.3), it is *entirely permissible to differentiate (g.f. derivative, D^p) the Fourier series of $F \in \mathscr{P}'_{2L}$ term by term; the resulting series is the Fourier series of D^pF.*

For example, from (6.14) and (6.15) are obtained in this fashion:

$$D^p\delta_{2L}(x-\xi) = \frac{1}{2L}\sum_{n=-\infty}^{\infty}(in\omega)^p e^{in\omega(x-\xi)} \quad (p = 0, 1, 2, \ldots), \tag{7.10}$$

$$D^{2p}\delta_{2L}(x-\xi) = \frac{1}{L}\sum_{n=1}^{\infty}(-1)^p(n\omega)^{2p}\cos n\omega(x-\xi) \quad (p = 1, 2, \ldots), \tag{7.11}$$

$$D^{2p-1}\delta_{2L}(x-\xi) = \frac{1}{L}\sum_{n=1}^{\infty}(-1)^p(n\omega)^{2p-1}\sin n\omega(x-\xi) \quad (p = 1, 2, \ldots). \tag{7.12}$$

Remark 4. Another advantageous feature of g.f. Fourier series is this: if $\lim_{n\to\infty} F_n = F$, then the Fourier coefficients of F_n converge to the corresponding coefficients of F. (For the converse see § 11.)

8. Ordinary Convergence of Fourier Series

From the g.f. theorems above can be deduced certain properties of convergence in the ordinary function sense of the Fourier series of continuous functions having ordinary derivatives.

We begin with this simple case:

Theorem 8.1. *If $F(x) \in C^2(R)$ has period $2L$ its Fourier series (real or complex form) converges to $F(x)$ uniformly on R.*

Proof. It suffices to prove it for the complex form (7.3) of the Fourier series of $F(x)$. By Lemma 1.2, this series converges uniformly to a continuous function $f(x)$. But uniform convergence entails g.f. convergence in $\mathscr{P}'_{2L}$ (compare Theorem II.B.6.1) so the Fourier series converges to $f(x)$ in the $\mathscr{P}'_{2L}$ sense. Since F is continuous, it follows from Theorem 2.1 that $F(x) \equiv f(x)$.

Before arriving at a relaxation in the hypotheses of this result, let us consider

Theorem 8.2 (Bessel's Inequality). *If $F(x) \in \mathscr{K}_{2L}$, its Fourier coefficients satisfy the inequalities ($N = 1, 2, \ldots$)*

$$\frac{a_0^2}{2} + \sum_{n=1}^{N}(a_n^2 + b_n^2) = \sum_{n=-N}^{N}|c_n|^2 \leqslant \frac{1}{2L}\int_{-L}^{L}|F(x)|^2\,dx. \tag{8.1}$$

Proof. The first equality in (8.1) results from the identities

$$c_0 = \frac{a_0}{2} \qquad c_n = a_n - ib_n \qquad (n > 0),$$

$$c_n = a_n + ib_n \qquad\qquad (n < 0)$$

which give

$$|c_n|^2 = a_n^2 + b_n^2 \qquad (n \neq 0).$$

To get the inequality on the right in (8.1) observe that

$$\frac{1}{2L}\int_{-L}^{L} |F(x) - \sum_{-N}^{N} c_n e^{in\omega x}|^2 \, dx \geqslant 0.$$

Expanding the integrand and performing the integrations in the light of the identities (1.7) [note that if $\bar{F}(x)$ designates the complex conjugate of $F(x)$ we have

$$\langle \bar{F}(x), e^{in\omega x}\rangle = \overline{\langle F(x), e^{-in\omega x}\rangle}]$$

gives

$$\frac{1}{2L}\int_{-L}^{L} |F(x)|^2 \, dx - \sum_{n=-N}^{N} |c_n|^2 \geqslant 0.$$

With the help of (8.1) the following generalization of Theorem 8.1 is achieved:

Theorem 8.3. *If $F(x) \in C(R)$ has period $2L$ and if, at all but a finite number of points in $[-L, L)$, it has an ordinary derivative $F'(x) \in \mathscr{K}_{2L}$ its Fourier series converges to $F(x)$ uniformly on R.*

Proof. When F is continuous DF and the g.f. $[DF]$ defined by $F'(x)$ coincide. Therefore

$$\begin{aligned}\langle DF(\xi), e^{-in\omega\xi}\rangle &= \langle F(\xi), in\omega e^{-in\omega\xi}\rangle \\ &= (in\omega)\langle F(\xi), e^{-in\omega\xi}\rangle,\end{aligned}$$

which, if c_n' denotes the Fourier coefficients of DF, while c_n denotes those of F, can be written

(8.2) $$c_n' = (in\omega)c_n \qquad (n \text{ integer}).$$

But $F' \in \mathscr{K}_{2L}$ is bounded, $|F'(\xi)| \leqslant B$, so by Bessel's inequality

$$\sum_{n=M}^{N} |c_n'|^2 \leqslant \frac{1}{2L}\int_{-L}^{L} |F'(\xi)|^2 \, d\xi \leqslant B^2.$$

Applying Schwarz's inequality (proof much like that for integrals, cf. Chapter II),

$$\sum_{n=M}^{N} |u_n v_n| \leqslant \sum_{n=M}^{N} |u_n|^2 \sum_{n=M}^{N} |v_n|^2$$

with $u_n = 1/n$, $v_n = c_n n$,

$$\sum_{\substack{n=M\\n\neq 0}}^{N} |c_n| = \sum_{\substack{n=M\\n\neq 0}}^{N} \frac{1}{n}|nc_n| = \sum_{n=M}^{N} \frac{1}{n}\frac{|c_n'|}{\omega} \leqslant \sqrt{\left(\sum_{n=M}^{N} \frac{1}{n^2}\right)} \cdot \frac{B}{\omega}.$$

It easily follows that $\sum_{-\infty}^{\infty} c_n e^{in\omega x}$ is absolutely and uniformly convergent; its sum is therefore a continuous function $f(x)$. By the concluding argument of Theorem 8.1, involving Theorem 2.1, we find $f(x) \equiv F(x)$.

A Fourier expansion theorem frequently quoted in elementary treatments [8] [11] of the subject is this extension of the preceding one:

Theorem 8.4. *If $F(x) \in \mathscr{K}'_{2L}$, its Fourier series converges to $F(x)$ uniformly in every closed interval that does not contain a point of discontinuity of $F(x)$.*

Principle of proof. The only difference with the hypotheses of Theorem 8.3 is that $F(x)$ itself is allowed to have jumps at a finite number of points in $[-L, L)$. Denote these points by $\xi_1, \xi_2, \ldots, \xi_m$ and let the jumps be

$$F(\xi_j + 0) - F(\xi_j - 0) = s_j \qquad (j = 1, 2, \ldots, l).$$

If $f(x)$ denotes the sawtooth function of Example 2, § 4, then $s_j f(x - \xi_j)$ has its single discontinuity in $[-L, L)$ at ξ_j and its jump there is s_j. Consequently, the function

$$G(x) = F(x) - \sum_{j=1}^{m} s_j f(x - \xi_j)$$

has all its jumps reduced to zero, and if $G(\xi_j)$ is defined to be $G(\xi_j + 0)$ we have a continuous function with an ordinary derivative $G'(x) \in \mathscr{K}_{2L}$. To this Theorem 8.3 applies, and the proof of Theorem 8.4 is reduced to showing that the Fourier series of $C(x) = \sum_{j=1}^{m} s_j f(x - \xi_j)$ converges uniformly in every closed interval not containing any ξ_j. Indeed, the same is then true of $F(x) = G(x) + C(x)$. For a proof of this property of $C(x)$ see [11] [12].

Remark. It should be noted that while the Fourier series of a $\mathscr{K}_{2L}$ function does not necessarily converge to it in the ordinary sense, it does converge in mean square

$$\left(\lim_{N\to\infty} \frac{1}{2L} \int_{-L}^{L} |F(x) - \sum_{-N}^{N} c_n e^{in\omega x}|^2 \, dx = 0 \right)$$

(cf. Exercises 7, 8, 9).

9. Primitive of a $\mathscr{P}'_{2L}$ G.F.

Following the terminology of ordinary calculus, the g.f., G, will be called a primitive of a given g.f., F, if it is a solution of the equation

$$DG = F. \tag{9.1}$$

When $F \in \mathscr{D}'_+$, this equation has a solution $G \in \mathscr{D}'_+$ and it is unique. This property was basic to the development of the direct operational calculus in which the operator D on $\mathscr{D}'_+$ has a unique inverse.

Such is no longer the case when $F \in \mathscr{P}'_{2L}$. Then either there exists no $G \in \mathscr{P}'_{2L}$ satisfying (9.1) or else there are an infinity of such $G \in \mathscr{P}'_{2L}$.

Theorem 9.1. *A necessary and sufficient condition for $F \in \mathscr{P}'_{2L}$ to have a primitive is that*

$$\langle F, 1 \rangle = 0. \tag{9.2}$$

Proof. The condition is necessary: if $F = DG$, then its value on the function 1 is

$$\langle DG, 1 \rangle = -\langle G, 1' \rangle = 0.$$

The condition is sufficient: if (9.2) holds, the coefficient c_0 of the Fourier series of F vanishes, so

$$F = \sum_{\substack{n=-\infty \\ n \neq 0}}^{\infty} c_n e^{in\omega x}. \tag{9.3}$$

Differentiation shows that

$$G = C + \sum_{n=-\infty}^{\infty} \frac{c_n}{in\omega} e^{in\omega x} \tag{9.4}$$

is a solution of (9.1), whatever value is assigned to the constant C.

(*Note.* In this proof, we have used a result of § 11; cf. Remark 2 of § 7. A proof which is independent of this result, in that it does not employ Fourier series, is suggested in Exercise 13.)

Suppose there exists a primitive, $G \in \mathscr{P}'_{2L}$, for a given F satisfying (9.1). Any function $f(x) \equiv C$ (constant) has $Df = Df = 0$ so $D(G + C) = F$ also, proving that the existence of one primitive entails that of an infinity of them. In fact it is a consequence of the following theorem that *all* the primitives of F are of the form $G + C$.

Theorem 9.2. *All the $\mathscr{P}'_{2L}$ solutions of the equation*

$$DG = 0 \tag{9.5}$$

are of the form $G(x) \equiv C$ with C an arbitrary complex number.

Before proving this, let us mention

Lemma. *A necessary and sufficient condition for $\psi(x) \in \mathscr{P}_{2L}$ to have a primitive function in $\mathscr{P}_{2L}$ is that*

$$\langle \psi, 1 \rangle = \int_{-L}^{L} \psi(x)\, dx = 0. \tag{9.6}$$

Though this is a particular case of Theorem 9.1, it can be proved separately.

Proof. $\psi(x)$ being continuous, all its primitives can be written in the form

$$\Psi(x) = \int_{-L}^{x} \psi(x)\, dx + C. \tag{9.7}$$

If $\Psi(x)$ is to have period $2L$, it is necessary that $\Psi(-L) = \Psi(L) = 0$ and this, by (9.7), is not possible unless (9.6) holds.

That (9.5) is sufficient also follows from (9.7) since it yields

$$\Psi(x + 2L) - \Psi(x) = \int_{-L}^{L} \psi(x)\, dx.$$

Proof of Theorem 9.2. Choose $\varphi_0 \in \mathscr{P}_{2L}$ such that

$$\int_{-L}^{L} \varphi_0(x)\, dx = 1. \tag{9.8}$$

To every $\varphi \in \mathscr{P}_{2L}$, we associate the function $\psi(x) \in \mathscr{P}$ defined$_{2L}$ by

$$\psi(x) = \varphi(x) - \varphi_0(x) \int_{-L}^{L} \varphi(x)\, dx.$$

From this relation and (9.8), it follows that $\psi(x)$ satisfies (9.6). In other words: given a fixed $\varphi_0 \in \mathscr{P}_{2L}$ for which (9.8) holds, every $\varphi(x) \in \mathscr{P}_{2L}$ can be decomposed in the form

$$\varphi(x) = \varphi_0(x) \int_{-L}^{L} \varphi(x)\, dx + \psi(x), \tag{9.9}$$

where ψ is the derivative of a $\mathscr{P}_{2L}$ function $\Psi(x)$. If G is a solution of (9.5), its value on $\varphi \in \mathscr{P}_{2L}$ can then be written as

$$\langle G, \varphi \rangle = \left(\int_{-L}^{L} \varphi(x)\, dx \right) \langle G, \varphi_0 \rangle + \langle G, \Psi' \rangle. \tag{9.10}$$

In view of the definition of DG and (9.5), we have

$$\langle G, \Psi' \rangle = (-1)\langle DG, \Psi \rangle = 0,$$

so that (9.10) becomes

$$\langle G, \varphi \rangle = C\langle 1, \varphi \rangle, \tag{9.11}$$

where $C = \langle G, \varphi_0 \rangle$ is the same for all $\varphi \in \mathscr{P}_{2L}$. This proves that $G = C \cdot 1$, which we write $G = C$ with the understanding that C is the function $f(x) \equiv C$.

The analogy of this result with that for ordinary functions is transparent: if $DG = 0$, it suffices to know the value of G at one "point" φ_0 of $\mathscr{P}_{2L}$ to have its value at every other "point" ($\langle G, \varphi \rangle = \langle G, \varphi_0 \rangle$).

10. The Finite Fourier Transforms

If $F(x)$ is piecewise continuous in the interval $[0, L]$ its finite sine and cosine transforms are defined for $n = 0, 1, 2, \ldots$, by

$$S(n) = \int_0^L F(x) \sin n\omega x \, dx,$$

$$C(n) = \int_0^L F(x) \cos n\omega x \, dx.$$

Thus to every function $F(x)$ of a large class correspond the sequences $\{S(n)\}_n$ and $\{C(n)\}_n$ of complex numbers; these sequences are the *images* under the finite sine and cosine transforms of the *object* function F. Such transforms are used to solve certain partial differential equation problems, in much the same way that the Laplace transform is used. When these transforms are couched in terms of g.f.'s, they serve the same purpose and some of the formulae that lie behind their usefulness take on a more symmetric form. We shall here sketch the theory of these transforms only cursorily, just enough to make apparent the principles involved.

With the $\mathscr{K}[0, L]$ function $F(x)$ are associated† its

(10.1) odd periodic extension:

$$F_0(x) = \begin{cases} -F(-x) & \text{if } -L \leqslant x \leqslant 0 \\ F(x) & \text{if } 0 \leqslant x \leqslant L \\ F_0(x + 2L), & x \in R; \end{cases}$$

(10.2) even periodic extension:

$$F_e(x) = \begin{cases} F(-x) & \text{if } -L \leqslant x \leqslant 0 \\ F(x) & \text{if } 0 \leqslant x \leqslant L \\ F_e(x + 2L), & x \in R. \end{cases}$$

[Note that if $F'(x)$ exists, $F_0'(x)$ is even and F_e' is odd.]

The (real form) Fourier series of F_0 contains only sine terms:

$$F_0(x) = \sum_{n=1}^{\infty} b_n \sin n\omega x, \tag{10.3}$$

$$b_n = \frac{1}{L} \langle F_0(x), \sin n\omega x \rangle. \tag{10.4}$$

---

† The terms "odd" and "even" are customarily reserved for real-valued functions; this practice is not followed here.

The Fourier series of F_e contains only cosine terms:

(10.5) $$F_e(x) = \frac{a_0}{2} + \sum_{n=1}^{\infty} a_n \cos n\omega x,$$

(10.6) $$a_n = \frac{1}{L}\langle F_e(x), \cos n\omega x\rangle.$$

As $F_0(x) \sin n\omega x$ is an even function

$$\int_{-L}^{L} F_0(x) \sin n\omega x\, dx = 2\int_0^L F(x) \sin n\omega x\, dx,$$

similarly

$$\int_{-L}^{L} F_e(x) \cos n\omega x\, dx = 2\int_0^L F(x) \cos n\omega x\, dx.$$

Let us then define the sine and cosine transforms by†

(10.7) $$S(F_0; n) = \tfrac{1}{2}\langle F_0(x), \sin n\omega x\rangle,$$

(10.8) $$C(F_e; n) = \tfrac{1}{2}\langle F_e(x), \cos n\omega x\rangle.$$

It follows from Theorem 7.3 that knowledge of either one of the sequences $\{C(n)\}$, $\{S(n)\}$ suffices to determine $F(x)$ as a g.f. since, by (10.3) and (10.5),

(10.9) $$F_0(x) = \frac{2}{L}\sum_{n=1}^{\infty} S(F_0; n) \sin n\omega x,$$

(10.10) $$F_e(x) = \frac{C(0)}{L} + \frac{2}{L}\sum_{n=1}^{\infty} C(F_e; n) \cos n\omega x,$$

where convergence is $\mathscr{P}'_{2L}$ convergence. These two relations are called the *inversion formulae for the finite sine and cosine transforms* respectively.

There is no need to limit ourselves to ordinary functions $F(x)$; we may just as well consider the transforms of two classes of $\mathscr{P}'_{2L}$ g.f.'s:

(a) the odd g.f.'s—whose real Fourier series contain only sine terms [examples: $\delta_{2L}(x - \xi) - \delta_{2L}(x + \xi)$, $D\delta_{2L}(x)$];

(b) the even g.f.'s—whose real Fourier series contain only cosine terms [examples: $\delta_{2L}(x - \xi) + \delta_{2L}(x + \xi)$, $D^2\delta_{2L}(x)$].

For applications to p.d.e.'s these identities are fundamental:

(10.11) $$S(D^2F_0; n) = -n^2\omega^2 S(F_0; n),$$

(10.12) $$C(D^2F_e; n) = -n^2\omega^2 C(F_e; n).$$

---

† The factor $\frac{1}{2}$ is included so that the definition coincides with the usual one for ordinary functions [7].

Let F_0 or F_e be the $\mathscr{K}^2_{2L}$ functions associated with a function $F(x)$ continuous in $(0, L)$ that has an ordinary first derivative $F'(x)$ continuous in $(0, L)$ and has an ordinary second derivative $F''(x)$ that is piecewise continuous. Then the discontinuities of $F_0(x)$ and $F_e(x)$ and their ordinary first derivatives are at $-L, 0, L$ only, where they have these jumps, as computed from (10.1):

at $x = 0$:

$$
\begin{aligned}
&F_0(+0) - F_0(-0) = F(+0) - (-F(+0)) = 2F(+0),\\
&F_e(+0) - F_e(-0) = 0 \quad (\text{because } F_e \text{ is even}),\\
&F_0'(+0) - F_0'(+0) = 0 \quad (\text{because } F_0' \text{ is an even function}),\\
&F_e'(+0) - F_e'(+0) = F'(+0) - (-F'(+0)) = 2F'(+0);
\end{aligned}
$$

at $x = -L$:

$$
\begin{aligned}
&F_0(-L+0) - F_0(-L-0) = -F(L-0) - F(L-0) = -2F(L-0),\\
&F_e(-L+0) - F_e(-L-0) = 0,\\
&F_0'(-L+0) - F_0'(-L-0) = 0 \quad (F_0' \text{ is even}),\\
&F_e'(-L+0) - F_e'(-L-0) = -F'(L-0) - F'(L-0) = -2F'(L-0).
\end{aligned}
$$

The relation between g.f. and ordinary derivatives consequently becomes

$$
\begin{aligned}
DF_0 &= [DF_0] + 2F(+0)\delta_{2L}(x) - 2F(L-0)\delta_{2L}(x-L),\\
D^2F_0 &= [D^2F_0] + 2F(+0)\delta'_{2L}(x) - 2F(L-0)\delta'_{2L}(x-L),\\
DF_e &= [DF_e],\\
D^2F_e &= [D^2F_e] + 2F'(+0)\delta_{2L}(x) - 2F'(L-0)\delta_{2L}(x-L).
\end{aligned} \tag{10.13}
$$

To get an idea as to how the finite Fourier transforms are applied, let us consider the problem of determining the temperature $u(x, t)$ in a homogeneous slab in space defined by $0 \leqslant x \leqslant \pi$. The initial temperature distribution $f(x)$ is known, and the temperature of the face $x = 0$ is held constantly at zero, while that at $x = \pi$ is constantly equal to T.

The usual mathematical description of this state of affairs is

$$\frac{\partial u}{\partial t} = k\frac{\partial^2 u}{\partial x^2} \qquad (0 < x < \pi, 0 < t), \tag{10.14}$$

$$\begin{cases} u(+0, t) = 0 & (t > 0),\\ u(\pi - 0, t) = T & (t > 0), \end{cases} \tag{10.15}$$

$$u(x, +0) = f(x) \qquad (0 < x < \pi). \tag{10.16}$$

(10.14) is the equation of heat conduction, k being a positive constant; (10.15) are the boundary values; (10.16) is the initial value.

We proceed as we did with the Laplace transform. To get a parametric equation of evolution, we start with the assumption that there is a solution $u(x, t)$ which, with $\partial u/\partial t$, $\partial u/\partial x$, and $\partial^2 u/\partial x^2$ is continuous in $x(0 < x < \pi)$ for every t. Denote by $U(x, t)$ the odd periodic extension of the original $u(x, t)$. Then, $U(x, t)$ being assumed continuous in the open region $0 < x < \pi$, there holds, by the second of relations (10.13), the equality

$$D_x^2 U = [D_x^2 U] + 2U(+0, t)\delta'_{2L}(x) - 2U(\pi - 0, t)\delta'_{2L}(x - \pi), \tag{10.17}$$

where $[D_x^2 U]$ is the g.f. defined by the $\mathscr{K}_{2L}$ function of x, $(\partial^2 U/\partial x^2)(x, t)$. Applying (10.15), this gives

$$D_x^2 U = [D_x^2 U] - 2T\delta'_{2L}(x - \pi). \tag{10.18}$$

[It is because the boundary conditions (10.15) bear on $u(x, t)$ that we chose for U the odd periodic extension—a glance at the last of the relations (10.13) indicates that had the boundary conditions concerned $\partial u/\partial x$, it is the even periodic extension that would have served.]

Solving (10.18) for $[D_x^2 U]$ and substituting in (10.14) we obtain the parametric equation

$$\frac{\partial U}{\partial t} = kD_x^2 U + 2kT\delta'_{2L}(x - \pi), \tag{10.19}$$

and, as replacement for (10.16), we adopt

$$\operatorname*{Lim}_{t \to +0} U(x, t) = F(x), \tag{10.20}$$

where $F(x)$ is the odd periodic extension of $f(x)$. Convergence and parametric differentiation in the variable t are, of course, understood in the sense of $\mathscr{P}'_{2L}$.

Now we simply take the sine transform of both sides of (10.19) and (10.20), obtaining with the help of (10.11) ($\omega = 1$ here),

$$\frac{\partial S(U; n)}{\partial t} = -n^2 kS(U; n) - kTn \cos n\pi \qquad (n = 1, 2, \ldots), \tag{10.21}$$

$$\lim_{t \to +0} S(U; n) = S(F; n) \qquad (n = 1, 2, \ldots). \tag{10.22}$$

This ordinary differential equation problem can easily be solved (by the direct operational method, for example) with the result [$\cos n\pi = (-1)^n$]

$$S(U; n) = e^{-n^2 kt}\left[S(F; n) + \frac{(-1)^n}{n} T\right] - \frac{(-1)^n}{n} T. \tag{10.23}$$

Next apply the inversion formula (10.9) with $L = \pi$. This gives the solution of (10.21) (10.20) in the form of the g.f. series

$$(10.24) \qquad U(x, t) = \frac{2}{\pi} \sum_{n=1}^{\infty} \left[S(F; n) + \frac{(-1)^n}{n} T \right] e^{-n^2 kt} \sin nx - \frac{2T}{\pi} \sum_{n=1}^{\infty} \frac{(-1)^n}{n} \sin nx.$$

It is easily checked (Exercise 16) that $-2 \sum_{n=1}^{\infty} \frac{(-1)^n}{n} \sin nx$ is the Fourier series of the odd periodic extension $\tilde{x}$ of $g(x) = x(0 < x < \pi)$ so

$$(10.25) \qquad U(x, t) = \frac{2}{\pi} \sum_{n=1}^{\infty} e^{-n^2 kt} \left[S(F; n) + \frac{(-1)^n}{n} T \right] \sin nx + \frac{\tilde{x} T}{\pi}.$$

So long as for some $M < \infty$ and integer $r \geqslant 0$,

$$(10.26) \qquad |S(F; n)| \leqslant M n^r \qquad (n = 1, 2, \ldots)$$

(as is the case for $F \in \mathscr{K}_{2L}$, for example; with $r = 0$), it follows from the inequalities (1.10) with $p = r + 4$ that for every $\varphi \in \mathscr{P}_{2L}$

$$(10.27) \qquad \sum_{n=1}^{\infty} \left| \left\langle \left[S(F; n) + \frac{(-1)^n}{n} T \right] e^{-n^2 kt} \sin nx, \varphi(x) \right\rangle \right| \leqslant \sum_{n=1}^{\infty} \left(\frac{M}{n^4} + \frac{T}{n^{r+5}} \right) e^{-n^2 kt} \max_{-L \leqslant x \leqslant L} |\varphi^{(r+4)}(x)|,$$

where the inequality actually applies term by term so that, by the Weierstrass M-test, the series on the left in (10.26) converges, for each x, uniformly in the region $t \geqslant 0$, and applying a classical theorem (cf. footnote, p. 287) one is assured that the parametric derivative U with respect to t of the series in (10.25) equals the series of the parametric derivatives of the individual terms. At the same time, the $\mathscr{P}'_{2L}$ g.f. differentiation operator D_x^2 can be applied term by term to this series, and it is then a trivial matter to see that (10.25) satisfies the equation of evolution. That condition (10.20) is satisfied follows from the uniform convergence of the series on the left in (10.27), which makes its sum a continuous function of t for $t \geqslant 0$.

A physically interesting case occurs when the heat conduction in a very thin homogeneous wire (the segment $0 < x < \pi$) is considered, the initial temperature distribution being $f(x) = 0$ on the rod except in the immediate neighborhood of the point ξ $(0 < \xi < \pi)$ where a very high temperature prevails. One idealizes such a situation by means of the equation of evolution (10.19) to which is adjoined an initial value $\operatorname{Lim}_{t \to +0} U(x, t)$, which in the interval $(0, \pi)$ presents a single impulse. For this impulse $c\delta_{2\pi}(x - \xi)$ will do as an idealization. However, our method of solution requires all inputs to be odd periodic g.f.'s with period 2π so we take for $F(x)$ in (10.20) the odd periodic extension of $c\delta_{2\pi}(x - \xi)$ which is

$$F(x) = c\delta_{2\pi}(x - \xi) - c\delta_{2\pi}(x + \xi), \tag{10.28}$$

as is easily seen from the fact that $\mathring{p}_n(x - \xi)$ of (2.8) has for its odd periodic extension $\mathring{p}_n(x - \xi) - \mathring{p}_n(-x - \xi)$.

In these circumstances, by (10.7),

$$S(F; n) = \tfrac{1}{2}c \sin (n\xi) - \tfrac{1}{2}c \sin (-n\xi) = c \sin n\xi, \tag{10.29}$$

which, substituted in (10.25), shows the temperature $U(x, t)$ to be, when $t \geqslant 0$,

$$U(x, t) = \frac{2}{\pi}\sum_{n=1}^{\infty}\left[c \sin n\xi \sin nx + \frac{(-1)^n T}{n} \sin nx\right]e^{-n^2kt} + \frac{\tilde{x}}{\pi} T \tag{10.30}$$

$$= \frac{2}{\pi}\sum_{n=1}^{\infty}\left[c \cos (x - \xi) - c \cos (x + \xi) + \frac{(-1)^n T}{n} \sin nx\right]e^{-n^2kt} + \frac{\tilde{x}}{\pi} T,$$

which, letting $t \to +0$, gives

$$U(x, +0) = \frac{2}{\pi}\sum_{n=1}^{\infty}\left[c \cos (x - \xi) - c \cos (x + \xi) + \frac{(-1)^n T}{n} \sin nx\right] + \frac{\tilde{x}}{\pi} T.$$

Referring to (6.15), and recalling the observation following (10.24), this is seen to be

$$U(x, +0) = c\delta_{2\pi}(x - \xi) - c\delta_{2\pi}(x + \xi),$$

in accord with (10.28).

Concerning the conditions on $F(x)$ under which the solution $U(x, t)$ of the parametric equation defines a solution $u(x, t)$ of the original problem (10.14)–(10.16), we merely observe that, if $F(x) \in \mathscr{K}_{2L}$, then $U(x, t)$, as given by (10.25), is a solution of the original problem. The proof, though not difficult, will not be given here. The interested reader can deduce it from §§ 46, 55 of [9].

Examples of applications of the finite Fourier transform are to be found in [8] [48].

**11. The Structure of $\mathscr{P}'_{2L}$ G.F.'s

With every $F \in \mathscr{P}'_{2L}$ is associated its Fourier series

$$\sum_{-\infty}^{\infty} c_n e^{in\omega x}, \qquad \text{where } c_n = \frac{1}{2L}\langle F(x), e^{-in\omega x}\rangle.$$

This series, however, converges only if c_n satisfies the inequalities (8.1) and then, when F is of the form (7.2), actually converges to F so that one says that it represents F.

This immediately brings up the question of the potency of the fundamental theorem on Fourier series: what $\mathscr{P}'_{2L}$ g.f.'s, if any, fail to be represented by their Fourier series? The answer is given by Theorem 11.2 below: none.

The investigation of this matter is closely tied to that of the structural properties of $\mathscr{P}'_{2L}$. We shall see that many parallels to ideas and results of Chapters V and VI present themselves very naturally—so much so that the proofs of many of them are best left to the reader as exercises.

Basic to what follows is

Theorem 11.1. *Let $F \in \mathscr{P}'_{2L}$. With the fundamental (on $\mathscr{P}_{2L}$) sequence $\{F_n\} \in F$ there are associated $M < \infty$ and an integer $r \geqslant 0$ such that*

$$(11.1) \qquad |\langle F_n(x), e^{ik\omega x}\rangle| \leqslant M\,|k|^r \qquad (\textit{integer } k \neq 0;\ n = 1, 2, \ldots).$$

Proof. By contradiction. The principle is this: We assume that (11.1) does not hold and apply the Lebesgue resonance method (§ VI.1) to simultaneously select a subsequence $\{F_{n_j}\}$ of $\{F_n\}$ and construct a $\varphi \in \mathscr{P}_{2L}$ for which

$$\lim_{j \to \infty} |\langle F_{n_j}, \varphi\rangle| = \infty.$$

Since

$$\lim_{n \to \infty} \langle F_n, \varphi\rangle = \langle F, \varphi\rangle$$

is finite for every $\varphi \in \mathscr{P}_{2L}$, it follows that the assumption of incorrectness for (11.1) is untenable. The details of the argument follow.

First, let us introduce the symbol $B(\varphi)$ defined for every $\varphi \in \mathscr{P}_{2L}$ by

$$(11.2) \qquad B(\varphi) = |\sup_n \langle F_n, \varphi\rangle|.$$

Suppose (11.1) to be invalid, and set

$$(11.3) \qquad \|F_l\| = \sup_{-L \leqslant x \leqslant L} |F_l(x)|.$$

Then, for every integer k

$$(11.4) \qquad |\langle F_l, e^{ik\omega x}\rangle| \leqslant 2L\,\|F_l\|,$$

so that, unless (11.1) were to hold with $r = 0$, $\{\|F_l\|\}$ must necessarily be unbounded and therefore contain a strictly monotonic increasing subsequence $\{\|F_{l_n}\|\}$. Since $\{F_l\}$ and $\{F_{l_n}\}$ are equivalent, we might just as well have started out with the latter in defining F. In fact, for the sake of convenience in notation, let us simply relabel elements and call this subsequence $\{F_n\}$, so that we may write

$$(11.5)\qquad 1 < \|F_1\| < \|F_2\| < \cdots < \|F_n\| < \cdots, \qquad \lim_{n\to\infty} \|F_n\| = +\infty.$$

If we now define

$$(11.6)\qquad M_n^r = \sup_{\substack{\text{integer } k\\ k\neq 0}} \frac{|\langle F_n, e^{ik\omega x}\rangle|}{|k|^r} \qquad (\text{integer } n, r \geqslant 1)$$

it follows from (11.4)† that for each (n, r) combination $(r \geqslant 1)$ there exists at least one finite integer $k(r, n)$ at which the supremum in (11.6) is actually reached, that is

$$(11.7)\qquad M_n^r = \frac{|\langle F_n, e^{ik(r,n)\omega x}\rangle|}{|k(r, n)|^r} \qquad (n, r = 1, 2, \ldots).$$

Consider the sequences $\{M_n^1\}_n, \ldots, \{M_n^r\}_n, \ldots$. If any one of these sequences were bounded, the rth one say, then (11.1) would hold for that value of r. Thus our initial assumption requires that we also suppose each $\{M_n^r\}_n$ to be unbounded.

In these circumstances, one could extract from each of these sequences one element, $M_{n_r}^r$ [which is more conveniently denoted by $M_{r'}^r$ $(r' = n_r)$] in such fashion as to produce the sequence $\{M_{r'}^r\}_r$ with these properties:

$$(11.8)\qquad 2 < M_{1'}^1 < M_{2'}^2 < \cdots < M_{r'}^r < \cdots,$$

$$(11.9)\qquad \lim_{r\to\infty} M_{r'}^r = +\infty.$$

One more observation should be made before we start on the main resonance routine: if $\{r_j\}$ is an increasing sequence of positive integers, any series of the form (recall that $r_j' = n_{r_j}$ in the notation established above)

$$(11.10)\qquad \sum_{j=1}^{\infty} a_j \frac{e^{ik(r_j, r'_j)\omega x}}{|k(r_j, r_j')|^{r_j}},$$

where $|a_j| \leqslant 1/2^j$, represents a $\mathscr{P}_{2L}$ function. This follows from the fact that if each term is differentiated p times, the resulting series is uniformly convergent by the Weierstrass M-test. Indeed, the absolute value of its jth term is bounded by

$$\frac{|k(r_j, r_j')\omega|^p}{2^j|k(r_j, r_j')|^{r_j}},$$

and this is the jth term of a convergent series of positive numbers (if $k > 1$, we could have let $|a_j| = 1$, in fact).

† Because $\lim_{k\to\infty} \dfrac{\|F_n\|}{k^r} = 0 (r \geqslant 1)$.

The set-up is now such that the inductive procedure of § VI.1 can be closely duplicated:

(i) By (11.8) the choice of integer $r_1 = 1$ gives $M^1_{1'} > 2$. Therefore, putting

$$\varphi_1(x) = \frac{e^{ik(1,1')\omega x}}{2\,|k(1, 1')|} \tag{11.11}$$

we have

$$1 < |\langle F_{1'}, \varphi_1\rangle|.$$

(ii) The jth step of the procedure ($j > 1$) employs (11.8) to find a positive integer $r_j > r_{j-1}$ such that the function

$$\varphi_j(x) = \frac{e^{ik(r_j,r'_j)\omega x}}{2^j\,\|F_{r'_{j-1}}\|\,|k(r_j, r'_j)|^{r_j}}$$

gives

$$|\langle F_{r'_j}, \varphi_j\rangle| > j + 2L + B(\varphi_1 + \varphi_2 + \cdots + \varphi_{j-1}). \tag{11.12}$$

(iii) The procedure produces the sequence $\{r_j\}_j$ of distinct positive integers and the sequence $\{\varphi_j\}_j$ of $\mathscr{P}_{2L}$ functions.

The series $\varphi(x) = \sum_{j=1}^{\infty} \varphi_j$ is a particular case of the series (11.10) with

$$a_j = \frac{1}{2^j\,\|F_{r'_{j-1}}\|} < \frac{1}{2^j}$$

[this last because of (11.5)] and, therefore, represents a $\mathscr{P}_{2L}$ function $\varphi(x)$.

Also, in the inequality

$$\left|\left\langle F_{r'_j}, \sum_{l=j+1}^{\infty} \varphi_l \right\rangle\right| \leqslant \|F_{r'_j}\| \sum_{l=j+1}^{\infty} \frac{1}{2^l\,\|F_{r'_{l-1}}\|}$$

we have but to observe the monotonicity of the $\|F_n\|$ described in (11.5) to see that the sum on the right is majorized by $\sum_{l=j+1}^{\infty} \frac{1}{2^l} < 1$, whence

$$\left|\left\langle F_{r'_j}, \sum_{l=j+1}^{\infty} \varphi_l \right\rangle\right| < 2L \tag{11.13}$$

Finally, applying (11.12) and (11.13),

$$|\langle F_{r'_j}, \varphi\rangle| \geqslant |\langle F_{r'_j}, \varphi_j\rangle| - \left|\left\langle F_{r'_j}, \sum_{l=1}^{j-1} \varphi_l \right\rangle\right| - \left|\left\langle F_{r'_j}, \sum_{l=j+1}^{\infty} \varphi_l \right\rangle\right| \geqslant j.$$

As this makes $\lim_{j\to\infty} |\langle F_{r'_j}, \varphi\rangle| = +\infty$, $\{F_n\}$ could not be a fundamental sequence on $\mathscr{P}_{2L}$. We conclude that (11.1) must hold for some finite integer r. ∎

Theorem 11.2. *Every $F \in \mathscr{P}'_{2L}$ is represented by its Fourier series.*

Proof. Let the fundamental sequence $\{F_n\} \in F$. Each of the $\mathscr{K}_{2L}$ functions in this sequence is represented by its Fourier series (Theorem 7.2):

$$F_n = \sum_{k=-\infty}^{\infty} c_k^{(n)} e^{ik\omega x}, \tag{11.14}$$

where, in view of Theorem 11.1,

$$|c_k^{(n)}| \leqslant \frac{M}{2L} |k|^r \qquad (k \neq 0) \tag{11.15}$$

for some $M < \infty$ and some integer $r \geqslant 0$ independent of n and k.

Given $\varphi \in \mathscr{P}_{2L}$, take $q = r + 2$ in (1.9) and use this with (11.15) (11.14) to get

$$\left|\langle F_n, \varphi\rangle - \left\langle \left(\sum_{k=-K}^{K} c_k^{(n)} e^{ik\omega x}\right), \varphi \right\rangle\right| \leqslant \frac{2MB_{r+2}(\varphi)}{2L} \sum_{k=K+1}^{\infty} \frac{1}{k^2}.$$

The right-hand side is independent of n so that letting $n \to \infty$, we find

$$\left|\langle F, \varphi\rangle - \left\langle \sum_{k=-K}^{K} c_k e^{ik\omega x}, \varphi \right\rangle\right| \leqslant \frac{MB_{r+2}(\varphi)}{L} \sum_{k=K+1}^{\infty} \frac{1}{k^2}, \tag{11.16}$$

in which

$$c_k = \lim_{n\to\infty} c_k^{(n)} = \frac{1}{2L} \lim_{n\to\infty} \langle F_n(\xi), e^{-ik\omega\xi}\rangle$$

is a Fourier coefficient of $F \in \mathscr{P}'_{2L}$.

We have only to let $K \to +\infty$ in (11.16) to conclude the proof. ∎

Corollary 11.2. *Every $F \in \mathscr{P}'_{2L}$ is the sum of a constant function and of a g.f. derivative of finite order p of a continuous function with period $2L$. (Thus every $F \in \mathscr{P}'_{2L}$ satisfies the hypotheses of Theorem 7.2.)*

Proof. By the previous theorem

$$F = c_0 + \sum_{n=-\infty}^{-1} c_n e^{in\omega x} + \sum_{n=1}^{\infty} c_n e^{in\omega x}, \tag{11.17}$$

where for some M and integer $r \geqslant 0$ provided for by Theorem 11.1:

$$|c_n| \leqslant M\,|n|^r \qquad (n \neq 0). \tag{11.18}$$

Let

$$G(x) = \left(\sum_{n=-\infty}^{-1} + \sum_{n=1}^{\infty}\right) \frac{c_n}{(in\omega)^{r+2}}\, e^{in\omega x}.$$

(11.18) and Lemma 1.2 show that $G(x)$ is a continuous function with period $2L$. From (11.17), we get

$$F(x) = c_0 \cdot 1 + D^{r+2} G(x) \quad ∎ \tag{11.19}$$

The above result indicates that $\mathscr{P}'_{2L}$ g.f.'s in a way resemble $\mathscr{D}'_+$ g.f.'s of finite order.

Corollary 11.3. *Every $F \in \mathscr{P}'_{2L}$ is a continuous linear functional on $\mathscr{P}_{2L}$ in the sense that F is both algebraically linear*

$$(\langle F, c_1\varphi_1 + c_2\varphi_2\rangle = c_1\langle F, \varphi_1\rangle + c_2\langle F, \varphi_2\rangle)$$

and continuous. By the latter is meant that for any sequence $\{\varphi_n\}$ of $\mathscr{P}_{2L}$ functions such that $\lim_{n\to\infty} \varphi_n^{(p)}(x) = 0$ uniformly on $[-L, L]$ (for each of $p = 0, 1, 2, \ldots$) there holds the relation

$$\lim_{n\to\infty} \langle F, \varphi_n\rangle = 0. \tag{11.20}$$

Proof. Since $\{\varphi_n^{(p)}\}_n$ tends to zero uniformly on $[-L, L]$ for every integer $p \geqslant 0$, it follows that, as $n \to \infty$,

$$\int_{-L}^{L} |\varphi_n(x)|\, dx \to 0 \quad \text{and that} \quad \int_{-L}^{L} |\varphi_n^{(r+2)}(x)|\, dx \to 0.$$

The expression (11.19) gives

$$|\langle F, \varphi_n\rangle| \leqslant |c_0| \frac{1}{2L}\int_{-L}^{L} |\varphi_n(x)|\, dx + \left(\max_{-L\leqslant x\leqslant L} |G(x)|\right)\frac{1}{2L}\int_{-L}^{L} |\varphi_n^{(r+2)}(x)|\, dx$$

from which (11.20) follows. ∎

Let it be noted that the converse of this corollary is true: every linear functional on $\mathscr{P}_{2L}$ that is continuous in the sense described is a g.f. of class $\mathscr{P}'_{2L}$. (This is used as a definition of $\mathscr{P}'_{2L}$ by L. Schwartz.) The proof, which follows the same general idea as Theorem V.A.4.1, is left to the reader as Exercise 19.

Remark 1. The exponent r was obtained in Theorem 11.1 in connection with a fundamental sequence $\{F_n\} \in F$. Equivalent sequences, however, do not necessarily lead to the same value of r, for, no matter how large r may be chosen, there exist fundamental sequences for the g.f. $0 \in \mathscr{P}'_{2L}$ for which no smaller r will do. [Example: $\{n^r \sin n\omega x\}_{n=1}^{\infty}$.] This phenomenon is scarcely different from the one encountered in $\mathscr{D}'_+$, where different fundamental sequences have indices of different order. Quite as there we may take for the r-index of $F \in \mathscr{P}'_{2L}$ the smallest non-negative r-index of all the fundamental sequences in the equivalence class F. Let us hereafter call this the order of $F \in \mathscr{P}'_{2L}$.

Remark 2. In the proof of Theorem 11.1, the fact that $\lim_{n\to\infty} \langle F_n, \varphi\rangle$ exists for every $\varphi \in \mathscr{P}_{2L}$ was not used directly. Only one of its consequences was really used: the existence of $B(\varphi)$ such that $|\langle F_n, \varphi\rangle| \leqslant B(\varphi)$ $(n = 1, 2, \ldots)$. Consequently, we actually proved a more general result: *every sequence of $\mathscr{K}_{2L}$ functions which is bounded in $\mathscr{P}'_{2L}$ has an $M < \infty$ and an $r \geqslant 0$, such that for integer $k \neq 0$*

$$|\langle F_n, e^{ik\omega x}\rangle| \leqslant M\,|k|^r \qquad (n = 1, 2, \ldots).$$

Remark 3. Let $\{F_n\}$ be a sequence of $\mathscr{P}'_{2L}$ g.f.'s that is bounded [i.e., $|\langle F_n, \varphi\rangle| \leqslant B(\varphi)$ $(n = 1, 2, \ldots)$]. Using the fact that to each F_n correspond M_n, r_n such that $|\langle F_n, e^{ik\omega x}\rangle| \leqslant M_n\,|k|^{r_n}$ $(k \neq 0)$ the proof of Theorem 11.1 can, with some simple changes in its early part, be adapted to show that there exist M and r such that for all integer $k \neq 0$

$$|\langle F_n, e^{ik\omega x}\rangle| \leqslant M\,|k|^r \qquad (n = 1, 2, \ldots). \tag{11.21}$$

Remark 4 (Completeness of $\mathscr{P}'_{2L}$). Any sequence of $\mathscr{P}'_{2L}$ g.f.'s such that $\lim_{n\to\infty} \langle F_n, \varphi\rangle$ exists for all $\varphi \in \mathscr{P}_{2L}$ is bounded and so also satisfies (11.21). But then the complex numbers

$$c_k = \frac{1}{2L} \lim_{n\to\infty} \langle F_n(x), e^{-ik\omega x}\rangle \qquad (\text{all integer } k \neq 0) \tag{11.22}$$

all have the bound

$$|c_k| \leqslant M\,|k|^r, \tag{11.23}$$

which we know (Theorem 7.1) suffices to ensure that $\sum_{-\infty}^{\infty} c_k e^{ik\omega x}$ converges to a $\mathscr{P}'_{2L}$ g.f., F. It is then easy to verify (reason as in Theorem 11.2) that

$$\lim_{n\to\infty} \langle F_n, \varphi\rangle = \langle F, \varphi\rangle \qquad \text{for every } \varphi \in \mathscr{P}_{2L},$$

so that in conclusion one has the **Theorem A:** *$\mathscr{P}'_{2L}$ is complete: to every sequence $\{F_n\}$ in $\mathscr{P}'_{2L}$ such that* $\lim_{n\to\infty} \langle F_n, \varphi\rangle$ *exists for every $\varphi \in \mathscr{P}_{2L}$ there corresponds $F \in \mathscr{P}'_{2L}$ such that* $\operatorname{Lim}_{n\to\infty} F_n = F$.

A very useful characterization of convergence in $\mathscr{P}'_{2L}$ is given by this **Theorem B:** *A necessary and sufficient condition for the sequence $\{F_n\}_{n=1}^{\infty}$ of $\mathscr{P}'_{2L}$ g.f.'s to converge to $F_0 \in \mathscr{P}'_{2L}$ is that for some $A < \infty$, $M < \infty$, and some integer $r \geqslant 0$ the Fourier coefficients*

$$c_{nk} = \frac{1}{2L} \langle F_n, e^{-ik\omega x}\rangle$$

satisfy the inequalities

$$|c_{n0}| \leqslant A \qquad (n = 0, 1, \ldots),$$
$$|c_{nk}| \leqslant M\,|k|^r \qquad (n = 0, 1, \ldots, \textit{integer } k \neq 0),$$

and that $\lim_{n\to\infty} c_{nk} = c_{0k}$ *for every integer k.*

Remark 5 (Relative Compactness of $\mathscr{P}'_{2L}$). *Every sequence $\{F_n\}$ bounded in $\mathscr{P}'_{2L}$ contains a convergent subsequence.* This property, the $\mathscr{P}'_{2L}$ analog of the Bolzano-Weierstrass Theorem, is easier to prove than in the $\mathscr{D}'_+$ case (Chapter VI). Indeed, setting

$$c_{nk} = \frac{1}{2L} \langle F_n, e^{-ik\omega x} \rangle, \tag{11.24}$$

it follows from (11.21) that, for some M and integer $r \geqslant 0$,

$$|c_{nk}| \leqslant M\,|k|^r \qquad (k \neq 0), \tag{11.25}$$

while the boundedness of $\{F_n\}$ ensures

$$|c_{n0}| \leqslant A. \tag{11.26}$$

Thus $\{c_{n0}\}_n$ is a bounded sequence of complex numbers and by the Bolzano-Weierstrass Theorem, it contains a subsequence $\{c_{n(0)0}\}_{n(0)}$ that converges to a complex number c_0.

By (11.25), with $k = 1$, the sequence $\{c_{n(0)1}\}_{n(0)}$ is bounded and by the Bolzano-Weierstrass Theorem it contains a subsequence $\{c_{n(1)1}\}_{n(1)}$ converging to a complex number c_1. Again by (11.25), but with $k = 2$, we get a subsequence $\{c_{n(2)2}\}_{n(2)}$ of $\{c_{n(1)2}\}_{n(1)}$ which converges to a complex number c_2.

Continuing in this manner, we have sequences of g.f.'s

$$\{F_{n(0)}\}, \quad \{F_{n(1)}\}, \quad \{F_{n(2)}\}, \quad \ldots, \quad \{F_{n(k)}\}, \quad \ldots,$$

each of which is a subsequence of the one preceding it (from left to right) and for which there exists

$$\lim_{n(k)\to\infty} \frac{1}{2L} \langle F_{n(k)}\, e^{-ik\omega x} \rangle = c_k. \tag{11.27}$$

Taking the diagonal sequence of integers $\{m_k\}_{k=0}^{\infty}$ defined by

$$\begin{aligned} m_0 &= \text{first element of } \{n(0)\}, \\ m_1 &= \text{second element of } \{n(1)\}, \\ m_k &= (k+1)\text{th element of } \{n(k)\} \end{aligned}$$

makes all but the first k elements, at most, of $\{F_{m_k}\}_{k=0}^{\infty}$ members of the sequence $\{F_{n(k)}\}$. Therefore, referring to (11.27), we get

$$\lim_{k\to\infty} \frac{1}{2L} \langle F_{m_k}, e^{-il\omega x} \rangle = c_l \qquad (\text{all integer } l), \tag{11.28}$$

where $|c_0| \leqslant A$ and $|c_l| \leqslant M\,|l|^r$. From Theorem B of Remark 4 it then follows that

$$\operatorname*{Lim}_{k\to\infty} F_{m_k} = F = \sum_{l=-\infty}^{\infty} c_l e^{il\omega x}. \quad \blacksquare$$

EXERCISES

[*Note:* All unmarked problems are of (*) level, insofar as they are related to a chapter of this category. Those marked with a (*) are supplementary.]

1. Verify the identities (1.4) for $f(x)$ piecewise continuous with period $2L$.

2. Prove Theorem 2.1.

3. Carry out the proof of Theorem 3.1.

4. Prove Theorem 3.2.

5. State and prove the $\mathscr{P}'_{2L}$ analogs of Theorems II.B.4.1 and II.B.4.2 and of the corollary to the latter [relation (VIII.5.3)].

6. Show that condition (7.1) is necessary for the convergence in $\mathscr{P}'_{2L}$ of the series $S(x) = \sum_{n=-\infty}^{\infty} c_n e^{in\omega x}$. [If (7.1) does not hold for any integer $r \geqslant 0$ a subsequence $\{n_p\}$ of the integers can be found such that $|n_{p+1}| > |n_p|$ $(p = 1, 2, \ldots)$ while $|c_{n_p}|/|n_p|^p$ is monotonically increasing to $+\infty$ as $p \to +\infty$. Consider

$$\varphi(x) = \sum_{p=1}^{\infty} \frac{e^{i\theta_p}}{|n_p|^p} e^{-in_p\omega x}$$

and take

$$\lim_{N\to\infty} \langle S_N(x), \varphi(x)\rangle,$$

where the S_N are the partial sums $\sum_{n=-N}^{N} c_n e^{in\omega x}$ and the θ_p are appropriately chosen.]

7. When $F, G \in \mathscr{K}_{2L}$ their finite convolution $F * G$ is defined by

$$C(x) = F * G = \frac{1}{2L}\int_{-L}^{L} F(x - \xi)G(\xi)\, d\xi.$$

Show that $C(x) \in \mathscr{K}_{2L}$ and that when $\sum_{-\infty}^{\infty} a_n e^{in\omega x}$, $\sum_{-\infty}^{\infty} b_n e^{in\omega x}$ are the Fourier series of F, G, respectively, the Fourier series of $C(x)$ is $\sum_{-\infty}^{\infty} a_n b_n e^{in\omega x}$. Further properties of this finite convolution operation are

$$F * G = G * F, \qquad F * (G + J) = F * G + F * J.$$

(Applications to the solution of linear D.E.'s with constant coefficients and periodic forcing terms will be found in [31]. The extension to $\mathscr{P}'_{2L}$ g.f.'s is straightforward if one defines $F * G$ as $D^{p+q}(A * B)$ whenever $F = D^p A$, $G = D^q B$ with $A, B \in \mathscr{K}_{2L}$.)

***8.** Given $F(x) \in \mathscr{K}_{2L}$, the integer $N \geqslant 0$, and the trigonometric polynomial $P_N(x) = \sum_{n=-N}^{N} d_n e^{in\omega x}$, expand

$$\frac{1}{2L}\int_{-L}^{L} |F(x) - P_N(x)|^2\, dx$$

and verify that this is a minimum when

$$d_n = \frac{1}{2L} \langle F(x), e^{-in\omega x} \rangle \qquad (n = -N, -N + 1, \ldots, N - 1, N).$$

This can be expressed in these words: the mean-square approximation of F by exponential polynomials of degree N of the form $P_N(x)$ is provided by the partial sum $S_N(x) = \sum_{n=-N}^{N} c_n e^{in\omega x}$ of the Fourier series of $F(x)$.

***9.** Let $\alpha_n(x)$ denote the function ρ_ε of (I.2.11), where $\varepsilon = 1/n (n = 1, 2, \ldots)$ and x replaces t. Given $F(x) \in \mathscr{K}_{2L}$ show that

$$F_n(x) = \int_{-\infty}^{\infty} \alpha_n(x - \xi) F(\xi)\, d\xi \in \mathscr{P}_{2L}.$$

Also show that

$$\lim_{n\to\infty} \frac{1}{2L} \int_{-L}^{L} |F(x) - F_n(x)|^2\, dx = 0.$$

***10.** By Theorem 6.2 each of the functions F_n defined in Exercise 9 has a Fourier series converging uniformly to it and satisfying (6.20). (a) Deduce from this and Exercise 9 the existence of a sequence of exponential polynomials of the form $P_N(x)$ such that

$$\lim_{n\to\infty} \frac{1}{2L} \int_{-L}^{L} |F(x) - P_N(x)|^2\, dx = 0.$$

(b) From (a) and the result of Exercise 8 deduce that

$$\lim_{n\to\infty} \frac{1}{2L} \int_{-L}^{L} |F(x) - S_N(x)|^2\, dx = 0.$$

(See the Remark at the conclusion of § 8.)

***11.** (A.R.) One of several alternative approaches to Theorem 6.2 starts from this result: if $f(x) \in \mathscr{K}_{2L}$ is real-valued and

$$(1) \quad \int_{-L}^{L} f(x) \cos n\omega x\, dx = \int_{-L}^{L} f(x) \sin n\omega x\, dx = 0$$

for $n = 0, 1, 2, \ldots$, then $f(x) \equiv 0$. The principle of its proof resembles that of Theorem VII.3.2: (a) Assume $f(x) \neq 0$, so there exists an interval

$$I = [\xi - \delta, \xi + \delta]\ (\xi \in [-L, L), \delta > 0)$$

such that $|f(x)| \geqslant c > 0$ throughout I; (b) let

$$P_N(x) = [1 + \cos \omega(x - \xi) - \cos \omega\delta]^N,$$

and show that as $N \to +\infty$ the contribution of

$$\int_{\xi-\delta}^{\xi+\delta} P_N(x) f(x)\, dx \quad \text{to} \quad \int_{-L}^{L} P_N(x) f(x)\, dx$$

is increasingly predominant so that the latter integral does not vanish when N is taken sufficiently large; as this contradicts the equalities (1) the conclusion follows.

***12.** (A.R.) Let $\varphi \in \mathscr{P}_{2L}$ be real-valued. By Lemma 1.1 its Fourier series

$$\frac{a_0}{2} + \sum_{n=0}^{\infty} (a_n \cos n\omega x + b_n \sin n\omega x)$$

is uniformly convergent and so represents a continuous $\mathscr{K}_{2L}$ function $S(x)$. Since

$$\int_{-L}^{L} [\varphi(x) - S(x)] \cos n\omega x \, dx = \int_{-L}^{L} [\varphi(x) - S(x)] \sin n\omega x \, dx = 0$$

$(n = 0, 1, 2, \ldots)$ it follows from the result of the preceding exercise that $S(x) = \varphi(x)$. Extending this to complex-valued $\varphi \in \mathscr{P}_{2L}$ furnishes the alternative proof of Theorem 6.2 mentioned in Exercise 11. The reader is asked to fill in the details and to observe that a direct (non-g.f.) proof of Theorem 8.1 can be obtained by the same procedure.

***13.** (A.R.) If $F \in \mathscr{P}'_{2L}$ has $\langle F, 1\rangle = 0$ there exists $G \in \mathscr{P}'_{2L}$ such that $F = DG$. Prove this without using Fourier series.

[Outline: (a) take a fundamental (on $\mathscr{P}_{2L}$) sequence $\{F_n\} \in F$, so

$$\lim_{n\to\infty} \langle F_n, 1\rangle = 0$$

and the sequence $\{E_n\}$, where $E_n(x) = F_n(x) - \langle F_n, 1\rangle \cdot 1$, is equivalent to $\{F_n\}$;

(b) let

$$G_n(x) = \int_{-L}^{x} E_n(t)\, dt,$$

so $G_n \in C(R) \cap \mathscr{K}_{2L}$ and $DG_n = E_n$;

(c) take any $\varphi_0 \in \mathscr{P}_{2L}$ that satisfies (9.8) and select a sequence $\{c_n\}$ of constants for which there exists

$$\lim_{n\to\infty} \langle G_n(x) + c_n, \varphi_0(x)\rangle$$

and use the decomposition (9.9) to express $\langle G_n(x) + c_n, \varphi(x)\rangle$ for arbitrary $\varphi \in \mathscr{P}_{2L}$;

(d) deduce that $\{G_n(x) + c_n\}$ is fundamental on $\mathscr{P}_{2L}$ and defines $G \in \mathscr{P}'_{2L}$ with $DG = F$.] (Compare Lemma V.B.2.1.)

14. By Theorem 9.1 δ_{2L} does not, but $(1/2L) - \delta_{2L}$ does have a primitive in $\mathscr{P}'_{2L}$. Take $L = \frac{1}{2}$, then $(1/2L) - \delta_{2L} = 1 - \delta_1$ has the primitive $P_1(x)$ which is the function with period 1 and equal to $x - \frac{1}{2}$ in the interval (0, 1) (see Example 2, § 4, for $\frac{1}{2} - x$ periodically extended). Verify that the Fourier series of this function is $\sum_{n=1}^{\infty} \frac{\sin 2n\pi x}{n\pi}$.

15. The Bernoulli periodic functions of period 1 are defined for $k = 0, 1, 2, \ldots$ by (1) $DP_k(x) = P_{k-1}(x)$ and (2) $\langle P_k(x), 1\rangle = 0$ with $P_0(x) = 1 - \delta_1$. Thus P_1 is the function defined in Exercise 14.

(a) Verify that the Fourier series for P_k are given by

$$P_{2k} = (-1)^{k-1} \sum_{n=0}^{\infty} \frac{\cos 2n\pi x}{2^{2k}(n\pi)^{2k+1}}$$

and

$$P_{2k+1} = (-1)^{k-1} \sum_{n=0}^{\infty} \frac{\sin 2n\pi x}{2^{2k}(n\pi)^{2k+1}};$$

(b) use the conditions (1) and (2) to derive from the ordinary function relations $dP_k(x)/dx = P_{k-1}(x)$ on (0, 1) and

$$\int_0^1 P_k(x)\, dx = 0 \qquad (k = 1, 2, 3, \ldots)$$

the fact that P_2, P_3, P_4 are periodic extensions of polynomials whose values on (0, 1) are

$$\frac{x^2}{2} - \frac{x}{2} + \frac{1}{12}, \quad \frac{x^3}{6} - \frac{x^2}{4} + \frac{x}{12}, \quad \frac{x^4}{24} - \frac{x^3}{12} + \frac{x^2}{24} - \frac{1}{720}$$

respectively ([19] [46]). [Note how the polynomial form of P_1 is suggested by the fundamental sequence $\{\mathring{p}_n\}$ for δ_{2L} defined in (2.8).]

16. Given that $F = \sum_{n=1}^{\infty} \frac{(-1)^{n+1}}{n} \sin nx$ and $L = \pi$ find a more compact expression for F. [Observing that

$$DF = \sum_{n=1}^{\infty} (-1)^{n+1} \cos nx$$

and recalling (6.15) we find

$$DF = \tfrac{1}{2} - \pi\delta_{2\pi}(x - \pi).$$

This is the sum of the $\mathscr{K}_{2\pi}$ function $\frac{1}{2}$ and of a $\delta_{2\pi}$ term. How such $\delta_{2\pi}$ terms arise is seen in Theorem 4.1, which suggests that F is the extension with period 2π of the function equal to $x/2$ on $(-\pi, \pi)$—a result whose correctness is checked by differentiating back. Another procedure consists in applying the method of Exercise 13 to find the primitive of DF.]

17. In the heat-transmission problem (10.14)–(10.16) the boundary conditions (10.15) are replaced by these:

$$\frac{\partial u(+0, t)}{\partial x} = \frac{\partial u(\pi - 0, t)}{\partial x} = 0 \qquad (t > 0).$$

Find $u(x, t)$ by means of an appropriate finite Fourier transform procedure in $\mathscr{P}_{2L}$.

$$[\textit{Ans. } u(x, t) = \frac{1}{\pi}\int_0^{\pi} f(\xi)\, d\xi + \frac{2}{\pi}\sum_{n=1}^{\infty} e^{-n^2kt} \cos nx \int_0^{\pi} f(\xi) \cos n\xi\, d\xi.]$$

18. Find $X \in \mathscr{P}'_{2L}$ such that

$$(aD^2 + bD + c)X = \delta_{2L}(x - \xi) \qquad (a, b, c, \xi \in R \text{ are constants})$$

by writing $X = \sum_{n=-\infty}^{\infty} a_n e^{in\omega x}$, expressing δ_{2L} in terms of its Fourier series and identifying coefficients. Justify this procedure.

****19.** Prove the converse of Corollary 11.3. [*Hint:* If F is a c.l.f. on $\mathscr{P}_{2L}$ the functions $\langle F(\xi), \mathring{p}_{1/n}(x - \xi)\rangle = F_n(x)$, where $\mathring{p}_\varepsilon$ is defined in (2.2), form a fundamental (on $\mathscr{P}_{2L}$) sequence.]

APPENDIX

Table of Inverse Operator Values

$P(D)$	$P^{-1}(D)\,\delta(t)^{(\dagger)(\ddagger)}$
D^p (integer $p > 0$)	$\dfrac{t^{p-1}}{(p-1)!}H(t)$
$(D-r)^p$ (integer $p > 0$)	$\dfrac{e^{rt}t^{p-1}}{(p-1)!}H(t) = \dfrac{1}{(p-1)!}\dfrac{\partial^{p-1}}{\partial r^{p-1}}[(D-r)^{-1}\,\delta(t)]$
$(D-r_1)(D-r_2)\cdots(D-r_l)$ ($r_1, r_2, \ldots, r_l$ distinct)	$\dfrac{e^{r_1t}H(t)}{(r_1-r_2)(r_1-r_3)\cdots(r_1-r_l)} + \dfrac{e^{r_2t}H(t)}{(r_2-r_1)(r_2-r_3)\cdots(r_2-r_l)} + \cdots + \dfrac{e^{r_lt}H(t)}{(r_l-r_1)(r_l-r_2)\cdots(r_l-r_{l-1})}$
$(D-r_1)^{p_1}(D-r_2)^{p_2}\cdots(D-r_l)^{p_l}$ ($r_1, r_2, \ldots, r_l$ distinct; $p_1, p_2, \ldots, p_l$ positive integers)	$\dfrac{1}{(p-1)!}\dfrac{1}{(p_2-1)!}\cdots\dfrac{1}{(p_l-1)!} \times \dfrac{\partial^{p_1+p_2+\cdots+p_l-l}}{\partial r_1^{p_1-1}\partial r_2^{p_2-1}\cdots\partial r_l^{p_l-1}} \times [(D-r_1)^{-1}(D-r_2)^{-1}\cdots(D-r_l)^{-1}\,\delta(t)]$
$(D-r_1)(D-r_2)$ ($r_1 \neq r_2$)	$\dfrac{H(t)}{r_2-r_1}(e^{r_2t}-e^{r_1t})$
D^2+r^2 ($r \neq 0$)	$\dfrac{H(t)}{r}\sin rt$
D^2-r^2 ($r \neq 0$)	$\dfrac{H(t)}{r}\sinh rt$
$(D-\alpha)^2+\beta^2$ ($\beta \neq 0$)	$\dfrac{H(t)}{\beta}e^{\alpha t}\sin\beta t$
D^3+r^3 ($r \neq 0$)	$\dfrac{H(t)}{3r^2}\left[e^{-rt} - e^{rt/2}\left(\cos\dfrac{rt\sqrt{3}}{2} - \sqrt{3}\sin\dfrac{rt\sqrt{3}}{2}\right)\right]$
$D(D^2+r^2)$ ($r \neq 0$)	$\dfrac{H(t)}{r^2}(1-\cos rt)$
$D^2(D^2+r^2)$ ($r \neq 0$)	$\dfrac{H(t)}{r^3}(rt-\sin rt)$
$(D^2+r^2)^2$ ($r \neq 0$)	$\dfrac{H(t)}{2r^3}(\sin rt - rt\cos rt)$
$(D^2-r^2)^2$ ($r \neq 0$)	$\dfrac{H(t)}{2r^3}(rt\cosh rt - \sinh rt)$
D^4-r^4 ($r \neq 0$)	$\dfrac{H(t)}{2r^3}(\sinh rt - \sin rt)$

† For any $f \in \mathscr{K}_+(R)$ $P^{-1}(D)f(t) = \int_{-\infty}^{t} G(t-\tau)f(\tau)\,d\tau$ (Section III.C.3).

‡ For any $F \in \mathscr{D}'_+$ $P^{-1}(D)F = G * F$ (Section III.C.5 and Section V.B.4).

Supplementary Table of Inverse Operator Values

$$(D - r)^{-p} e^{\alpha t} \frac{t^{n-1}}{(n-1)!} H(t) = H(t) e^{\alpha t} \sum_{l=0}^{n-1} \binom{l+p-1}{p-1} \frac{(-1)^l}{(\alpha - r)^{l+p}} \frac{t^{n-l-1}}{(n-l-1)!}$$

$$+ H(t) e^{rt} \sum_{l=0}^{p-1} \binom{l+n-1}{n-1} \frac{(-1)^l}{(r-\alpha)^{l+n}} \frac{t^{p-l-1}}{(p-l-1)!}$$

$$= \frac{1}{(p-1)!} \frac{1}{(n-1)!} \frac{\partial^{p+n-2}}{\partial \alpha^{n-1} \partial r^{p-1}} \left(\frac{e^{\alpha t} - e^{rt}}{\alpha - r} \right)$$

(integers $p, n \geqslant 1$)

$$D^{-p} \log t_+ = H(t) \frac{t^p}{p!} \left(\log t - \sum_{k=1}^{p} \frac{1}{k} \right) \qquad \text{(integer } p \geqslant 1\text{)}$$

$$D^{-p} t^{\lambda} \log t_+ = \frac{H(t) t^{\lambda+p}}{(\lambda+1)(\lambda+2) \cdots (\lambda+p)} \left(\log t - \sum_{k=1}^{p} \frac{1}{\lambda+k} \right)$$

($\lambda \neq -1, -2, \ldots$; integer $p \geqslant 1$)

$$(D - r)^{-p} e^{\alpha t} \frac{t_+^{\lambda-1}}{\Gamma(\lambda)} = H(t) \sum_{k=0}^{\infty} \frac{t^{\lambda+p+k-1}}{\Gamma(\lambda+p+k)} \sum_{m=0}^{k} \binom{m+p-1}{p-1} r^m \frac{\alpha^{k-m}}{(k-m)!}$$

(integer $p \geqslant 1$)

$$(D - r)^{-p} t^{\lambda} \log t_+ = H(t) e^{rt} \sum_{n=0}^{\infty} \frac{(-r)^n}{n!} \frac{t^{\lambda+n+p}}{(\lambda+n+1) \cdots (\lambda+n+p)}$$

$$\times \left(\log t - \sum_{k=1}^{p} \frac{1}{\lambda+n+k} \right) \qquad (\lambda \neq -1, -2, \ldots \text{; integer } p \geqslant 1$$

$$(D - r)^{-1} t_+^{-1/2} = \frac{e^{rt}}{\sqrt{2r}} \int_0^{\sqrt{2rt}} e^{-v^2/2}\, dv$$

Table of Laplace Transforms

$F(t)$	$\mathscr{L}\{F; s\}$
$t^p H(t)$	$\dfrac{p!}{s^{p+1}}$ (integer $p \geqslant 0$)
$e^{rt} t^p H(t)$	$\dfrac{p!}{(s-r)^{p+1}}$ (integer $p \geqslant 0$)
$\dfrac{e^{r_1 t} H(t)}{(r_1 - r_2) \cdots (r_1 - r_l)} + \dfrac{e^{r_2 t} H(t)}{(r_2 - r_1)(r_2 - r_3) \cdots (r_2 - r_l)} + \cdots + \dfrac{e^{r_l t} H(t)}{(r_l - r_1) \cdots (r_l - r_{l-1})}$	$(s - r_1)^{-1}(s - r_2)^{-1} \cdots (s - r_l)^{-1}$ ($r_1, \ldots, r_l$ distinct)
$H(t) \sin rt$	$\dfrac{r}{s^2 + r^2}$
$H(t) \cos rt$	$\dfrac{s}{s^2 + r^2}$
$H(t) e^{\alpha t} \sin \beta t$	$\dfrac{\beta}{(s - \alpha)^2 + \beta^2}$
$H(t) e^{\alpha t} \cos \beta t$	$\dfrac{s - \alpha}{(s - \alpha)^2 + \beta^2}$
t_+^λ	$\dfrac{\Gamma(\lambda + 1)}{s^{\lambda+1}}$ ($\lambda \neq -1, -2, \ldots$)
$\delta(t)$	1
$\delta^{(p)}(t)$	s^p (integer $p > 0$)
$\delta^{(p)}(t - h)$	$e^{-sh} s^p$ (integer $p \geqslant 0$, $h \geqslant 0$)
$e^{-a^2/4t} \dfrac{H(t)}{t^{3/2}}$	$\dfrac{2\sqrt{\pi}}{a} e^{-a\sqrt{s}}$
$\log t_+$	$\dfrac{\Gamma'(1) - \log s}{s}$ ($\Gamma'(1) \approx -0.5772$)
$t^\lambda \log t_+$ ($\lambda \neq -1, -2, \ldots$)	$\dfrac{\Gamma'(\lambda + 1) - \Gamma(\lambda + 1) \log s}{s^{\lambda+1}}$

BIBLIOGRAPHY

1. Apostol, T., *Mathematical Analysis*, 1957, Addison-Wesley, Reading, Massachusetts.
2. Birkoff, G. D., and S. MacLane, *A Survey of Modern Algebra*, 1948, Macmillan, New York.
3. Blanc, C., *Les équations différentielles de la technique*, 1947, Griffon, Lausanne.
4. Bochner, S., *Vorlesungen über Fouriersche Integrale*, 1932, Chelsea, New York, 110–144.
5. Bromwich, J. T. Ia., "Normal coordinates in dynamical systems," *Proc. London Math. Soc.*, **15** (1916).
6. Buck, R. C., *Advanced Calculus*, 1956, McGraw, New York.
7. Carslaw and Jaeger, *Operational Methods in Applied Mathematics*, 1941, Oxford.
8. Churchill, R. V., *Operational Mathematics*, 1958, McGraw, New York.
9. Churchill, R. V., *Fourier Series and Boundary-value Problems*, 1941, McGraw, New York.
10. Coddington and Levinson, *Theory of Ordinary Differential Equations*, 1955, McGraw, New York.
11. Courant, R., *Differential and Integral Calculus*, vol. I, 1937, Interscience, New York.
12. Courant and Hilbert, *Methods of Mathematical Physics*, vol. I, 1953, Interscience, New York.
13. Dirac, P. A. M., "The physical interpretation of quantum mechanics," *Proc. Roy. Soc. London*, **A113** (1926–27), 621–641.
14. Doetsch, G., *Handbuch der Laplace Transformation*, 1955, Birkhäuser, Basel.
15. Ehrenpreis, L., "Theory of infinite derivatives," *Amer. J. Math.*, **LXXXI:4** (1959), 799–845.
16. Erdélyi, A., "From Delta functions to distributions," pp. 5–50 of *Modern Mathematics for the Engineer*, Second Series, ed. E. F. Beckenbach, 1961, McGraw, New York.
17. Erdélyi, A., *Operational Calculus and Generalized Functions*, 1962, Holt, Rinehart & Winston, New York.
18. Fantappié, L., "Les nouvelles méthodes d'intégration en termes finis des équations aux dérivees partielles," pp. 95–128, *1954 Colloquium on Part. Dif. Eqs.*, Brussels.
19. Franklin, P., *Treatise on Advanced Calculus*, 1940, Wiley, New York.
20. Friedman, B., *Principles and Techniques of Applied Mathematics*, 1956, Wiley, New York.
21. Gál, I. S., "Sur la méthode de résonance et sur un théorème concernant le espaces de type (B)," *Annales de l'Institut Fourier, Grenoble*, **III** (1951), 23–30.
22. Gel'fand, I. M., and Šilov, "Quelques applications de la théorie des fonctions generalisées," *Journal de Mathématiques*, **XXXV**, fasc. 4 (1956), 383–413.

23. Gel'fand, I. M., and Šilov, *Verallgemeinerte Funktionen*, vol. I, 1960, D.V.W., Berlin (trans. from Russian 1958 edition).
24. Ghosh, P. K., "Mathematical foundations of physically observable functions," *Bull. Calcutta Math. Soc.*, **49** (1957), 25–28.
25. Goffman, C., *Real Functions*. 1953, Holt, Rinehart & Winston, New York.
26. Halperin, I., *Introduction to the Theory of Distributions*, 1952, Toronto University Press, Toronto.
27. Hosemann, R., and S. N. Bagchi, "Begründung einer Algebra physikalisch beobachtbarer Funktionen," *Z. Physik*, **135** (1953), 50–84.
28. Jeffreys, H., *Operational Methods in Mathematical Physics*, 1927, Cambridge University Press, New York.
29. Jeffreys, H., and B. Jeffreys, *Methods of Mathematical Physics*, 3rd ed., 1956, Cambridge University Press, New York.
30. Joos, G., *Theoretical Physics*, 3rd ed., 1954, Hafner, New York.
31. Kaplan, W., *Operational Methods for Linear Systems*, 1962, Addison-Wesley, Reading, Mass.
32. Korevaar, J., "Distributions defined from the point of view of applied mathematics," *Nederl. Akad. Wetensh. Proc.*, **A58** (1955), 368–389, 483–503, 663–674.
33. Lavoine, J., *Calcul symbolique*, 1959, C.N.R.S., Paris.
34. Lighthill, M. J., *Introduction to Fourier Analysis and Generalized Functions*, 1958, Cambridge University Press, New York.
35. Łojasiewicz, S., "Sur la valeur et la limite d'une distribution en un point," *Studia Math.*, **16** (1957), 1–36.
36. Mandelbrojt, S., "Analytic functions and classes of infinitely differentiable functions," *Rice Institute Pamphlet*, **29** (1942), 1.
37. Mikusiński, J. G., "Sur la méthode de généralisation de L. Schwartz et sur la convergence faible," *Fund. Math.*, **35** (1948), 235–239.
38. Mikusiński, J. G., "Sur les fondements du calcul opératoire," *Studia Math.*, **11** (1949) 41–70.
39. Mikusiński, J. G., *Operational Calculus*, 1959, Pergamon, New York (trans. from Polish 1953 edition).
40. Mikusiński, J. G., and R. Sikorski, "The elementary theory of distributions," *Rozprawy Matematyczne*, **12** (1957).
41. Ravetz, J. R., "Distributions defined as limits," *Proc. Cambridge Phil. Soc.*, **53** (1957), 76–92.
42. Saltzer, C. R., "The theory of distributions," *Advances in Appl. Mech.*, **5** (1958), 91–110.
43. Schwartz, L., *Théorie des distributions*, vols. I, II, 1950–1951, Hermann, Paris.
44. Schwartz, L., "Sur l'impossibilité de la multiplication des distributions," *Comptes Rendus*, Paris, **239** (1954), 847–848.
45. Schwartz, L., "Transformation de Laplace des distributions," *Math. Seminar, Lund Univ.*, volume dedicated to M. Riesz (1952), 196–206.
46. Schwartz, L., *Cours de Méthodes Mathématiques de la Physique*, 1955, C.D.U., Univ. of Paris, Paris.
47. Sikorski, R., "A definition of the notion of distribution," *Bull. Acad. Pol. Sci.* Classe III, **2** (1954), 209–211.
48. Sneddon, I. N., *Fourier Transforms*, 1951, McGraw, New York.

49. Taylor, A. E., *Advanced Calculus*, 1955, Ginn, Boston.
50. Temple, G., "Theories and applications of generalised functions," *J. London Math. Soc.*, **28** (1953), 134–148.
51. Temple, G., "The theory of generalised functions," *Proc. Roy. Soc. London*, **A228** (1955), 175–190.
52. Van der Pol, B., and H. Bremmer, *Operational Calculus Based on the Two-sided Laplace Transform*, 1950, Cambridge University Press, New York.
53. Whittaker, E., and G. Robinson, *The Calculus of Observations*, 4th ed., 1944, Blackie, Glasgow.
54. Widder, D. V., *Advanced Calculus*, 2nd ed., 1961, Prentice-Hall, Englewood, Cliffs, New Jersey.
55. Widder, D. V., *The Laplace Transform*, 1946, Princeton University Press, Princeton, New Jersey.

Supplementary Bibliography

1s. McShane, E. J., "A canonical form for antiderivatives," *Illinois Jour. of Math.*, **3** (1959), 334–351.
2s. Mirkil, H., "Differentiable functions, formal power series and moments," *Proceedings Am. Math. Soc.*, **7** (1956) # 4, 650–652.
3s. Mohr, E., "Integration von gewöhnlichen Differentialgleichungen mit konstanten koeffizienten mittels Operatorenrechnung," *Mathematische Nachrichten* **10** (1953), pp. 1–49.

INDEX OF NOTATION

Some current symbols, with their meanings, as employed in this text, are listed here for reference.

Symbol	*Meaning*
$\Rightarrow$	implies, has the consequence (thus $A \Rightarrow B$ means statement A implies statement B)
$\Leftrightarrow$	if and only if (thus $A \Leftrightarrow B$ means statements A and B are equivalent)
$\in$	belongs to, is an element of (thus $x \in A$ means x is an element of the set A)
$\subset$	$A \subset B$ means the set A is a subset of the set B (i.e., $x \in A \Rightarrow x \in B$) (Similarly, $A \supset B$ means that B is a subset of A)
R	the set of real numbers
C	the set of complex numbers
$[a, b]$	the closed interval $[a, b]$ (this is the set of all real numbers x verifying $a \leqslant x \leqslant b$)
(a, b)	the open interval (a, b) (this is the set of all real numbers x verifying $a < x < b$)
$[a, b)$	half-open interval (the set of real numbers x verifying $a \leqslant x < b$) (similarly $(a, b]$ stands for the real x with $a < x \leqslant b$) (the symbols $[a, +\infty)$ and $(-\infty, b]$ are now self-explanatory).
$A \cap B$	the intersection of the sets A and B (i.e., the set of elements belonging to both the sets A and B)
$A \cup B$	the union of the sets A and B (i.e., the set of elements belonging either to A, or to B, or to A and B)
$\bar{A}$	the closure of the set A (i.e., the union of A and of the set of limit points of A)
$\{a_n\}$	the sequence $a_1, a_2, a_3, \ldots, a_n, \ldots$
$\{a_{mn}\}_n$	the sequence $a_{m1}, a_{m2}, a_{m3}, \ldots, a_{mn}, \ldots$ $\{a_n\}_{n=-\infty}^{n=+\infty}$ stands for a sequence in which n ranges over *all* the integers)

$\lim_{n\to\infty} a_n = l$ — the limit of a_n as $n \to \infty$ is l. *In this text, the expressions "the limit exists", "has a limit", "converges", always mean* that l is a finite real or complex number, unless an explicit indication is given to the contrary (in the form $\lim_{n\to\infty} a_n = +\infty$)
(Similar observation for the symbol $\lim_{\lambda\to\lambda_0} a_\lambda$)

$f(a+0)$ — $\lim_{\varepsilon\to 0} f(a+\varepsilon)$, $\varepsilon > 0$ (when $a = 0$ we write $f(+0)$)

$f(a-0)$ — $\lim_{\varepsilon\to 0} f(a-\varepsilon)$, $\varepsilon > 0$ (when $a = 0$ we write $f(-0)$).

Special symbols, each with a page number indicating where it is defined in the text, are listed below:

a_n, b_n	Real Fourier coefficients, p. 301
c_n	Complex Fourier coefficients, pp. 297, 299
$C^k(R)$, $C^\infty(R)$	p. 14
$C(F; n)$	Cosine transform, p. 308
D^p $(p \geqslant 0)$	pp. 17, 49, 90, 291
D^p $(p < 0)$	pp. 20, 93
$[Df]$	pp. 58, 292
$\dfrac{\partial F_{\lambda_0}}{\partial \lambda}$	parametric derivative at λ_0, p. 76
δ, $\delta(t)$	Dirac delta g.f., p. 42
δ_{2L}, $\delta_{2L}(t)$	Periodic delta g.f., p. 289
$\mathscr{D}$	p. 35 (Problem 8)
$\mathscr{D}'$	p. 84 (Problem 6)
$\mathscr{D}_-$	p. 14
$\mathscr{D}'_-$	p. 57
$\mathscr{D}_+$	p. 28
$\mathscr{D}'_+$	p. 41
$\mathscr{E}$, $\mathscr{E}'$	p. 84, 85
$\langle F, \varphi \rangle$	pp. 41, 288
f^{*p}	Convolution exponent, p. 128
$\Vert f \Vert_I$	p. 186
$G(t)$	Green's function, pp. 107, 129
$G_{ij}(t)$	p. 156
$H(t)$	Heaviside function, p. 42
$\mathscr{K}_+(R)$	p. 39

$\mathscr{K}_{2L}$	p. 287
$\operatorname{Lim}_{n\to\infty} F_n$	g.f. limit, pp. 65, 294
$\operatorname{Lim}_{\lambda\to\lambda_0} F_\lambda$	g.f. limit, p. 71
$\log t_+$	p. 79
ω	pp. 115, 284
$p_n(t)$	rectangular pulse function, p. 39
$\mathring{p}_n(t)$	periodic pulse function, p. 289
$\dot{+}$	p. 39
$\bar{P}(D)$	transpose of $P(D)$, p. 91
$\bar{P}^{-1}(D)$	transpose of $P^{-1}(D)$, p. 95
$\mathscr{P}_{2L}$	p. 287
$\mathscr{P}'_{2L}$	p. 288
$S(F; n)$	sine transform, p. 308
T^p	translation operator, p. 171
t_+^λ	p. 80

References to other parts of the text are made as follows: if, in the course of Chapter III, mention is made of (A.5.11), this means formula 11 of §5 of part A of Chapter III. If formula 11 of §5 of part A of Chapter III is mentioned elsewhere than in Chapter III, this reference is given in the form (III. A.5.11).

INDEX

Abel's integral equation, 182, ex. 21
Ascoli-Arzelà Theorem, 230, 236, 319 (*see also* Relative compactness)

Backward half-line, 14
Bernoulli periodic functions, 322, ex. 15
Bessel functions, 265
Bessel's inequality, 302
Beta function, 29
Bochner, S., 196
Bolzano-Weierstrass Theorem, 216, 230, 319 (*see also* Relative compactness)
Boundary term:
  in equation of evolution, 105
  in system, 148
Boundary-value problems for ordinary d.e., 165
  mixed b.v.-i.v. problems, 265, 276, 309
Bounded sequence:
  in $\mathscr{D}'_+$, 220
  in $\mathscr{P}'_{2L}$, 318
Bremmer, H., 237
Bromwich, T. J., 11

Cantor, G., 8, 56, 57, 216
Carrier:
  of $\mathscr{D}'_+$ g.f., 207
  of function, 14
  half-line as carrier of $\mathscr{D}'_+$ g.f., 44
Cauchy sequence, 216 (*see also* Completeness; Fundamental sequence)
Change of variable in g.f., 85, ex. 10
Churchill, R. V., 275
Commutativity:
  of convolution, 126, 133, 211
  of operator multiplication, 4, 18, 36, ex. 10; 94 (A.2.15)
Compactness (*see* Relative compactness)
Compatibility of i.v. and forcing term in system of d.e.'s, 164
Completeness, 216
  of $\mathscr{D}'$, 234, exs. 10, 12
  of $\mathscr{D}'_+$, 225
  of $\mathscr{E}'$, 234, ex. 12
  of $\mathscr{P}'_{2L}$, 318
Continuation by zero:
  for difference equation, 175
  for d.e., 61, 105
  for p.d.e., 267 (10.5), 276 (13.5)
  for system of d.e.'s, 142, 147
Continuity:
  of operators on $\mathscr{D}'_+$, 99, 211
  of operators on $\mathscr{P}'_{2L}$, 294
  of parametric g.f., 75, 87, ex. 38
Continuous linear functional:
  on $\mathscr{D}$, 214, ex. 14
  on $\mathscr{D}_-$, 186, 193
  on $\mathscr{E}$, 214, ex. 16
  on $\mathscr{P}_{2L}$, 317
Continuous operator on $\mathscr{D}'_+$, 100
Convergence:
  Cauchy principle in $\mathscr{D}'_+$, 67
  in $\mathscr{D}$, 213, ex. 14
  in $\mathscr{D}_-$, 191
  in $\mathscr{D}'_+$, 65, 71
  in $\mathscr{E}$, 214, ex. 16
  in $\mathscr{P}'_{2L}$, 294, 318
  mean square, 75, 321, ex. 9
  unconditional, 285, 297
  uniform, 64, 74, 192, 286
Convolution product:
  continuity of, 211
  of $\mathscr{D}'_+$, functions of finite K-order 133
  of $\mathscr{D}'_+$ g.f., 209
  of $\mathscr{K}_+$ (R) functions, 124
  of $\mathscr{K}_{2L}$ functions, 320, ex. 7
  Laplace transformation of, 247
Convolution quotient, 179
C-order, 200, 203, 204
Critical damping, 114, 117

Definite integral of a parametric $\mathscr{D}'_+$ g.f. 77, 227
Derivative of Heaviside function, 49
Derivative polynomial:
  on $\mathscr{D}_-$, 18
  on $\mathscr{D}'_+$, 90
  inverse of:
    on $\mathscr{D}_-$, 24
    on $\mathscr{D}'_+$, 94
  partial fraction expansion of, 25, 95
  transpose, 91, 99
Derivatives of Dirac delta function, 49

Derivatives of g.f. (*see also* Parametric derivative):
  of class $\mathscr{D}'$, 85, ex. 12
  of class $\mathscr{D}'_+$, 47, 58, 73
  of class $\mathscr{E}'$, 85, ex. 13
  of class $\mathscr{P}_{2L}$, 291, 292
  limit definition, 196
  relation between ordinary and generalized derivative, 58, 292
Determinants:
  Chiò method, 153
  Cramer's rule, 152
  operator, 149
Differential equations (*see* Linear differential equations)
Differentiation (*see also* Parametric derivative):
  of $\mathscr{D}_-$ test functions, 17, 30
  of $\mathscr{D}'_+$ g.f., 47
  of $\mathscr{P}'_{2L}$ g.f., 291
Dirac delta function, 6, 42
  Fourier series, 297
  periodic, 289
Direct operational method, 11, 243
Division:
  of derivative polynomials, 19 (*see also* Inverse; Operator, rational)
  of g.f. of class $\mathscr{D}'_+$, 227
Doetsch, G., 12, 13, 237

Ehrenpreis, L., 12
Equation of evolution, 62
  of i.v. problems for linear difference equations, 176
  of mixed i.v.-b.v. problems for p.d.e.'s, 266, 277, 310
  of ordinary i.v. problems, 105, 148
Equicontinuity, 199, 230
Equivalence class of fundamental sequences, 44, 289
Equivalence relation, 44
Erdelyi, A., 178
Exponential order of a $\mathscr{K}_{++}$ function, 238
Exponential type of $\mathscr{D}'_{++}$ g.f., 250

Fibonacci numbers, 182, ex. 25
Finite Fourier transforms, 308
  inversion formulae, 308
Finite *K*-order of $\mathscr{D}'_+$ g.f., 73n., 133
Forcing term, 62, 105, 111, 117
Forward half-line, 14
  carrier of $\mathscr{D}'_+$ g.f., 44
Fourier series:
  for any $\mathscr{P}_{2L}$ function, 297
  for any $\mathscr{P}'_{2L}$ g.f., 301, 316
Function:
  of class $\mathscr{K}_+(R)$, 39
  of class $\mathscr{K}^p_+(R)$, 57
  of class $\mathscr{K}_{++}(R)$, 238
  of class $\mathscr{K}_{2L}$, 287
  complex-valued, 14, 33
  periodic extensions, 307
  piecewise continuous, 38
  pulse, 5
  test (*see* Test function)
Functional, 38
  continuous linear on $\mathscr{D}$, 213, ex. 14
  continuous linear on $\mathscr{D}_-$, 193
  continuous linear on $\mathscr{E}$, 214, ex. 16
  continuous linear on $\mathscr{P}_{2L}$, 317
  on $\mathscr{D}_-$, 40
  linear, 38
Fundamental sequence:
  on $\mathscr{D}$, 84, ex. 6
  on $\mathscr{D}_-$, 40, 202
  on $\mathscr{D}^p_-$, 85, ex. 14
  on $\mathscr{E}$, 84, ex. 7
  on $\mathscr{P}_{2L}$, 288

Gamma function, 28
Gel'fand, I. M., 12, 195
Generalized derivative, 47, 58
Generalized functions:
  carried in a half-line, 44
  of class $\mathscr{D}'$, 84, ex. 6; 213, exs. 13, 14, 20; 233, exs. 9, 10
  of class $\mathscr{D}'_-$, 57, 101
  of class $\mathscr{D}'_+$, 41, 195
  of class $\mathscr{D}'^p_+$, 85, ex. 14
  of class $\mathscr{D}'_{++}$, 250
  of class $\mathscr{E}$, 84, ex. 7; 214, exs. 15, 16; 234, ex. 12
  of class $\mathscr{P}_{2L}$, 288
  continuous linear functionals on $\mathscr{D}_-$, 195
  convolution (*see* Convolution product)
  division of, 227
  exponential type, 250
  finite *K*-order, 73n., 133
  homogeneous, 88, exs. 47, 48
  multiplication of, 45, 47, 140, ex. 36
  parametric, 71
Green's function:
  for ordinary i.v. problems, 120, 129
  for p.d.e. i.v. problems, 275

Halperin, I., 12, 195
Heat equation, 276, 309
Heaviside, O., 11
Heaviside function, 42
Homogeneous $\mathscr{D}'_+$ g.f., 88, exs. 47, 48

Image function space, 243
Image sequence, 307
Indirect operational method, 11, 243
Initial-value problems (*see* Integral equations; Integro-difference equations; Linear difference equations)
Integral equations, 166
Integral-non-linear equations, 282, ex. 18
Integrals of parametric $\mathscr{D}'_+$ g.f.:
  definite integrals, 77, 226
  improper integrals, 78, 233, ex. 8
Integro-difference equation, 166
Inverse:
  of derivative polynomials (*see* Derivative polynomials)
  left, 20
  of operator, 20
  right, 20

Inversion of operators (*see* Inverse)

Jump, of function at point, 58

Korevaar, J., 196, 202, 250

Laplace transform:
of $\mathscr{D}'_{++}$ g.f., 253
of $\mathscr{K}'_{++}(R)$ function, 238
Lavoine, J., 250
Lebesque, H., 53, 111, 217
method of resonance, 217, 222, 234, ex. 11; 313
Leibnitz formula, 31, 35, ex. 2; 63
Lerch's Theorem, 247
Lighthill, M. J., 12, 196, 283
Limit point, 71
Linear difference equations, 174
Linear functional, 38
Linear ordinary differential equations:
b.v. problem, 165
equation of evolution, 62, 105
existence and uniqueness of solution in $\mathscr{D}_-$, 24
existence and uniqueness of solution in $\mathscr{D}'_+$, 94
i.v. problem with constant coefficients, 104, 110
i.v. problem for a forced vibrating system, 117
i.v. problem for free vibrating system, 112
simultaneous (*see* Systems)
Linear p.d.e.'s
Green's function, 275
heat equation, 276, 309
operational solution of an ib.v. problem, 9
operational solution of an i.v. problem, 8
wave equation, 266
Linear space, 16
Local identification of $\mathscr{D}'_+$ g.f., 54

Mach, Ernst, 11
McShane, E. J., 204
Mandelbrojt, S., 56n.
Matrix equation of evolution, 149
Mikusinski, J. G., 178, 202
Mikusinski operators, 202
Mirkil, H., 213, ex. 11
Mixed difference-differential equations, 258
M-norm, 186
Multiplication of g.f., 45, 47, 140, ex. 36

Natural frequency, 116
Non-linear integral equation, 282, ex. 18
Nonnormal systems, 148, 159
Norm, 186
Normal systems, 148, 155
Nullity set of a $\mathscr{D}'_+$ g.f., 207

Object function space, 243
Object g.f., 253

Operational calculi, 3, 8, 9, 11
Operators, 17
continuous on $\mathscr{D}'_+$, 100
derivative polynomial (*see* Derivative polynomial)
identity, 20, 90
inverse, 20
rational, 25
translation, 171
transpose, 91, 95, 99, 257
Ordinary i.v. problem, 104, 147
Overdamping, 113, 117

Parametric derivatives:
of $\mathscr{D}'_+$ g.f., 76, 100, 136, exs. 6, 7; 139, ex. 30; 227
of $\mathscr{D}'_{++}$ g.f., 267
of $\mathscr{P}'_{2L}$ g.f., 294, 310
Parametric equation of evolution, 267, 310
Parametric integrals:
of $\mathscr{D}'_+$ g.f., 77, 100, 140, 226, 233, ex. 8
of $\mathscr{P}'_{2L}$ g.f., 294
Physical relevance of g.f., 6, 59, 164, 275, 311
Point-masses, 58
Positive $\mathscr{D}'_+$ g.f., 185, 197
Primitive:
of $\mathscr{D}'$ g.f., 86, ex. 32
of $\mathscr{P}'_{2L}$ g.f., 304, 322, exs. 13, 14, 15
Prolongation by zero of function (*see* Continuation by zero)
Pseudo-function, 81, 89, ex. 49

Ravetz, J. R., 215n.
Relative compactness:
of $\mathscr{D}'_+$, 230, 236, ex. 21
of $\mathscr{P}'_{2L}$, 319
Resonance, 118
method of, 217, 222, 234, ex. 11; 313

Saltus, 58, 292
Saltzer, C. R., 195
Sawtooth function, 60, 293
Schwartz, L., vii, viii, xi, 3, 12, 13, 178, 184, 195, 207, 215, 250, 283, 295, 317
Schwarz's inequality, 74, 303
Shift relation:
on $\mathscr{D}_-$, 19, 22
on $\mathscr{D}'_+$, 91, 94
Sikorski, R., 202
Ŝilov, G. E., 12, 195
Supporting set (*see* Carrier)
Systems of linear d.e.'s:
equations of evolution, 142, 148
i.v. problem for system, 147
normal systems, 148, 155

Taylor formula:
for complex-valued functions, 34
for parametric $\mathscr{D}'_+$ g.f., 87, ex. 40
Temple, G., viii, xi, 12, 13, 196, 283
Test function:
of class $\mathscr{D}$, 35, ex. 8
of class $\mathscr{D}_-$, 14

Test function (contd.)
  of class $\mathscr{D}_+$, 28
  of class $\mathscr{E}$, 84, ex. 7
  of class $\mathscr{P}_{2L}$, 287
  of class $\mathscr{L}$, 35, ex. 7
Translation of g.f., 45
Translation operators, 171
Translation polynomials, 174
Transpose of derivative:
  polynomial operator on $\mathscr{D}'_+$, 91, 99

Unconditional convergence, 285, 297
Underdamping, 115, 117
Unit solution, 120, 129, 275 (*see also* Green's function)
Unstable physical system, 119

Van der Pol, B., 237

Wave equation, 266
Weak Cauchy sequence of $\mathscr{D}'_+$ g.f., 216 (*see also* Completeness)
Weak completeness, 217, 318 (*see also* Completeness)
Weak convergence in $\mathscr{D}'_+$, 65 (*see also* Convergence)
Weakly bounded sequence, 220 (*see also* Bounded sequence)
Whittaker, E. T., 11
Widder, D. V., 13, 237